The Ultimate Pub Quiz Book

Geoff Tibballs

p

This is a Parragon Book
First published in 2002

Parragon
Queen Street House
4 Queen Street
Bath BA1 1HE, UK

Produced by Magpie Books, an imprint of
Constable & Robinson Ltd, London

Copyright © Parragon 2002

ISBN 0-75258-764-1

A copy of the British Library Cataloguing-in-Publication Data
is available from the British Library

Printed and bound in the UK

Cover and illustrations courtesy of Slatter-Anderson, London

Contents

Music 11

Pot Luck 1 12
Fifties 1 13
One-Hit Wonders 1 14
Eric Clapton 1 15
Heavy Metal 1 16
Duos 1 17
Name Changes 1 18
Spice Girls 1 19
Rap 1 20
Name Changes 2 21
Boy Bands 1 22
Albums 1 23
R&B 1 24
Number Twos 1 25
Pot Luck 2 26
Name Changes 3 27
Cover Versions 1 28
Pot Luck 3 29
Chart Toppers 1 30
The Police 1 31
Girl Bands 1 32
Chart Toppers 2 33
Pot Luck 4 34
Prince 1 35
Nineties 1 36
Heavy Metal 2 37
Pot Luck 5 38
One-Hit Wonders 2 39
Pot Luck 6 40
Jazz 1 41
Chart Toppers 3 42
Bay City Rollers 1 43
Pot Luck 7 44
Christmas Hits 1 45
Country and Western 1 46
Nineties 2 47
George Michael 1 48
Cover Versions 2 49
Solo Artists 1 50
Seventies 1 51
Eighties 1 52
Elvis 1 53
Pot Luck 8 54
Glam Rock 1 55
Lyrics 1 56
Pink Floyd 1 57

Pot Luck 9 58
Solo Artists 2 59
Pot Luck 10 60
One-Hit Wonders 3 61
Rock 'n' Roll 1 62
Seventies 2 63
Eighties 2 64
Bon Jovi 1 65
Singer/Songwriters 1 66
Pot Luck 11 67
Nineties 3 68
Classical Gas 1 69
Glam Rock 2 70
Singer/Songwriters 2 71
Seventies 3 72
Girl Bands 2 73
Pot Luck 12 74
Sinatra 1 75
Solo Artists 3 76
Sixties 1 77
Pot Luck 13 78
Country and Western 2 79
Name Changes 4 80
Cover Versions 3 81
Number Twos 2 82
Seventies 4 83
Simon and Garfunkel 1 84
Solo Artists 4 85
One-Hit Wonders 4 86
Lyrics 2 87
Cover Versions 4 88
Merseybeat 1 89
Seventies 5 90
The Who 1 91
Pot Luck 14 92
Dance 1 93
Lyrics 3 94
One-Hit Wonders 5 95
Number Twos 3 96
David Bowie 1 97
Pot Luck 15 98
Five 1 99
Motown 1 100
Eighties 3 101
Folk 1 102
Indie 1 103
Pot Luck 16 104

Stevie Wonder 1	105
Fifties 2	106
Film Tracks 1	107
Bee Gees 1	108
Chart Toppers 4	109
Pot Luck 17	110
Albums 2	111
Sixties 2	112
Girl Bands 3	113
Eurovision 1	114
New Wave 1	115
Stairway to Heaven 1	116
Pot Luck 18	117
Novelty Numbers 1	118
Lyrics 4	119
Eighties 4	120
Soul 1	121
Indie 2	122
Pot Luck 19	123
Jimi Hendrix 1	124
Number Twos 4	125
Dance 2	126
Sixties 3	127
John Lennon 1	128
Albums 3	129
Pot Luck 20	130
Punk 1	131
Lyrics 5	132
Home Towns 1	133
Rap 2	134
Sixties 4	135
Chart Toppers 5	136
Pot Luck 21	137
Albums 4	138
Indie 3	139
Film Tracks 2	140
Pot Luck 22	141
Novelty Numbers 2	142
Tina Turner 1	143
Pot Luck 23	144
The Sex Pistols 1	145
Folk 2	146
Duos 2	147
Pot Luck 24	148
Chart Toppers 6	149
Disco 1	150
Backstreet Boys 1	151
Fifties 3	152
Motown 2	153
Indie 4	154
Pot Luck 25	155
Tom Jones 1	156
Number Twos 5	157
Name Changes 5	158
Albums 5	159
Chart Toppers 7	160
Cover Versions 5	161
Blues 1	162
Nineties 4	163
Boyzone 1	164
One-Hit Wonders 6	165
Eighties 5	166
Novelty Numbers 3	167
Pot Luck 26	168
Soul 2	169
Lyrics 6	170
Cher 1	171
Film Tracks 3	172
Albums 6	173
Pot Luck 27	174
Punk 2	175
Chart Toppers 8	176
Seventies 6	177
Number Twos 6	178
Dance 3	179
Pot Luck 28	180
The Rolling Stones 1	181
Classical Gas 2	182
Rock 'n' Roll 2	183
Football	**185**
Transfer Trail 1	186
Livingston 1	187
Stockport County 1	188
The World Game 1	189
Scotland 1	190
Football League 1	191
Liverpool 1	192
Gillingham 1	193
World Cup 1	194
Who Said That?	195
Sheffield United 1	196
Name the Year 1	197
Sunderland 1	198
Football League 2	199
The World Game 2	200
Republic of Ireland 1	201
Managers 1	202
Manchester United 1	203

On the Spot 1	204	Premiership 4	254
Barnsley 1	205	Scottish Scene 2	255
World Cup 2	206	Grimsby Town 1	256
Premiership 1	207	European Cups 3	257
The World Game 3	208	FA Cup 2	258
Portsmouth 1	209	Manchester United 2	259
Millwall 1	210	European Championship 3	260
The World Game 4	211	Nicknames 1	261
Managers 2	212	League Cup 1	262
Premiership 2	213	European Championship 4	263
Leeds United 1	214	Transfer Trail 3	264
England 1	215	FA Cup 3	265
FA Cup 1	216	On the Spot 2	266
Football League 3	217	England 2	267
Whistle Happy 1	218	Non-League 2	268
Wales 1	219	Rangers 1	269
Motherwell 1	220	Whose Home? 3	270
Sharpshooters 1	221	Goalkeepers 2	271
Manchester City 1	222	Germany 1	272
European Championship 1	223	Newcastle United 1	273
Managers 3	224	Southampton 1	274
Aston Villa 1	225	Sharpshooters 2	275
Wolverhampton Wanderers 1	226	Transfer Trail 4	276
Oddballs 1	227	England 3	277
Scottish Scene 1	228	Sheffield Wednesday 1	278
European Championship 2	229	Managers 5	279
Brazil 1	230	Dundee United 1	280
Oddballs 2	231	The World Game 6	281
The World Game 5	232	France 1	282
Crystal Palace 1	233	FA Cup 4	283
European Cups 1	234	Who Said That? 3	284
Norwich City 1	235	Oddballs 4	285
Hibernian 1	236	Bolton Wanderers 1	286
Whose Home? 1	237	Derby County 1	287
Coventry City 1	238	On the Spot 3	288
Goalkeepers 1	239	World Cup 3	289
Name the Year 2	240	Manchester United 3	290
Premiership 3	241	European Cups 4	291
Arsenal 1	242	Premiership 5	292
European Cups 2	243	Birmingham City 1	293
Non-League 1	244	Football League 4	294
Oddballs 3	245	Leeds United 2	295
Wimbledon 1	246	Name the Year 3	296
Whose Home?	247	England 4	297
Managers 4	248	Whose Home? 4	298
Everton 1	249	Tottenham Hotspur 1	299
Who Said That? 2	250	Preston North End 1	300
Transfer Trail 2	251	Transfer Trail 5	301
Italy 1	252	Sharpshooters 3	302
Dunfermline Athletic 1	253	Scotland 2	303

Watford 1	304	Aston Villa 2	354
Oddballs 5	305	France 2	355
Arsenal 2	306	Oddballs 7	356
The World Game 7	307	Managers 7	357
Football League 5	308		
Kilmarnock 1	309		
Early Baths 1	310	**General**	**359**
Goalkeepers 3	311	General Quiz 1	360
Burnley 1	312	General Quiz 2	361
Liverpool 2	313	General Quiz 3	362
League Cup 2	314	General Quiz 4	363
Argentina 1	315	General Quiz 5	364
Name the Year 4	316	General Quiz 6	365
West Bromwich Albion 1	317	General Quiz 7	366
Germany 2	318	General Quiz 8	367
Dundee 1	319	General Quiz 9	368
Football League 6	320	General Quiz 10	369
England 5	321	General Quiz 11	370
FA Cup 5	322	General Quiz 12	371
Nicknames 2	323	General Quiz 13	372
The World Game 8	324	General Quiz 14	373
Managers 6	325	General Quiz 15	374
Bradford City 1	326	General Quiz 16	375
Nicknames 3	327	General Quiz 17	376
The World Game 9	328	General Quiz 18	377
FA Cup 6	329	General Quiz 19	378
Oddballs 6	330	General Quiz 20	379
Whose Home? 5	331	General Quiz 21	380
Walsall 1	332	General Quiz 22	381
Managers 7	333	General Quiz 23	382
Football League 7	334	General Quiz 24	383
The World Game 10	335	General Quiz 25	384
Chelsea 1	336	General Quiz 26	385
World Cup 4	337	General Quiz 27	386
Scottish Scene 3	338	General Quiz 28	387
World Cup 5	339	General Quiz 29	388
Transfer Trail 6	340	General Quiz 30	389
Northern Ireland 1	341	General Quiz 31	390
Football League 8	342	General Quiz 32	391
The World Game 11	343	General Quiz 33	392
Name the Year 5	344	General Quiz 34	393
League Cup 3	345	General Quiz 35	394
Transfer Trail 7	346	General Quiz 36	395
Fulham 1	347	General Quiz 37	396
Scottish Scene 4	348	General Quiz 38	397
The World Game 12	349	General Quiz 39	398
Transfer Trail 8	350	General Quiz 40	399
European Cups 5	351	General Quiz 41	400
Non-League 3	352	General Quiz 42	401
St Johnstone 1	353	General Quiz 43	402

General Quiz 44	403	General Quiz 94	453
General Quiz 45	404	General Quiz 95	454
General Quiz 46	405	General Quiz 96	455
General Quiz 47	406	General Quiz 97	456
General Quiz 48	407	General Quiz 98	457
General Quiz 49	408	General Quiz 99	458
General Quiz 50	409	General Quiz 100	459
General Quiz 51	410	General Quiz 101	460
General Quiz 52	411	General Quiz 102	461
General Quiz 53	412	General Quiz 103	462
General Quiz 54	413	General Quiz 104	463
General Quiz 55	414	General Quiz 105	464
General Quiz 56	415	General Quiz 106	465
General Quiz 57	416	General Quiz 107	466
General Quiz 58	417	General Quiz 108	467
General Quiz 59	418	General Quiz 109	468
General Quiz 60	419	General Quiz 110	469
General Quiz 61	420	General Quiz 111	470
General Quiz 62	421	General Quiz 112	471
General Quiz 63	422	General Quiz 113	472
General Quiz 64	423	General Quiz 114	473
General Quiz 65	424	General Quiz 115	474
General Quiz 66	425	General Quiz 116	475
General Quiz 67	426	General Quiz 117	476
General Quiz 68	427	General Quiz 118	477
General Quiz 69	428	General Quiz 119	478
General Quiz 70	429	General Quiz 120	479
General Quiz 71	430	General Quiz 121	480
General Quiz 72	431	General Quiz 122	481
General Quiz 73	432	General Quiz 123	482
General Quiz 74	433	General Quiz 124	483
General Quiz 75	434	General Quiz 125	484
General Quiz 76	435	General Quiz 126	485
General Quiz 77	436	General Quiz 127	486
General Quiz 78	437	General Quiz 128	487
General Quiz 79	438	General Quiz 129	488
General Quiz 80	439	General Quiz 130	489
General Quiz 81	440	General Quiz 131	490
General Quiz 82	441	General Quiz 132	491
General Quiz 83	442	General Quiz 133	492
General Quiz 84	443	General Quiz 134	493
General Quiz 85	444	General Quiz 135	494
General Quiz 86	445	General Quiz 136	495
General Quiz 87	446	General Quiz 137	496
General Quiz 88	447	General Quiz 138	497
General Quiz 89	448	General Quiz 139	498
General Quiz 90	449	General Quiz 140	499
General Quiz 91	450	General Quiz 141	500
General Quiz 92	451	General Quiz 142	501
General Quiz 93	452	General Quiz 143	502

General Quiz 144	503
General Quiz 145	504
General Quiz 146	505
General Quiz 147	506
General Quiz 148	507
General Quiz 149	508
General Quiz 150	509
General Quiz 151	510
General Quiz 152	511
General Quiz 153	512
General Quiz 154	513
General Quiz 155	514
General Quiz 156	515
General Quiz 157	516
General Quiz 158	517
General Quiz 159	518
General Quiz 160	519
General Quiz 161	520
General Quiz 162	521
General Quiz 163	522
General Quiz 164	523
General Quiz 165	524
General Quiz 166	525
General Quiz 167	526
General Quiz 168	527
General Quiz 169	528
General Quiz 170	529
General Quiz 171	530
General Quiz 172	531
TV	**533**
Cop Shows 1	534
Sport 1	535
Children's TV 1	536
Pot Luck 1	537
Comedy 1	538
Corrie 1	539
Wildlife 1	540
Dramas 1	541
EastEnders 1	542
Pot Luck 2	543
Quiz & Game Shows 1	544
Cop Shows 2	545
Comedy 2	546
Soaps 1	547
Name the Year 1	548
Catchphrases 1	549
Dramas 2	550
Pot Luck 3	551

Emmerdale 1	552
Comedy 3	553
Cop Shows 3	554
Children's TV 2	555
Soaps 2	556
Locations 1	557
Dramas 3	558
Brookside 1	559
Children's TV 3	560
Pot Luck 4	561
Soaps 3	562
Cop Shows 4	563
Comedy 4	564
Corrie 2	565
Dramas 4	566
Children's TV 4	567
Cop Shows 5	568
Comedy 5	569
Pot Luck 5	570
Locations 2	571
Soaps 4	572
Sport 2	573
Name the Year 2	574
Westerns 1	575
Comedy 6	576
Pot Luck 6	577
Cop Shows 6	578
Emmerdale 2	579
Children's TV 5	580
Dramas 5	581
Comedy 7	582
Soaps 5	583
Music 1	584
Pot Luck 7	585
Locations 3	586
Sci Fi 1	587
Comedy 8	588
Pot Luck 8	589
TV Chefs 1	590
Dramas 6	591
Corrie 3	592
Comedy 9	593
Pot Luck 9	594
Soaps 6	595
Quiz & Game Shows 2	596
Wildlife 2	597
Comedy 10	598
Dramas 7	599
Corrie 4	600
Children's TV 6	601

Comedy 11	602	Comedy 17	652
Westerns 2	603	Pot Luck 14	653
Children's TV 7	604	Dramas 14	654
EastEnders 2	605	Quiz & Game Shows 6	655
Emmerdale 3	606	Locations 6	656
Children's TV 8	607	Emmerdale 4	657
Dramas 8	608	Children's TV 12	658
Pot Luck 10	609	Sci Fi 5	659
Comedy 12	610	Soaps 11	660
TV Chefs 2	611	Cop Shows 9	661
Soaps 7	612	Dramas 15	662
Sci Fi 2	613	Music 3	663
Cop Shows 7	614	Comedy 18	664
Name the Year 3	615	Soaps 12	665
Comedy 13	616	Comedy 19	666
Quiz & Game Shows 3	617	Pot Luck 15	667
Locations 4	618	Name the Year 5	668
Dramas 9	619	Brookside 3	669
Chat Shows 1	620	Comedy 20	670
Pot Luck 11	621	Commercials 1	671
Sport 3	622	Dramas 16	672
Soaps 8	623	Pot Luck 16	673
Comedy 14	624	Music 4	674
Children's TV 9	625	Pot Luck 17	675
Brookside 2	626	Dramas 17	676
Sci Fi 3	627	Children's TV 13	677
Quiz & Game Shows 4	628	Comedy 21	678
Dramas 10	629	Soaps 13	679
Soaps 9	630	Sci Fi 6	680
Children's TV 10	631	Locations 7	681
Wildlife 3	632	Quiz & Game Shows 7	682
Name the Year 4	633	Children's TV 14	683
Comedy 15	634	Sci Fi 7	684
Music 2	635	Brookside 4	685
Dramas 11	636	Cop Shows 10	686
Locations 5	637	Children's TV 15	687
Corrie 5	638	Catchphrases 3	688
Pot Luck 12	639	Soaps 14	689
Quiz & Game Shows 5	640	Sci Fi 8	690
Sci Fi 4	641	Comedy 22	691
Children's TV 11	642	Chat Shows 2	692
Dramas 12	643	EastEnders 4	693
EastEnders 3	644	Sci Fi 9	694
Pot Luck 13	645	Pot Luck 18	695
Comedy 16	646	Docusoaps 1	696
Catchphrases 2	647	Comedy 23	697
Soaps 10	648	Cop Shows 11	698
Dramas 13	649	Comedy 24	699
Cop Shows 8	650	Pot Luck 19	700
News 1	651	Commercials 2	701

Music

Pot Luck 1

Answers on page 14

1. Who produced 'I'm The Urban Spaceman' for The Bonzo Dog Doo-Dah Band under the pseudonym Apollo C. Vermouth?

2. Who was charged with indecent exposure during a 1969 concert in Miami?

3. Which film star's eyes were the subject of a Kim Carnes hit of 1981?

4. Who wrote The Jackson Five's 'Doctor My Eyes'?

5. What taste did Acker Bilk have in 1963?

6. What were Pinkerton's Assorted Colours looking into in 1966?

7. What nationality were The Mixtures?

8. And what was the title of their only UK hit?

9. Who was 'Frozen' in 1998?

10. Which band's number one of 1979 was their first UK singles hit for 12 years?

11. With which successful Sixties band did Van Morrison play before going solo?

12. Who released the 1991 album 'Out Of Time'?

13. Who asked 'How Am I Supposed To Live Without You' in 1990?

14. 'Gertcha' was a hit for which Cockney duo?

15. Who recounted 'Mary's Prayer' in 1987?

16. Elkie Brooks and Robert Palmer sang together in which band?

Answers to page 14
ONE-HIT WONDERS 1: **1.** The Connells **2.** Buzz Clifford **3.** Oran 'Juice' Jones **4.** Janet Kay **5.** Father Christmas **6.** Hotshots **7.** 'Three Wheels On My Wagon' **8.** The Seashells **9.** Randy Vanwarmer **10.** 'You Keep Me Hanging On' **11.** 'Here I Go Again' **12.** Oliver **13.** Don Robertson **14.** 'More Than In Love' **15.** Stan Ridgway **16.** Rich Kids ('Rich Kids')

Fifties 1

Answers on page 15

1. Which was the biggest-selling single in the UK for 1958?

2. Who was 'Puttin' On The Style' in 1957?

3. Who had a hit with 'Be Bop A Lula' in 1956?

4. Who backed Joan Regan on her 1953 hit 'Ricochet'?

5. Which three artists had UK hits with 'Only Sixteen' in 1959?

6. Which 1958 number one for Tommy Edwards became a hit again for The Four Tops 12 years later?

7. Which British female singer's first chart entry was a version of Harry Belafonte's 'Banana Boat Song'?

8. Who sang the theme tune from the TV series *Rawhide*?

9. From which Hitchcock film was the Doris Day hit 'Que Sera Sera' taken?

10. How old was Frankie Lymon when he sang his 1956 number one 'Why Do Fools Fall In Love'?

11. Which two songs were placed equal at the top of the UK charts on 18 December 1959?

12. Who had hits in 1959 with 'Sea Of Love' and 'Bad Boy'?

13. For which two artists were 'Kisses Sweeter Than Wine' in 1957?

14. Dave King and Dean Martin both had hits with which song in 1956?

15. Who sang about the 'Gal With The Taller Shoes'?

16. Which capital city gave Frankie Vaughan his first hit in 1954?

Answers to page 15
ERIC CLAPTON 1: **1.** 1966 **2.** 'I Feel Free' **3.** 'Disraeli Gears' **4.** 1968 **5.** Blind Faith **6.** Derek and The Dominos ('Layla') **7.** 'I Shot The Sheriff' **8.** 'Slowhand' **9.** 'Wonderful Tonight' **10.** *Water* **11.** 'I Was Made To Love Her' **12.** 'Unplugged' **13.** 'Tears In Heaven' **14.** 'Love Can Build A Bridge' **15.** Elton John **16.** *Phenomenon*

One-Hit Wonders 1

Answers on page 12

1. Which act's only incursion into the UK charts was with ''74–'75' in 1995?

2. Who had a hit with 'Baby Sittin' Boogie' in 1961 and hasn't been heard of since?

3. Who took 'The Rain' to number four in 1986?

4. In 1979 'Silly Games' provided which artist with her only chart success?

5. Who did Greg Lake believe in to give him his only hit as a solo artist?

6. A cover version of 'Snoopy Versus The Red Baron' was a one-off success for which British group in 1973?

7. Which song about a Cherokee Indian ambush gave The New Christy Minstrels their only UK hit?

8. Who had a 1972 hit with a cover version of Lesley Gore's 'Maybe I Know'?

9. 'Just When I Needed You Most' was a 1979 top ten hit for which American artist?

10. What was the title of Vanilla Fudge's 1967 version of a Supremes song, itself later covered by Kim Wilde?

11. Which song gave Twiggy her only hit?

12. Who had a hit with 'Good Morning Starshine' from the musical *Hair*?

13. Who was 'The Happy Whistler' in 1956?

14. Which song from *Crossroads* went to number 1 in 1981 sung by Kate Robbins?

15. Who had a 1986 top five hit with 'Camouflage'?

16. In 1978, which UK band's only hit was named after them?

Answers to page 12
POT LUCK 1: **1.** Paul McCartney **2.** Jim Morrison **3.** Bette Davis
4. Jackson Browne **5.** 'A Taste Of Honey' **6.** 'Mirror, Mirror'
7. Australian **8.** 'The Pushbike Song' **9.** Madonna **10.** Pink Floyd
11. Them **12.** R.E.M. **13.** Michael Bolton **14.** Chas and Dave **15.** Danny Wilson **16.** Vinegar Joe

Eric Clapton 1

Answers on page 13

1. In which year were Cream formed?
2. What was the title of Cream's debut single?
3. From which Cream album was 'Sunshine Of Your Love' taken?
4. In which year did Cream break up?
5. Which band did Clapton form with Ginger Baker and Steve Winwood?
6. Which alias did Clapton adopt for a 1972 hit about George Harrison's wife, Patti Boyd?
7. Which song gave Clapton a US number one in 1974?
8. What was the title of Clapton's 1977 solo album?
9. Which 1978 ballad was the second song Clapton wrote about Patti Boyd?
10. In which Michael Caine film did Clapton make a cameo appearance?
11. Which Stevie Wonder song did Clapton select when he was a guest on *Desert Island Discs*?
12. Which Clapton collection won Album Of The Year at the 1993 Grammy Awards?
13. Which song was written about his dead son Conor who tragically fell to his death from the 53rd floor of a New York apartment block in 1991?
14. On which 1995 Comic Relief song did Clapton team up with Cher, Chrissie Hynde and Neneh Cherry?
15. With whom did Clapton duet on 'Runaway Train'?
16. From the soundtrack of which film was the single 'Change The World' taken?

Answers to page 13
FIFTIES 1: 1. 'Jailhouse Rock' 2. Lonnie Donegan 3. Gene Vincent
4. The Squadronaires 5. Sam Cooke, Craig Douglas and Al Saxon 6. 'It's All In The Game' 7. Shirley Bassey 8. Frankie Laine 9. *The Man Who Knew Too Much* 10. 13 11. 'What Do You Want' (Adam Faith) and 'What Do You Want To Make Those Eyes At Me For' (Emile Ford and The Checkmates) 12. Marty Wilde 13. Jimmie Rodgers and Frankie Vaughan 14. 'Memories Are Made Of This' 15. Michael Holliday 16. 'Istanbul'

Heavy Metal 1

Answers on page 18

1. Which heavy metal frontman formed an unlikely double act with Mr Bean on a 1992 single?

2. Which Aerosmith album featured 'Walk This Way'?

3. Which band chose their name after rejecting Heads Of Amazon and AIDS?

4. Which glove puppet was frequently lowered onstage at Iron Maiden concerts at the request of drummer Nicko McBrain?

5. Which band were famous for their painted faces?

6. 'Geezer' Butler is bassist with which band?

7. Who released the live album 'Made In Japan'?

8. Which heavy metal keyboard player was married to Cher?

9. Which band got to number 13 in the UK charts in 1987 with 'Wanted Dead Or Alive'?

10. Who was sacked from Hawkwind in 1975 for spending five days in a Canadian jail for drug possession?

11. Which band rejected the name Bastard before settling on their new identity?

12. What was Hawkwind's only UK top thirty hit?

13. From which film was the Aerosmith single 'I Don't Want To Miss A Thing' taken?

14. Richie Sambora, David Bryan and Tico Torres were founder members of which band?

15. Who strongly advised: 'Run To The Hills' in 1982?

16. Whose albums included 'The Razor's Edge' and 'Ballbreaker'?

Answers to page 18
NAME CHANGES 1: 1. The Delfonics 2. Terence 3. The Communards
4. Brenda Lee 5. Ewan MacColl 6. Carole King 7. George 8. Steve Tyler
9. Theodore 10. Edwin Starr 11. Aneka ('Japanese Boy') 12. Kiss
13. Chris Farlowe 14. Nina Simone 15. Slash 16. Sweetshop

Duos 1

Answers on page 19

1. Who teamed up with Nancy Sinatra for the 1971 hit 'Did You Ever'?

2. Who links Yazoo and Erasure?

3. Who was Jimmy Somerville's partner in The Communards?

4. Which cover of an Elvis song gave The Pet Shop Boys a number one in 1987?

5. Who joined Billy Preston on the 1979 hit 'With You I'm Born Again'?

6. Which two singers joined forces in 1986 for 'On My Own'?

7. Which Sixties duo could have been called Stewart and Clyde?

8. Which band had a 1986 hit with 'Sometimes'?

9. Which pair pleaded 'Don't Stay Away Too Long' in 1974?

10. What was the title of The Pet Shop Boys' second UK number one?

11. Which girl duo got to number five in the charts in 1984 with 'Since Yesterday'?

12. What was Peter and Gordon's follow-up to 'A World Without Love'?

13. With whom did Elton John release a live version of 'Don't Let The Sun Go Down On Me' in 1991?

14. For whom was it 'Yesterday Once More' in 1973?

15. Which Everly Brothers classic was a hit for Bobbie Gentry and Glen Campbell in 1969?

16. Which two country artists got together for 'Islands In The Stream' in 1983?

Answers to page 19
SPICE GIRLS 1: **1.** Simon Fuller **2.** Geri **3.** 1996 **4.** 1998 **5.** Emma Bunton **6.** Victoria Beckham (with Sophie Ellis Bextor, daughter of Janet Ellis) **7.** 'Say You'll Be There' **8.** Mel B **9.** Melanie C **10.** 'When You're Gone' **11.** 'Mama/Who Do You Think You Are' **12.** *Spiceworld: The Movie* **13.** Richard E. Grant **14.** 'Goin' Down' **15.** 'Look At Me' **16.** 'Mi Chico Latino'

Name Changes 1

Answers on page 16

1. Which Philly band were previously known as The Four Gents?

2. What is the real Christian name of 'Geezer' Butler?

3. Which duo were formerly called The Committee but changed it in honour of a group of 19th-century French Republicans?

4. Which Sixties American singer shortened her name from Brenda Mae Tarpley?

5. Which folk singer did Jimmie Miller become?

6. Which singer/songwriter found something more regal than Carole Klein?

7. What is Zoot Money's real name?

8. Which heavy metal singer was born Steve Tallarico?

9. What prefix did Supergrass drop from their name?

10. Which Motown artist changed his name from Charles Hatcher?

11. What stage name did Mary Sandeman adopt for her Oriental-sounding number one?

12. Which rock band were previously called Wicked Lester?

13. Which British Sixties R & B singer was born John Deighton?

14. Which singer began life as Eunice Waymon?

15. As which heavy metal guitarist is Saul Hudson better known?

16. What were Sweet originally called?

Answers to page 16
HEAVY METAL 1: 1. Bruce Dickinson 2. 'Toys In The Attic' 3. Guns 'N' Roses 4. Sooty 5. Kiss 6. Black Sabbath 7. Deep Purple 8. Greg Allman 9. Bon Jovi 10. Lemmy 11. Motörhead 12. 'Silver Machine' 13. *Armageddon* 14. Bon Jovi 15. Iron Maiden 16. AC/DC

Spice Girls 1

Answers on page 17

1. Who was The Spice Girls' manager?

2. Of the original line-up, who was the oldest Spice Girl?

3. In which year did 'Wannabe' reach number one in the UK?

4. When did Geri leave the band?

5. Which Spice Girl once played a mugger in *EastEnders*?

6. Which Spice Girl has had a running feud with the daughter of a former *Blue Peter* presenter?

7. What was the title of The Spice Girls' second number one?

8. Which Spice Girl presented a TV talent show in 2001?

9. Which Spice Girl recorded a duet with Bryan Adams?

10. What was its title?

11. Which 1997 double A-side was a charity record in aid of Comic Relief's Red Nose Day?

12. What was the name of The Spice Girls' first film?

13. Who played the girls' manager in that film?

14. What was the title of Melanie C's second single?

15. What was Geri Halliwell's first solo single?

16. Which song gave Geri Halliwell her first solo UK number one?

Answers to page 17
DUOS 1: **1.** Lee Hazlewood **2.** Vince Clarke **3.** Richard Coles **4.** 'Always On My Mind' **5.** Syreeta **6.** Patti Labelle and Michael McDonald **7.** Chad and Jeremy **8.** Erasure **9.** Peters and Lee **10.** 'It's A Sin' **11.** Strawberry Switchblade **12.** 'Nobody I Know' **13.** George Michael **14.** The Carpenters **15.** 'All I Have To Do Is Dream' **16.** Kenny Rogers and Dolly Parton

Rap 1

Answers on page 22

1. From which film was Snoop Doggy Dog's 'We Just Wanna Party With You' taken?

2. Who was The Fresh Prince in DJ Jazzy Jeff and The Fresh Prince?

3. Which rap artist had a number one in 1995 with 'Gangsta's Paradise'?

4. Which Stevie Wonder song was sampled on 'Gangsta's Paradise'?

5. Which Will Smith hit was dedicated to his son Tre?

6. What does LL Cool J stand for?

7. Which Bill Withers track was sampled on LL Cool J's single 'Phenomenon'?

8. Whose albums include 'Raising Hell' and 'Tougher Than Leather'?

9. Who released 'Rapper's Delight' in 1979?

10. Which mainstream band had a 1981 hit with 'Rapture'?

11. Who was often backed by The Furious Five?

12. Which Grandmaster was born Melvin Glover?

13. Which rap act are known as 'The Black Sex Pistols'?

14. What was the title of Vanilla Ice's 1990 UK number one?

15. And which Queen and David Bowie song did it sample?

16. Whose 1993 album was called 'Home Invasion'?

Answers to page 22
BOY BANDS 1: 1. Andy Williams 2. Donnie Wahlberg 3. 'Rollercoaster' 4. New Kids On The Block 5. 'Night To Remember' 6. 'The Journey' 7. 'The Proud One' 8. 'Love Me For A Reason' 9. Bad Boys Inc. 10. 'Crazy Horses' 11. Point Break 12. 'If You Go Away' 13. 1973 14. Alan 15. Boston 16. 'Don't Make Me Wait'

Name Changes 2

Answers on page 23

1. Who changed his name from August Darnell?

2. What is Ginger Baker's real first name?

3. What is Eric Clapton's real surname?

4. Which rap artist decided that Robert Van Winkle just wasn't cool enough?

5. Which US band who weren't afraid of dying started out as The Stalk-Forrest Group?

6. What was Louise's maiden name?

7. Which band who have had hits spanning five decades used to be known as The Rattlesnakes?

8. Which sinister British pop star of the Sixties changed his name from David Holgate Grundy?

9. Which rap artist was born Artis Ivey?

10. What was Eden Kane's real name?

11. Which mixer changed his name from William Wainwright?

12. Which Sixties girl group were previously called The Poquellos?

13. Who is William Johnson better known as?

14. Which falsetto singer was born Francis Castelluccio?

15. Who shortened her name from Eithne Ni Bhraonain?

16. Which keyboard player/producer started life as Thomas Morgan Robertson before opting for a better sound?

Answers to page 23
ALBUMS 1: **1.** Foreigner **2.** 'Everything Must Go' **3.** Leo Sayer **4.** Mike Oldfield **5.** Abba **6.** 'Rumours' (Fleetwood Mac) **7.** A cigarette **8.** 'Songs From The Big Chair' **9.** The Who **10.** David Bowie **11.** The Police **12.** Catatonia **13.** 'Our Town' **14.** Robson and Jerome **15.** Pink Floyd ('Wish You Were Here') **16.** Bryan Ferry

Boy Bands 1

Answers on page 20

1. On which singer's US TV show did The Osmonds first come to prominence?

2. Which member of New Kids On The Block fell through an unlocked trapdoor on stage mid-way through a New York concert in 1990?

3. What was the title of Let Loose's second album?

4. Which band were sued by three girl fans and a mother for 'pain and suffering' following a stampede at a 1991 concert?

5. A cover of which Shalamar track gave 911 their first hit?

6. What was the title of 911's debut album?

7. Which Four Seasons track did The Osmonds cover in 1975?

8. What was The Osmonds' only UK number one?

9. Which British band had a 1994 top ten hit with 'More To This World'?

10. What was The Osmonds' first UK top five hit?

11. 'Do We Rock' was a first UK hit for which boy band?

12. Which New Kids On The Block single shared the same title as a Terry Jacks hit from 1974?

13. In which year did The Osmonds release 'Let Me In'?

14. Who is the oldest Osmond?

15. From which American city do New Kids On The Block originate?

16. What was 911's first UK top ten single?

Answers to page 20
RAP 1: **1.** *Men In Black* **2.** Will Smith **3.** Coolio **4.** 'Pastime Paradise'
5. 'Just The Two Of Us' **6.** Ladies Love Cool James (his real name is James Smith) **7.** 'Who Is He And What Is He To You' **8.** Run D.M.C.
9. The Sugarhill Gang **10.** Blondie **11.** Grandmaster Flash
12. Grandmaster Melle Mel **13.** Public Enemy **14.** 'Ice Ice Baby'
15. 'Under Pressure' **16.** Ice-T

Albums 1

Answers on page 21

1. Which US band had a number one album with 'Agent Provocateur' in 1984?

2. Which Manic Street Preachers album contains 'A Design For Life'?

3. Which solo singer released the album 'Silver Bird' which reached number two in 1974?

4. Who recorded 'Hergest Ridge'?

5. Which band had the biggest-selling UK albums for both 1976 and 1977?

6. The title of which band's best-selling album from 1977 was taken from the crumbling relationships occurring within the unit?

7. What is Paul McCartney holding in his right hand on the cover of 'Abbey Road'?

8. Which Tears For Fears album features 'Shout' and 'Everybody Wants To Rule The World'?

9. Whose greatest hits album was titled 'Meaty, Beaty, Big and Bouncy'?

10. Whose 1972 album was definitely 'Hunky Dory'?

11. 'Outlandos D'Amour', 'Reggatta De Blanc' and 'Zenyatta Mondatta' were the first three albums by which band?

12. Whose 2001 album was called 'Papers, Scissors, Stone'?

13. What was the title of Deacon Blue's 1994 Greatest Hits album?

14. Which duo had the best-selling UK album of 1995?

15. The title of whose 1975 album sounded like a holiday invitation to Judith Chalmers?

16. Whose 1978 album was called 'The Bride Stripped Bare'?

Answers to page 21
NAME CHANGES 2: 1. Kid Creole 2. Peter 3. Clapp 4. Vanilla Ice
5. Blue Oyster Cult 6. Nurding 7. The Bee Gees 8. Dave Berry
9. Coolio 10. Richard Sarstedt 11. William Orbit 12. The Shirelles
13. Holly Johnson 14. Frankie Valli 15. Enya 16. Thomas Dolby

R & B 1

Answers on page 26

1. Under what name did Barry White perform in the early Sixties?

2. Which guitarist was the mainstay of Ten Years After?

3. Simon Kirke was drummer with which major R & B band?

4. Who recorded the posthumous 1971 album 'Pearl'?

5. Which member of Free was the son of a well-known actor?

6. Which replacement as drummer for Ringo Starr in Rory Storm and The Hurricanes went on to form his own R & B band?

7. Which R & B artist duetted with Celine Dion on the 1998 hit 'I'm Your Angel'?

8. Which Eric Clapton song was taken to number three in the charts by Damage in 1997?

9. Which band's debut album was titled 'Tons Of Sobs'?

10. Who featured on the Another Level hit 'Summertime'?

11. Who had the 'Love Of A Lifetime' in 1999?

12. Whose 1998 album was titled 'Anutha Zone'?

13. What was Barry White's only UK number one?

14. Which Barry White single reached number two in the UK charts in 1976?

15. Who featured on the Destiny's Child hit 'No No No'?

16. What was the title of the second album by Destiny's Child?

Answers to page 26
POT LUCK 2: 1. Carl Douglas 2. Ray Sawyer 3. Drums 4. Scotland
5. The Doobie Brothers 6. Ruby Flipper 7. Don 8. Jesus Jones
9. Jefferson Airplane 10. The Housemartins 11. Jerome 12. Jon Lord and Nick Simper 13. The Turtles 14. Tim and Neil Finn 15. A Mississippi steamboat 16. Bob Geldof

Number Twos 1

Answers on page 27

Which artists reached number two in the UK charts with the following singles?

1. 'Annie I'm Not Your Daddy' (1982)

2. 'Church Of The Poison Mind' (1983)

3. 'Then He Kissed Me' (1963)

4. 'Opposites Attract' (1990)

5. 'Night Of Fear' (1967)

6. 'The Bitterest Pill (I Ever Had To Swallow)' (1982)

7. 'A Man Without Love' (1968)

8. 'Someone Else's Baby' (1960)

9. 'Why Can't I Wake Up With You?' (1993)

10. 'Can't Get By Without You' (1976)

11. 'Morningtown Ride' (1966)

12. '(Dancing) On A Saturday Night' (1973)

13. 'Dreaming' (1979)

14. 'Private Investigations' (1982)

15. 'Save A Prayer' (1982)

16. 'Cindy Incidentally' (1973)

Answers to page 27
NAME CHANGES 3: **1.** Gene Vincent **2.** Rory Storm **3.** Ten Years After **4.** Engelbert Humperdinck **5.** James **6.** Warsaw **7.** Tom Jones **8.** Betty Boo **9.** Peter Smith **10.** Lieutenant Pigeon **11.** Jack Bruce **12.** J.J. Barrie **13.** Karl Denver **14.** The Grateful Dead **15.** The Dreamers **16.** The Four Tops

Pot Luck 2

Answers on page 24

1. Who was 'Kung Fu Fighting' in 1974?

2. Which member of Dr Hook wore an eye patch?

3. What instrument does Bill Bruford play?

4. In which country was Talking Heads' David Byrne born?

5. Which Seventies band took their name from the slang for a marijuana cigarette?

6. Who replaced Pan's People on *Top of the Pops?*

7. Who was the older of The Everly Brothers?

8. Which band's debut album was called 'Liquidizer'?

9. From which band did Jefferson Starship evolve?

10. Which Eighties chart band had a bass player named Stan Cullimore?

11. What did the J in the J. Geils Band stand for?

12. Which two members of Deep Purple were previously in The Flowerpot Men?

13. Flo and Eddie were an off-shoot from which Sixties group?

14. Which brothers were members of Split Enz and Crowded House?

15. What was 'Proud Mary' in the 1969 hit for Creedence Clearwater Revival?

16. Which former punk has the middle names Frederick Zenon?

Answers to page 24
R & B 1: 1. Barry Lee 2. Alvin Lee 3. Free 4. Janis Joplin 5. Paul Kossoff (son of David) 6. Keef Hartley 7. R. Kelly 8. 'Wonderful Tonight' 9. Free 10. TQ 11. Honeyz 12. Dr John 13. 'You're The First, The Last, My Everything' 14. 'You See The Trouble With Me' 15. Wyclef Jean 16. 'The Writing's On The Wall'

Name Changes 3

Answers on page 25

1. Which rock 'n' roller was born Eugene Craddock?

2. Which Merseybeat band leader sought something more tempestuous than Alan Caldwell?

3. Which British R & B band changed their name from The Jaybirds?

4. Who is Gerry Dorsey better known as?

5. What is Midge Ure's real Christian name?

6. As what were Joy Division previously known?

7. Which international star was born Thomas Woodward?

8. Who changed her name from Alison Clarkson?

9. What was Crispian St Peters's less impressive real name?

10. Which band who had a novelty hit in the Seventies started out as Stavely Makepiece?

11. Which member of a key R & B threesome of the late Sixties was born John Asher Simon Bruce?

12. What name did Barrie Authors use to reach the top of the charts in 1976?

13. Which Sixties frontman of a trio Americanised his name from Angus McKenzie?

14. Which US acid rock band of the Sixties were formerly known as The Warlocks?

15. Which Sixties backing band used to be called The Kingfishers?

16. To what did The Four Aims change their name?

Answers to page 25
NUMBER TWOS 1: **1.** Kid Creole and The Coconuts **2.** Culture Club **3.** The Crystals **4.** Paula Abdul **5.** The Move **6.** The Jam **7.** Engelbert Humperdinck **8.** Adam Faith **9.** Take That **10.** The Real Thing **11.** The Seekers **12.** Barry Blue **13.** Blondie **14.** Dire Straits **15.** Duran Duran **16.** The Faces

Cover Versions 1

Answers on page 30

1. Which Canadian chanteuse had the original hit with Boyzone's 'You Needed Me'?

2. Which song links The Real Thing, Sonia and Sean Maguire?

3. Which Bad Company track did Pauline Henry cover in 1993?

4. Who discovered that 'The First Cut Is The Deepest' ten years before Rod Stewart?

5. Faith No More covered which Commodores single in 1993?

6. The McCoys and The Sandpipers both had hits with which song?

7. In 1988, who covered The Isley Brothers hit 'Harvest For The World'?

8. The Detroit Emeralds, Forrest and Shakin' Stevens have all had hits with which song?

9. Which Elton John song was covered by Oleta Adams in 1991?

10. Kavana recorded which Shalamar hit in 1997?

11. Who originally had a UK hit with David Cassidy's 1972 chart topper 'How Can I Be Sure'?

12. Which Donna Summer hit did Arsenal Football Club re-record in 1998?

13. Which title was a hit for both Michael Jackson and Marti Webb?

14. Which track links Harold Faltermeyer and Clock?

15. Which Sweet song did Def Leppard cover in 1994?

16. The Kinks and The Stranglers both had top ten hits with which song?

Answers to page 30
CHART TOPPERS 1: 1. 1973 2. 1998 3. 1995 4. 1966 5. 1959 6. 1987 7. 1982 8. 1975 9. 1997 10. 1963 11. 1969 12. 1979 13. 1987 14. 1990 15. 1993 16. 1977

Pot Luck 3

Answers on page 31

1. In which month of the year was Wizzard's 'Rock 'n' Roll Winter' released?
2. Which 52-year-old had a number one hit in 1998?
3. Which band took their name from a David Lynch film?
4. Who had more UK top ten hits than any other act in the first half of the Eighties?
5. Which divine American female artist once worked as a pineapple chunker in Hawaii?
6. Which district of London was mentioned in Marillion's 'Kayleigh'?
7. Which Mark Knopfler song was used as the theme tune for Britain's 1986 challenge for the America's Cup yachting prize?
8. What were Harold and Herbie known as when they joined the ranks of one-hit wonders in 1958?
9. Donald Fagen and Walter Becker were the prime movers in which band?
10. Who was the lead singer with The Gingerbreads?
11. Which footballer teamed up with Lindisfarne for a 1990 version of 'Fog On The Tyne'?
12. John Phillips and Denny Doherty were the male members of which Sixties foursome?
13. How did Jimi Hendrix attract headlines at the 1967 Monterey Pop Festival?
14. Which Peter, Paul and Mary song was a 1963 hit for Trini Lopez?
15. Which member of Darts went on to present *Tiswas*?
16. Who were the first overseas act to have their first three singles reach number one in the UK?

Answers to page 31
THE POLICE 1: 1. 'The Dream Of The Blue Turtles' 2. CIA agent
3. Henry Padovani 4. Alberto Y Lost Trios Paranoias 5. 1978 6. Ace
7. The Kennedy Space Centre, Houston 8. 'Invisible Sun' 9. *Rumble Fish*
10. 'Spread A Little Happiness' 11. 'Synchronicity' 12. 'Synchronicity'
13. 'Every Breath You Take' 14. 'Message In A Bottle' 15. Andy Summers
16. Trudie Styler

Chart Toppers 1

Answers on page 28

In which years did the following singles reach number one in the UK?

1. 'Get Down' (Gilbert O'Sullivan)

2. 'No Matter What' (Boyzone)

3. 'Think Twice' (Celine Dion)

4. 'Sunny Afternoon' (The Kinks)

5. 'Only Sixteen' (Craig Douglas)

6. 'Respectable' (Mel and Kim)

7. 'The Lion Sleeps Tonight' (Tight Fit)

8. 'January' (Pilot)

9. 'Beetlebum' (Blur)

10. 'She Loves You' (The Beatles)

11. 'Albatross' (Fleetwood Mac)

12. 'Video Killed The Radio Star' (Buggles)

13. 'It's A Sin' (The Pet Shop Boys)

14. 'A Little Time' (The Beautiful South)

15. 'Pray' (Take That)

16. 'When I Need You' (Leo Sayer)

Answers to page 28
COVER VERSIONS 1: **1.** Anne Murray **2.** 'You To Me Are Everything'
3. 'Feel Like Making Love' **4.** P.P. Arnold **5.** 'Easy' **6.** 'Hang On Sloopy'
7. The Christians **8.** 'Feel The Need In Me' **9.** 'Don't Let The Sun Go
Down On Me' **10.** 'I Can Make You Feel Good' **11.** Dusty Springfield
12. 'Hot Stuff' **13.** 'Ben' **14.** 'Axel F' **15.** 'Action' **16.** 'All Day And All Of
The Night'

The Police 1

Answers on page 29

1. What was the title of Sting's first solo album?

2. What did Stewart Copeland's father do for a living?

3. Which member of The Police quit the band in 1977, leaving them as a trio?

4. Which band did The Police support on their first UK tour?

5. In which year was 'Roxanne' released as a single?

6. Which character did Sting play in the film *Quadrophenia*?

7. Where did The Police film the video for 'Walking On The Moon'?

8. Which Police single was inspired by the troubles in Northern Ireland?

9. For which Francis Ford Coppola movie of 1982 did Stewart Copeland write the score?

10. What was Sting's first solo single?

11. Which album was written by Sting at Ian Fleming's former Jamaican home?

12. From which album was 'Every Breath You Take' extracted as a single?

13. Which Police track was named Song Of The Year at the 1984 Grammy Awards?

14. Which was the band's first UK number one?

15. Which band member released the solo album 'XYZ'?

16. Who did Sting marry in 1992?

Answers to page 29
POT LUCK 3: 1. April 2. Cher 3. Erasure (*Eraserhead*) 4. Madness
5. Bette Midler 6. Belsize Park 7. 'Going Home' 8. The Kalin Twins
9. Steely Dan 10. Goldie 11. Paul Gascoigne 12. Mamas and The Papas
13. By burning his guitar 14. 'If I Had A Hammer' 15. Den Hegarty
16. Aqua

Girl Bands 1

Answers on page 34

1. Which band had Nineties hits with 'Creep', 'No Scrubs' and 'Unpretty'?

2. How many UK top ten singles hits did The Nolans have?

3. Which girl group had a 1963 hit with 'Then He Kissed Me'?

4. Who enquired: 'Is that Jimmy's ring you're wearing'?

5. Which member of The Bangles co-wrote 'Eternal Flame'?

6. Sarah, Keren and Siobhan were better known as which group?

7. Who sang lead vocals with The Chiffons until 1969?

8. 'Right Now' was a number one album in 2001 for which girl band?

9. 'Power Of A Woman' and 'I Am Blessed' were 1995 hits for which band?

10. Which two sisters were members of Eternal?

11. In which year did Louise leave Eternal?

12. Which girl band turned down The Crystals' US number one 'He's A Rebel' because they were afraid the title would stir up trouble in the south?

13. With which band did The Supremes record the album 'The Magnificent 7'?

14. Who did The Ronettes support on a 1964 tour of Britain?

15. Which Bananarama single was originally titled 'Big Red Motorbike'?

16. Which Martha Reeves and The Vandellas track was originally released in the UK in 1964 but did not become a top ten hit until 1969?

Answers to page 34
POT LUCK 4: 1. Eyes 2. Gary Numan 3. Chuck Berry 4. Björk 5. Dave Berry 6. Blue Oyster Cult 7. Brad Roberts 8. The Grateful Dead 9. 1969 10. Roy Wood 11. Ugly Kid Joe 12. Dog kennels 13. Val Doonican 14. 'Lazy River' 15. Gorillaz 16. Petula Clark

Chart Toppers 2

Answers on page 35

In which years did the following tracks top the UK charts?

1. 'Skweeze Me, Please Me' (Slade)

2. 'Don't Give Up On Us' (David Soul)

3. 'Everlasting Love' (Love Affair)

4. 'Distant Drums' (Jim Reeves)

5. 'Mr Vain' (Culture Beat)

6. 'I Believe I Can Fly' (R. Kelly)

7. 'Pipes Of Peace' (Paul McCartney)

8. 'Running Bear' (Johnny Preston)

9. 'The Name Of The Game' (Abba)

10. 'Start' (The Jam)

11. 'Do You Really Want To Hurt Me' (Culture Club)

12. 'Two Tribes' (Frankie Goes To Hollywood)

13. 'Never Ever' (All Saints)

14. 'Vogue' (Madonna)

15. 'I Should Have Known Better' (Jim Diamond)

16. 'Blackberry Way' (The Move)

Answers to page 35
PRINCE 1: 1. The Revolution 2. *Purple Rain* 3. 'The Most Beautiful Girl In The World' 4. 'For You' 5. Most of the tour was cancelled due to poor ticket sales 6. James Brown 7. 1984 8. Elaine Paige and Barbara Dickson 9. Alexander Nevermind 10. 1987 11. A squiggle 12. A lollipop 13. 'Batdance' 14. 'Betcha By Golly Wow' 15. Christopher Tracy 16. A huge pink Cadillac

Pot Luck 4

Answers on page 32

1. Which word was in both of Art Garfunkel's UK number ones?

2. Which rock star tried to fly around the world, only to end up in an Indian military zone?

3. Which Fifties rock 'n' roll star spent three years in jail as a teenager for armed robbery?

4. Which artist's surname is Gudmundsdóttir?

5. Who had a Sixties hit with 'The Crying Game'?

6. Who said '(Don't Fear) The Reaper'?

7. Who was the lead singer with Crash Test Dummies?

8. Which US acid rock band chose their name at random in 1965 from the pages of the Oxford English Dictionary?

9. In which year was the Woodstock Festival?

10. Which colourful British star's real first names are Ulysses Adrian?

11. Who had a 1993 hit with 'Cats In The Cradle'?

12. What did Cyndi Lauper used to clean for a living?

13. Who got out of his rocking chair and tried to 'Walk Tall' in 1964?

14. Which Hoagy Carmichael song was a number two UK hit for Bobby Darin in 1961?

15. Which cartoon group were formed by Damon Albarn?

16. In 1967, who was convinced that the other man's grass was always greener?

Answers to page 32
GIRL BANDS 1: **1.** TLC **2.** Three **3.** The Crystals **4.** The Shangri-Las ('Leader Of The Pack') **5.** Susanna Hoffs **6.** Bananarama **7.** Judy Craig **8.** Atomic Kitten **9.** Eternal **10.** Easther and Vernie Bennett **11.** 1995 **12.** The Shirelles **13.** The Four Tops **14.** The Rolling Stones **15.** 'Shy Boy' **16.** 'Dancing In The Street'

Prince 1

Answers on page 33

1. What was the name of Prince's occasional backing band?

2. From which film was 'When Doves Cry' taken?

3. What was Prince's first UK number one single?

4. What was the title of his debut album?

5. What happened when Prince first came to the UK in 1981?

6. Seeing which artist in concert inspired Prince to become a musician?

7. In which year did the film *Purple Rain* open?

8. Which duo kept '1999/Little Red Corvette' off the UK top spot?

9. Under which pseudonym did Prince write 'Sugar Walls' for Sheena Easton?

10. In which year was the album 'Sign Of The Times' released?

11. To what did Prince change his name in 1993?

12. What did Prince suck throughout the 1995 American Music Awards?

13. Which was the first Prince single to be taken from the movie *Batman*?

14. Which Stylistics song did Prince cover in 1996?

15. Which pseudonym did Prince use when writing 'Manic Monday' for The Bangles?

16. In what did Prince enter the stage on his 1988 'Lovesexy' tour?

Answers to page 33
CHART TOPPERS 2: 1. 1973 2. 1977 3. 1968 4. 1966 5. 1993 6. 1997
7. 1984 8. 1960 9. 1977 10. 1980 11. 1982 12. 1984 13. 1998 14. 1990
15. 1984 16. 1969

Nineties 1

Answers on page 38

Which artists had top ten UK hits with the following tracks in the Nineties?

1. 'Slam Dunk (Da Funk)'

2. 'Smack My Bitch Up'

3. 'North Country Boy'

4. 'Not Over You Yet'

5. 'My Oh My'

6. 'Mary Had A Little Boy'

7. 'The Millennium Prayer'

8. 'If You Buy This Record Your Life Will Be Better'

9. 'Doodah!'

10. 'Shiny Happy People'

11. 'Satan'

12. 'Stupid Girl'

13. 'Sailing On The Seven Seas'

14. 'You Stole The Sun From My Heart'

15. 'Get The Message'

16. 'Get Get Down'

Answers to page 38
POT LUCK 5: **1.** The Jackson Five (to honour Michael's 30 years in showbiz) **2.** Orchestral Manoeuvres in the Dark **3.** Australian **4.** The Shades **5.** Salt 'N' Pepa **6.** Sailor **7.** 10cc **8.** Al Green **9.** Frank Zappa **10.** Benny and Graham **11.** Staind **12.** Freddie and The Dreamers **13.** Because the title was seen as promoting the magazine **14.** Jon Moss **15.** One **16.** 'Night Owl'

Heavy Metal 2

Answers on page 39

1. Who was lead singer with Whitesnake?

2. What was the name of the final Deep Purple studio album?

3. John Kay was the singer with which Sixties band?

4. Which band's debut album was 'Bleach'?

5. Which Guns 'N' Roses song is on the soundtrack to *End of Days*?

6. Which German band was founded by Rudolf and Michael Schenker in 1971?

7. Whose 1980 album was titled 'Strong Arm Of The Law'?

8. 'Since You Been Gone' was a 1979 hit for which band?

9. Who were 'Back In Black' in 1980?

10. Which former member of Deep Purple joined Rainbow in 1979?

11. Which ex-member of Deep Purple and Rainbow used to play in Screaming Lord Sutch's band?

12. Which Scorpions single reached number two in the UK charts in 1991?

13. Which Guns 'N' Roses album contained a song written by Charles Manson?

14. Which Whitesnake album got to number two in the UK charts in 1981?

15. Which band were formed in 1976 by bass guitarist Steve Harris?

16. Who joined Deep Purple as vocalist in 1969?

Answers to page 39
ONE-HIT WONDERS 2: **1.** Renaissance **2.** The Rattles **3.** Nana Mouskouri **4.** *Full Metal Jacket* **5.** Al Matthews **6.** Keith Marshall **7.** McFadden and Whitehead **8.** Maureen McGovern **9.** Mary McGregor **10.** Gino Latino **11.** Rodney Franklin **12.** 'Peppermint Twist' **13.** Anne-Marie David **14.** Johnny Cymbal **15.** Louise Cordet **16.** Bimbo Jet

Pot Luck 5

Answers on page 36

1. Which group reunited in September 2001 for the first time since 1984?

2. What does OMD stand for?

3. What nationality is Helen Reddy?

4. With which group did Lou Reed make his recording debut in 1957?

5. Cheryl James and Sandra Denton were better known as which American duo?

6. Which nautical band enthused about 'Girls Girls Girls' in 1976?

7. Hotlegs were the forerunners of which Seventies supergroup?

8. Who had hits with 'Tired Of Being Alone' and 'Let's Stay Together'?

9. Who was leader of the Mothers Of Invention?

10. What are the Christian names of Seventies duo Gallagher and Lyle?

11. Who had a number one album in 2001 with 'Break The Cycle'?

12. Who encouraged us to 'Do The Freddie'?

13. Why did the BBC ban Dr Hook's 'The Cover Of Rolling Stone'?

14. Who was drummer with Culture Club?

15. How old was Marti Pellow when 'Love Is All Around' was a hit for The Troggs?

16. What was Gerry Rafferty's follow-up to 'Baker Street'?

Answers to page 36
NINETIES 1: **1.** Five **2.** The Prodigy **3.** The Charlatans **4.** Diana Ross **5.** Aqua **6.** Snap! **7.** Cliff Richard **8.** Tamperer featuring Maya **9.** Cartoons **10.** R.E.M. **11.** Orbital **12.** Garbage **13.** OMD **14.** Manic Street Preachers **15.** Electronic **16.** Paul Johnson

One-Hit Wonders 2

Answers on page 37

1. Which band's only UK hit was 'Northern Lights' in 1978?

2. Which German group charted with 'The Witch' in 1970?

3. Which Greek singer's only UK hit single was 'Only Love'?

4. The title track from which film gave Abigail Mead and Nigel Goulding a number two hit in 1987?

5. In 1975, 'Fool' gave which American singer his only UK chart action?

6. Who was 'Only Crying' in 1981?

7. Which duo were wrong when they said 'Ain't No Stoppin' Us Now' in 1979?

8. Who was doing 'The Continental' in 1976?

9. Who was 'Torn Between Two Lovers' in 1977?

10. Which Italian artist reached the UK top twenty with 'Welcome' in 1990?

11. Who got to number seven with 'The Groove' in 1980?

12. Joey Dee and The Starliters had a hit with which dance record in 1962?

13. Which 1973 Eurovision Song Contest winner had a 'Wonderful Dream'?

14. Which singer, also named after a musical instrument, extolled the virtues of 'Mr Bass Man' in 1963?

15. Which French artist said 'I'm Just A Baby' in 1962?

16. Which French act had a 1975 hit with 'El Bimbo'?

Answers to page 37
HEAVY METAL 2: **1.** David Coverdale **2.** Abandon **3.** Steppenwolf **4.** Nirvana **5.** 'Oh My God' **6.** The Scorpions **7.** Saxon **8.** Rainbow **9.** AC/DC **10.** Roger Glover **11.** Ritchie Blackmore **12.** 'Wind Of Change' **13.** 'The Spaghetti Incident' **14.** 'Come And Get It' **15.** Iron Maiden **16.** Ian Gillan

Pot Luck 6

Answers on page 42

1. Rob Pilatus and Fabrice Morvan were otherwise known as which disgraced duo?

2. Which Monkee used to be a jockey?

3. Rick Witter was the singer with which Nineties band?

4. Who was Dirk McQuickly?

5. Who was the lead singer with Free?

6. Which blue comedian joined Smokie for a 1995 version of 'Living Next Door To Alice'?

7. Who was 'Addicted To Love' in 1986?

8. Which former Australian soap star had a 1997 hit with 'Torn'?

9. Which Status Quo single was originally a country track recorded by Hank Thompson?

10. Who played bongos on The Shadows' 'Apache'?

11. What was the title of The Moody Blues' first UK number one album?

12. Which singing miners had a top twenty hit in 1973 with 'Vaya Con Dios (May God Be With You)'?

13. Ray Manzarek was keyboard player with which Sixties band?

14. What was Dr Hook's full name in the band's early years?

15. Which 1977 Barbara Dickson hit was taken from the musical *Evita*?

16. What nationality are The Cuban Boys?

Answers to page 42
CHART TOPPERS 3: 1. The Troggs 2. Floyd Cramer 3. Maya 4. The Goombay Dance Band 5. 'Town Called Malice' and 'Beat Surrender' 6. 'Karma Chameleon' 7. Johnny Kidd and The Pirates 8. 'Mouldy Old Dough' 9. 'Bad Moon Rising' 10. 'Devil Gate Drive' 11. Babylon Zoo 12. 'Never Gonna Give You Up' and 'China In Your Hand' 13. Livin' Joy 14. 'Hey Girl Don't Bother Me' 15. The Walker Brothers 16. Frank Ifield

Jazz 1

Answers on page 43

1. In which year did Dizzy Gillespie die?

2. What instrument is associated with James Moody?

3. Which jazz guitarist recorded the 1987 album 'Spontaneous Combustion'?

4. Which drummer's Big Band featured the vocals of Anita O'Day and the trumpet solos of Roy Eldridge during the early Forties?

5. Which jazzman's orchestra had a 1961 hit with 'African Waltz'?

6. Which 1976 track gave Acker Bilk his first UK hit for 13 years?

7. Which girl was the subject of a 1961 hit for Kenny Ball?

8. From which Bing Crosby/Frank Sinatra film was the tune taken?

9. With which instrument was Clyde Hart associated?

10. Which Big Band leader's first recording with Capitol in 1943 was 'Artistry In Rhythm'?

11. Which jazz singer teamed up with James Galway for the 1980 hit 'Sometimes When We Touch'?

12. Which Cleo Laine hit of 1961 was originally recorded by Patti Page?

13. Which British jazz band released the 1960 album 'Elite Syncopations'?

14. Which band leader had a 1962 hit with 'The Green Leaves Of Summer'?

15. From which John Wayne film was it taken?

16. What was Louis Armstrong's nickname?

Answers to page 43
BAY CITY ROLLERS 1: **1.** Stuart Wood **2.** 1973 **3.** 'Remember'
4. Tartan scarves **5.** 1975 **6.** Six **7.** 'Once Upon A Star' **8.** Alan Longmuir
9. Ian Mitchell **10.** Les McKeown **11.** 'It's A Game' **12.** 'Give A Little
Love' **13.** 'You Made Me Believe In Magic' **14.** Les McKeown
15. Jonathan King **16.** Bill Martin and Phil Coulter

Chart Toppers 3

Answers on page 40

1. 'With A Girl Like You' was a 1966 number one for which group?

2. Who was 'On The Rebound' in 1961?

3. Who featured on Tamperer's 1998 number one 'Feel It'?

4. Who topped the charts in 1982 with 'Seven Tears'?

5. Which two tracks were UK number ones for The Jam in 1982?

6. What was the best-selling UK single of 1983?

7. Who were 'Shakin' All Over' in 1960?

8. Which 1972 number one was recorded in the front room of a Coventry semi?

9. Which 1969 number one was used 12 years later in the film *An American Werewolf in London*?

10. Which song gave Suzi Quatro a 1974 UK chart topper?

11. Who had a 1996 number one with 'Spaceman'?

12. Which two singles each spent five weeks at number one in 1987?

13. Who had a 1995 chart topper with 'Dreamer'?

14. What was the title of The Tams' number one from 1971?

15. 'Make It Easy On Yourself' was a 1965 hit for which American group?

16. Who had the 'Lovesick Blues' in 1962?

Answers to page 40
POT LUCK 6: **1.** Milli Vanilli **2.** Davy Jones **3.** Shed Seven **4.** The Rutles version of Paul McCartney **5.** Paul Rodgers **6.** Roy 'Chubby' Brown **7.** Robert Palmer **8.** Natalie Imbruglia **9.** 'Wild Side Of Life' **10.** Cliff Richard **11.** 'On The Threshold Of A Dream' **12.** Millican and Nesbitt **13.** The Doors **14.** Dr Hook and The Medicine Show **15.** 'Another Suitcase In Another Hall' **16.** British

Bay City Rollers 1

Answers on page 41

1. What was Woody's full name?

2. When did Les McKeown join the Rollers?

3. What was the first single to be released with McKeown as lead singer?

4. What did the Rollers' fans wrap around their wrists?

5. In which year did 'Bye Bye Baby' get to number one?

6. How many weeks did it stay at the top of the UK charts?

7. What was the title of the Rollers' second UK number one album?

8. Who quit the band in 1976, thinking he was too old?

9. Who replaced him?

10. In 1976, which band member was acquitted of shooting an air rifle at a girl fan?

11. Which Rollers hit was recorded originally by String Driven Thing?

12. What was the Rollers' second number one of 1975?

13. Which was the Rollers' last UK hit?

14. Who released the 1979 solo album 'All Washed Up'?

15. Who produced and sang on the Rollers' first single 'Keep On Dancing'?

16. Which pair wrote most of the Rollers' hits?

Answers to page 41
JAZZ 1: 1. 1993 2. Saxophone 3. Barney Kessel 4. Gene Krupa
5. Johnny Dankworth 6. 'Aria' 7. 'Samantha' 8. *High Society* 9. Piano
10. Stan Kenton 11. Cleo Laine 12. 'You'll Answer To Me' 13. Chris
Barber's Jazz Band 14. Kenny Ball 15. *The Alamo* 16. 'Satchmo'

Pot Luck 7

Answers on page 46

1. Who sang on Rockwell's 1984 hit 'Somebody's Watching Me'?

2. Whose song about the death of her biker boyfriend 'Terry' caused a mild furore in 1964?

3. Who sang about 'The Young New Mexican Puppeteer' in 1972?

4. What did the J stand for in Billy J. Kramer?

5. Which country star's first name is really Troyal?

6. What were the names of the twins in Bros?

7. Martin Lee and Lee Sheridan are the male half of which quartet?

8. Jay Aston was a member of which Eurovision-winning group?

9. Which band were named after a stalwart of the 18th-century Agricultural Revolution?

10. Who was the original drummer with 10cc?

11. What was the name of Kid Creole's backing band?

12. Who was 'Torn Between Two Lovers' in 1977?

13. Who invited you to ride on their 'Paper Plane' in 1973?

14. Mike Barson was the keyboard player with which Eighties band?

15. Who was the leader of ELO?

16. Who had a hit in 2001 with 'Little L'?

Answers to page 46
COUNTRY AND WESTERN 1: 1. 'Lucille' 2. Dolly Parton 3. Tammy Wynette 4. 'You're Still The One' 5. Chris Gaines 6. 'Blue' 7. Elton John 8. *Aida* 9. Shania Twain ('That Don't Impress Me Much') 10. Alvin and The Chipmunks 11. Kenny Rogers 12. Mac David 13. Sheena Easton 14. 'We've Got Tonight' 15. Trisha Yearwood 16. 'Stand By Your Man'

Christmas Hits 1

Answers on page 47

1. Who was simply having a 'Wonderful Christmastime' in 1979?

2. Which DJ had a 1975 hit with 'Renta Santa'?

3. And what was the title of his 1976 festive follow-up?

4. Who was 'Rockin' Around The Christmas Tree' in 1962?

5. For which duo was 1985 the 'Last Christmas'?

6. What colour Christmas did Elvis Presley experience in 1964?

7. Who sent out the invitation to 'Step Into Christmas' in 1973?

8. Who was 'Driving Home For Christmas' in 1988?

9. In 1975 who announced 'Santa Claus Is Coming To Town'?

10. What did Dora Bryan want for Christmas in 1963?

11. Who told the story of 'A Winter's Tale' in 1982?

12. What misfortune had befallen Santa Claus, according to Spitting Image in 1986?

13. Who saw 'Christmas Through Your Eyes' in 1992?

14. Which Christmas ditty was a 1959 hit for Max Bygraves?

15. Which Irish singer offered 'A Christmas Kiss' in 1999?

16. What advice did Chuck Berry offer to Santa's head reindeer in 1963?

Answers to page 47
NINETIES 2: **1.** Oasis **2.** Monaco **3.** Weezer **4.** Pink Floyd **5.** Piper **6.** 'To The End' **7.** Sinead O'Connor **8.** 'Any Dream Will Do' **9.** Ash ('1977') **10.** Bryan Adams **11.** Depeche Mode **12.** Miles Hunt **13.** Suede **14.** The Prodigy **15.** Kylie Minogue **16.** S Club 7

45

Country and Western 1

Answers on page 44

1. Which Kenny Rogers number one was originally recorded by Johnny Darrell?

2. Who had a 1976 hit with 'Jolene'?

3. Which country star sang lead vocals on the 1991 KLF hit 'Justified And Ancient'?

4. What was Shania Twain's first UK top ten hit?

5. As which fictional character from the film *The Lamb* did Garth Brooks record 'Lost In You' in 1999?

6. Which song, written for Patsy Cline who died before she could record it, became a hit for LeAnn Rimes in 1998?

7. With whom did LeAnn Rimes duet on the 1999 hit 'Written In The Stars'?

8. And from which Walt Disney film was the song taken?

9. Who was hard to impress in 1999?

10. Which cartoon critters joined forces with Billy Ray Cyrus for a Christmas version of 'Achy Breaky Heart'?

11. 'Something's Burning' was a 1970 hit in the UK for which country artist?

12. Who recorded the song originally?

13. Who duetted with Kenny Rogers on a 1983 cover of a Bob Seger song?

14. What was the title of the song?

15. Whose 1998 album was called 'Where Your Road Leads'?

16. In 1975, which country song became a number one in the UK seven years after it had first entered the US charts?

Answers to page 44
POT LUCK 7: 1. Michael Jackson 2. Twinkle 3. Tom Jones 4. Nothing 5. Garth Brooks 6. Matt and Luke Goss 7. Brotherhood Of Man 8. Bucks Fizz 9. Jethro Tull 10. Kevin Godley 11. The Coconuts 12. Mary McGregor 13. Status Quo 14. Madness 15. Jeff Lynne 16. Jamiroquai

Nineties 2

Answers on page 45

1. Who hit number one in 1998 with 'All Around The World'?

2. Which New Order splinter band had a 1997 hit with 'What Do You Want From Me'?

3. Rivers Cuomo was the singer with which goofy US band?

4. Whose 1995 album was titled 'Pulse'?

5. What was Billie's surname before she married Chris Evans?

6. Laetitia from Stereolab provided backing vocals on which Blur single from 'Parklife'?

7. Who had a number one album 'I Do Not Want What I Haven't Got'?

8. What was Jason Donovan's last UK number one?

9. The title of which band's debut album reflected the year in which two-thirds of them were born?

10. Who insisted that he would be '18 Til I Die'?

11. Who had hits in the Nineties with 'In Your Room' and 'Barrel Of A Gun'?

12. Who was the lead singer with The Wonder Stuff?

13. Which band released the 1994 album 'Dog Man Star'?

14. Keith Flint is a singer with which band?

15. Who pleaded 'Confide In Me' in 1994?

16. Jo O'Meara is a member of which band?

Answers to page 45
CHRISTMAS HITS 1: **1.** Paul McCartney **2.** Chris Hill **3.** 'Bionic Santa'
4. Brenda Lee **5.** Wham! **6.** Blue **7.** Elton John **8.** Chris Rea **9.** The
Jackson Five **10.** A Beatle **11.** David Essex **12.** He was on the dole
13. Gloria Estefan **14.** 'Jingle Bell Rock' **15.** Daniel O'Donnell **16.** 'Run
Rudolph Run'

George Michael 1

Answers on page 50

1. How old was George Michael when he wrote 'Careless Whisper'?

2. Who played piano on Wham!'s 1986 number one 'Edge Of Heaven'?

3. With whom did George Michael duet on 'I Knew You Were Waiting (For Me)'?

4. Which George Michael number one sampled Patrice Rushen's 'Forget Me Nots'?

5. Which 1997 single (with Toby Bourke) did George Michael dedicate to his late mother?

6. Who joined George Michael on a duet for the 1999 hit 'As'?

7. On which Stevie Wonder album did 'As' originally appear?

8. Where did George Michael and Andrew Ridgeley record demos of 'Wham Rap!', 'Club Tropicana' and 'Careless Whisper'?

9. What was Wham!'s first hit single?

10. From which Wham! album was 'Club Tropicana' taken?

11. Which single was inspired by a note Andrew Ridgeley left lying in his bedroom?

12. In which year did George Michael become the youngest-ever recipient of the Songwriter Of The Year trophy at the Ivor Novello Awards?

13. In August 1985, Wham! became the first pop group to perform live in which country?

14. What was George Michael's second solo single?

15. In which year did Wham! split up?

16. What was the title of George Michael's first solo album?

Answers to page 50
SOLO ARTISTS 1: **1.** Veronica **2.** Andy Gibb **3.** Debbie Gibson
4. 'Temma Harbour' **5.** Rita Coolidge **6.** Vanessa Paradis **7.** Tiffany
8. Shakin' Stevens **9.** 'When I Need You' **10.** Jimmy Page **11.** 'Rubber Ball'
12. Sinead O'Connor **13.** Billy Ocean **14.** Joe Jackson **15.** Phil Collins
16. George Harrison ('My Sweet Lord')

Cover Versions 2

Answers on page 51

1. How did Brian Hyland and Jason Donovan choose to seal their letters?

2. The Equals and Pato Banton both took which song to number one?

3. Betty Everett, Linda Lewis and Cher have all had hits with which song?

4. What was an important date for Cliff Richard and Donny Osmond?

5. Which Elvis hit did ZZ Top cover in 1992?

6. Which song links Dionne Warwick, The Stranglers and Gabrielle?

7. Which Dion hit was covered by Status Quo in 1984?

8. 'Too Good To Be Forgotten' was a UK hit for which two bands?

9. Engelbert Humperdinck in 1967 and Elvis Presley in 1971 both enjoyed UK top ten hits with which song?

10. What were Tommy Steele in 1956 and Daniel O'Donnell in 1994 both doing?

11. Who originally recorded 'She's Not There', a 1977 hit for Santana?

12. Which Bread song was a hit for Let Loose in 1996?

13. Who was the first artist to have a UK hit with 'Lovely Day'?

14. Which song links Bill Withers, Mud, Club Nouveau and Michael Bolton?

15. Which Eddie Cochran chart topper was a number two hit for Showaddywaddy in 1975?

16. Who took their two-tone version of Smokey Robinson's 'Tears Of A Clown' to number six in the UK charts in 1979?

Answers to page 51
SEVENTIES 1: **1.** Les Gray **2.** Boston **3.** Yes **4.** Neil Young **5.** The Bee Gees **6.** 'Rockin' All Over The World' **7.** 'Bye Bye Baby' **8.** David Gates **9.** 1978 **10.** Genesis **11.** David Essex **12.** Keith Emerson **13.** Neil Diamond **14.** Jane **15.** 'Paper Roses' **16.** 'Mother And Child Reunion'

Solo Artists 1

Answers on page 48

1. What is Randy Crawford's real first name?
2. Which youngest of the Gibb brothers enjoyed a moderately successful solo career before his death in 1988?
3. Which young American singer, who had hits with 'Shake Your Love' and 'Foolish Beat' in the late Eighties, had previously made TV commercials for Oxydol detergent and Wendy's burger restaurants?
4. Which harbour did Mary Hopkin sing about in 1970?
5. Which singer did Kris Kristofferson marry in 1973?
6. Who was hailed for her rendition of 'Joe Le Taxi' in 1988?
7. Who had a number one with 'I Think We're Alone Now' after performing free in shopping malls across the US?
8. Which Welsh rock 'n' roller played the king on stage in the West End musical *Elvis* before enjoying a lucrative solo career in the Eighties?
9. Which Leo Sayer single gave Chrysalis Records their first-ever number one?
10. Who played guitar on P.J. Proby's 1964 hit 'Hold Me'?
11. Which bouncy number from Bobby Vee was written by Gene Pitney?
12. Which Irish singer spent part of her early life in a residential centre run by nuns?
13. Whose first UK hit was 'Love Really Hurts Without You'?
14. Whose 1982 album was titled 'Night And Day'?
15. Which future singer played the Artful Dodger in a London stage production of *Oliver* at 14 before touring the UK promoting Smith's crisps?
16. Whose was the biggest-selling UK single of 1971?

Answers to page 48
GEORGE MICHAEL 1: 1. 16 2. Elton John 3. Aretha Franklin
4. 'Fastlove' 5. 'Waltz Away Dreaming' 6. Mary J. Blige 7. 'Songs In The Key Of Life' 8. In Ridgeley's parents' front room 9. 'Young Guns (Go For It)' 10. 'Fantastic' 11. 'Wake Me Up Before You Go Go' 12. 1985
13. China 14. 'A Different Corner' 15. 1986 16. 'Faith'

Seventies 1

Answers on page 49

1. Who was the lead singer with Mud?

2. Which US band hit the UK charts in 1977 with 'More Than A Feeling'?

3. Which progressive rock band released the albums 'Fragile' and 'Close To The Edge'?

4. Which Canadian singer/songwriter had a 'Heart Of Gold' in 1972?

5. Which prolific songwriters penned Candi Staton's hit 'Nights On Broadway'?

6. Which Status Quo anthem was originally recorded by John Fogerty?

7. With which Four Seasons song did The Bay City Rollers enjoy their first UK number one?

8. Who was the chief songwriter with Bread?

9. In which year did The Commodores get to number one with 'Three Times A Lady'?

10. Whose 1976 album was called 'A Trick Of The Tail'?

11. Who played Jim MacLaine in *That'll Be The Day*?

12. Which keyboard player, famous for stabbing his instrument with knives, injured his hands in San Francisco in 1973 when his organ, rigged to explode as a stunt during the set, detonated prematurely?

13. Who released the live double album 'Hot August Night' in 1972?

14. To whom did Slade say Gudbuy in 1972?

15. What was the title of Marie Osmond's solo single?

16. Which song did Paul Simon write after eating egg fried rice and chicken in a Chinese restaurant?

Answers to page 49
COVER VERSIONS 2: **1.** With a kiss **2.** 'Baby Come Back' **3.** 'It's In His Kiss (The Shoop Shoop Song)' **4.** 'The Twelfth Of Never' **5.** 'Viva Las Vegas' **6.** 'Walk On By' **7.** 'The Wanderer' **8.** The Chi-Lites and Amazulu **9.** 'There Goes My Everything' **10.** 'Singing The Blues' **11.** The Zombies **12.** 'Make It With You' **13.** Bill Withers **14.** 'Lean On Me' **15.** 'Three Steps To Heaven' **16.** The Beat

Eighties 1

Answers on page 54

1. Which band's debut album was titled 'Bridge Of Spies'?

2. In 1987, which band had their fifth UK number one in total, but their first for eight years?

3. Who were 'Showing Out' in 1986?

4. Which Asian trouble spot was the title of a Kim Wilde hit of 1981?

5. Steve Grant was the male singer in which chart-topping Eighties trio?

6. In which year did 'The Land Of Make Believe' reach number one for Bucks Fizz?

7. Which city links Eighties hits for Elvis Costello and Kajagoogoo?

8. Who wanted to 'Kiss The Bride' in 1983?

9. Which solo artist had hits with 'New Song' and 'What Is Love'?

10. What was Barry Manilow's only UK top ten hit of the decade?

11. Who thought of herself as a 'Modern Girl' in 1980?

12. 'Wide Boy' was a 1985 hit for which diminutive UK artist?

13. What is the Christian name of the Bronski in Bronski Beat?

14. Which band were Dave Stewart and Annie Lennox in before The Eurythmics?

15. Who is vocalist with Erasure?

16. Who had a 1986 number one before deciding to join the police force six years later?

Answers to page 54
POT LUCK 8: **1.** Edwyn Collins **2.** The Emerald Express **3.** The Aces **4.** Del Amitri **5.** 'Look Away' **6.** The Beverley Sisters **7.** Mick Jones **8.** Curved Air **9.** The Crystals **10.** Randy Crawford **11.** Sam Cooke **12.** Welsh **13.** Bobby Brown **14.** The Beat **15.** The Bangles **16.** Mia Farrow

Elvis 1

Answers on page 55

1. 'Teddy Bear' was on the soundtrack of which film?

2. In which year was 'King Creole' released as a single?

3. Which Elvis number one was recorded originally by Vaughn Deleath in 1927?

4. How many UK number ones did Elvis have in 1961?

5. How many UK number ones did Elvis have in total?

6. What was his last UK number one before his death?

7. Which mansion did Elvis buy in 1957?

8. In which city is it located?

9. Which unique event took place on 2 March 1960?

10. Who recorded the original version of 'Crying In The Chapel'?

11. On a cold and grey Chicago morning where was another little baby child born?

12. Which 1969 single gave Elvis his first US number one for seven years?

13. In which year was Elvis's marriage to Priscilla dissolved?

14. Besides English, in which language did Elvis sing on 'Wooden Heart'?

15. Who sold Elvis from Sun for $35,000?

16. How many weeks did 'Heartbreak Hotel' remain at number one in the US charts?

Answers to page 55
GLAM ROCK 1: 1. Alvin Stardust 2. Frank Torpey 3. 'Wig Wam Bam'
4. Nicky Chinn and Mike Chapman 5. David Bowie 6. The US moon launch 7. 'My Coo Ca Choo' 8. 'Jealous Mind' 9. Gary Glitter 10. Mark McManus (*Taggart*) 11. The Glitter Band 12. Alvin Stardust 13. T. Rex 14. 1973 15. 'The Groover' 16. Alvin Stardust

Pot Luck 8

Answers on page 52

1. Which singer/guitarist was with Orange Juice before going solo?

2. Which fiddle section joined Dexy's Midnight Runners in 1982?

3. What was the name of Desmond Dekker's backing group?

4. Which Glaswegian band were formed by Justin Currie and Iain Harvie?

5. What was Big Country's last UK top ten hit?

6. Which British female trio saw Mommy kissing Santa Claus in 1953?

7. Which member of The Clash formed Big Audio Dynamite?

8. Sonja Kristina was the singer with which Seventies band?

9. Dee Dee Kennibrew and La La Brooks were part of which girl group of the Sixties?

10. Who reached number two in the charts in 1980 with 'One Day I'll Fly Away'?

11. Who was lead singer with The Soul Stirrers between 1951 and 1956 before going solo?

12. What nationality were Budgie?

13. Which singer married Whitney Houston in 1992?

14. Which two-tone band had a rapper by the name of Ranking Roger?

15. 'All Over The Place' was the debut album from which girl band?

16. Which actress's sister was the subject of The Beatles' 'Dear Prudence'?

Answers to page 52
EIGHTIES 1: 1. T'Pau 2. The Bee Gees 3. Mel and Kim 4. 'Cambodia' 5. Tight Fit 6. 1981 7. New York (Elvis Costello sang about 'New Amsterdam' (New York's former name) and Kajagoogoo had a hit titled 'Big Apple') 8. Elton John 9. Howard Jones 10. 'I Wanna Do It With You' 11. Sheena Easton 12. Nik Kershaw 13. Steve 14. The Tourists 15. Andy Bell 16. Nick Berry (who went on to star in *Heartbeat*)

Glam Rock 1

Answers on page 53

1. Which glam rocker's previous incarnations included Bernard Jewry and Shane Fenton?

2. Who did Andy Scott replace as guitarist in Sweet?

3. For which song did Sweet dress up as Native American Indians?

4. Which glam rock writers were commonly known as Chinnichap?

5. Whose early backing groups included The King Bees, The Lower Third and The Buzz?

6. Which real-life event was Bowie's 'Space Oddity' released to coincide with?

7. What was Alvin Stardust's first hit?

8. And which was his first UK number one?

9. Who pleaded 'Remember Me This Way'?

10. Sweet singer Brian Connolly was later revealed to be the half-brother of which actor who played a TV cop?

11. Pete Phipps was one of the drummers in which band?

12. Which glam rock star went on to advise youngsters of the importance of road safety?

13. 'Solid Gold Easy Action' was a 1972 hit for which band?

14. In which year was Marc Bolan/T. Rex's last UK top ten hit?

15. What was the title of the track?

16. Who ended up playing a pub landlord in *Hollyoaks*?

Answers to page 53
ELVIS 1: **1.** *Loving You* **2.** 1958 **3.** 'Are You Lonesome Tonight?' **4.** Four **5.** 17 **6.** 'The Wonder Of You' **7.** Graceland **8.** Memphis **9.** Elvis set foot on British soil for the only time, during his plane's refuelling stop at Prestwick Airport in Scotland **10.** Sonny Til and The Orioles **11.** 'In The Ghetto' **12.** 'Suspicious Minds' **13.** 1973 **14.** German **15.** Sam Phillips **16.** Eight

Lyrics 1

Answers on page 58

From which songs are the following lyrics taken?

1. 'Why do birds suddenly appear every time you are near'

2. 'To insure yourself you've got to provide communication constantly'

3. 'But now there's nowhere to hide since you pushed my love aside'

4. 'I gave you my heart and my soul to keep'

5. 'Touch me now, I close my eyes and dream away'

6. 'But is her sweet expression worth more than my love and affection'

7. 'You can't start a fire without a spark'

8. 'I play my part and you play your game'

9. 'I wish I could fly right up to the sky but I can't'

10. 'When you're weary, feeling small, when tears are in your eyes I will dry them all'

11. 'When I was down, I was your clown'

12. 'People say I'm crazy and that I'm blind, risking it all in a glance'

13. 'And once again I'm thinking about taking the easy way out'

14. 'I need a man who'll take a chance on a love that burns hot enough to last'

15. 'Recreation is our destination so don't wait up for us tonight'

16. 'It's not how it used to be, you've taken my life away, ruining everything'

Answers to page 58
POT LUCK 9: **1.** Neil Tennant (The Pet Shop Boys) **2.** Little Anthony **3.** Chuck Berry **4.** The Twist **5.** The Three Degrees **6.** Dexy's Midnight Runners ('Jackie Wilson Said') **7.** He didn't exist **8.** Norman **9.** Candy **10.** Bobby Goldsboro ('Honey') **11.** Wyclef Jean **12.** Peter Bardens **13.** Jean Jacques **14.** José Feliciano **15.** Kate Bush **16.** 'Elstree'

Pink Floyd 1

Answers on page 59

1. How did Pink Floyd get their name?

2. Which radio station banned 'Arnold Layne' because of its transvestite subject matter?

3. Which *Juke Box Jury* panellist and Radio 1 DJ described Pink Floyd as a 'con'?

4. What was the title of Pink Floyd's first album?

5. Why was the Floyd's 1967 US tour cancelled?

6. Who replaced Syd Barrett in 1968?

7. Which album became a UK number one in 1970?

8. 'Obscured By Clouds' was the soundtrack to which film?

9. Who is Pink Floyd's drummer?

10. Which album never became a UK number one despite spending over 350 weeks in the charts?

11. Who guested to sing 'Shine On You Crazy Diamond' on the album 'Wish You Were Here'?

12. Which violinist made an uncredited contribution to 'Wish You Were Here'?

13. In which year was 'The Wall' released?

14. Who left the band in 1980?

15. Who starred in the film version of 'The Wall'?

16. Which Pink Floyd album was named after an item of parliamentary procedure?

Answers to page 59
SOLO ARTISTS 2: 1. Geri Halliwell 2. Clodagh Rodgers 3. Leo Sayer
4. Boz Scaggs 5. Billy Preston 6. Betty Boo 7. Sandie Shaw 8. 'When You Say Nothing At All' 9. Sean Maguire 10. Michelle Gayle 11. Jona Lewie 12. Red 13. Ringo Starr 14. 'Jarrow Song' 15. Curtis Mayfield 16. *Opportunity Knocks*

Pot Luck 9

Answers on page 56

1. Which half of a pop duo used to be British editor of *Marvel Comics*?
2. Who fronted The Imperials?
3. Who invented the Duck Walk?
4. Which Sixties dance craze was pioneered by Chubby Checker?
5. Who faced a 'Year Of Decision' in 1974?
6. Which band, appearing on *Top of the Pops*, were surprised to be playing in front of a blow-up picture of darts player Jocky Wilson instead of one of singer Jackie Wilson?
7. What was the twist about the Bonzo Dog Doo-Dah Band's Urban Spaceman?
8. What was the name of Marmalade's cousin?
9. According to Brian Hyland what was Ginny as sweet as?
10. Which grieving husband encouraged his friends to 'See the tree, how big it's grown'?
11. Who sampled The Bee Gees' 'Stayin' Alive' in his 1997 hit 'We Trying To Stay Alive'?
12. Which keyboard player fronted Camel?
13. What does the J.J. in J.J. Cale stand for?
14. Which Latin guitarist, who had a 1968 hit with 'Light My Fire', was born blind?
15. Who kept 'Running Up That Hill' in 1985?
16. About which film studios did Buggles sing?

Answers to page 56
LYRICS 1: 1. 'Close To You' (The Carpenters) 2. 'Tell Her About It' (Billy Joel) 3. 'Hopelessly Devoted To You' (Olivia Newton-John) 4. 'In Too Deep' (Belinda Carlisle) 5. 'It Must Have Been Love' (Roxette) 6. 'Stop In The Name Of Love' (The Supremes) 7. 'Dancing In The Dark' (Bruce Springsteen) 8. 'You Give Love A Bad Name' (Bon Jovi) 9. 'Orville's Song' (Keith Harris and Orville) 10. 'Bridge Over Troubled Water' (Simon and Garfunkel) 11. 'Don't Go Breaking My Heart' (Elton John and Kiki Dee) 12. 'As Long As You Love Me' (Backstreet Boys) 13. 'If I Let You Go' (Westlife) 14. 'I Wanna Dance With Somebody (Who Loves Me)' (Whitney Houston) 15. 'Respectable' (Mel and Kim) 16. 'What Do You Want From Me?' (Monaco)

Solo Artists 2

Answers on page 57

1. Who reached number one in 1999 with 'Lift Me Up'?
2. Which Irish singer had a 1969 hit with 'Goodnight Midnight'?
3. Which Seventies singer appeared in a clown's costume to promote his first hit?
4. Which Boz was 'Lowdown' in 1976?
5. In 1969 who maintained 'That's The Way God Planned It'?
6. Who appeared on *Top of the Pops* as a singer in 1990 a couple of years after she had been turned down by the BBC for a sound engineer's course?
7. Which Sixties singer married fashion designer Jeff Banks?
8. What was Ronan Keating's first solo hit?
9. Which ex-*EastEnder* recorded a cover version of Hamilton, Joe Frank and Reynolds's 1971 hit 'Don't Pull Your Love'?
10. Which ex-*EastEnder* had a top five hit with 'Sweetness' in 1994?
11. Who did you always find in the kitchen at parties?
12. What colour were roses for Bobby Vinton in 1962?
13. Who went solo and had hits with 'Back Off Boogaloo' and 'Photograph'?
14. Which Alan Price hit recalled a workers' march of 1926?
15. Who said 'Move On Up' in 1971?
16. For which TV talent show did Engelbert Humperdinck fail an audition?

Answers to page 57
PINK FLOYD 1: **1.** Syd Barrett named the band after bluesmen Pink Anderson and Floyd Council **2.** Radio London **3.** Pete Murray **4.** 'The Piper At The Gates Of Dawn' **5.** Syd Barrett refused to mime properly on a US TV show **6.** Dave Gilmour **7.** 'Atom Heart Mother' **8.** *La Vallée* **9.** Nick Mason **10.** 'The Dark Side Of The Moon' **11.** Roy Harper **12.** Stephane Grappelli **13.** 1979 **14.** Rick Wright **15.** Bob Geldof **16.** 'The Division Bell'

Pot Luck 10

Answers on page 62

1. Which singer killed in a 1966 car crash was famous for wearing an eye patch?

2. What middle name was John Lennon given at birth?

3. In 1974, who became the first woman to win the Ivor Novello Songwriting Award?

4. Which band's 1973 album was titled 'Can't Buy A Thrill'?

5. Which three solo artists with the surname Preston had UK hits in the Sixties?

6. Which sister of a pop star had a 1991 hit with 'Love And Kisses'?

7. Which member of Duran Duran co-produced Kajagoogoo's only number one?

8. Which band named themselves after a pep pill?

9. What was the surname of Delaney and Bonnie?

10. Who did it 'All For Leyna' in 1980?

11. Which two Sixties artists had hits about girls named Jennifer?

12. In which year did The Moody Blues first release 'Nights In White Satin'?

13. Who was 'Living On The Front Line' in 1979?

14. Who worked as a bookmaker's clerk before joining The Rolling Stones?

15. Which girl did Gerry Monroe take to number four in the charts in 1970?

16. Which family group reckoned they were 'The Chosen Few' in 1979?

Answers to page 62
ROCK 'N' ROLL 1: 1. Little Richard 2. Chuck Berry 3. Jerry Lee Lewis 4. The Teenagers (Frankie Lymon's group) 5. Little Richard 6. Marty Wilde 7. Adam Faith 8. Smiley Lewis 9. English 10. Tony Meehan 11. 'Rave On' 12. Billy Fury 13. 'Lonely Teenager' 14. Chuck Berry 15. Rapp 16. Marty Wilde

One-Hit Wonders 3

Answers on page 63

1. Which actor had a hit with 'MacArthur Park'?

2. What was the title of Mr Bloe's only hit?

3. Who reached number three with 'Jungle Rock' in 1957?

4. On which thoroughfare could The Maisonettes be found in 1982?

5. Which politically incorrect title took Carl Malcolm into the top ten in 1975?

6. Who sang about 'Something Old, Something New' in 1971?

7. 'A Way Of Life' was a hit for which band in 1969?

8. Which song by Honeybus went on to be used in TV adverts for Nimble bread?

9. Who was 'Gonna Make You An Offer You Can't Refuse' in 1973?

10. The UK top ten hit 'I See A Star' was the 1974 Dutch Eurovision entry for which ill-matched duo?

11. Which American artist recorded 'The Clapping Song'?

12. Who got to number three in the UK charts in 1957 with 'Little Darlin''?

13. What was Danny and The Juniors' only success in the UK?

14. Who had a 1963 hit with 'Rhythm Of The Rain'?

15. Yannis Markopoulos had a 1977 hit with the theme from which BBC television series?

16. Whose only hit was a 1964 version of The Beatles' 'I Should Have Known Better'?

Answers to page 63
SEVENTIES 2: 1. Sweet 2. Don Powell 3. Suzi Quatro 4. 'Bicycle Race'
5. Pickettywitch 6. The New Seekers 7. Tom Jones 8. 'Song For Guy'
9. The Isley Brothers 10. Heatwave 11. 'Under My Thumb' 12. 'Rubber
Bullets' 13. The Delfonics 14. Chicago 15. Fox 16. Thin Lizzy

Rock 'n' Roll 1

Answers on page 60

1. As a child, which rock 'n' roller used to sing with The Tiny Tots Quartet?

2. Who released 'Roll Over Beethoven' in 1956?

3. 'Whole Lotta Shakin' Goin' On' became a hit on both sides of the Atlantic for which flamboyant performer?

4. What were Sherman Garnes, Joe Negroni, Herman Santiago and Jimmy Merchant known as collectively?

5. Who wrote and recorded 'Tutti Frutti'?

6. Which rock 'n' roller worked in a south London timber yard before being discovered?

7. Whose first movie was the X-rated *Beat Girl* with Shirley Ann Field?

8. Who originally recorded 'One Night', a UK number one for Elvis in 1959?

9. In what subject did Cliff Richard (then known as Harry Webb) gain his only 'O' Level pass?

10. Which drummer joined Cliff Richard's backing band in November 1958?

11. Which Buddy Holly single was recorded originally by Sonny West?

12. Which budding rock star used to work as a deckhand on the River Mersey tug boats?

13. What was the title of Dion's first solo single?

14. Which rock star was born in St Louis, Missouri, in 1926 and later landed a job with General Motors?

15. What was the surname of Danny from Danny and The Juniors?

16. Which rock 'n' roller married one of The Vernons Girls?

Answers to page 60
POT LUCK 10: **1.** Johnny Kidd **2.** Winston **3.** Lynsey De Paul **4.** Steely Dan **5.** Billy, Johnny and Mike **6.** Dannii Minogue **7.** Nick Rhodes **8.** Dexy's Midnight Runners (dexedrine) **9.** Bramlett **10.** Billy Joel **11.** Donovan ('Jennifer Juniper') and The Hollies ('Jennifer Eccles') **12.** 1967 **13.** Eddy Grant **14.** Bill Wyman **15.** 'Sally' **16.** The Dooleys

Seventies 2

Answers on page 61

1. Who were proud of their 'Little Willy' in 1972?

2. Who was the drummer with Slade?

3. Which Detroit-born rocker sang about the "48 Crash' in 1973?

4. Which Queen track formed a double A-side with 'Fat Bottomed Girls'?

5. Who experienced 'That Same Old Feeling' in 1970?

6. Lyn Paul and Eve Graham were the singers with which Seventies group?

7. Who charted with 'Daughter Of Darkness' in 1970?

8. Which Elton John single was a tribute to Rocket Records' motorcycle messenger boy who had died in an accident aged 17?

9. Which former Motown band had hits with 'Highway Of My Life' and 'Summer Breeze'?

10. Whose biggest hit was 'Boogie Nights' in 1977?

11. Which cover of a Rolling Stones track gave Wayne Gibson a UK top twenty record in 1974?

12. Which 10cc single received little radio play because of the weaponry used by the British Army in Northern Ireland?

13. In 1971 which Philly band asked 'Didn't I (Blow Your Mind This Time)'?

14. '25 Or 6 To 4' was a hit for which American band in 1970?

15. Who wanted to sleep in a 'S-S-S-Single Bed'?

16. Who were 'Live And Dangerous' on their 1978 album?

Answers to page 61
ONE-HIT WONDERS 3: 1. Richard Harris 2. 'Groovin' With Mr Bloe'
3. Hank Mizell 4. 'Heartache Avenue' 5. 'Fattie Bum Bum' 6. The
Fantastics 7. Family Dogg 8. 'I Can't Let Maggie Go' 9. Jimmy Helms
10. Mouth and McNeal 11. Shirley Ellis 12. The Diamonds 13. 'At The
Hop' 14. The Cascades 15. *Who Pays The Ferryman?* 16. The Naturals

Eighties 2

Answers on page 66

1. Which aunt of Whitney Houston had a US number one in 1977 with a song which become a UK number one in 1986 for The Communards?

2. Who had a 1986 number one with 'I Wanna Wake Up With You'?

3. Which five acts, all featuring female vocalists, filled the top five places in the UK singles chart in November 1986?

4. Who released the 1980 album 'Tears And Laughter'?

5. Who had a 1980 hit with 'I Am The Beat'?

6. In 1986, who became the second Swedish act to top the UK singles charts?

7. A spin-off group from which group recorded the original version of The Housemartins' 'Caravan Of Love'?

8. Which former Rubette was a member of The Firm who had a 1987 number one with 'Star Trekkin''?

9. Who was the singer with Berlin?

10. Who featured on Soul II Soul's 1989 hit 'Back To Life (However Do You Want Me)'?

11. Who was the singer with Transvision Vamp?

12. Which band, fronted by a present-day actress, had top ten hits with 'Happy Birthday' and 'I Could Be Happy'?

13. Who was the third member of Bros?

14. Which 1987 chart topper was the first since 'Je T'Aime...Moi Non Plus' to be sung entirely in a foreign language?

15. And in what language was it sung?

16. Which T'Pau single was originally titled 'Intimate Strangers'?

Answers to page 66
SINGER/SONGWRITERS 1: 1. Alanis Morissette 2. 'We Do What We Can' 3. 'Songs Of Leonard Cohen' 4. Brother Love 5. Neil Sedaka 6. Billy Joel 7. 'True Love' 8. 23 9. 'Rocky Mountain High' 10. 'W-O-L-D' 11. 'Cat's In The Cradle' 12. Bobby Vee 13. 'Run, Baby, Run' 14. John Denver 15. Don McLean 16. 'Son Of My Father' by Chicory Tip

Bon Jovi 1

Answers on page 67

1. What did Jon Bon Jovi's mother used to be?

2. And what was his father?

3. Which 1986 single reached number 14 in the UK singles chart?

4. How many weeks did the album 'Slippery When Wet' spend at number one in the US?

5. In which year was 'Livin' On A Prayer' released?

6. Which Bon Jovi manager was convicted of drug offences in 1988?

7. Which 1988 Bon Jovi album became the first to reach the top spot in the UK?

8. The acoustic version of which Bon Jovi song, played at the 1989 MTV Video Music Awards, inspired the Unplugged series of the Nineties?

9. Which Bon Jovi song was the theme to the movie *Young Guns II*?

10. In which year was 'Keep The Faith' released?

11. Which actress did Bon Jovi guitarist Richie Sambora marry in 1994?

12. What is the name of Bon Jovi's drummer?

13. In which country did ticketless fans riot in 1995 after forcing their way into a Bon Jovi concert?

14. What was the title of Bon Jovi's debut album?

15. Which film gave Jon Bon Jovi his first acting role?

16. Which Bon Jovi track reached two in the UK charts in 1994?

Answers to page 67
POT LUCK 11: **1.** Tina Weymouth **2.** Billy Swan **3.** Mick Talbot **4.** 'The Very Best Of Slim Whitman' **5.** The Hollies **6.** The Stylistics **7.** American **8.** The Family Stone **9.** Shocking Blue ('Venus') **10.** Helen Shapiro **11.** Tom Robinson **12.** Saffron **13.** 1963 **14.** KC **15.** Evan Dando **16.** Sam Cooke

Singer/Songwriters 1

Answers on page 64

1. Which singer/songwriter once appeared in a short-lived US sitcom *Just One of the Girls*?

2. On which Sheryl Crow track from the 'Tuesday Night Music Club' album did her father Wendell play trumpet?

3. On which Leonard Cohen album did 'Suzanne' first appear?

4. Whose Travelling Salvation Show was created by Neil Diamond?

5. Apart from Led Zeppelin, which American artist penned a song called 'Stairway To Heaven'?

6. Who said 'We Didn't Start The Fire' in 1989?

7. Which Fifties song did Elton John revive with Kiki Dee in 1993?

8. How many singles had Chris De Burgh released before 'Lady In Red'?

9. What was John Denver's first US top ten album?

10. Which Harry Chapin song told the story of a morning DJ on a radio station?

11. And which Harry Chapin song that became a US number one was based on a poem by his wife about a neglectful father?

12. For which artist did Carole King write 'It Might As Well Rain Until September'?

13. What was Sheryl Crow's first single?

14. Which artist had 16 UK hit albums but only one hit single – a number one in 1974?

15. Who had his debut album 'Tapestry' rejected by 34 record labels?

16. Which song kept Don McLean's 'American Pie' from the top of the UK singles chart?

Answers to page 64
EIGHTIES 2: **1.** Thelma Houston ('Don't Leave Me This Way') **2.** Boris Gardiner **3.** Berlin, Kim Wilde, The Bangles, Mel and Kim and Swing Out Sister **4.** Johnny Mathis **5.** The Look **6.** Europe ('The Final Countdown') **7.** The Isley Brothers (Isley Jasper Isley) **8.** Tony Thorpe **9.** Terri Nunn **10.** Caron Wheeler **11.** Wendy James **12.** Altered Images (Clare Grogan) **13.** Craig Logan **14.** 'La Bamba' **15.** Spanish **16.** 'Sex Talk'

Pot Luck 11

Answers on page 65

1. What was the name of the only female in Talking Heads?

2. Who worked as a janitor at Columbia Studios before having a US number one with 'I Can Help'?

3. Who was Paul Weller's partner in Style Council?

4. Which country album spent six weeks at the top of the UK charts in 1976?

5. Who knew a 'Long Cool Woman In A Black Dress'?

6. Which Seventies group's hits included 'Betcha By Golly Wow' and 'I'm Stone In Love With You'?

7. What nationality are Smashing Pumpkins?

8. Who backed Sly?

9. Which Dutch group had a US number one in 1970?

10. Which teenage pop star of the Sixties ended up in the short-lived Eighties TV soap *Albion Market*?

11. Who had a 1983 UK top ten hit with 'War Baby'?

12. Who was recruited from being part of The Prodigy's stage act to singing with Republica?

13. In which year did *Ready, Steady, Go!* start?

14. Who was the leader of The Sunshine Band?

15. Who was the singer with The Lemonheads?

16. Who was 'Twistin' The Night Away' in 1962?

Answers to page 65
BON JOVI 1: **1.** Playboy bunny girl **2.** A hairdresser **3.** 'You Give Love A Bad Name' **4.** 15 **5.** 1986 **6.** Doc McGee **7.** 'New Jersey' **8.** 'Wanted Dead Or Alive' **9.** 'Blaze Of Glory' **10.** 1992 **11.** Heather Locklear **12.** Tico Torres **13.** Indonesia **14.** 'Bon Jovi' **15.** *Young Guns II* **16.** 'Always'

Nineties 3

Answers on page 70

Which artists had UK hits with the following tracks?

1. 'Don't Marry Her'

2. 'Come As You Are'

3. 'Promise Me'

4. 'Because We Want To'

5. 'Bitter Sweet Symphony'

6. 'Twilight Zone'

7. 'Flying Without Wings'

8. 'Fairground'

9. 'The Universal'

10. 'Whoops Now'

11. 'Beautiful Ones'

12. 'To You I Belong'

13. 'You Are Not Alone'

14. 'Boom! Shake The Room'

15. 'Rhythm Is A Dancer'

16. 'The Fly'

Answers to page 70
GLAM ROCK 2: 1. Marc Bolan 2. Nicky Chinn and Mike Chapman
3. Sweet 4. Gary Glitter 5. Gary Glitter 6. Rob Davis 7. 'Blockbuster'
8. 'Tie A Yellow Ribbon' 9. 1972 10. 'I Love To Boogie' 11. Marc Bolan
12. Mike Leander 13. Four 14. Sweet 15. Gerry Sheppard 16. 1976

Classical Gas 1

Answers on page 71

1. Who composed *Peter And The Wolf*?

2. In which century did Vivaldi die?

3. Which Russian composer, born at Oneg in 1873, went to live in the USA following the 1917 Revolution?

4. What was Purcell's Christian name?

5. Who composed the ballet *Boléro*?

6. What nationality was *Bartók*?

7. Who wrote the *Symphonie Fantastique*?

8. Who composed the *New World Symphony*?

9. Which Austrian composer once said: 'To write a symphony is, for me, to construct a world'?

10. In which German town was Bach born?

11. In which year did Bizet compose his most famous opera, *Carmen*?

12. How many piano sonatas did Beethoven compose?

13. How old was Beethoven when he was stricken by deafness?

14. For whom did Handel write his *Water Music*?

15. Which Handel masterpiece was first performed in Dublin in 1842?

16. Which musicologist catalogued Mozart's works chronologically 70 years after the composer's death?

Answers to page 71
SINGER/SONGWRITERS 2: **1.** 'All By Myself' **2.** John Denver
3. 'Watermark' **4.** Tanita Tikaram **5.** 'Tapestry' **6.** Joe Jackson **7.** 'The Way It Is' **8.** 'Our Last Song Together' **9.** Leonard Cohen **10.** David Gray
11. Bob Dylan **12.** Kirsty MacColl **13.** Mandy **14.** Clifford T. Ward
15. Neil Diamond **16.** They share the same birthday – 30 July

Glam Rock 2

Answers on page 68

1. Which glam rock star was born Mark Feld?

2. Who composed most of Sweet's hits?

3. Which glam rock group were banned by the Mecca dancehall circuit for what was considered to be an overtly sexual stage act?

4. Who released a version of George Harrison's 'Here Comes The Sun' under the name of Paul Monday?

5. In 1973, who put old records and photos of his former persona, Paul Raven, in a coffin and let them sink into the Thames?

6. Which Mud guitarist used to wear a dress on stage?

7. Which Sweet number has an identical riff to David Bowie's 'The Jean Genie'?

8. Which song kept Sweet's 'Hellraiser' off the top of the UK charts in 1973?

9. In which year did T. Rex hit number one with 'Telegram Sam'?

10. Which T. Rex single was based on 'Teenage Boogie' by Webb Pierce?

11. Which glam rock star had an earlier existence as London folk singer Toby Tyler?

12. Who produced and co-wrote Gary Glitter's early hits?

13. How many weeks did 'I'm The Leader Of The Gang (I Am)' spend at the top of the UK charts?

14. Who went on a Ballroom Blitz in 1973?

15. Who was lead singer with The Glitter Band?

16. When did Gary Glitter first announce his retirement?

Answers to page 68
NINETIES 3: 1. The Beautiful South 2. Nirvana 3. Beverley Craven
4. Billie 5. The Verve 6. 2 Unlimited 7. Westlife 8. Simply Red 9. Blur
10. Janet Jackson 11. Suede 12. B*Witched 13. Michael Jackson 14. Jazzy
Jeff and The Fresh Prince 15. Snap! 16. U2

Singer/Songwriters 2

Answers on page 69

1. Which Eric Carmen single was based on a Rachmaninov melody from his Piano Concerto No 2 in C Minor?

2. Who released the 1972 album 'Rocky Mountain High'?

3. From which album was Enya's 'Orinoco Flow' taken?

4. Whose debut hit was 'Good Tradition' in 1988?

5. Which Carole King album spent 90 weeks in the UK charts following its 1971 release?

6. Who reckoned 'It's Different For Girls'?

7. Which Bruce Hornsby single dealt with racial discrimination?

8. Which Neil Sedaka song was penned in tribute to his former writing partner Howard Greenfield?

9. Which melancholic, Canadian-born songwriter composed 'Suzanne'?

10. Whose best-selling album is 'White Ladder'?

11. Who released the 1966 album 'Blonde On Blonde'?

12. Who was 'Walking Down Madison' in 1991?

13. Which Barry Manilow song was inspired by Scott English's 'Brandy'?

14. Which Seventies artist had hits with 'Gaye' and 'Scullery'?

15. 'Tap Root Manuscript' was the first album to chart in the UK for which American singer/songwriter?

16. Other than the song 'Wuthering Heights', what else links Kate Bush to Emily Brontë?

Answers to page 69
CLASSICAL GAS 1: **1.** Prokofiev **2.** 18th **3.** Rachmaninov **4.** Henry **5.** Ravel **6.** Hungarian **7.** Berlioz **8.** Dvořák **9.** Mahler **10.** Eisenach **11.** 1875 **12.** 32 **13.** 31 **14.** King George I **15.** *Messiah* **16.** Ludwig von Köchel

Seventies 3

Answers on page 74

1. 'Five Minutes' and 'Duchess' were hits for which punk band?

2. Which two members of Showaddywaddy are fathers of noted sportsmen?

3. How many sisters were there in Pussycat?

4. Jeffrey Calvert and Max West were better known as which 1975 chart-topping act?

5. Who requested 'Don't Play Your Rock 'N' Roll To Me' in 1975?

6. Which Australian winners of *Opportunity Knocks*, who had a 1971 hit with 'Tom Tom Turnaround', were at the centre of a vote-rigging storm?

7. Which band's first UK hit was 'Only You Can' in 1975?

8. Which island did The Gibson Brothers sing about in 1979?

9. 'You Don't Have To Be In The Army To Fight In The War' was a 1971 hit for which band?

10. 'Dyna-Mite' was which band's UK top ten debut?

11. Who played the violin with Slade?

12. Which bopping bird was a 1972 hit for Michael Jackson?

13. Which British R & B band had a 1972 hit with 'Burlesque'?

14. Which member of *The Partridge Family* did David Cassidy play?

15. How many UK top ten hits did Abba have in 1979?

16. Which Yorkshire brass band found themselves at number two in the charts in 1977 with their version of 'The Floral Dance'?

Answers to page 74
POT LUCK 12: **1.** Everything But The Girl **2.** The Shondells **3.** 1964
4. Curiosity Killed The Cat **5.** Carousel ('On A Carousel') **6.** Wings
7. Red Hot Chili Peppers **8.** The Strokes **9.** Tom Jones **10.** Jeremy Clyde
(Chad and Jeremy) **11.** Jon Anderson (Yes) **12.** Deacon Blue **13.** Dollar
14. Edison Lighthouse **15.** Dexy's Midnight Runners **16.** Huey Lewis and
The News

Girl Bands 2

Answers on page 75

1. What family trait links The Ronettes and Eternal?

2. Which girl group had a 1963 hit with 'One Fine Day'?

3. What was All Saints' first UK number one?

4. Which member of Bananarama left in 1988 and married Dave Stewart of The Eurythmics?

5. Who replaced her in Bananarama?

6. The Ganser sisters were members of which Sixties girl group?

7. Bernie, Linda and Ann were members of which Seventies singing sisters?

8. Which Sixties singer wrote 'He's A Rebel' for The Crystals?

9. Which girl band split up in 1989, months after having a number one single on both sides of the Atlantic?

10. Which Ronette married Phil Spector?

11. Which artist, now an international star, sang backing vocals on The Ronettes' 1963 hit 'Be My Baby'?

12. Which girl band had a 1999 hit with 'So Long'?

13. Which pet is Atomic in a current girl band?

14. Who wanted to know when 'Jimmy Mack' was coming back in 1967?

15. Which Steam hit charted for Bananarama in 1983?

16. 'Deep Sea Skiving' was the title of which girl band's first hit album?

Answers to page 75
SINATRA 1: **1.** 'Three Coins In The Fountain' **2.** Albert **3.** Nelson Riddle **4.** Sammy Davis Jnr **5.** Whispering Jack Smith **6.** 'Strangers In The Night' **7.** 1969 **8.** 'Love's Been Good To Me' **9.** 'Songs For Swinging Lovers' **10.** The Wine ('I Will Drink The Wine') **11.** 'My Way' **12.** Bono **13.** 'Granada' **14.** New York **15.** 'Chicago' **16.** 'My Way'

Pot Luck 12

Answers on page 72

1. Which duo took their name from a second-hand furniture shop in Hull?

2. What was the name of Tommy James's backing group?

3. In which year was *Top of the Pops* first broadcast?

4. Ben Volpelière-Pierrot was lead singer with which band?

5. Which fairground ride was a big hit with The Hollies in 1967?

6. Who had a 1974 hit with 'Band On The Run'?

7. 'Antwan The Swan' and 'Flea' are members of which US band?

8. Whose 2001 album was titled 'Is This It'?

9. Which international singing star made his professional debut at the Treforest Non-Political Working Men's Club in 1957?

10. Which member of a Sixties duo is now a TV actor?

11. Which singer with a progressive rock group once went solo under the name of Hans Christian Anderson?

12. Which Scottish band got their name from a Steely Dan song?

13. Who asked 'Who Were You With In The Moonlight'?

14. 'It's Up To You Petula' was which band's follow-up to a number one?

15. Violinist Helen O'Hara joined which band in 1982?

16. Who was 'Stuck With You' in 1986?

Answers to page 72
SEVENTIES 3: **1.** The Stranglers **2.** Romeo Challenger (father of international athlete Ben) and Trevor Oakes (father of professional footballer Scott) **3.** Three **4.** Typically Tropical **5.** Smokie **6.** New World **7.** Fox **8.** 'Cuba' **9.** Mungo Jerry **10.** Mud **11.** Jim Lea **12.** 'Rockin' Robin' **13.** Family **14.** Keith **15.** Five **16.** Brighouse and Rastrick

Sinatra 1

Answers on page 73

1. Which title song from a 1954 film gave Sinatra his first UK number one?

2. What was Sinatra's middle name?

3. Whose orchestra backed Sinatra on his 1955 hit 'Learnin' The Blues'?

4. With whom did Sinatra duet on the 1962 hit 'Me And My Shadow'?

5. Who recorded the original version of 'Me And My Shadow' back in 1927?

6. Which 1966 UK chart topper was taken from the film *A Man Could Get Killed*?

7. In which year did Sinatra release 'My Way'?

8. Which 1969 hit for Sinatra was first recorded by Rod McKuen?

9. What was the title of Sinatra's landmark album from 1958?

10. What did Sinatra say he would drink in 1971?

11. Which Sinatra track spent a record 124 weeks on the UK singles chart?

12. Which Irish rock star joined Sinatra for a 1993 version of 'I've Got You Under My Skin'?

13. Which Sinatra hit from 1961 was originally recorded by Frankie Laine?

14. According to Sinatra, which city is so good they named it twice?

15. Where did Sinatra say was 'My Kind Of Town'?

16. Claude François recorded the original version of which Sinatra classic?

Answers to page 73
GIRL BANDS 2: **1.** Both had pairs of Bennett sisters **2.** The Chiffons **3.** 'Never Ever' **4.** Siobhan Fahey **5.** Jacqui Sullivan **6.** The Shangri-Las **7.** The Nolans **8.** Gene Pitney **9.** The Bangles **10.** Veronica 'Ronnie' Bennett **11.** Cher **12.** Fierce **13.** Kitten **14.** Martha Reeves and The Vandellas **15.** 'Na Na Hey Hey Kiss Him Goodbye' **16.** Bananarama

Solo Artists 3

Answers on page 78

1. Which Eagle aired his 'Dirty Laundry' after going solo?

2. Which member of the Jackson family had a number one album with 'Control'?

3. 'Steppin' Out' was a track from which Joe Jackson album?

4. What is Cyndi Lauper's real first name?

5. Who wrote 'Step Inside Love', a 1968 hit for Cilla Black?

6. What nationality is Björk?

7. Which hit band did Björk used to be a member of?

8. Which Texan singer's biggest chart success was 'It Must Be Him' in 1967?

9. Whose debut solo album was the 1972 offering 'Cherish'?

10. Which Gloria Gaynor anthem was remixed to chart again 14 years on in 1993?

11. Who sang about 'Games Without Frontiers' in 1980?

12. And which female singer provided supporting vocals for 'Games Without Frontiers'?

13. Which Richie opened the Woodstock Festival in 1969?

14. Who took Billie Holliday's 'That Ole Devil Called Love' to number two in the UK in 1985?

15. Which 1990 UK number one for a solo artist was written by Prince and originally recorded by The Family?

16. Who could see clearly now in 1972?

Answers to page 78
POT LUCK 13: 1. Pilot 2. The Cruisers 3. David Clayton-Thomas
4. 'Parallel Lines' 5. Sloopy ('Hang On Sloopy') 6. 'Jennifer Eccles'
7. Peter Shelley 8. Prince 9. A grocery store 10. Kate Bush 11. Lilac
12. The Cufflinks 13. Foreigner 14. Africa 15. 2 16. 'Breakout'

Sixties 1

Answers on page 79

Which artists had UK hits with the following tracks in the Sixties?

1. 'Still I'm Sad'

2. 'To Whom It Concerns'

3. 'Time For Living'

4. 'Little Town Flirt'

5. 'Just Like Eddie'

6. 'Gimme A Little Sign'

7. 'Gimme Some Loving'

8. 'Baby Make It Soon'

9. 'Am I That Easy To Forget'

10. 'Barbara Ann'

11. 'Early In The Morning'

12. 'Dick-A-Dum-Dum'

13. 'Multiplication'

14. 'My Little Lady'

15. 'My Mind's Eye'

16. 'The Wedding'

Answers to page 79
COUNTRY AND WESTERN 2: **1.** His collie dog **2.** The Oak Ridge Boys **3.** Shania Twain **4.** Dolly Parton **5.** Kenny Rogers ('Ruby, Don't Take Your Love To Town') **6.** Donegal **7.** Willie Nelson **8.** Waylon Jennings **9.** 'Lucille' **10.** 'Man! I Feel Like A Woman!' **11.** John Denver **12.** Charlie Rich **13.** Kenny O'Dell **14.** Marty Robbins **15.** LeAnn Rimes **16.** 'The Wayward Wind'

Pot Luck 13

Answers on page 76

1. David Paton was the singer with which Seventies band?

2. What was the name of Dave Berry's backing group?

3. Who was the best-known lead vocalist with Blood, Sweat and Tears?

4. Which Blondie album contained 'Hanging On The Telephone'?

5. Who did The McCoys say 'lives in a very bad part of town'?

6. Whose satchel did The Hollies used to carry?

7. Who issued the ultimatum: 'Love Me Love My Dog'?

8. Who sang about '1999' in 1985?

9. Where did Anthony work in Billy Joel's 'Movin' Out'?

10. Who had a 1980 hit with 'Babooshka'?

11. What colour wine was on Elkie Brooks's lips in 1978?

12. Which US group of the late Sixties scored hits with 'Tracy' and 'When Julie Comes Around'?

13. Which American band were 'Waiting For A Girl Like You' in 1981?

14. Which continent was a hit with Toto in 1983?

15. What position in the UK charts did The Tremeloes' '(Call Me) Number One' reach?

16. What was Swing Out Sister's first UK hit?

Answers to page 76
SOLO ARTISTS 3: **1.** Don Henley **2.** Janet Jackson **3.** 'Night And Day **4.** Cynthia **5.** Paul McCartney **6.** Icelandic **7.** The Sugarcubes **8.** Vikki Carr **9.** David Cassidy **10.** 'I Will Survive' **11.** Peter Gabriel **12.** Kate Bush **13.** Richie Havens **14.** Alison Moyet **15.** 'Nothing Compares 2 U' (Sinead O'Connor) **16.** Johnny Nash

Country and Western 2

Answers on page 77

1. Three years after Jim Reeves died, what was buried at his feet?

2. Wally Fowler was leader of which American country band?

3. Whose 1995 album was titled 'The Woman In Me'?

4. Who had a country hit with a song called 'Dumb Blonde'?

5. Who lamented: 'It's hard to love a man whose legs are bent and paralysed'?

6. In which Irish county was Daniel O'Donnell born?

7. Which veteran country star teamed up with Julio Iglesias for the 1984 hit 'To All The Girls I've Loved Before'?

8. Whose theme for the TV series *The Dukes of Hazzard* made the US top thirty?

9. Who picked a fine time to leave Kenny Rogers?

10. In which song did Shania Twain want to 'go totally crazy, forget I'm a lady'?

11. Who said 'Thank God I'm A Country Boy' in 1975?

12. Who had a 1974 UK hit with 'Behind Closed Doors'?

13. But who recorded the song originally?

14. Which country singer had hits in the early Sixties with 'El Paso' and 'Devil Woman'?

15. Which American singer went 'Crazy' in 1999?

16. Which Tex Ritter hit of 1956 later became a number one for Frank Ifield?

Answers to page 77
SIXTIES 1: 1. The Yardbirds 2. Chris Andrews 3. The Association
4. Del Shannon 5. Heinz 6. Brenton Wood 7. Spencer Davis Group
8. Marmalade 9. Engelbert Humperdinck 10. The Beach Boys 11. Vanity
Fare 12. Des O'Connor 13. Bobby Darin 14. The Tremeloes 15. The
Small Faces 16. Julie Rogers

Name Changes 4

Answers on page 82

1. Which Australian rock band were previously called The Farriss Brothers?

2. As which rap artist is Sean Combs better known?

3. Which Sixties group started out as The Howlin' Wolves?

4. What is Jet Harris's real name?

5. Which international band were previously known as Feedback?

6. Which jazz singer was born Clementina Dinah Campbell?

7. Who was born Georgios Kyriacos Panayiotou?

8. What is Fats Domino's real name?

9. Which singer with a Scottish band changed his name from Mark McLoughlin?

10. As which rapper is André Young better known?

11. Which Sixties group who were into something good were previously known as The Heartbeats?

12. Which head of the family was born Sylvester Stewart?

13. Which member of Roxy Music changed his name from Philip Targett Adams?

14. To what did The Dalton Brothers change their name?

15. Which singer started out as a member of Café Society?

16. Which Eighties chart-toppers were previously called Caviar?

Answers to page 82
NUMBER TWOS 2: **1.** 1975 **2.** 1982 **3.** 1982 **4.** 1969 **5.** 1974 **6.** 1997 **7.** 1984 **8.** 1964 **9.** 1969 **10.** 1975 **11.** 1961 **12.** 1980 **13.** 1995 **14.** 1983 **15.** 1979 **16.** 1983

Cover Versions 3

Answers on page 83

1. In 1974, whose eyes did smoke get in, 15 years after it had first affected The Platters?

2. Who first had a UK hit in 1971 with 'Softly Whispering I Love You', revived by Paul Young in 1990?

3. Which Jonathan King project covered The Archies' 'Sugar Sugar'?

4. What song links Bobby Hebb, Georgie Fame and Boney M?

5. Who originally had a hit with Glamma Kid's 'The Sweetest Taboo'?

6. Which Searchers number one was taken to number three by C.J. Lewis in 1994?

7. Which group covered Billie Davis's 'Tell Him' in 1974?

8. Which Isaac Hayes track was revived by Eddy and The Soulband in 1985?

9. What did both The Carpenters in 1970 and Gwen Guthrie in 1986 long to be?

10. Who first had success with 'The Three Bells', a hit for Brian Poole and The Tremeloes in 1965?

11. What did both R. Dean Taylor and The Fall discover 13 years apart?

12. Who had the original hit with 'This Old Heart Of Mine', covered by Rod Stewart in 1989?

13. What identical message was sent out by The Four Tops, Gloria Gaynor and Michael Bolton?

14. Which Andrew Gold song did Undercover turn their attention to?

15. In 1971, who covered the aptly named 'It's The Same Old Song' by The Four Tops?

16. Which park was frequented by both The Small Faces and M People?

Answers to page 83
SEVENTIES 4: 1. Gary Numan (his uncle, Jess Lidyard, was the drummer with Tubeway Army) 2. Led Zeppelin 3. David Cassidy 4. Denny Laine 5. Dr Hook 6. Abba, Demis Roussos and Pussycat 7. Tony Orlando 8. Jeff 9. Ray Dorset (Mungo Jerry) 10. Andrea True 11. The Ramones 12. Paul Nicholas (*Just Good Friends*) 13. Nazareth 14. 'Julie Ann' 15. Andrew Gold 16. Creedence Clearwater Revival

Number Twos 2

Answers on page 80

In which years did the following tracks reach number two in the UK charts?

1. 'Glass Of Champagne' (Sailor)

2. 'Mirror Man' (Human League)

3. 'Just An Illusion' (Imagination)

4. 'Goodbye' (Mary Hopkin)

5. 'Never Can Say Goodbye' (Gloria Gaynor)

6. 'Stand By Me' (Oasis)

7. 'Wild Boys' (Duran Duran)

8. 'Bits And Pieces' (Dave Clark Five)

9. 'I'm Gonna Make You Mine' (Lou Christie)

10. 'There's A Whole Lot Of Loving' (Guys and Dolls)

11. 'Wild Wind' (John Leyton)

12. 'Dance Yourself Dizzy' (Liquid Gold)

13. 'Hold Me, Thrill Me, Kiss Me, Kill Me' (U2)

14. 'Wings Of A Dove' (Madness)

15. 'Pop Muzik' (M)

16. 'They Don't Know' (Tracey Ullman)

Answers to page 80
NAME CHANGES 4: **1.** INXS **2.** P Diddy **3.** Simon Dupree and The Big Sound **4.** Terence **5.** U2 **6.** Cleo Laine **7.** George Michael **8.** Antoine Domino **9.** Marti Pellow **10.** Dr Dre **11.** Herman's Hermits **12.** Sly Stone **13.** Phil Manzanera **14.** The Walker Brothers **15.** Tom Robinson **16.** Bros

Seventies 4

Answers on page 81

1. Whose uncle played in his band on their 1979 chart topper?

2. Who released the 1976 album 'Presence'?

3. Which teen idol was just a 'Daydreamer' in 1973?

4. Which Moody Blue became one of Wings?

5. Dennis Locorriere was one of the singers with which band?

6. Which three European acts had number one singles in the UK in 1976?

7. Who was the lead singer with Dawn?

8. What was the first name of Christie who had a 1970 number one with 'Yellow River'?

9. Who was working as a laboratory researcher when his song reached number one in 1970 and had to ask for time off to appear on *Top of The Pops*?

10. Whose Connection wanted 'More More More' in 1976?

11. Who told us in 1977: 'Sheena Is A Punk Rocker'?

12. Which actor who appeared in a long-running Eighties sit-com had three top twenty singles in 1976?

13. 'My White Bicycle' was a 1975 hit for which band?

14. Which girl gave Kenny a top ten hit in 1975?

15. Who was a 'Lonely Boy' in 1977?

16. 'Up Around The Bend' was a 1970 hit for which US band?

Answers to page 81
COVER VERSIONS 3: 1. Bryan Ferry 2. The Congregation 3. Sakkarin 4. 'Sunny' 5. Sade 6. 'Sweets For My Sweet' 7. Hello 8. 'Theme From *Shaft*' 9. 'Close To You' 10. The Browns 11. 'There's A Ghost In My House' 12. The Isley Brothers 13. 'Reach Out I'll Be There' 14. 'Never Let Her Slip Away' 15. The Weathermen 16. Itchycoo Park

Simon and Garfunkel 1

Answers on page 86

1. What did Paul Simon call himself in the late Fifties?
2. What was the title of Simon and Garfunkel's debut album?
3. Which song did Paul Simon dedicate to his then girlfriend Kathy Chitty?
4. Which trio covered 'The Sound of Silence' in the UK?
5. Which track from the album 'Sounds Of Silence' was originally recorded solo by Simon in 1964?
6. In 1967, who covered Simon's '59th Street Bridge Song (Feelin' Groovy)'?
7. How many Simon and Garfunkel tracks featured in *The Graduate*?
8. In which year was the album 'Bookends' released?
9. Which Paul Simon song was named Record of The Year at the 1969 Grammy Awards?
10. For how many weeks did 'Bridge Over Troubled Water' occupy the number one spot in the UK singles chart?
11. Which architect was the subject of a song on the 'Bridge Over Troubled Water' album?
12. Which Everly Brothers hit was covered on 'Bridge Over Troubled Water' in a live recording?
13. How many hours did it reportedly take Simon and Garfunkel to complete the recording of the 'Bridge Over Troubled Water' album?
14. For the recording of which song did the duo reunite briefly in 1975?
15. Which year saw the release of the double live set, 'The Concert In Central Park'?
16. In which school production did Simon and Garfunkel first appear together?

Answers to page 86
ONE-HIT WONDERS 4: 1. Chris Spedding 2. Mason Williams 3. 'Four In The Morning' 4. Dan Hill 5. Our Kid 6. 'I'd Rather Jack' 7. Redbone 8. 'Shame, Shame, Shame' 9. '(How Much Is) That Doggie In The Window' 10. Angry Anderson 11. Laurie Anderson 12. 'Love Games' 13. 'Chantilly Lace' 14. Graham Bonney 15. 'I'm The Urban Spaceman' 16. Sophie Lawrence

Solo Artists 4

Answers on page 87

1. 'Boys Cry' was a 1964 hit for which singer?
2. According to Jilted John, who was a moron?
3. How old was Little Jimmy Osmond when he recorded 'Long Haired Lover From Liverpool'?
4. Who was 'King Of The Road' in 1965?
5. Cilla Black's 1964 number one 'You're My World' was translated from which language?
6. Who turned down 'It's Not Unusual' because she didn't think it was suited to her talents?
7. Who recorded a version of 'I Know Him So Well' in a duet with her mother Cissy on her 1987 album?
8. Which 1961 Ben E. King song became a UK number one 26 years later after featuring in a jeans commercial?
9. Which Labi Siffre track was sampled on Eminem's 'My Name Is'?
10. Which Gloria Estefan single was the official anthem of the 1996 Olympics?
11. Who was the uncredited singer on Mike Oldfield's 'Moonlight Shadow'?
12. What was David Essex's first UK hit?
13. What is Lonnie Donegan's real Christian name?
14. Which 1970 number one for Dave Edmunds was originally recorded by Smiley Lewis?
15. On which road did Robbie Williams find himself in 2001?
16. Who saw the light in 1973?

Answers to page 87
LYRICS 2: **1.** 'Waterloo' (Abba) **2.** '(I Just) Died In Your Arms Tonight' (Cutting Crew) **3.** '(I've Had) The Time Of My Life' (Bill Medley and Jennifer Warnes) **4.** 'Wonderwall' (Oasis) **5.** 'I Have Nothing' (Whitney Houston) **6.** 'You Needed Me' (Boyzone) **7.** 'Love Really Hurts Without You' (Billy Ocean) **8.** 'The Longest Time' (Billy Joel) **9.** 'Desperado' (The Eagles) **10.** 'New Year's Day' (U2) **11.** 'Surfin' USA' (The Beach Boys) **12.** 'Easy Lover' (Phil Collins and Philip Bailey) **13.** 'Drive' (The Cars) **14.** 'Livin' On A Prayer' (Bon Jovi) **15.** 'What Can I Do' (The Corrs) **16.** 'With A Little Help From My Friends' (Joe Cocker)

One-Hit Wonders 4

Answers on page 84

1. After sweating in a Wombles costume on *Top of the Pops*, whose only hit in human guise was 'Motor Bikin'' in 1975?
2. 'Classical Gas' was the only hit for which instrumentalist?
3. What was Faron Young's favourite time of day?
4. Which Canadian singer hit the UK charts in 1978 with 'Sometimes When We Touch'?
5. Which juvenile band took 'You Just Might See Me Cry' to number two in 1976?
6. Which song provided The Reynolds Girls with their 15 minutes of fame?
7. Which American band got to number two in 1971 with 'The Witch Queen of New Orleans'?
8. Which song was a 1975 hit for Shirley and Company?
9. Which pet-shop lament – the young Margaret Thatcher's favourite song – was a 1953 hit for Patti Page?
10. Who was unhappy about Scott and Charlene getting married in *Neighbours* even though the wedding song, 'Suddenly', gave him his only UK hit?
11. 'O Superman' was which American singer's solitary chart entry?
12. Which 1974 Eurovision entry marked the beginning and end for Belle and The Devotions?
13. What was The Big Bopper's only UK hit?
14. Who had his only UK hit with 'Super Girl' in 1966?
15. Which novelty number charted for The Bonzo Dog Doo-Dah Band?
16. Which ex-*EastEnder* got to number 21 in 1991 with 'Love's Unkind'?

Answers to page 84
SIMON AND GARFUNKEL 1: 1. Jerry Landis 2. 'Wednesday Morning, 3 A.M.' 3. 'Homeward Bound' 4. The Bachelors 5. 'I Am A Rock' 6. Harpers Bizarre 7. Five 8. 1968 9. 'Mrs Robinson' 10. Three 11. Frank Lloyd Wright 12. 'Bye Bye Love' 13. 800 14. 'My Little Town' 15. 1982 16. *Alice in Wonderland*

Lyrics 2

Answers on page 85

From which songs are the following lyrics taken?

1. 'And how could I ever refuse, I feel like I win when I lose'
2. 'It must've been some kind of kiss, I should've walked away'
3. 'Now with passion in our eyes there's no way we could disguise it secretly'
4. 'There are many things that I would like to say about you but I don't know how'
5. 'I won't hold it back again, this passion inside, can't run from myself, there's nowhere to hide'
6. 'You put me high upon a pedestal, so high that I could almost see eternity'
7. 'You run around town like a fool and you think that it's groovy'
8. 'I don't care what consequence it brings, I have been a fool for lesser things'
9. 'Don't you draw the queen of diamonds, boy, she'll beat you if she's able'
10. 'And so we're told this is the golden age, and gold is the reason for the wars we wage'
11. 'If everybody had an ocean across the USA'
12. 'She'll take your heart but you won't feel it'
13. 'Who's gonna pay attention to your dreams, who's gonna plug their ears when you scream'
14. 'We've got each other and that's a lot for love, we'll give it a shot'
15. 'I haven't slept at all in days, it's been so long since we have talked'
16. 'What would you do if I sang out of tune, would you stand up and walk out on me'

Answers to page 85
SOLO ARTISTS 4: **1.** Eden Kane **2.** Gordon **3.** Nine **4.** Roger Miller
5. Italian **6.** Sandie Shaw **7.** Whitney Houston **8.** 'Stand By Me'
9. 'I Got The' **10.** 'Reach' **11.** Maggie Reilly **12.** 'Rock On' **13.** Anthony
14. 'I Hear You Knocking' **15.** 'The Road To Mandalay' **16.** Todd
Rundgren

Cover Versions 4

Answers on page 90

1. Which Beatles number one was covered by Ray Charles two years later?

2. Which one-time 'High Priestess of Punk' recorded a version of Martha and The Muffins' 'Echo Beach' in 1987?

3. Which song was a hit for both The Big Bopper in 1958 and Jerry Lee Lewis in 1972?

4. Which song links Elvis Presley, Andy Williams, The Stylistics and UB40?

5. Who first recorded the Dave Edmunds hit 'Born To Be With You'?

6. Which hit for Elvis in 1956 and for The Marcels in 1961 was revived by Showaddywaddy in 1980?

7. Which XTC song did The Crash Test Dummies cover in 1995 for the film *Dumb and Dumber*?

8. Who recorded the original hit version of Simply Red's 'Angel'?

9. Which song by Prince and the Revolution was covered by Art Of Noise featuring Tom Jones?

10. Which two groups charted with The Beatles' 'Ob-La-Di Ob-La-Da' in 1968?

11. Which Bee Gees song was revived by Adam Garcia in 1998?

12. Who first charted in the UK with 'Now That We've Found Love', a 1991 hit for Heavy D and The Boyz?

13. Which city song links Gary 'US' Bonds, Harley Quinne and Gillan?

14. Which Supremes hit did Bananarama cover in 1988?

15. Who covered Tommy James's 'Mony Mony' in 1987?

16. Who had a hit with 'Make The World Go Away' nine years before Donny and Marie Osmond?

Answers to page 90
SEVENTIES 5: **1.** Derek Longmuir **2.** Gilbert O'Sullivan **3.** Mud **4.** Paper Lace **5.** 'Billy Don't Be A Hero' **6.** Les Gray of Mud **7.** Bjorn Ulvaeus **8.** Donny Osmond **9.** The Four Seasons **10.** Midge Ure **11.** J. J. Barrie ('No Charge') **12.** Madeline Bell and Roger Cook **13.** Barry White **14.** Alice Cooper ('School's Out') **15.** Roxy Music **16.** 'Amoureuse'

Merseybeat 1

Answers on page 91

1. How far did 'A Little Loving' go for The Fourmost in 1964?

2. Who wrote Gerry and The Pacemakers' first two number ones?

3. Who was lead singer with The Mojos?

4. Which former member of The Merseybeats hit the charts again in 1976 with Liverpool Express?

5. Who replaced Tony Jackson as bass guitarist with The Searchers?

6. What was The Searchers' third UK number one?

7. Which band had a 1964 hit with 'You're No Good'?

8. Which artist destined for stardom co-wrote The Searchers' 'Needles And Pins'?

9. Who wrote the first three hits for Billy J. Kramer and The Dakotas?

10. Which Bacharach and David song did Billy J. Kramer cover in 1965?

11. Which infamous event took place on the same day in August 1963 that The Searchers had their first UK number one?

12. Who were the first act, apart from The Beatles, to top the charts with a Lennon and McCartney composition?

13. And what was the title of the song?

14. Who were the first Liverpool group to reach number one?

15. Which Merseybeat singer had previously worked for British Railways?

16. Which madcap comedian had his own Merseybeat group called The Midnighters?

Answers to page 91
THE WHO 1: **1.** The Ivy League **2.** *Ready, Steady, Go!* **3.** 'My Generation' **4.** Miles **5.** 'You Better You Bet' **6.** 13 (his grandmother had complained about the noise) **7.** 'The Carnival Is Over' by The Seekers **8.** 1966 **9.** 'Pictures Of Lily' (the picture was of Lily Bayliss) **10.** Herman's Hermits **11.** Tony Blackburn **12.** Pete Townshend **13.** Keith Moon **14.** Keith Moon **15.** *Lisztomania* **16.** Kenney Jones

Seventies 5

Answers on page 88

1. Which member of The Bay City Rollers later worked as a nurse?

2. Whose 1971 album was titled 'Himself'?

3. 'The Cat Crept In' for which band in 1974?

4. Which band dressed as American Civil War soldiers to promote their 1974 number one?

5. And what was the title of the song?

6. Which singer was dubbed 'Leslie Presley' for his vocal impersonations of the 'king'?

7. Which member of Abba had previously been a member of The Hootenanny Singers?

8. Who was Britain's favourite Mormon in 1973?

9. Which New Jersey band, who topped the charts in 1976, named themselves after the cocktail lounge in a local bowling alley?

10. Which chart topper with Slik nearly joined The Sex Pistols but became one of The Rich Kids instead?

11. Which former comedian and manager of Blue Mink had a spoken number one in 1976?

12. Who were the two vocalists with Blue Mink?

13. Who had a bigger UK hit with 'Just The Way You Are' than its composer Billy Joel?

14. Which minister's son outraged parents with his 1972 number one?

15. Who released the 1979 album 'Manifesto'?

16. Veronique Sanson recorded the original version of which Kiki Dee hit?

Answers to page 88
COVER VERSIONS 4: 1. 'Eleanor Rigby' 2. Toyah 3. 'Chantilly Lace'
4. 'Can't Help Falling In Love' 5. The Chordettes 6. 'Blue Moon' 7. 'The Ballad Of Peter Pumpkinhead' 8. Aretha Franklin 9. 'Kiss' 10. Marmalade and The Bedrocks 11. 'Night Fever' 12. Third World 13. 'New Orleans' 14. 'Nathan Jones' 15. Billy Idol 16. Eddy Arnold

The Who 1

Answers on page 89

1. Which Sixties falsetto group did backing vocals on 'I Can't Explain'?

2. The Who's second hit, 'Anyway Anyhow Anywhere', was chosen as the new theme to which TV show?

3. Which was The Who's first top three hit?

4. For how far could The Who see in 1967?

5. What was The Who's last UK top ten single?

6. At what age did Pete Townshend smash his first guitar, and why?

7. Which song prevented 'My Generation' from reaching number one in the UK?

8. In which year was 'I'm A Boy' released?

9. Which Who single was inspired by a photo of an old vaudeville star hanging on a wall in Pete Townshend's girlfriend's house?

10. Which British band did The Who support on their first US tour?

11. Which Radio 1 DJ described the rock opera *Tommy* as 'sick'?

12. Which member of The Who produced Thunderclap Newman's 'Something In The Air'?

13. Which non-driving member of The Who accidentally ran over and killed his chauffeur while trying to escape from a gang of skinheads?

14. Which of The Who played J.D. Clover in the film *That'll Be The Day*?

15. In which 1975 Ken Russell film did Roger Daltrey star?

16. Who replaced Keith Moon as drummer in 1979?

Answers to page 89
MERSEYBEAT 1: 1. A long long way 2. Mitch Murray 3. Stu James 4. Billy Kinsley 5. Frank Allen 6. 'Don't Throw Your Love Away' 7. The Swinging Blue Jeans 8. Sonny Bono 9. Lennon and McCartney 10. 'Trains And Boats And Planes' 11. The Great Train Robbery 12. Billy J. Kramer and The Dakotas 13. 'Bad To Me' 14. Gerry and The Pacemakers 15. Billy J. Kramer 16. Freddie Starr

Pot Luck 14

Answers on page 94

1. Which Shadow became a Jehovah's Witness in 1973?

2. Which Rolling Stone is the son of a lorry driver?

3. What was Bob Marley's middle name?

4. Paddy McAloon is the leader of which band?

5. Dave Mount was the drummer with which Seventies band?

6. Which country star had four children and several miscarriages by the time she was 18?

7. Which singer was once employed wrapping chamber pots in a Cardiff factory?

8. Which band got their name from a TV listing guide which gave details of a forthcoming discussion programme?

9. At the time which rock classic was described as a 'novelty foxtrot'?

10. From which country do Midnight Oil come?

11. Who had a hit with 'The Joker'?

12. Derek Quinn, Roy Crewsdon, Pete Birrell and Bernie Dwyer formed which Sixties backing group to an energetic singer?

13. Who was sacked from his job with the Precision Tool Company in 1951 for being under age?

14. Who was sacked from his job stacking shelves at Tesco because he kept wearing the store's carrier bags?

15. Who wrote and performed 'Time In A Bottle'?

16. Who was the singer with Creedence Clearwater Revival?

Answers to page 94
LYRICS 3: 1. 'Hand On Your Heart' (Kylie Minogue) 2. 'Don't Look Back In Anger' (Oasis) 3. 'All I Want For Christmas Is You' (Mariah Carey) 4. 'Uptown Girl' (Billy Joel) 5. 'The Greatest Love Of All' (George Benson) 6. 'Mamma Mia' (Abba) 7. 'Take On Me' (a-ha) 8. 'Eternal Flame' (The Bangles) 9. 'Love Me For A Reason' (The Osmonds) 10. 'Linger' (The Cranberries) 11. 'Honesty' (Billy Joel) 12. 'A View To A Kill' (Duran Duran) 13. 'That Don't Impress Me Much' (Shania Twain) 14. 'Happy Together' (The Turtles) 15. 'Until The Time Is Through' (Five) 16. 'Oops!…I Did It Again' (Britney Spears)

Dance 1

Answers on page 95

1. Who was the guiding light behind Beats International's 'Dub Be Good To Me'?

2. Prince Markie Dee was a member of which New York dance band?

3. Who was the founder of Enigma?

4. Which young brother of New Kids On The Block's Donnie Wahlberg was once an underwear model for Calvin Klein?

5. Who changed her name to MC Kinky?

6. Daddy G and Mushroom were among the founding fathers of which Bristol-based dance/rap outfit?

7. Who had a 2001 hit with 'Castles In The Sky'?

8. Who released the album 'Strange Cargo'?

9. What is the real name of D.M.C. from Run D.M.C.?

10. Who had a 1997 hit with his version of the James Bond theme from *Tomorrow Never Dies*?

11. Which dance band were the UK's entrants in the 1995 Eurovision Song Contest?

12. Which Paul Hardcastle hit featured spoken news reports about the Vietnam War?

13. Who had a 1998 hit with 'The Rockafeller Skank'?

14. Who remixed Cornershop's 'Brimful Of Asha' to take it to number one in 1998?

15. What nationality are Black Box?

16. Which track earned Black Box a UK number one single in 1989?

Answers to page 95
ONE-HIT WONDERS 5: 1. Wild Cherry 2. Lipps Inc. 3. Harmony Grass 4. 'Race With The Devil' 5. First Class 6. 'Twilight Café' 7. 'Also Sprach Zarathustra' 8. Paul Davidson 9. The Weather Girls 10. Sunny 11. Red Sovine 12. 'My Resistance Is Low' 13. Pseudo Echo 14. Ohio Express 15. 1910 Fruitgum Company 16. 'The Shifting Whispering Sands'

Lyrics 3

Answers on page 92

From which songs are the following lyrics taken?

1. 'Look me in the eye and tell me we are really through'

2. 'You ain't ever gonna burn my heart out'

3. 'I just want you for my own more than you could ever know'

4. 'And when she's walking she's looking so fine'

5. 'I decided long ago never to walk in anyone's shadow'

6. 'Look at me now, will I ever learn, I don't know how, but I suddenly lose control'

7. 'Today's another day to find you shying away'

8. 'Do you feel my heart beating, do you understand'

9. 'My initial reaction is, honey, give me love, not a facsimile of'

10. 'But I'm in so deep, you know I'm such a fool for you'

11. 'If you look for truthfulness you might just as well be blind'

12. 'That fatal kiss is all we need'

13. 'I can't believe you kiss your car goodnight'

14. 'Me and you and you and me, no matter how they toss the dice it has to be, the only one for me is you and you for me'

15. 'Without your love I'd be half a man, maybe one day you'll understand'

16. 'It might seem like a crush but it doesn't mean that I'm serious'

Answers to page 92
POT LUCK 14: **1.** Hank Marvin **2.** Charlie Watts **3.** Nesta **4.** Prefab Sprout **5.** Mud **6.** Loretta Lynn **7.** Shirley Bassey **8.** Talking Heads **9.** 'Rock Around The Clock' **10.** Australia **11.** The Steve Miller Band **12.** The Dreamers (Freddie and The Dreamers) **13.** Elvis Presley **14.** Boy George **15.** Jim Croce **16.** John Fogerty

One-Hit Wonders 5

Answers on page 93

1. Whose only hit was 'Play That Funky Music' in 1976?

2. Who reached number two with 'Funky Town' in 1980 before disappearing without trace?

3. Which group had their solitary hit with 'Move In A Little Closer' in 1969?

4. What was Gun's only hit?

5. Which band's moment of triumph was 'Beach Baby' in 1974?

6. With a song about which eaterie did Susan Fassbender enjoy chart success in 1981?

7. Which instrumental reached number seven for Deodato in 1973?

8. Who had a top ten hit with 'Midnight Rider' in 1975?

9. For whom was it 'Raining Men' in 1984?

10. Who issued 'Doctor's Orders' in 1974?

11. Which American artist's only UK chart success was a number four hit with 'Teddy Bear' in 1981?

12. In 1976, which cover version of an old Hoagy Carmichael song gave Robin Sarstedt his only hit?

13. Which Australian band reached number eight in 1987 with 'Funky Town'?

14. Which bubblegum group had a 1968 hit with 'Yummy Yummy Yummy'?

15. Who got to number two in 1968 with 'Simon Says'?

16. Which 1956 release gave Eamonn Andrews his only chart entry?

Answers to page 93
DANCE 1: 1. Norman Cook 2. The Fat Boys 3. Michael Cretu
4. Marky Mark 5. Caron Geary 6. Massive Attack 7. Ian Van Dahl
8. William Orbit 9. Darryl McDaniels 10. Moby 11. Love City Groove
12. '19' 13. Fatboy Slim 14. Norman Cook 15. Italian 16. 'Ride On Time'

Number Twos 3

Answers on page 98

In which years did the following singles reach number two in the UK charts?

1. 'Starting Together' (Su Pollard)

2. 'You Take Me Up' (The Thompson Twins)

3. 'Alternate Title' (The Monkees)

4. 'Welcome To The Pleasure Dome' (Frankie Goes To Hollywood)

5. 'Bend It' (Dave Dee, Dozy, Beaky, Mick and Tich)

6. 'The Jean Genie' (David Bowie)

7. 'Gold' (Spandau Ballet)

8. 'True Love Ways' (Peter and Gordon)

9. 'Song 2' (Blur)

10. 'If You Gotta Go Go Now' (Manfred Mann)

11. 'Yester-Me Yester-You Yesterday' (Stevie Wonder)

12. 'Only You' (Yazoo)

13. 'Love Of The Common People' (Paul Young)

14. 'Sandy' (John Travolta)

15. 'Call Me Number One' (The Tremeloes)

16. 'Ghostbusters' (Ray Parker Jnr)

Answers to page 98
POT LUCK 15: 1. Little Jimmy Osmond ('Long Haired Lover From Liverpool') 2. 'Arnold Layne' 3. Al Green 4. Hues Corporation 5. Cousin 6. Rod Argent (Argent) 7. 'House Of The Rising Sun' 8. Judas Priest 9. Nick Beggs 10. The Who 11. Marty Wilde 12. New Zealander 13. Clare Grogan 14. Mari Wilson 15. Swedish 16. 'Old Red Eyes Is Back'

David Bowie 1

Answers on page 99

1. Which Bowie novelty track originally released in 1967 finally became a hit in 1973?

2. Who co-wrote and provided backing vocals on 'Fame'?

3. What was the original title of the 'Space Oddity' album in the UK?

4. On which Sixties show did Bowie make his TV debut with The Manish Boys?

5. Who originally recorded 'China Girl'?

6. Who recorded backing vocals on 'Sound And Vision'?

7. With whom did Bowie record the double A-side duet 'Peace On Earth' and 'Little Drummer Boy'?

8. In which year did 'Let's Dance' get to number one?

9. Which film theme did Bowie take to number two in the singles charts in 1986?

10. Who played guitar on 'Buddha Of Suburbia'?

11. Who joined Bowie for the 1996 single 'Hallo Spaceboy'?

12. Who did Bowie tell 'I'm Only Dancing' in 1972?

13. When did Davy Jones, as he was originally billed, decide to change his name?

14. Why did he choose the surname Bowie?

15. In which year was 'Aladdin Sane' released?

16. Which Bowie composition was a 1971 hit for Peter Noone?

Answers to page 99
FIVE 1: 1. Jason Brown 2. Sean 3. Birmingham 4. Abidin 5. 'Slam Dunk Da Funk' 6. Ritchie and Scott 7. Four 8. 1 9. Abs 10. Turkey 11. 'We Will Rock You' 12. 'Everybody Get Up' 13. Abs 14. Scott 15. Ritchie and J 16. Sweden

Pot Luck 15

Answers on page 96

1. Who admitted in 1972 that he had no idea where Liverpool was?

2. Which Pink Floyd song was about a boy who stole women's underwear?

3. Who became a preacher after hot grits was poured on him in the bath by an ex-girlfriend who then shot herself?

4. Hubert Ann Kelly, St Clair Lee and Fleming Williams made up which trio who had a 1974 hit with 'Rock The Boat'?

5. What relation is Dionne Warwick to Whitney Houston?

6. Which keyboard player with The Zombies went on to form his own band?

7. Which four and a half minute Sixties classic was about a New Orleans brothel?

8. Which heavy metal band were formed in Birmingham in 1969 by K. K. Downing and Ian Hill?

9. Who took over singing duties with Kajagoogoo following Limahl's exit?

10. Who could see for miles in 1967?

11. Which British rock 'n' roller wrote Status Quo's 'Ice In The Sun'?

12. What nationality was John Rowles who had a 1968 top three hit with 'If I Only Had Time'?

13. Who was the lead singer with Altered Images?

14. Who was 'Neasden's queen of soul'?

15. What nationality are Roxette?

16. Which Beautiful South song dealt with alcoholism?

Answers to page 96
NUMBER TWOS 3: 1. 1986 2. 1984 3. 1967 4. 1985 5. 1966 6. 1972
7. 1983 8. 1965 9. 1997 10. 1965 11. 1969 12. 1982 13. 1983 14. 1978
15. 1969 16. 1984

Five 1

Answers on page 97

1. What is J's full name?

2. Who was the youngest member of the group?

3. In which city was Ritchie Neville born?

4. What is Abs short for?

5. What was the title of Five's first UK single?

6. Which two members sang the lead vocals on 'Until The Time Is Through'?

7. How many singles were released from Five's first album?

8. What number in the UK charts did 'Keep On Movin'' reach?

9. Which band member went to the Italia Conti Performing Arts College?

10. Which country is Abs's father from?

11. Which Five single featured Brian May?

12. What was the title of Five's fourth single?

13. Which former band member does not drink alcohol?

14. Who took time off in 2001 because his girlfriend had a baby?

15. Which two members ended up in court after a fight in a Dublin bar?

16. In which country did Five record the single 'Slam Dunk Da Funk'?

Answers to page 97
DAVID BOWIE 1: 1. 'The Laughing Gnome' 2. John Lennon 3. 'David Bowie' 4. *Gadzooks! It's All Happening* 5. Iggy Pop 6. Mary Hopkin 7. Bing Crosby 8. 1983 9. 'Absolute Beginners' 10. Lenny Kravitz 11. The Pet Shop Boys 12. John 13. When Davy Jones signed up as one of The Monkees 14. From the Bowie knife in honour of his idol Mick Jagger, a jagger being an old English knife 15. 1973 16. 'Oh You Pretty Thing'

Motown 1

Answers on page 102

1. Who was lead singer and saxophonist with The Commodores before going solo?

2. Which Motown artist enjoyed a 1981 UK number one with 'Being With You'?

3. Which Four Tops hit was originally a US number five for Left Banke?

4. How old was Stevie Wonder when he signed for Motown?

5. Which Stevie Wonder hit was inspired by Bob Marley's 'Jamming'?

6. What did The Miracles and Diana Ross and The Supremes both second?

7. Which Four Tops hit was taken from the film *Buster*?

8. Where were The Four Tops standing in 1967?

9. Which Temptation sued Motown for $5 million in 1968?

10. Who had a top three hit with 'War' in 1970?

11. Who replaced David Ruffin in The Temptations and went on to sing lead vocals on 'Papa Was A Rolling Stone'?

12. 'Help Me Make It Through The Night' was a 1972 hit for which Motown group?

13. Who contributed backing vocals on Lionel Richie's 'Hello'?

14. Which Motown girl group had 'Nowhere To Run' in 1965?

15. What was Marvin Gaye too busy thinking about in 1969?

16. Which 20-year-old artist married Motown boss Berry Gordy's 37-year-old sister Anna?

Answers to page 102
FOLK 1: 1. *Tonight* 2. Gordon Giltrap 3. American 4. Fairport Convention 5. Salford 6. The Kingston Trio 7. Arlo Guthrie (son of Woody Guthrie) 8. Clannad 9. Glenn Yarbrough 10. The Seekers 11. Australian 12. 'I Get A Kick Out Of You' 13. 'Green Green' 14. Gene Clark 15. Joni Mitchell 16. Donovan

Eighties 3

Answers on page 103

1. Who are Neil Tennant and Chris Lowe?

2. Which 1986 number one was written by Pal Waaktaar?

3. Who played harmonica on Chaka Khan's 'I Feel For You'?

4. Which 1984 chart topper wrote the theme for the TV series *Boon*?

5. What were Squeeze pulling from the shell in 1980?

6. Which band's only top ten hit was 'When You Ask About Love' in 1980?

7. Who had a 1988 number one with 'Nothing's Gonna Change My Love For You'?

8. Which song was named International Hit Of The Year at the 1983 Ivor Novello Awards?

9. Which Hall and Oates hit from 1983 was a cover of a Mike Oldfield track?

10. Which Mike Oldfield song was a tribute to John Lennon?

11. Neville Staples, Lynval Golding and Jerry Dammers were members of which band?

12. John Pickles and Ian Morgan were better known as which hitmakers?

13. Who reached the top of the UK singles chart in 1988 with 'The First Time'?

14. What was the title of Big Country's only UK number one album?

15. Who had a 1982 hit with 'Torch'?

16. John Keeble was the drummer with which Eighties band?

Answers to page 103
INDIE 1: 1. New Order 2. 'Black Eyed Boy' 3. R.E.M. 4. Blur
5. Arabacus 6. 'Cloudcuckooland' 7. Joy Division 8. Deacon Blue
9. John Power 10. 'Female Of The Species' 11. Counting Crows
12. Brian Eno 13. 'The One And Only' by Chesney Hawkes
14. Radiohead 15. Suede 16. Stone Roses masks (after the Roses had cancelled their headline appearance)

Folk 1

Answers on page 100

1. Robin Hall and Jimmie MacGregor were regulars on which TV news magazine series of the early Sixties?

2. Who released the 1977 album 'Perilous Journey'?

3. What nationality is Julie Felix?

4. Iain Matthews, Judy Dyble, Ashley Hutchings, Richard Thompson, Simon Nicol and Martin Lamble were the original members of which group?

5. Which district of Manchester inspired Ewan MacColl to write 'Dirty Old Town'?

6. Which trio had a hit with 'Tom Dooley' in 1958?

7. Which son of a famous folk singer sang about 'Alice's Restaurant'?

8. Which band took their name from the Gaelic for 'family'?

9. Who was lead vocalist with the Sixties folk group The Limeliters?

10. Bruce Woodley and Keth Potger were members of which folk quartet from Down Under?

11. What nationality is Gary Shearston?

12. And what was his only UK chart success?

13. What colour gave The New Christy Minstrels a UK hit in 1963?

14. Who left The New Christy Minstrels after a few months and went on to form The Byrds?

15. Who recorded the 1974 album 'Court And Spark'?

16. Which Sixties folk singer was labelled 'Britain's answer to Bob Dylan'?

Answers to page 100
MOTOWN 1: **1.** Lionel Richie **2.** Smokey Robinson **3.** 'Walk Away Renee' **4.** Ten **5.** 'Masterblaster' **6.** That Emotion **7.** 'Loco In Acapulco' **8.** 'Standing In The Shadows Of Love' **9.** David Ruffin **10.** Edwin Starr **11.** Dennis Edwards **12.** Gladys Knight and The Pips **13.** Richard Marx **14.** Martha and The Vandellas **15.** My Baby **16.** Marvin Gaye

Indie 1

Answers on page 101

1. Which band had a 2001 hit with 'Crystal'?

2. In which 1997 single did Texas re-create the sound of The Supremes?

3. Who released the 1995 single 'Crush With Eyeliner'?

4. Which band's debut album was titled 'Leisure'?

5. What prefix did Pulp drop from their original name?

6. 'Pure' was a track from which Lightning Seeds album?

7. New Order were the successors to which band?

8. Who had hits with 'Dignity' and 'Real Gone Kid'?

9. Which bassist formed Cast following the break-up of The La's?

10. Which was more deadly than the male according to Space?

11. 'August & Everything After' was the debut album of which Van Morrison-inspired US band?

12. Who produced the 'Laid' album for James?

13. Which song prevented 'Sit Down' by James from reaching number one in the UK in 1991?

14. Who released the album 'The Bends'?

15. Which band were named Hype of the Year in the 1994 *Rolling Stone Music Awards* Critics' Picks?

16. What did Supergrass wear on stage at the 1995 Glastonbury Festival?

Answers to page 101
EIGHTIES 3: 1. The Pet Shop Boys 2. 'The Sun Always Shines On TV' (a-ha) 3. Stevie Wonder 4. Jim Diamond 5. Mussels 6. Matchbox 7. Glenn Medeiros 8. 'Ebony And Ivory' 9. 'Family Man' 10. 'Moonlight Shadow' 11. The Specials 12. Jive Bunny 13. Robin Beck 14. 'Steeltown' 15. Soft Cell 16. Spandau Ballet

Pot Luck 16

Answers on page 106

1. Which movie star sang backing vocals on Billy Ocean's 1986 hit 'When The Going Gets Tough (The Tough Get Going)'?

2. Which older sister of Janet Jackson had a minor US hit in 1984 with 'Hearts Don't Lie'?

3. Who played bass on Midge Ure's 'If I Was'?

4. Who played a housewife in the 1979 film *Union City*?

5. Which former teen idol did washing powder commercials in the Sixties?

6. Which singer/songwriter used to be employed at a New York brewery?

7. Which Scottish singer was once married to a Bee Gee?

8. Bobby Farrell was the chief dancer in which Seventies group?

9. Clem Burke was the drummer with which Eighties band?

10. Why does Sheryl Crow have two false front teeth?

11. Which artist, who had a UK number one, founded Dr West's Medicine Show and Junk Band?

12. Who had a 1996 hit with 'Stripper Vicar'?

13. What do PJ Harvey's initials stand for?

14. Which member of Poco left to found The Eagles?

15. Who wrote 'Simon Smith And His Amazing Dancing Bear'?

16. Gary Brooker was the singer and pianist with which Sixties band?

Answers to page 106
FIFTIES 2: **1.** Ronnie Hilton ('Veni, Vidi, Vici') **2.** The Hilltoppers and The Platters **3.** The Checkmates **4.** 'What Do You Want To Make Those Eyes At Me For?' **5.** October **6.** 'On The Street Where You Live' **7.** Vic Damone **8.** Pat Boone **9.** 'Diana' **10.** The Ramblers **11.** 'Living Doll' **12.** Paul Anka **13.** 'I Can't Tell A Waltz From A Tango' **14.** 'Long Tall Sally' **15.** *The Sweetest Girl in Town* **16.** Brenda Lee

Stevie Wonder 1

Answers on page 107

1. Which Stevie Wonder single was part of his campaign to have Martin Luther King's birthday recognised as a US holiday?

2. With whom did Stevie Wonder duet on 'My Love'?

3. What was Stevie Wonder's first UK hit single?

4. Who recorded the original version of 'For Once In My Life'?

5. What caused Stevie Wonder's blindness?

6. Which French title gave Stevie Wonder a hit on both sides of the Atlantic in 1969?

7. Which singer did he marry in 1970?

8. For whom was 'Superstition' originally written?

9. Which 1973 single gave Stevie Wonder his first US number one for ten years?

10. What did Stevie Wonder lose after a car crash in 1973?

11. Which female artist took a Stevie Wonder song to number one in the US in 1975?

12. What kept 'Happy Birthday' off the top of the UK singles chart?

13. What sport did Stevie Wonder play while hosting NBC TV's *Saturday Live* in 1983?

14. On which Elton John song did Stevie Wonder play harmonica?

15. To whom did Stevie Wonder dedicate his 1985 Oscar for Best Song, awarded for 'I Just Called To Say I Love You'?

16. In which year was the album 'Innervisions' released?

Answers to page 107
FILM TRACKS 1: 1. *Jubilee* 2. *Girl's Town* 3. 'When You Believe'
4. Barbra Streisand 5. *Up Close and Personal* 6. 'More Than A Woman'
7. 'You're The One That I Want', 'Summer Nights', 'Sandy' and 'Greased Lightning' 8. *Xanadu* 9. 'Hopelessly Devoted To You' 10. Anthony Newley
11. 'Living In America' 12. Boy George 13. Doris Day 14. Duane Eddy
15. *King Creole* 16. *Fun in Acapulco*

Fifties 2

Answers on page 104

1. Who came, saw and conquered the charts in 1954?

2. Which two groups had UK top ten hits in the Fifties with 'Only You'?

3. What was the name of Emile Ford's backing group?

4. And what were they asking in 1959?

5. In which month of 1959 did 'Here Comes Summer' top the UK charts?

6. Which 1958 UK number one was taken from the musical *My Fair Lady*?

7. And which American singer took it to the top of the charts?

8. 'I'll Be Home' was a first UK number one single for which artist?

9. Which number one did Paul Anka write about his babysitter?

10. Which group backed Perry Como on his chart-topping 'Don't Let The Stars Get In Your Eyes'?

11. Which was the biggest-selling UK single of 1959?

12. Which 12-year-old won $35 for impersonating Johnnie Ray in a 1953 amateur talent contest?

13. Which Alma Cogan hit suggested she had two left feet?

14. Which girl gave Little Richard his first UK top ten hit?

15. Which film featured Jackie Wilson's 'Reet Petite'?

16. Who was billed as 'Little Miss Dynamite'?

Answers to page 104
POT LUCK 16: **1.** Michael Douglas **2.** LaToya Jackson **3.** Mark King (Level 42) **4.** Debbie Harry **5.** Craig Douglas **6.** Barry Manilow **7.** Lulu (Maurice Gibb) **8.** Boney M **9.** Blondie **10.** The originals fell out when she tripped up on stage early in her career **11.** Norman Greenbaum **12.** Mansun **13.** Polly Jean **14.** Randy Meisner **15.** Randy Newman **16.** Procol Harum

Film Tracks 1

Answers on page 105

1. Adam and The Ants' 'Deutscher Girls' was a 1982 hit from which 1977 film?
2. From which film was Paul Anka's 1959 hit 'Lonely Boy' taken?
3. Mariah Carey and Whitney Houston duetted on which song from *The Prince of Egypt*?
4. Who sang the theme from *The Way We Were*?
5. Celine Dion's 1996 hit 'Because You Loved Me' was the theme from which film?
6. Which Tavares hit, written by The Bee Gees, came from *Saturday Night Fever*?
7. Which four singles from *Grease* featured John Travolta?
8. The Olivia Newton-John/Cliff Richard duet 'Suddenly' was taken from which film?
9. Which *Grease* single did Olivia Newton-John take to number two in the UK charts as a solo artist?
10. Who recorded 'I've Waited So Long' in 1959 from *Idle on Parade*?
11. Which James Brown single was taken from *Rocky IV*?
12. Who released the theme from *The Crying Game* in 1992?
13. In 1955, who recorded 'Ready, Willing And Able' from *Young at Heart*?
14. The theme from *Because They're Young* was a 1960 hit for which guitar man?
15. Elvis's 'Hard-Headed Woman' came from which film?
16. 'Bossa Nova Baby' was an Elvis hit from which film?

Answers to page 105
STEVIE WONDER 1: 1. 'Happy Birthday' 2. Julio Iglesias 3. 'Uptight (Everything's Alright)' 4. Tony Bennett 5. After birth, he was given too much oxygen while in an incubator 6. 'My Cherie Amour' 7. Syreeta 8. Jeff Beck 9. 'Superstition' 10. His sense of smell 11. Minnie Riperton ('Lovin' You') 12. 'Green Door' by Shakin' Stevens 13. Tennis 14. 'I Guess That's Why They Call It The Blues' 15. Nelson Mandela 16. 1973

Bee Gees 1

Answers on page 110

1. Which Bee Gees hit was originally written for, but turned down by, Otis Redding?

2. Which industrial tragedy gave The Bee Gees their first hit single in the UK?

3. For which American female singer was 'How Deep Is Your Love' originally written?

4. On which island were the Gibb brothers born?

5. Which former child actor joined The Bee Gees as drummer in 1967?

6. Which was the band's first number one in Australia?

7. In which year did Maurice Gibb say that it is 'very probable The Bee Gees will be non-existent in two years from now'?

8. Which was the last Bee Gees hit on which Colin Petersen and Vince Melouney appeared?

9. Which brother left the band in 1969 to pursue a solo career?

10. Whose UK TV show did The Bee Gees walk off in protest at his mickey-taking?

11. Which single got to number one in the US in 1977?

12. From which album was 'Nights On Broadway' taken?

13. Who played guest percussion on 'You Should Be Dancing'?

14. Which Bee Gees single set a Billboard Hot 100 record by remaining in the US top ten for 17 weeks in a row?

15. In which year was 'Tragedy' a number one on both sides of the Atlantic?

16. 'Tragedy' was a track on which Bee Gees album?

Answers to page 110
POT LUCK 17: **1.** Eric Clapton **2.** The Big Blue **3.** Monsieur Dupont
4. 'Could It Be Magic' **5.** 'A Lover's Concerto' **6.** 'God Save The Queen'
7. 'Ventura Highway' **8.** John Lennon **9.** Paul McCartney **10.** 1964
11. Mike Oldfield **12.** The Monkees **13.** Ozzy Osbourne **14.** Slade
15. The Modern Lovers **16.** Crispian St Peters

Chart Toppers 4

Answers on page 111

1. Who entered the record books in March 2002 by having the fastest-selling UK single ever?

2. Dennis D'Ell was the singer with which 1964 chart toppers?

3. From which Duran Duran album was 'The Reflex' taken?

4. What didn't Eddy Grant want to do in the title of his 1982 number one?

5. Which 1982 number one by a group of Birmingham schoolboys was originally a Jamaican song about pot-smoking?

6. Which American youngsters had a 1983 number one with 'Candy Girl'?

7. Tim Hauser, Janis Siegel, Laurel Massé and Alan Paul made up which 1977 chart toppers?

8. And which French love song took them to number one?

9. Who got smoke in their eyes in 1959?

10. How many weeks did Whitney Houston stay at the top of the UK charts with 'I Will Always Love You'?

11. Who had a posthumous number one with 'Living On My Own' in 1993?

12. Which 1994 single was the 700th UK number one since the charts began?

13. Which 1982 number one by a German techno band started out on the B-side of a track called 'Computer Love'?

14. What was the name of Georgie Fame's backing group on his 1965 hit 'Yeh Yeh'?

15. Which singer with a group who had a 1964 UK number one went on to present *Play School*?

16. And which girl did his band sing about?

Answers to page 111
ALBUMS 2: 1. Whitesnake 2. Blondie 3. 10cc 4. The Smiths 5. Melanie C 6. The Small Faces 7. Queen 8. Kate Bush 9. Alison Moyet 10. Tanita Tikaram 11. Roxy Music 12. Deep Purple 13. Leo Sayer 14. Haircut 100 15. Simply Red 16. The Rolling Stones

Pot Luck 17

Answers on page 108

1. As a 16-year-old which future guitar legend took a Christmas job as a relief postman in Surrey?

2. With which band did the Pop Idols work on their big band album in 2002?

3. Which Frenchman did Sandie Shaw sing about in 1969?

4. Which Barry Manilow song was inspired by Chopin's Prelude in C Minor?

5. And which hit for The Toys was adapted from Bach's Minuet in G?

6. Which Sex Pistols track was banned by the BBC for being too anarchic?

7. Which highway did America drive down in 1972?

8. Who called himself Dr Winston O'Boogie when playing on Elton John's version of 'Lucy In The Sky With Diamonds'?

9. Who produced Mary Hopkin's 1968 chart topper 'Those Were The Days'?

10. In which year was Jim Reeves killed in a plane crash?

11. Who recorded his own version of the *Blue Peter* theme?

12. Which Sixties pop group starred in the film *Head*?

13. Which Black Sabbath wild man once reputedly bit off a bat's head on stage?

14. Which Seventies band dropped the prefix 'Ambrose' from their original name?

15. What was the name of Jonathan Richman's backing group?

16. In 1966, who was convinced he was the 'Pied Piper'?

Answers to page 108
BEE GEES 1: 1. 'To Love Somebody' 2. 'New York Mining Disaster 1941'
3. Yvonne Elliman 4. Isle of Man 5. Colin Petersen 6. 'Spicks And Specks'
7. 1968 8. 'I Started A Joke' 9. Robin 10. Clive Anderson 11. 'Jive Talkin''
12. 'Main Course' 13. Stephen Stills 14. 'How Deep Is Your Love'
15. 1979 16. 'Spirits Having Flown'

Albums 2

Answers on page 109

Who recorded the following albums?

1. 'Come And Get It' (1981)

2. 'Eat To The Beat' (1979)

3. 'The Original Soundtrack' (1975)

4. 'Hatful Of Hollow' (1984)

5. 'Northern Star' (1999)

6. 'Ogden's Nut Gone Flake' (1968)

7. 'Sheer Heart Attack' (1974)

8. 'The Sensual World' (1989)

9. 'Raindancing' (1987)

10. 'Ancient Heart' (1988)

11. 'Avalon' (1982)

12. 'Burn' (1974)

13. 'Endless Flight' (1976)

14. 'Pelican West' (1982)

15. 'Love And The Russian Winter' (1999)

16. 'Emotional Rescue' (1980)

Answers to page 109
CHART TOPPERS 4: 1. Will Young 2. The Honeycombs 3. 'Seven And The Ragged Tiger' 4. Dance 5. 'Pass The Dutchie' (Musical Youth) 6. New Edition 7. Manhattan Transfer 8. 'Chanson D'Amour' 9. The Platters 10. Ten 11. Freddie Mercury 12. 'Twist And Shout' by Chaka Demus and Pliers with Jack Radics and Taxi Gang 13. 'The Model' 14. The Blue Flames 15. Lionel Morton (The Four Pennies) 16. Juliet

Sixties 2

Answers on page 114

1. What was the name of Screaming Lord Sutch's backing group?

2. Grocer Jack was the central figure in which innovative Sixties hit?

3. And who was the singer?

4. Which group did The Ivy League become in 1967?

5. Bobby Elliott was the drummer for which popular Sixties group?

6. Who had a 1962 hit with 'Ginny Come Lately'?

7. Which son of a famous actor sang about 'Windmills Of Your Mind' in 1969?

8. In which baffling song did someone leave the cake out in the rain?

9. Which group, who had a hit with the mild protest song 'It's Good News Week', were all ex-members of the RAF?

10. Who sang about 'The House That Jack Built' in 1967?

11. What was the title of Frank Ifield's fourth and final UK number one single?

12. Which comedian had the biggest-selling UK single of 1965?

13. Who conjured up a 'Strange Brew' in 1967?

14. Which singer with The Zombies later enjoyed a successful solo career?

15. What was the name of Chris Farlowe's backing band?

16. Under what name did accomplished songwriters Roger Cook and Roger Greenaway perform?

Answers to page 114
EUROVISION 1: **1.** Switzerland **2.** They both sang barefoot **3.** Celine Dion **4.** Michael Ball **5.** At 16th, she was the lowest-ever UK finisher **6.** Alphabeta **7.** German **8.** Vicky Leandros **9.** Patricia Bredin (1957) **10.** Denmark **11.** Five **12.** Matt Monro **13.** Scott Fitzgerald **14.** Ronnie Carroll (1962, 1963) **15.** 1985 **16.** The New Seekers

Girl Bands 3

Answers on page 115

1. How many members are there in the Irish girl group B*Witched?

2. The single 'He Loves U Not' by Dream was remixed by which male rap star?

3. What does the 'C' in TLC stand for?

4. 'It's About Time You Were Mine' was a single by which group?

5. The All Saints single 'Pure Shores' was a song from the soundtrack to which film?

6. Which group released 'Deep Deep Down'?

7. Sporty Spice was also known as who?

8. Which single did Precious enter in the Eurovision Song Contest?

9. Fiona, Mim, Kate and Leanne make up which girl group?

10. Which group released 'Girls On Top'?

11. Which country are the group M2M from?

12. How many members of Madasun are there?

13. Who had a single titled 'Shut Your Mouth'?

14. What was the first UK chart success for Honeyz?

15. Which girl group had hits with 'Days Like That' and 'So Long' in 1999?

16. What was the title of TLC's second album?

Answers to page 115
NEW WAVE 1: **1.** XTC **2.** Edward Tudor-Pole (Tenpole Tudor) **3.** Paul Carrack **4.** Bottles of blood **5.** The Teardrop Explodes **6.** Buggles **7.** 'Brass In Pocket' **8.** The Kinks **9.** Elvis Costello **10.** 'Drive' **11.** 'I Can't Stand Up For Falling Down' **12.** 'Private Life' **13.** The Police **14.** Tenpole Tudor **15.** The Pretenders (Martin Chambers) **16.** 'Sgt Rock (Is Going To Help Me)'

Eurovision 1

Answers on page 112

1. Which country did Israeli-born Esther Ofarim represent in the 1963 Eurovision Song Contest?

2. What did Sandie Shaw in 1967 have in common with Spain's Remedios Amaya in 1983?

3. Which Canadian-born international star won the Eurovision for Switzerland in 1988?

4. Which West End musical star represented the UK in 1992?

5. What dubious distinction does the 2000 UK entry Nicki French hold?

6. What was the name of Izhar Cohen's backing group in Israel's victorious year of 1978?

7. What nationality was Nicole who got to number one in the UK with her 1982 Eurovision winner, 'A Little Peace'?

8. Who won for Luxembourg in 1972 with 'Come What May'?

9. Who was the UK's first Eurovision entrant?

10. The Olsen Brothers won the 2000 contest for which country?

11. How many times have the United Kingdom won the Eurovision?

12. Who was runner-up in 1964 for the UK with 'I Love The Little Things'?

13. Who finished runner-up for the UK in 1988 with 'Go' yet only reached number 52 in the charts?

14. Who is the only singer to have represented the UK two years in a row?

15. In which year did Norway win the Eurovision for the first time?

16. Who came second in 1972 with 'Beg, Steal Or Borrow'?

Answers to page 112
SIXTIES 2: 1. The Savages 2. 'Excerpt From A Teenage Opera' 3. Keith West 4. The Flowerpot Men 5. The Hollies 6. Brian Hyland 7. Noel Harrison (son of Rex) 8. 'MacArthur Park' 9. Hedgehoppers Anonymous 10. Alan Price 11. 'Confessin'' 12. Ken Dodd ('Tears') 13. Cream 14. Colin Blunstone 15. The Thunderbirds 16. David and Jonathan

New Wave 1

Answers on page 113

1. Andy Partridge, Colin Moulding, Dave Gregory and Terry Chambers lined up in which new wave band?

2. Which leader of an Eighties band went on to present *The Crystal Maze*?

3. Who sang lead vocals on Squeeze's 'Tempted'?

4. What were thrown at Squeeze during a gig at a veterinary college in Bournemouth?

5. Which band's biggest hit was 'Reward'?

6. Who were Trevor Horn and Geoff Downes better known as?

7. What was The Pretenders' first UK number one?

8. Who originally recorded The Pretenders' 'Stop Your Sobbing'?

9. Who produced the Squeeze album 'East Side Story'?

10. Which Cars song provided backing for film footage of the famine in Ethiopia during Live Aid?

11. Which cover of a Sam and Dave song gave Elvis Costello a UK top five hit in 1980?

12. Which Chrissie Hynde song was covered by Grace Jones?

13. Who had a 1981 hit titled 'De Do Do Do, De Da Da Da'?

14. 'Swords Of A Thousand Men' was a 1981 hit for which band?

15. Which band's drummer injured both his hands in separate incidents within the space of two months in 1981, causing dates to be cancelled?

16. Which comic-book hero came to the aid of XTC?

Answers to page 113
GIRL BANDS 3: 1. Four 2. Puff Daddy 3. Chilli 4. Thunderbugs 5. *The Beach* 6. Hepburn 7. Melanie Chisholm 8. 'Say It Again' 9. 21st Century Girls 10. Girl Thing 11. Norway 12. Three 13. Made In London 14. 'Finally Found' 15. Fierce 16. 'Fanmail'

Stairway to Heaven 1

Answers on page 118

1. Thousands of fans showed up for a free 1981 concert from which singer/songwriter, not knowing that he had just died in a car crash on the Long Island Expressway?
2. Which velvet-voiced singer died from anorexia nervosa at the age of 32?
3. Which Memphis-based rock 'n' roller drowned in a California boating accident in 1964?
4. Which prolific songwriter for The Monkees shot himself dead in 1994?
5. Which former member of Wings died from heart failure in 1979?
6. How did Sonny Bono die?
7. Which member of The Temptations shot himself dead in his car near the Motown studios in 1973?
8. How did Steve Took, Marc Bolan's partner in T. Rex, meet his end in 1980?
9. Who died of a 1996 heart attack halfway through 'Tiptoe Thru The Tulips'?
10. How did Viv Stanshall of The Bonzo Dog Doo-Dah Band die in 1995?
11. Which member of The Temptations died from a drug overdose in 1991?
12. Which controversial manager, born Andreas Cornelius Van Kuijk, died of a stroke in 1997?
13. Which Sixties singer, whose hits included 'Dream Baby' and 'It's Over', died of a heart attack while visiting his mother in 1988?
14. Who had the only US number one to be sung entirely in Japanese before being killed in a plane crash 22 years later?
15. In which year did The Doors' Jim Morrison die?
16. How old was John Lennon when he was killed?

Answers to page 118
NOVELTY NUMBERS 1: **1.** Charlie Drake **2.** Alexei Sayle **3.** Hylda Baker and Arthur Mullard **4.** Father Abraham **5.** Peter Sellers and Sophia Loren **6.** 'Bangers and Mash' **7.** 'Combine Harvester' **8.** 'Brand New Key' **9.** 'Elected' **10.** 'I Am A Cider Drinker' **11.** Harry Enfield **12.** The Woolpackers **13.** *Emmerdale* **14.** The Goodies **15.** Dudley Moore **16.** *Not Only…But Also*

Pot Luck 18

Answers on page 119

1. Which Rolling Stone used to work as a relief porter at Bexley Mental Hospital?

2. What is the name of the Abba tribute band from Australia?

3. Which band were named after the HMV dog Nipper?

4. Which band were stripped of their 1989 Grammy for Best New Artist after it emerged that they hadn't sung on any of their releases?

5. What was the name of Reparata's backing group?

6. Which movie star was waiting for Bananarama in 1984?

7. Who had a bit of a 'Rama Lama Ding Dong' in 1978?

8. Who released 'Ooh-Wakka-Doo-Wakka-Day' in 1972?

9. Who tried to '(Remember The Days Of The) Old School Yard'?

10. Who sang with The Flowerpot Men, Edison Lighthouse and Pipkins?

11. Zal Cleminson was a colourful member of which band?

12. What is former Queen drummer Roger Taylor's full name?

13. Who were 'The In Betweenies' in 1974?

14. Which two artists fought out the 'Battle Of New Orleans' in 1959?

15. Who sang about 'Handbags & Gladrags' in 1967?

16. What was John Wayne according to Haysi Fantayzee?

Answers to page 119
LYRICS 4: **1.** 'You're Still The One' (Shania Twain) **2.** 'This Night' (Billy Joel) **3.** 'Like A Prayer' (Madonna) **4.** 'Don't Speak' (No Doubt) **5.** 'Genie In A Bottle' (Christina Aguilera) **6.** 'If You Had My Love' (Jennifer Lopez) **7.** 'Marblehead Johnson' (The Bluetones) **8.** 'Help!' (The Beatles) **9.** 'A Little Respect' (Erasure) **10.** 'With Or Without You' (U2) **11.** 'You Make Me Feel Like Dancing' (Leo Sayer) **12.** 'I'm Not In Love' (10cc) **13.** 'Good Vibrations' (The Beach Boys) **14.** 'It Must Be Love' (Madness) **15.** 'Lazy Sunday' (The Small Faces) **16.** 'Baby…One More Time' (Britney Spears)

Novelty Numbers 1

Answers on page 116

1. Which pint-sized comedian wailed: 'My Boomerang Won't Come Back'?

2. Who enquired: 'Ullo John! Gotta New Motor'?

3. Which grotesque duo tried to outdo Travolta and Livvy with their own version of 'You're The One That I Want'?

4. Who was the bearded leader of The Smurfs?

5. Which actor and actress played doctor and patient for the 1960 hit 'Goodness Gracious Me'?

6. And what was the title of their culinary follow-up?

7. What was The Wurzels' only number one?

8. And which Melanie song did they adapt?

9. Which Alice Cooper song was covered by Mr Bean and Bruce Dickinson?

10. What was the title of The Wurzels' version of 'Una Paloma Blanca'?

11. Who had 'Loadsamoney' in 1988?

12. Who danced to the 'Hillbilly Rock Hillbilly Roll' in 1966?

13. And from which TV soap did they come?

14. Who suggested 'Make A Daft Noise For Christmas' in 1975?

15. Who said 'Goodbye-ee' with Peter Cook in 1965?

16. And in which TV series was it the closing song?

Answers to page 116
STAIRWAY TO HEAVEN 1: **1.** Harry Chapin **2.** Karen Carpenter
3. Johnny Burnette **4.** Tommy Boyce **5.** Jimmy McCulloch **6.** In a skiing accident **7.** Paul Williams **8.** He choked on a cherry pip **9.** Tiny Tim
10. In a fire **11.** David Ruffin **12.** Colonel Tom Parker **13.** Roy Orbison
14. Kyu Sakamoto ('Sukiyaki') **15.** 1971 **16.** 40

Lyrics 4

Answers on page 117

From which songs are the following lyrics taken?

1. 'Looks like we made it, look how far we've come my baby'

2. 'How many nights have I been thinking about you, wanting to hold you but knowing you would not be there'

3. 'I hear your voice, it's like an angel sighing'

4. 'It looks as though you're letting go, and if it's real, well, I don't want to know'

5. 'You're licking your lips and blowing kisses my way'

6. 'Tell me who can I trust if I can't trust you'

7. 'And now my heart's possessed with 18-carat gold regrets'

8. 'My independence seems to vanish in the haze'

9. 'I'm so in love with you, I'll be forever blue'

10. 'See the stone set in your eyes, see the thorn twist in your side'

11. 'You've got a cute way of talking, you got the better of me'

12. 'It's just a silly phase I'm going through'

13. 'I love the colourful clothes she wears and the way the sunlight plays upon her hair'

14. 'As soon as I wake up, every night, every day'

15. 'Hallo, Mrs Jones, how's your Bert's lumbago – mustn't grumble'

16. 'My loneliness is killing me, I must confess, I still believe'

Answers to page 117
POT LUCK 18: **1.** Mick Jagger **2.** Björn Again **3.** Bow Wow Wow
4. Milli Vanilli **5.** The Delrons **6.** Robert De Niro **7.** Rocky Sharpe and
The Replays **8.** Gilbert O'Sullivan **9.** Cat Stevens **10.** Tony Burrows
11. The Sensational Alex Harvey Band **12.** Roger Meddows-Taylor
13. The Goodies **14.** Lonnie Donegan and Johnny Horton **15.** Chris
Farlowe **16.** Big Leggy

Eighties 4

Answers on page 122

1. Carol Decker was the fiery singer with which band?

2. Who were dancing with tears in their eyes in 1984?

3. Who had a number one album in 1982 with 'The Gift'?

4. Which band reached number two in 1980 with 'What You're Proposing'?

5. Which former lead singer with The Undertones had a number one in 1985 with 'A Good Heart'?

6. Which 1986 number one was a girl's heartfelt plea to her father not to criticise her for getting pregnant?

7. Which sisters nearly made the top of the charts with 'Automatic'?

8. From which country did the girl group Mai Tai originate?

9. Who said 'The Lunatics (Have Taken Over The Asylum)'?

10. Thereze Bazar and David Van Day were better known as which duo?

11. Which Bruce Springsteen number one album of 1987 had the same title as a track on Dire Straits' 'Making Movies'?

12. Which country singer was the first solo artist to have a UK number one in the Eighties?

13. And what was the name of the song?

14. Who was 'Guilty', according to the title of her 1980 album?

15. Who sang about 'Don Quixote' in 1985?

16. Who had a 1989 hit with a remixed version of 'I'm Every Woman'?

Answers to page 122
INDIE 2: **1.** Pearl Jam **2.** Blur **3.** Pulp **4.** 'Sit Down' **5.** 'The Man Who'
6. 'Yellow' **7.** Radiohead **8.** The Lightning Seeds **9.** 'If You Tolerate This
Your Children Will Be Next' **10.** 'This Is My Truth Tell Me Yours'
11. 1991 **12.** John Squire **13.** Food **14.** 'The Last Time' **15.** ''D'You Know
What I Mean?' **16.** James

Soul 1

Answers on page 123

1. Who covered The Beatles' 'Hey Jude' in 1969?

2. Who sang 'It's A Man's Man's Man's World' in 1966?

3. Who liked to make 'Sweet Soul Music' in 1967?

4. Which band backed James Brown on his first three UK hits?

5. Who is known as 'The Queen of Soul'?

6. What are Charles and Eddie's surnames?

7. Which Eddie had a 1974 hit with '(Hey There) Lonely Girl'?

8. In 1976, who promised: 'You'll Never Find Another Love Like Mine'?

9. Who was the oldest of The Jacksons?

10. Which of The Jacksons was really named Sigmund Esco?

11. What was the title of The Jacksons' first UK number one?

12. Who wrote 'Respect', a hit for Aretha Franklin in 1967?

13. Who originally recorded 'I Say A Little Prayer', which Aretha Franklin took to number four in the UK in 1968?

14. Whose hits included 'I Get The Sweetest Feeling' and '(Your Love Keeps Lifting Me) Higher And Higher'?

15. Which soul singer liked to describe himself as a 'sex machine'?

16. Which song gave Otis Redding his first UK hit?

Answers to page 123
POT LUCK 19: 1. 1972 2. 1997 3. 1956 4. 1958 5. 1999 6. 1971
7. 1992 8. 1972 9. 1978 10. 1989 11. 1976 12. 1972 13. 1962 14. 1978
15. 1981 16. 1967

Indie 2

Answers on page 120

1. Which band were formed by Jeff Ament and Stone Gossard in Seattle?

2. Alex James is a member of which band?

3. Which Indie band formed in 1979 had to wait until 1995 for their first UK top ten hit?

4. Which James song only reached number 77 in 1989 but then got to number two in 1991?

5. 'Driftwood' and 'Turn' are tracks from which Travis album?

6. Which colour brought chart success for Coldplay?

7. Who released 'Creep' in 1993?

8. Whose 1994 album was titled 'Jollification'?

9. Which track gave the Manic Street Preachers their first UK number one?

10. And from which number one album was it taken?

11. In which year did Blur release 'There's No Other Way'?

12. Which member of The Stone Roses once worked as a set-maker on a TV adaptation of *The Wind in the Willows*?

13. With which record label have Blur spent most of their career?

14. Which Rolling Stones track was sampled on The Verve's 'Bitter Sweet Symphony'?

15. What was the title of Oasis's 1997 UK number one?

16. Who were 'Waltzing Alone' in 1997?

Answers to page 120
EIGHTIES 4: 1. T'Pau 2. Ultravox 3. Jam 4. Status Quo 5. Feargal Sharkey 6. 'Papa Don't Preach' 7. The Pointer Sisters 8. Holland 9. Fun Boy Three 10. Dollar 11. 'Tunnel Of Love' 12. Kenny Rogers 13. 'Coward Of The County' 14. Barbra Streisand 15. Nik Kershaw 16. Chaka Khan

Pot Luck 19

Answers on page 121

In which years were the following tracks UK top ten hits?

1. 'Goodbye To Love' (The Carpenters)

2. 'Drop Dead Gorgeous' (Republica)

3. 'Blue Suede Shoes' (Carl Perkins)

4. 'Born Too Late' (The Poni-Tails)

5. 'Honey To The Bee' (Billie)

6. 'It Don't Come Easy' (Ringo Starr)

7. 'It Only Takes A Minute' (Take That)

8. 'Look Wot You Dun' (Slade)

9. 'Oh What A Circus' (David Essex)

10. 'Song For Whoever' (The Beautiful South)

11. 'You Should Be Dancing' (The Bee Gees)

12. 'Tumbling Dice' (The Rolling Stones)

13. 'Ramblin' Rose' (Nat King Cole)

14. 'Instant Replay' (Dan Hartman)

15. 'I Could Be Happy' (Altered Images)

16. 'Hey Joe' (Jimi Hendrix Experience)

Answers to page 121
SOUL 1: 1. Wilson Pickett 2. James Brown 3. Arthur Conley 4. The Famous Flames 5. Aretha Franklin 6. Pettigrew and Chacon 7. Eddie Holman 8. Lou Rawls 9. Jackie 10. Jackie 11. 'Show You The Way To Go' 12. Otis Redding 13. Dionne Warwick 14. Jackie Wilson 15. James Brown 16. 'My Girl'

Jimi Hendrix 1

Answers on page 126

1. Who originally recorded 'All Along The Watchtower'?

2. Hendrix was a member of whose backing band in 1965?

3. What was the debut single of The Jimi Hendrix Experience?

4. On stage, what did Hendrix like to play his guitar with?

5. In which year was 'Purple Haze' released as a single?

6. What was the title of Hendrix's debut album?

7. Which Hendrix single had previously been recorded by The Leaves and Tim Rose?

8. In which country did Hendrix spend a night in jail after wrecking a hotel room during a fight with band member Noel Redding?

9. Which was Hendrix's third UK hit single?

10. With which British singer did Hendrix perform a duet on a 1968 TV series?

11. Which Animal was responsible for bringing Hendrix to the UK?

12. Who was drummer with the Experience?

13. What was the title of Hendrix's second album?

14. Why did some shops refuse to display the album 'Electric Ladyland'?

15. What final message did Hendrix leave on his manager's answering machine?

16. Which track topped the UK chart two months after Hendrix's death?

Answers to page 126
DANCE 2: 1. 'Silk' 2. Goldie 3. Lindy Layton 4. Norman Cook (aka Fatboy Slim) 5. Missy Elliott 6. MC Remedee 7. Jason Nevins 8. Larry Heard 9. Stephen Morris and Gillian Gilbert 10. New Order 11. 'Just For The Money' 12. Gang Starr 13. Coldcut 14. Beats International 15. Black Box 16. Geir Jenssen

Number Twos 4

Answers on page 127

1. Which Fifties throwback band reached number two in the UK charts in 1977 with 'You Got What It Takes'?

2. Which band got to number two in 1979 with 'Some Girls'?

3. Which track spelt success for Ottawan in 1980?

4. Who made it to the number two spot with 'Let's Dance' in 1962?

5. 'Do You Want To Know A Secret' was a 1963 hit for which Merseybeat group?

6. Which Elton John song nearly had lift-off to number one in 1972?

7. Which group scored a number two hit with 'I'm Telling You Now' in 1963?

8. Emerson, Lake and Palmer got to second spot with which piece in 1977?

9. 'Another Day In Paradise' fell one short of the promised land for which singer?

10. Who took his cover of 'Freedom' to number two in 1996?

11. Who got to number two in 1960 with 'Someone Else's Baby'?

12. Minus their leader, who had a 1975 hit with 'Goodbye My Love'?

13. 'Radio Gaga' narrowly missed out on pole position in 1984 for which band?

14. Who was 'Going In With My Eyes Open' in 1977?

15. Who had a 1986 hit with 'Every Beat Of My Heart'?

16. Which comedienne got to number two in 1983 with a Kirsty MacColl song?

Answers to page 127
SIXTIES 3: 1. Kenney Jones 2. Crispian St Peters 3. Brian Poole 4. The New Vaudeville Band 5. Keith Emerson 6. The Migil Five 7. Mike D'Abo 8. The Vagabonds 9. Marianne Faithfull 10. Simon Dupree and The Big Sound 11. The Dave Clark Five 12. Cliff Bennett and The Rebel Rousers 13. 1964 14. 'The Green Green Grass Of Home' 15. Roy Orbison 16. Bobby Darin

Dance 2

Answers on page 124

1. What is Steve Hurley's nickname?

2. Which artist is distinguishable by his gold-inlaid front teeth?

3. Who sang on Beats International's 'Dub Be Good To Me'?

4. Whose aliases have included Pizzaman, Fried Funk Food and Mighty Dub Katz?

5. Which New York hip-hop artist used to be part of a group called Sista?

6. Which member of Cookie Crew used to be a chef for the Ministry of Defence?

7. Which remixer has called himself Plastick Project, Crazee Tunes and The Experience?

8. Which house music DJ is better known as Mr Fingers?

9. Who comprised The Other Two?

10. The Other Two were a splinter group from which band?

11. The voices of Lord Olivier and Bob Hoskins were heard on which Paul Hardcastle track about the Great Train Robbery?

12. Guru Keith E and DJ Premier make up which hip-hop band?

13. Whose albums include 'What's That Noise' and 'Some Like It Cold'?

14. Whose debut album was titled 'Let Them Eat Bingo'?

15. Who are Daniele Divoli, Mirko Limoni and Valerio Simplici better known as?

16. Which Bleep mainman went on to create Biosphere?

Answers to page 124
JIMI HENDRIX 1: 1. Bob Dylan 2. Little Richard 3. 'Hey Joe' 4. His teeth 5. 1967 6. 'Are You Experienced' 7. 'Hey Joe' 8. Sweden 9. 'The Wind Cries Mary' 10. Dusty Springfield 11. Chas Chandler 12. Mitch Mitchell 13. 'Axis: Bold As Love' 14. The cover showed Hendrix surrounded by naked women 15. 'I need help bad, man' 16. 'Voodoo Chile'

Sixties 3

Answers on page 125

1. Who was drummer with The Small Faces?

2. Who claimed he was better than Elvis and The Beatles after a hit with 'You Were On My Mind' but sank without trace within a year?

3. Who left The Tremeloes at the start of 1966?

4. Henry Harrison formed which quirky band modelled on a pre-war jazz sound?

5. Who was keyboard player with The Nice?

6. Mike Felix was the singer with which band that had a hit with 'Mockingbird Hill'?

7. Who replaced Paul Jones as lead singer with Manfred Mann?

8. What was the name of Jimmy James's backing group?

9. Who had a 1964 hit with 'As Tears Go By'?

10. 'Kites' flew high for which band in 1967?

11. Denny Payton played saxophone with which London chart toppers?

12. Whose hits included 'One Way Love' and 'Got To Get You Into My Life'?

13. In which year did Ken Dodd release 'Happiness'?

14. Which was the biggest-selling UK single of 1966?

15. Who was the only male solo artist to have a UK number one in 1964?

16. Which American singer had a top three hit with 'Things' in 1962?

Answers to page 125
NUMBER TWOS 4: **1.** Showaddywaddy **2.** Racey **3.** 'D.I.S.C.O.' **4.** Chris Montez **5.** Billy J. Kramer and The Dakotas **6.** 'Rocket Man' **7.** Freddie and The Dreamers **8.** 'Fanfare For The Common Man' **9.** Phil Collins **10.** Robbie Williams **11.** Adam Faith **12.** The Glitter Band **13.** Queen **14.** David Soul **15.** Rod Stewart **16.** Tracey Ullman ('They Don't Know')

John Lennon 1

Answers on page 130

1. Who raised young Lennon after his parents' separation?

2. In which Richard Lester film did Lennon play Private Gripweed?

3. Why was Lennon's album 'Unfinished Music No 1 – Two Virgins' distributed in brown paper bags?

4. To what did Lennon change his middle name in 1969?

5. In which city did John and Yoko spend eight days in a bed to promote world peace?

6. On which Lennon composition did Petula Clark appear?

7. What did Lennon return to Buckingham Palace in 1969?

8. Who produced 'Instant Karma'?

9. In which year was the album 'Imagine' released?

10. The 'Imagine' track 'How Do You Sleep' was a thinly veiled attack on whom?

11. What was the name of Lennon's new backing band for 1972?

12. What was the full name of Lennon's first wife?

13. Which band recorded a tribute version of Lennon's 'Jealous Guy'?

14. On 9 October 1990 which track was played simultaneously in 130 countries to mark what would have been Lennon's 50th birthday?

15. Who pronounced himself 'the number one John Lennon fan' in 1994?

16. With which number did Lennon have a strange fixation?

Answers to page 130
POT LUCK 20: **1.** Half Man Half Biscuit **2.** French **3.** Adam Faith
4. Earth, Wind and Fire **5.** Beaky **6.** Rod Stewart **7.** Manfred Mann and
Sweet **8.** 'Bernadette' **9.** Samantha **10.** Blackberry ('Blackberry Way')
11. 'If I Said You Have A Beautiful Body Would You Hold It Against Me'
12. Syd Barrett (Pink Floyd) **13.** The title isn't featured in the song's
lyrics **14.** 'Love Is Life' **15.** The News **16.** It Bites

Albums 3

Answers on page 131

Which artists released the following albums?

1. 'Tango In The Night' (1987)

2. 'The Rhythm Of The Saints' (1990)

3. 'Ooh-La-La' (1973)

4. 'It's Better To Travel' (1987)

5. 'Dig Your Own Hole' (1997)

6. 'Medusa' (1995)

7. 'Black Tie White Noise' (1993)

8. 'Kings Of The Wild Frontier' (1981)

9. 'On The Level' (1975)

10. 'Highway 61 Revisited' (1965)

11. 'Oceans Of Fantasy' (1979)

12. 'Hush' (1999)

13. 'Move To This' (1991)

14. 'The Joshua Tree' (1987)

15. 'No Sleep Till Hammersmith' (1981)

16. 'Journey To The Centre Of The Earth' (1974)

Answers to page 131
PUNK 1: 1. The Undertones 2. Stuart Adamson 3. The Jam 4. Bob
Geldof 5. 'Denis' (it was a cover of 'Denise' by Randy & The Rainbows)
6. '(I'm Not Your) Stepping Stone' 7. The Undertones 8. Buckingham
Palace 9. 'Peaches' 10. The Stranglers 11. The Clash 12. The Motors
13. Secret Affair 14. The Slits 15. Siouxsie and The Banshees 16. The
Banshees (*Cry of the Banshee*)

Pot Luck 20

Answers on page 128

1. Whose song titles have included '99% Of Gargoyles Look Like Bob Todd' and 'I Love You Because (You Like Jim Reeves)'

2. What nationality is Johnny Hallyday?

3. Which pop star played Budgie on TV?

4. Maurice White was the leader of which nine-piece Seventies disco group?

5. Which member of Dave Dee, Dozy, Beaky, Mick and Tich was born John Dymond?

6. Which rock star once worked as a gravedigger at Highgate Cemetery in London?

7. Which two groups had hits with different songs titled 'Fox On The Run'?

8. Which girl did The Four Tops take into the UK charts in 1967 and 1972?

9. What did Sam become after Cliff Richard had said goodbye to her in 1970?

10. Which fruit was in the title of a Move hit?

11. Which Bellamy Brothers hit had 51 letters in its title?

12. Which reclusive rock star used to use margarine as hair gel?

13. What do 'Bohemian Rhapsody', 'Space Oddity' and 'Tubthumping' have in common?

14. What was Hot Chocolate's first UK hit?

15. What was the name of Huey Lewis's band?

16. Who were 'Calling All The Heroes' in 1986?

Answers to page 128
JOHN LENNON 1: **1.** His Aunt Mimi **2.** *How I Won The War* **3.** The cover was a naked full-frontal of John and Yoko **4.** Ono **5.** Montreal **6.** 'Give Peace A Chance' **7.** His MBE **8.** Phil Spector **9.** 1971 **10.** Paul McCartney **11.** Elephant's Memory **12.** Cynthia Powell **13.** Roxy Music **14.** 'Imagine' **15.** Paul McCartney **16.** 9

Punk 1

Answers on page 129

1. Which band sang about 'Teenage Kicks'?

2. Who left The Skids in order to form Big Country?

3. Which band reached number three with 'The Eton Rifles'?

4. Which member of The Boomtown Rats was previously a journalist on the *NME*?

5. Which song had a sex change when becoming a 1978 hit for Blondie?

6. Which Paul Revere and The Raiders song was covered by The Sex Pistols in 1980?

7. Who had a Perfect Cousin in 1980?

8. Outside which tourist attraction did The Sex Pistols sign for A&M Records in 1977?

9. Which Stranglers A-side of 1977 was banned by the BBC for its offensive lyrics?

10. Who sang 'Nice 'N' Sleazy' does it in 1978?

11. Whose top three album was titled 'Give 'Em Enough Rope'?

12. Bram Tchaikovsky and Ricky Slaughter were members of which band?

13. Who said that 1979 was the 'Time For Action'?

14. Which punk band originally had a drummer called Palmolive?

15. Which band had a hit with 'Hong Kong Garden'?

16. Which band took their name from a 1970 Vincent Price movie?

Answers to page 129
ALBUMS 3: 1. Fleetwood Mac 2. Paul Simon 3. The Faces 4. Swing Out Sister 5. The Chemical Brothers 6. Annie Lennox 7. David Bowie 8. Adam and The Ants 9. Status Quo 10. Bob Dylan 11. Boney M 12. Texas 13. Cathy Dennis 14. U2 15. Motorhead 16. Rick Wakeman

Lyrics 5

Answers on page 134

From which songs are the following lyrics taken?

1. 'It's two hearts living in two separate worlds'
2. 'Don't say you're easy on me, you're about as easy as a nuclear war'
3. 'I've shivers down my spine and it feels divine'
4. 'Oh, look what has happened with just one kiss, I never knew that I could be in love like this'
5. 'Head over heels when toe to toe, this is the sound of my soul'
6. 'I love her, I'm hoping that I never recover'
7. 'Spirits move me every time I'm near you, whirling like a cyclone in my mind'
8. 'I'm a man without conviction, I'm a man who doesn't know how to sell a contradiction'
9. 'I blame you for the moonlit sky and the dream that died with the eagle's flight'
10. 'But then the sound of my desperate calls echoes off these dungeon walls'
11. 'And it's too late to wash my hands, caught in a trap set for a man'
12. 'I play it off but I'm dreamin' of you'
13. 'Showin' how funky and strong is your fight, it doesn't matter who's wrong or right'
14. 'When it seems all your hopes and dreams are a million miles away I will reassure you'
15. 'Hey baby, you really got my tail in a spin, hey baby, I don't even know where to begin'
16. 'What's love but a second-hand emotion'

Answers to page 134
RAP 2: **1.** Eve featuring Gwen Stefani **2.** Snoop Doggy Dogg **3.** *Beavis and Butthead Do America* **4.** Dr Dre **5.** Vanilla Ice **6.** 'U Can't Touch This'
7. 'Pray' **8.** 'Addams Groove' **9.** Notorious B.I.G. **10.** 'Can't Nobody Hold Me Down' **11.** 'I'll Be Missing You' **12.** 'No Way Out' **13.** JC001
14. Notorious B.I.G. **15.** Grandmaster Flash and Melle Mel **16.** 'It's Like That'

Home Towns 1

Answers on page 135

1. In which Scottish town were The Jesus and Mary Chain formed?

2. Which well-coiffeured Eighties band came from Beckenham, Kent?

3. Which firestarters hail from Braintree in Essex?

4. Which southern town was home to Cliff Bennett and The Rebel Rousers?

5. In which city did Ten Years After start their career?

6. Which city are The Stone Roses from?

7. From which city did The Specials hail?

8. Which Lancashire town was home to The Four Pennies?

9. Which mouldy old Seventies outfit came from Coventry?

10. From which city did Them originate?

11. In which seaside resort did Procol Harum have their roots?

12. They may have sounded American, but in reality The Nashville Teens came from which Surrey town?

13. Rockers King Crimson hailed from which genteel English resort?

14. Which city were The Sensational Alex Harvey Band from?

15. Which city did The Fortunes come from?

16. What was the home town of Simon Dupree and The Big Sound?

Answers to page 135
SIXTIES 4: **1.** The Rebel Rousers **2.** Neil Diamond **3.** Tom Jones **4.** Roy Orbison **5.** The Byrds **6.** Neil Sedaka **7.** Seven **8.** The Move **9.** 'The Good, The Bad And The Ugly' **10.** Hugo Montenegro **11.** Johnny Keating **12.** The Four Seasons **13.** Frank Ifield ('I Remember You') **14.** Herman's Hermits **15.** 'Glad All Over' (The Dave Clark Five) **16.** Cat Stevens

Rap 2

Answers on page 132

1. Who had a 2001 hit with 'Let Me Blow Ya Mind'?
2. Whose debut album was titled 'Doggy Style'?
3. From which film was LL Cool J's 'Ain't Nobody' taken?
4. Who joined LL Cool J on the 1998 hit 'Zoom'?
5. Which rap artist covered Wild Cherry's 'Play That Funky Music' in 1991?
6. What was M.C. Hammer's first UK hit?
7. Which M.C. Hammer single was based around Prince's 'When Doves Cry'?
8. Which M.C. Hammer hit was taken from the film *The Addams Family*?
9. Which American rap artist, whose first album was called 'Ready To Die', was murdered in 1997?
10. Which Puff Daddy single sampled Grandmaster Flash and The Furious Five's 'The Message'?
11. Which Puff Daddy number one sampled The Police's 'Every Breath You Take'?
12. What was the title of Puff Daddy's debut album?
13. Which rap artist collaborated with The Beatmasters on 'Boulevard Of Broken Dreams'?
14. Which rapper's real name was Christopher Wallace?
15. Who had a 1984 hit with the anti-drug message 'White Lines (Don't Don't Do It)'?
16. What was the title of Run D.M.C.'s first UK number one?

Answers to page 132
LYRICS 5: 1. 'Sacrifice' (Elton John) 2. 'Is There Something I Should Know?' (Duran Duran) 3. 'Show Me Heaven' (Maria McKee) 4. 'I Only Want To Be With You' (Dusty Springfield) 5. 'True' (Spandau Ballet) 6. 'Never Let Her Slip Away' (Andrew Gold) 7. 'Could It Be Magic' (Barry Manilow) 8. 'Karma Chameleon' (Culture Club) 9. 'Sleeping Satellite' (Tasmin Archer) 10. 'Chains' (Tina Arena) 11. 'Forbidden City' (Electronic) 12. 'I Try' (Macy Gray) 13. 'Beat It' (Michael Jackson) 14. 'Reach' (S Club 7) 15. 'Life Is A Rollercoaster' (Ronan Keating) 16. 'What's Love Got To Do With It?' (Tina Turner)

Sixties 4

Answers on page 133

1. Which Sixties backing group took their name from a Duane Eddy track?

2. Who wrote The Monkees' 'I'm A Believer'?

3. Who experienced 'Funny Familiar Forgotten Feelings' in 1967?

4. Who had a 1963 hit with 'Blue Bayou'?

5. Which American band charted in 1965 with 'All I Really Want To Do' and 'Turn! Turn! Turn!'?

6. 'Happy Birthday Sweet Sixteen' was a number three hit for which artist in 1961?

7. How many members were there in Amen Corner?

8. Which band were successfully sued by Prime Minister Harold Wilson over a nude caricature of him on a promotional postcard?

9. Which 1968 theme from a spaghetti Western became the first instrumental for five years to top the UK charts?

10. And whose orchestra and chorus recorded it?

11. Which orchestra leader had a 1962 top ten hit with the theme from *Z Cars*?

12. Which band's first two UK hits were 'Sherry' and 'Big Girls Don't Cry'?

13. Which solo artist had the biggest-selling UK single of 1962?

14. Who ordered 'No Milk Today' in 1966?

15. Which song knocked 'I Want To Hold Your Hand' off the top of the UK charts?

16. 'Matthew And Son' was a 1967 top three hit for which artist?

Answers to page 133
HOME TOWNS 1: **1.** East Kilbride **2.** Haircut 100 **3.** The Prodigy
4. Slough **5.** Nottingham **6.** Manchester **7.** Coventry **8.** Blackburn
9. Lieutenant Pigeon **10.** Belfast **11.** Southend **12.** Weybridge
13. Bournemouth **14.** Glasgow **15.** Birmingham **16.** Portsmouth

Chart Toppers 5

Answers on page 138

1. Scott Engel, John Maus and Gary Leeds were better known as which 1966 chart toppers?

2. Which singer with a band who had a 1976 number one returned to the limelight in 1987 when his Afghan hound was Supreme Champion at Crufts?

3. What was the title of Tony Di Bart's 1994 chart topper?

4. What was The Prodigy's second number one of 1996?

5. Junior Campbell was a guitarist with which Scottish chart toppers of 1969?

6. Which member of The Mamas and The Papas wrote 'San Francisco (Be Sure To Wear Some Flowers In Your Hair)' for Scott McKenzie?

7. Which 1983 number one told the story of a fictitious woman who accused Michael Jackson of being the father of her illegitimate son?

8. Which 1984 single spent nine weeks at number one in the UK but lost out as the year's best-seller to Band Aid?

9. Who had a 1980 number one with 'The Tide Is High'?

10. Whose 1973 chart topper was titled 'Angel Fingers'?

11. Who were the only duo to reach number one in the UK in 1968?

12. In 1958, which American singer reached the top spot with 'On The Street Where You Live'?

13. Which two former Shadows knocked their old mates off the UK number one perch in 1963?

14. And with which tune did they do it?

15. Who wanted to 'Paint It Black' in 1966?

16. Which Australian band had a UK number one in 1983?

Answers to page 138
ALBUMS 4: 1. 'Animals' 2. Bob Dylan 3. 'Parallel Lines' 4. Donna Summer 5. The Smiths 6. 'We Can't Dance' 7. 'For Your Pleasure' 8. 'Urban Hymns' 9. 'Labour Of Love' 10. Prince 11. 'Bridge Over Troubled Water' 12. Kate Bush 13. Culture Club 14. Luther Vandross 15. 'Blue' 16. Hanson

Pot Luck 21

Answers on page 139

1. In 1986, who became the first band named after a European city to have a UK number one?

2. What does KLF stand for?

3. German music students Ralf Hutter and Florian Schneider-Esleben were the founders of which Seventies band?

4. What links Lenny Kravitz, Slash from Guns 'N' Roses and Marla McKee?

5. What is Dionne Warwick's first name?

6. Who backed Junior Walker?

7. Who is the bass player with U2?

8. What was the title of Spandau Ballet's debut single?

9. Which girl duo took their name from a Smiths' song?

10. In which country was Sade born?

11. Which DJ introduced the first edition of *Top of the Pops*?

12. Guitarist Phil Manzanera was a member of which Seventies band?

13. Who went 'Crazy' after leaving Adamski?

14. Which Seventies singer married her band's guitarist Len Tuckey?

15. Which rock star's sister was a member of the girl band Fanny?

16. Which Eighties band developed their New York docker image from Robert De Niro's film *Mean Streets*?

Answers to page 139
INDIE 3: 1. Swedish 2. 1998 3. Tom Jones 4. Catatonia 5. The Verve
6. 'Hush' 7. The Bluetones 8. Ash 9. Blur 10. Ian Broudie 11. Travis
12. Suede 13. Ocean Colour Scene 14. 'Moseley Shoals' 15. The
Stereophonics 16. Space

Albums 4

Answers on page 136

1. Which Pink Floyd album cover depicted an inflatable pig over Battersea Power Station?

2. Who released the 1968 album 'John Wesley Harding'?

3. Which Blondie album was the UK best-seller for 1979?

4. Which disco diva's 1977 album was titled 'I Remember Yesterday'?

5. 'The Queen Is Dead' was a 1986 album by which band?

6. What was the title of the 1992 number one album from Genesis?

7. What was Roxy Music's second album?

8. Which Verve album featured 'Bitter Sweet Symphony'?

9. Which was UB40's first UK number one album?

10. Who recorded the 1990 album 'Graffiti Bridge'?

11. 'The Boxer' was a track on which Simon and Garfunkel album?

12. 'Hounds Of Love' was the title of a 1985 album by which female artist?

13. Which band fronted by Boy George topped the album charts in 1983?

14. 'Give Me The Reason' was a top five album for which R & B artist in 1987?

15. What colour was the title of Simply Red's number one album in 1998?

16. Which US pop band were in the 'Middle Of Nowhere' in 1997?

Answers to page 136
CHART TOPPERS 5: **1.** The Walker Brothers **2.** Chris Amoo (The Real Thing) **3.** 'The Real Thing' **4.** 'Breathe' **5.** Marmalade **6.** John Phillips **7.** 'Billie Jean' **8.** 'Two Tribes' (Frankie Goes To Hollywood) **9.** Blondie **10.** Wizzard **11.** Esther and Abi Ofarim **12.** Vic Damone **13.** Jet Harris and Tony Meehan **14.** 'Diamonds' **15.** The Rolling Stones **16.** Men At Work ('Down Under')

Indie 3

Answers on page 137

1. What nationality are The Cardigans?

2. In which year did The Cardigans' 'My Favourite Game' first enter the UK charts?

3. Who teamed up with The Cardigans for the 1999 hit 'Burning Down The House'?

4. Who were 'Dead From The Waist Down' in 1999?

5. Which Indie band released the album 'A Northern Soul' in 1995?

6. Which cover of a Deep Purple track was a hit for Kula Shaker?

7. 'Return To The Last Chance Saloon' was a 1998 album by which Indie band?

8. Who released the 1998 album 'Nu-Clear Sounds'?

9. Who reckoned 'Modern Life Is Rubbish'?

10. Who composed 'Three Lions', England's football anthem at Euro 96?

11. Fran Healy is the frontman of which Indie band?

12. Who sang about a 'Filmstar' in 1997?

13. 'The Day We Caught The Train' was a top ten hit for which band?

14. And from which album was it taken?

15. Who encouraged us to 'Have A Nice Day' in 2001?

16. Tommy Scott is the lead singer with which band?

Answers to page 137
POT LUCK 21: **1.** Berlin **2.** Kopywright Liberation Front **3.** Kraftwerk
4. They were all contemporaries at Beverly Hills High School **5.** Marie
6. The All Stars **7.** Adam Clayton **8.** 'To Cut A Long Story Short'
9. Shakespear's Sister **10.** Nigeria **11.** Jimmy Savile **12.** Roxy Music
13. Seal **14.** Suzi Quatro **15.** Suzi Quatro (her sister Patti was in Fanny)
16. Dexy's Midnight Runners

Film Tracks 2

Answers on page 142

1. Seal's 'Kiss From A Rose' was the theme from which film?

2. Who reached number one with 'Nothing's Gonna Stop Us Now' from the film *Mannequin*?

3. Which track from *Sister Act 2: Back in the Habit* was a 1994 hit for Aretha Franklin?

4. Which of the Monty Python team sang 'Always Look On The Bright Side Of Life'?

5. And which film did it close?

6. Who had a hit with 'Two Hearts' from the film *Buster*?

7. Natalie Cole's 1990 hit 'Wild Women Do' was from the soundtrack of which Julia Roberts film?

8. Which film featured the 1954 Dean Martin hit 'That's Amore'?

9. The 1961 hit 'Moon River' was taken from which film?

10. Which film spawned the Frank Sinatra song 'High Hopes'?

11. Who sang 'Step By Step' from the film *The Preacher's Wife*?

12. Who had a UK top five hit with 'Where Do I Begin', the theme from *Love Story*?

13. Who sang the theme from the 1967 film *The Valley of the Dolls*?

14. Which film featured 'Tonight', a hit for Shirley Bassey in 1962?

15. Madonna's number one single 'Into The Groove' was a track from which film?

16. The Brenda Lee hit 'Speak To Me Pretty' came from which film?

Answers to page 142
NOVELTY NUMBERS 2: **1.** Bob The Builder **2.** 'The Chicken Song'
3. Leapy Lee **4.** 1981 **5.** His Cast Of Idiots **6.** 'Disco Duck' **7.** Doc Cox
8. The Goons **9.** Lonnie Donegan **10.** Billy Howard **11.** Brown Sauce
12. 'I Wanna Be A Winner' **13.** Joy Sarney **14.** Mel Brooks **15.** Hale and
Pace **16.** Kevin the Gerbil

Pot Luck 22

Answers on page 143

1. Which Manchester band took their name from a New Order song?

2. 'Rich Girl' was a US number one in 1977 for which duo?

3. Mike Score was the lead singer with which Eighties band?

4. What is the surname of Morten from a-ha?

5. Which Seventies band got their name from the first letters of the four members' Christian names?

6. Before she became a singer, who used to choreograph the cheerleaders of the LA Lakers Basketball team?

7. Who had a 1985 hit with 'Every Time You Go Away'?

8. Shaun Ryder was the singer with which band?

9. Which musical knight used to work in a Peterborough pea factory?

10. Who sang 'I'll Be There For You', the theme from *Friends*?

11. In 1997, which song took over from 'White Christmas' as the biggest-selling single in the world?

12. In which year was 'White Christmas' first released?

13. Which sinister Caribbean mystery provided the title for a Barry Manilow hit in 1981?

14. With whom did Billy Paul have 'a thing going on' in 1973?

15. Which California foursome had a 1966 hit with 'I Saw Her Again'?

16. In 1986, which band were giving 'Lessons In Love'?

Answers to page 143
TINA TURNER 1: 1. 'We Don't Need Another Hero' 2. Bonnie Tyler
3. Bryan Adams 4. 1989 5. Tony Joe White 6. Jeff Beck 7. 'Nutbush City Limits' 8. 'I Don't Wanna Fight' 9. Sting 10. 'Break Every Rule'
11. 'What's Love Got To Do With It' 12. Aunty Entity 13. Edgar Winter
14. Rod Stewart 15. 'Disco Inferno' 16. Phil Spector

Novelty Numbers 2

Answers on page 140

1. Which handyman covered 'Mambo No. 5' in 2001?

2. Which fowl number topped the charts for Spitting Image in 1986?

3. Who fired 'Little Arrows' in 1968?

4. In which year did The Tweets inflict 'The Birdie Song' on an unsuspecting nation?

5. Who backed Rick Dees on his 1976 hit single?

6. What was the title of the Rick Dees track that drove everyone quackers?

7. Which *That's Life* presenter charted under the name of Ivor Biggun?

8. Who were Walking Backwards For Christmas?

9. Who asked: 'Does Your Chewing Gum Lose Its Flavour On The Bedpost Overnight'?

10. Who did impressions of TV detectives on the Roger Miller parody 'King Of The Cops'?

11. Under what name did presenters from *Multi-Coloured Swap Shop*, led by Noel Edmonds, enter the charts in 1981?

12. And what was the inspirational title of their song?

13. Who did Punch and Judy impressions on 'Naughty Naughty Naughty'?

14. Which film producer charted with 'The Hitler Rap' in 1984?

15. Which pair had a Comic Relief number one with 'The Stonk'?

16. Which rodent covered Cliff Richard's 'Summer Holiday' in 1984?

Answers to page 140
FILM TRACKS 2: 1. *Batman Forever* 2. Starship 3. 'A Deeper Love'
4. Eric Idle 5. *The Life of Brian* 6. Phil Collins 7. *Pretty Woman* 8. *The Caddy* 9. *Breakfast At Tiffany's* 10. *A Hole in the Head* 11. Whitney Houston 12. Andy Williams 13. Dionne Warwick 14. *West Side Story* 15. *Desperately Seeking Susan* 16. *Two Little Bears*

Tina Turner 1

Answers on page 141

1. Which Tina Turner hit single was taken from the film *Mad Max: Beyond Thunderdome*?

2. Who originally recorded 'The Best'?

3. With whom did Tina Turner duet on 'It's Only Love'?

4. In which year was 'The Best' released?

5. Who recorded the original version of 'Steamy Windows'?

6. Who played guitar on 'Private Dancer'?

7. What was Tina Turner's last UK hit with husband Ike?

8. Lulu joined Tina Turner on which 1993 single?

9. Who contributed backing vocals for the 1996 hit 'On Silent Wings'?

10. What was the title of Tina Turner's second solo album?

11. Which Tina Turner single won Record Of The Year at the 1985 Grammy Awards?

12. Which part did Tina Turner play in *Mad Max: Beyond Thunderdome*?

13. Who played the saxophone solo on 'The Best'?

14. With whom did Turner duet on 'It Takes Two', an update of the Marvin Gaye/Tammi Terrell song?

15. Which Trammps song did Turner cover in 1993?

16. Who produced 'River Deep Mountain High'?

Answers to page 141
POT LUCK 22: **1.** Happy Mondays ('Blue Monday') **2.** Daryl Hall and John Oates **3.** A Flock Of Seagulls **4.** Harket **5.** Abba (Agnetha, Bjorn, Benny and Anni-Frid) **6.** Paula Abdul **7.** Paul Young **8.** Happy Mondays **9.** Sir Bob Geldof **10.** The Rembrandts **11.** 'Candle In The Wind' (Elton John) **12.** 1942 **13.** 'Bermuda Triangle' **14.** Mrs Jones ('Me And Mrs Jones') **15.** The Mamas and The Papas **16.** Level 42

Pot Luck 23

Answers on page 146

1. What do Otis Redding, Jim Reeves, Laurel and Hardy, and Jimi Hendrix have in common?

2. Which Scottish band took their name from a line in a Scritti Politti song?

3. Which heavy metal frontman has a B.A. and can speak four languages?

4. What was the original title of The Beatles' 'Hey Jude'?

5. Which TV presenters enjoyed chart success as PJ and Duncan?

6. Which group backed Peter Jay?

7. Which band knocked Band Aid's 'Do They Know It's Christmas' off the top of the UK charts?

8. Which self-promoting star of the late Eighties was once a regional Golden Gloves boxing champion in Florida?

9. Who is the singer with The Cure?

10. Which future chart toppers played their first gig in Liverpool in 1980 as support act to Hambi and The Dance?

11. Roger Chapman was lead singer with which Seventies band?

12. Who was 'Mr Soft' in 1974?

13. Which American state did Ernie Ford put before his name?

14. Who backed Reparata?

15. What nationality was Edmund Hockridge?

16. What was the name of Bruce Hornsby's backing band?

Answers to page 146
FOLK 2: 1. Tommy Makem 2. 'Catch The Wind' 3. Jimmy Page 4. Bob Dylan 5. The Band 6. Ewan MacColl 7. Don McLean 8. 'Letter From America' 9. Three 10. 'Silver Threads And Golden Needles' 11. 'All Around My Hat' was produced by chief Womble Mike Batt 12. Dave Swarbrick 13. 'You've Got A Friend' 14. Donovan 15. James Taylor 16. Suzanne Vega

The Sex Pistols 1

Answers on page 147

1. Who was the drummer with The Sex Pistols?

2. How did Johnny Rotten get his name?

3. Who joined the band in 1976?

4. What milestone in The Sex Pistols history occurred on 1 December 1976?

5. Out of 19 scheduled dates for the 'Anarchy In The UK' tour, how many went ahead?

6. Which record label dropped The Pistols at the start of 1977?

7. How many days did The Sex Pistols stay with the A & M label?

8. Why did A & M sack The Sex Pistols?

9. Workers at a record factory refused to press copies of which Pistols' single?

10. Outside which buildings did The Pistols perform 'Anarchy In The UK' in June 1977 in a boat travelling along the Thames?

11. Which track did the band perform on their *Top of the Pops* debut?

12. Who was the Pistols' manager?

13. What was the title of the planned Sex Pistols film?

14. In which city did the Pistols play their last-ever gig?

15. Which band did Johnny Rotten form after The Sex Pistols split up?

16. Which Sex Pistol covered 'My Way'?

Answers to page 147
DUOS 2: 1. Jaki Graham 2. Bobbie Gentry 3. 'Back Together Again'
4. Phil Collins and Philip Bailey 5. Lennie Peters (Peters and Lee) 6. 'We Close Our Eyes' 7. 'King Of Wishful Thinking' 8. Alisha's Attic 9. 1969
10. 'West End Girls' 11. Liza Minnelli ('Losing My Mind') 12. Yazoo
13. Sonny and Cher 14. Chris Norman 15. Sarah Brightman 16. 'Deep Purple'

Folk 2

Answers on page 144

1. Which whistle player joined The Clancy Brothers?

2. What was the title of Donovan's first UK hit single?

3. Which guitar legend played on Donovan's 'Sunshine Superman'?

4. Who had a hit with 'Subterranean Homesick Blues' in 1965?

5. Who originally recorded 'The Night They Drove Old Dixie Down', a 1971 hit for Joan Baez?

6. Which folk singer wrote 'The First Time Ever I Saw Your Face'?

7. Which American folk singer wrote 'And I Love You So', which became an international success for Perry Como?

8. What was The Proclaimers' first hit?

9. How many members of The Springfields were there?

10. Which country standard gave The Springfields their biggest US hit?

11. What is the link between Steeleye Span and The Wombles?

12. Which violinist joined Fairport Convention in 1972?

13. Which song from Carole King's 'Tapestry' album became a hit for James Taylor?

14. Who had a 1969 hit with 'Goo Goo Barabajagal?

15. Who released the album 'Sweet Baby James'?

16. 'Luka' was a 1987 hit for which female singer?

Answers to page 144
POT LUCK 23: **1.** They all had their biggest hits after they had died
2. Wet Wet Wet **3.** Gene Simmons **4.** 'Hey Jules' (after Julian Lennon)
5. Ant and Dec **6.** The Jaywalkers **7.** Foreigner **8.** Terence Trent D'Arby
9. Robert Smith **10.** Frankie Goes To Hollywood **11.** Family **12.** Steve
Harley (and Cockney Rebel) **13.** Tennessee **14.** The Delrons
15. Canadian **16.** The Range

Duos 2

Answers on page 145

1. Who joined David Grant on a 1985 version of The Detroit Spinners' 'Could It Be I'm Falling In Love'?

2. Which artist combined with Glen Campbell for a 1969 cover of 'All I Have To Do Is Dream'?

3. Which song did Roberta Flack and Donny Hathaway take to number three in the UK charts in 1980?

4. Which two Phils joined forces on the 1985 number one 'Easy Lover'?

5. The Kray Twins were said to be old friends of which half of a successful Seventies duo?

6. What was Go West's first UK hit?

7. Which Go West single appeared in the film *Pretty Woman*?

8. 'I Am, I Feel' was a hit for which Nineties duo?

9. In which year did Simon and Garfunkel chart with 'The Boxer'?

10. Which Pet Shop Boys song was named Best Single Of The Year at the 1987 Brit Awards?

11. Which American diva gained her UK chart debut in 1989 courtesy of a song produced by The Pet Shop Boys?

12. 'Only You' and 'Don't Go' were Eighties hits for which duo?

13. Which duo topped the UK charts in 1965?

14. Which Smokie singer was Suzi Quatro 'Stumblin' In' with in 1978?

15. Which star of musicals linked with Cliff Richard on the 1986 hit 'All I Ask Of You'?

16. Which colour was a hit for Nino Tempo and April Stevens in 1963?

Answers to page 145
THE SEX PISTOLS 1: 1. Paul Cook 2. His catchphrase was 'You're rotten, you are' 3. Sid Vicious 4. They were interviewed by Bill Grundy on *Today* 5. Three 6. EMI 7. Six 8. Other A & M artists complained about signing them 9. 'God Save The Queen' 10. The Houses of Parliament 11. 'Pretty Vacant' 12. Malcolm McLaren 13. *Who Killed Bambi?* 14. San Francisco 15. Public Image Ltd 16. Sid Vicious

Pot Luck 24

Answers on page 150

1. Which hit song came to Tommy James while he was sitting in a hotel room watching the flashing neon sign of the Mutual of New York building?

2. Which band had a 'Perfect Skin' in 1984?

3. Which Sixties band's compilation album was called '25 Thumping Great Hits'?

4. Peter Cetera was the singer with which band named after a US city?

5. Which US band who were invariably on the road included Bob 'The Bear' Hite and Al 'Blind Owl' Wilson?

6. In what gear was King Midas according to a 1967 Hollies hit?

7. Who sang the first solo part on USA For Africa's 'We Are The World'?

8. Which of the Jackson Five married the daughter of Motown boss Berry Gordy?

9. Which UK number one hit of 1966 was recorded originally as a TV commercial jingle for petrol?

10. What is Missy short for, as in Missy Elliott?

11. From what cartoon character did Stephen Duffy take his nickname?

12. What was the title of Dire Straits' fourth UK number one album?

13. Which Uncle had a 2001 top five hit with 'Follow Me'?

14. On which Kinks album did 'Waterloo Sunset' first appear?

15. What is Santana's first name?

16. Which Prince was a profound influence on Madness?

Answers to page 150
DISCO 1: 1. Amii Stewart 2. Six 3. 'In The Navy' 4. *Can't Stop The Music*
5. Donna Summer 6. The Bee Gees 7. Tina Charles 8. Baccara
9. 'Son Of My Father' (Chicory Tip) 10. The Village People 11. Chic
12. *Thank God It's Friday* 13. Chic 14. B. Devotion 15. French
16. Hamilton Bohannon

Chart Toppers 6

Answers on page 151

1. Which 1965 UK number one by an Australian foursome was written and produced by Tom Springfield, brother of Dusty?

2. Who went all the way with a 'Sailor' in 1961?

3. Which American female artist had two number ones in 1958?

4. Who featured on Eternal's 1997 chart topper, 'I Wanna Be The Only One'?

5. 'Professional Widow (It's Got To Be Big)' was a 1997 hit for which Cornflake Girl?

6. Who played the 'Pipes Of Peace' to the top spot in 1984?

7. Which disco favourite was the best-selling UK single of 1979?

8. Which group spent eight weeks at number one in 1969 even though they didn't exist in the flesh?

9. Which 1961 hit from The Shadows was named after Thor Heyerdahl's raft?

10. Which band originally recorded 'If', a 1975 number one for Telly Savalas?

11. Two Philadelphia groups, The Percussions and The Monarchs, merged to form which 1975 chart toppers?

12. And what was the title of their number one?

13. Which number one had the chorus, 'Heathcliff, it's me, I'm Cathy come home again'?

14. Who had a 1968 UK number one with a Lennon and McCartney song but had to wait another 15 years before getting as high as number seven again?

15. Which trio reached the top in 1965 with 'Make It Easy On Yourself'?

16. Who had a 1999 number one with 'If I Let You Go'?

Answers to page 151
BACKSTREET BOYS 1: 1. Brian and Nick 2. Gene 3. Four 4. 'Black And Blue' 5. 'Millennium' 6. A.J. 7. Nick 8. Two 9. 'Black And Blue' 10. Brian 11. Kevin 12. 'Millennium' 13. 'Answer To Our Life' and 'Time' 14. Nick 15. 1999 16. Four

Disco 1

Answers on page 148

1. Who decided to 'Knock On Wood' in 1979?

2. How many Village People were there?

3. What was The Village People's follow-up to 'Y.M.C.A.'?

4. In which 1980 movie did The Village People appear?

5. Who had a 1977 top ten hit with 'Love's Unkind'?

6. 'Too Much Heaven' was a 1978 top three hit for which band?

7. Whose second UK top ten hit was titled 'Dance Little Lady Dance'?

8. Which disco divas were the first female duo to have a UK number one?

9. Donna Summer's 'I Feel Love' was the second Giorgio Moroder composition to reach number one in the UK, but what was the first?

10. Which group's second album was titled 'Macho Man'?

11. Nile Rodgers was the leader of which US disco group?

12. In which film did Donna Summer make her acting debut?

13. 'Le Freak' sold over four million copies for which band?

14. Who backed Sheila?

15. And what nationality was she?

16. Who did the 'Disco Stomp'?

Answers to page 148
POT LUCK 24: 1. 'Mony Mony' 2. Lloyd Cole and The Commotions
3. The Dave Clark Five 4. Chicago 5. Canned Heat 6. Reverse ('King Midas In Reverse') 7. Lionel Richie 8. Jermaine 9. 'Get Away'
10. Misdemeanor 11. 'Tin Tin' 12. 'On Every Street' 13. Uncle Kracker
14. 'Something Else' 15. Carlos 16. Prince Buster

Backstreet Boys 1

Answers on page 149

1. Which two Backstreet Boys wrote 'Ain't That Cute' for Aaron Carter's debut album?

2. What is Nick Carter's middle name?

3. How many siblings does Nick Carter have?

4. 'More Than That', 'Get Another Boyfriend' and 'It's True' are tracks off which album?

5. Which Backstreet Boys album went diamond?

6. Which member of the group was nicknamed 'Bone Daddy'?

7. Which Backstreet Boy was a licensed scuba diver?

8. What number in the UK charts did 'Quit Playing Games (With My Heart)' reach in 1997?

9. Which album features an a cappella version of 'All I Have To Give'?

10. Which former band member's nickname is 'B-Rok'?

11. Who co-wrote 'Back To Your Heart'?

12. And on which album did it appear?

13. Which two tracks on 'Black And Blue' were written by the whole group?

14. Who sang lead vocals on 'I Need You Tonight'?

15. In which year were The Backstreet Boys 'Larger Than Life'?

16. How many UK top ten hits did the band have in 1997?

Answers to page 149
CHART TOPPERS 6: 1. 'I'll Never Find Another You' (The Seekers)
2. Petula Clark 3. Connie Francis 4. Bebe Winans 5. Tori Amos 6. Paul McCartney 7. 'Y.M.C.A.' 8. The Archies 9. 'Kon-Tiki' 10. Bread 11. The Stylistics 12. 'Can't Give You Anything (But My Love)' 13. 'Wuthering Heights' 14. Joe Cocker 15. The Walker Brothers 16. Westlife

Fifties 3

Answers on page 154

1. Which three singers had UK charts hits in 1955 with 'Yellow Rose Of Texas'?

2. Who had a 1958 hit with 'Deck Of Cards'?

3. Although Ronnie Hilton recorded a UK version, which American singer had the number one with 'Magic Moments'?

4. The theme from which TV Western gave Frankie Laine a UK top ten hit in 1959?

5. Lita Roza and Patti Page both had hits with which tender tale in 1953?

6. About what did Doris Day tell the golden daffodils in 1954?

7. Which Pat Boone song was the UK's biggest-selling single of 1956?

8. Who recorded the theme from the film *April Love*?

9. Who warned in 1955: 'Never Do A Tango With An Eskimo'?

10. Which British singer said 'Arrivederci Darling' in 1955?

11. Who were the resident band on the TV pop show *Oh Boy!*?

12. Whose appearance on *Oh Boy!* brought a flood of criticism over his 'crude exhibitionism'?

13. Which pair of brothers replaced another pair of brothers at the top of the UK charts in 1958?

14. Where was Emile Ford born?

15. Which was the biggest-selling UK single of 1954?

16. How many UK top twenty hits did Russ Conway have in 1959?

Answers to page 154
INDIE 4: 1. U2 2. Soul Asylum 3. Space 4. Travis 5. Cerys Matthews
6. Train 7. 'Girls And Boys' 8. Dodgy 9. Cast 10. 'Goldfinger' 11. Ocean
Colour Scene 12. The Verve 13. After a long dispute with Verve Records
14. The Lightning Seeds 15. Ash 16. 'You Showed Me'

Motown 2

Answers on page 155

1. Which Temptations hit bemoaned the disintegrating fabric of American society?

2. Who did Diana Ross oust as The Supremes' lead singer?

3. Which group's 1970 debut single became the fastest-selling record in Motown history?

4. What was Mary Wells's only UK top ten hit?

5. Where were The Miracles going in 1966?

6. In 1967, who replaced Florence Ballard in The Supremes?

7. With which fellow Motown band did The Supremes record 'I'm Gonna Make You Love Me'?

8. Who had the 1965 hit 'Uptight (Everything's Alright)'?

9. What was Marvin Gaye's first solo hit in the UK?

10. Who were stuck in 'Seven Rooms Of Gloom' in 1967?

11. Who was too busy thinking about his baby in 1969?

12. What was The Four Tops' last UK top ten hit before quitting Motown in 1972?

13. What was the first UK hit for Gladys Knight and The Pips?

14. Who told what life was like 'Behind A Painted Smile' in 1969?

15. Who had a 1967 hit with 'The Happening'?

16. What lesson in the alphabet did The Jackson Five provide?

Answers to page 155
POT LUCK 25: **1.** The Kinks **2.** Darius Rucker **3.** J. Geils Band
4. Squeeze **5.** Bobby G **6.** Kirsty MacColl **7.** Nadinia **8.** Van Morrison
9. Bob Seger **10.** *All You Need Is Cash* **11.** Dean Friedman **12.** Neil Sedaka
13. John Parr **14.** Dandy Livingstone **15.** 'Raindrops Keep Falling On My Head' **16.** Tuesday

Indie 4

Answers on page 152

1. Who released the album 'Achtung Baby'?

2. Which American band caught a 'Runaway Train' in 1993?

3. Who sang about their beautiful 'Neighbourhood' in 1996?

4. Whose 1997 album was titled 'Good Feeling'?

5. Who was the singer with Catatonia?

6. Who had a 2001 album called 'Drops Of Jupiter'?

7. Which was the first single to be taken from Blur's 'Parklife'?

8. Who were 'Staying Out For The Summer' in 1994?

9. Whose second album was titled 'Mother Nature Calls'?

10. Which hit for Ash was also the title of a Bond film?

11. Simon Fowler is the vocalist with which Indie band?

12. Whose 1993 album was titled 'A Storm In Heaven'?

13. Why were Verve renamed The Verve?

14. 'Sugar Coated Iceberg' was a 1997 hit for which band?

15. Which Indie band's first chart single was 'Kung Fu'?

16. Which Lightning Seeds hit was previously recorded back in the Sixties by both The Byrds and The Turtles?

Answers to page 152
FIFTIES 3: **1.** Mitch Miller, Gary Miller and Ronnie Hilton **2.** Wink Martindale **3.** Perry Como **4.** *Rawhide* **5.** '(How Much Is) That Doggie In The Window?' **6.** 'Secret Love' **7.** 'I'll Be Home' **8.** Pat Boone **9.** Alma Cogan **10.** Anne Shelton **11.** Lord Rockingham's XI **12.** Cliff Richard **13.** The Kalin Twins replaced The Everly Brothers **14.** The Bahamas **15.** 'Secret Love' **16.** Five

Pot Luck 25

Answers on page 153

1. The 1972 single 'Supersonic Rocket Ship' was which band's last UK hit for nine years?

2. Who is the lead singer of Hootie and the Blowfish?

3. Whose baby was on the 'Centerfold' in 1982?

4. Chris Difford and Glenn Tilbrook were the songwriting partnership of which band?

5. Which member of Bucks Fizz recorded the theme from the TV series *Big Deal*?

6. Who joined The Pogues in a 'Fairytale Of New York'?

7. What is Alanis Morissette's real Christian name?

8. Which Irish singer released the 1970 album 'Moondance'?

9. Who fronted The Silver Bullet Band?

10. George Harrison, Mick Jagger and Paul Simon all appeared in which Rutles film?

11. Which American singer/songwriter had a number three hit in 1978 with 'Lucky Stars'?

12. Who sang about 'Laughter In The Rain' in 1974?

13. 'St Elmo's Fire' was a 1986 hit for which artist?

14. Who warned 'Suzanne Beware Of The Devil'?

15. What identical meteorological sensation was experienced by Bobbie Gentry, Sacha Distel and B.J. Thomas in 1970?

16. What day was everything for Chairmen Of The Board in 1971?

Answers to page 153
MOTOWN 2: 1. 'Ball Of Confusion' 2. Florence Ballard 3. The Jackson Five ('I Want You Back') 4. 'My Guy' 5. To A Go-Go 6. Cindy Birdsong 7. The Temptations 8. Stevie Wonder 9. 'How Sweet It Is' 10. The Four Tops 11. Marvin Gaye 12. 'Simple Game' 13. 'Take Me In Your Arms And Love Me' 14. The Isley Brothers 15. The Supremes 16. 'ABC'

Tom Jones 1

Answers on page 158

1. Who recorded the original version of 'Green Green Grass Of Home'?

2. In which year was 'Delilah' released?

3. Who wrote 'She's A Lady'?

4. From which film was the single 'A Boy From Nowhere' taken?

5. What was Tom Jones's first UK number one?

6. Who managed both Tom Jones and Engelbert Humperdinck?

7. What was the name of Jones's backing band in the mid-Sixties?

8. What was the title of his debut album?

9. Which Tom Jones hit was written and originally recorded by Lonnie Donegan?

10. Which three successive Tom Jones singles all got stuck at number two in the UK charts?

11. Which 1987 song gave Jones his first UK top ten success for 15 years?

12. What was the title of Jones's first single?

13. On which Prince song did he collaborate with Art Of Noise?

14. What did 27-year-old Katherine Berkery do to Jones in 1989?

15. Which Bond theme did Jones record in 1966?

16. Which 1971 single was recorded originally by Roger Williams in 1957?

Answers to page 158
NAME CHANGES 5: **1.** Bag Of Blues **2.** Mungo Jerry **3.** Gene Simmons **4.** Culture Club **5.** Johnny Rotten **6.** Doris Day **7.** Kool (And The Gang) **8.** Paul and Barry Ryan **9.** Family **10.** Ranking Roger **11.** Bobby Rydell **12.** The Sex Pistols **13.** Tom Jones **14.** The Cure **15.** Dr Hook **16.** Devo

Number Twos 5

Answers on page 159

Which artists reached number two in the UK singles charts with the following tracks?

1. 'Are You Sure' (1961)

2. 'True Love Ways' (1965)

3. 'The Most Beautiful Girl' (1974)

4. 'Going In With My Eyes Open' (1977)

5. 'Up The Junction' (1979)

6. 'What You're Proposing' (1980)

7. 'You Drive Me Crazy' (1981)

8. 'Every Beat Of My Heart' (1986)

9. 'Golden Brown' (1982)

10. 'Part Of The Union' (1973)

11. 'Heart Full Of Soul' (1965)

12. 'Let's Hear It For The Boy' (1984)

13. 'Heartbreaker' (1982)

14. 'Holding Out For A Hero' (1985)

15. 'You Can Get It If You Really Want' (1970)

16. 'I Did What I Did For Maria' (1971)

Answers to page 159
ALBUMS 5: 1. The Bay City Rollers 2. Queen 3. Style Council 4. Boyzone 5. 'True Blue' 6. 10cc 7. Curiosity Killed The Cat 8. Spandau Ballet 9. The Cure 10. 'The Great Escape' 11. 'Steptacular' 12. Elton John 13. Wet Wet Wet 14. It was circular 15. Paris 16. 'Abbey Road'

Name Changes 5

Answers on page 156

1. What were Jethro Tull previously known as?

2. Which Sixties band changed their name from The Good Earth?

3. Which heavy rock frontman was born Chaim Witz?

4. Which flamboyant Eighties band started out as In Praise Of Lemmings?

5. Who changed his name from John Lydon and then adopted it again later?

6. Which singer looked for something easier to pronounce than Doris von Kappelhoff?

7. Which gang leader did Robert Bell become?

8. Who began their lives as Paul and Barry Sapherson?

9. Which Seventies band were previously called The Farinas?

10. What stage name did Roger Charlery adopt when joining the two-tone movement?

11. What shorter name did Robert Ridarelli choose for himself?

12. Which band used to be called The Swankers?

13. Who did 'Tommy' of Tommy Scott and The Senators go on to become?

14. Which band were once known as The Goat Band?

15. Who started their career as The Chocolate Papers?

16. Which American band was reduced from the De-Evolution Band?

Answers to page 156
TOM JONES 1: 1. Johnny Darrell 2. 1968 3. Paul Anka 4. *Matador*
5. 'It's Not Unusual' 6. Gordon Mills 7. The Squires 8. 'Along Came Jones' 9. 'I'll Never Fall In Love Again' 10. 'I'll Never Fall In Love Again', 'I'm Coming Home' and 'Delilah' 11. 'A Boy From Nowhere' 12. 'Chills And Fever' 13. 'Kiss' 14. She successfully filed a paternity suit against him 15. 'Thunderball' 16. 'Till'

Albums 5

Answers on page 157

1. Which tartan horde released the 1975 album 'Once Upon A Star'?

2. Whose 1980 number one album was titled 'The Game'?

3. 'Our Favourite Shop' was a 1985 album by which band?

4. Whose debut album in 1995 was 'Said And Done'?

5. Which Madonna album was the UK best-seller for 1986?

6. Which band recorded the 1974 album 'Sheet Music'?

7. 'Keep Your Distance' was a 1987 number one album for which band?

8. Who released a 1986 album titled 'Through The Barricades' which bore a single of the same name?

9. Whose 1992 chart-topping album was called 'Wish'?

10. Which Blur album contained 'Stereotypes' and 'Country House'?

11. What was the title of Steps' UK number one album of 1999?

12. Who was 'Sleeping With The Past' in 1990?

13. Who had 'Popped In Souled Out' in 1988?

14. What was revolutionary about the cover of The Small Faces' album 'Ogden's Nut Gone Flake'?

15. In which city was Simple Minds' 'Live In The City Of Light' recorded?

16. Which album was the UK best-seller of 1969?

Answers to page 157
NUMBER TWOS 5: **1.** The Allisons **2.** Peter and Gordon **3.** Charlie Rich **4.** David Soul **5.** Squeeze **6.** Status Quo **7.** Shakin' Stevens **8.** Rod Stewart **9.** The Stranglers **10.** The Strawbs **11.** The Yardbirds **12.** Deniece Williams **13.** Dionne Warwick **14.** Bonnie Tyler **15.** Desmond Dekker and The Aces **16.** Tony Christie

Chart Toppers 7

Answers on page 162

1. Which was the first UK number one to have the number 'two' in the title?

2. Which was the first UK number one to have a boy's name in the title?

3. Which was the first UK number one to feature a girl's name in the title?

4. Which was the first UK number one to mention the word 'Christmas' in the title?

5. Which was the first UK number one to include a capital city in the title?

6. Which was the first UK number one with the colour 'blue' in the title?

7. Which was the first UK number one to include the name of a breed of bird?

8. Which was the first UK number one with the name of a musical instrument in the title?

9. Excluding 'Maggie May', which was the first UK number one with a month in the title?

10. Which was the first UK number one with a reptile in the title?

11. Which was the first UK number one to include the colour 'red' in the title?

12. Which was the first UK number one with 'gold' in the title?

13. Which was the first UK number one with 'black' in the title?

14. Which was the first UK number one with the name of an insect in the title?

15. Which was the first UK number one to include the name of a mammal in the title?

16. Which was the first UK number one to include a rodent in the title?

Answers to page 162
BLUES 1: **1.** John Lee Hooker **2.** B.B. King **3.** 'The Kid' **4.** Muddy Waters **5.** Memphis Slim **6.** John Mayall **7.** Magic Slim **8.** CCS **9.** Freddie King **10.** Elmore James **11.** Etta James **12.** 1995 **13.** 'Champion Jack' **14.** Fats Domino **15.** Chicago **16.** Ray Charles

Cover Versions 5

Answers on page 163

1. Which US singer covered Wings' 'Let 'Em In' in 1977?

2. Coast To Coast had a 1981 hit with 'Let's Jump The Broomstick', but which female singer had a UK hit with it 20 years earlier?

3. Which Scottish duo revived P.J. Proby's 'Hold Me' in 1981?

4. Which song has been a hit for both The Chi-Lites and M.C. Hammer?

5. Who originally had a hit with the Rolling Stones' 1986 chartbuster 'Harlem Shuffle'?

6. Which Mamas and The Papas song did Bitty McLean cover in 1994?

7. Lee Lawrence had the original hit with which Elvis number one?

8. Which Beach Boys song did David Cassidy take to number 16 in the UK charts in 1975?

9. Who recorded the original version of Don McLean's 1980 number one 'Cryin''?

10. Which two artists have had number ones with 'Baby Come Back'?

11. Who had a 1987 hit with Tommy James's 'Mony Mony'?

12. Who had a 1965 UK hit with 'The Promised Land', ten years before Elvis?

13. Which song links Maurice Williams and The Zodiacs, The Hollies and Jackson Browne?

14. Which Fun Boy Three hit of 1982 was recorded by Al Martino 22 years previously?

15. Which Beach Boys song was covered by Aaron Carter in 1998?

16. In 1986, which band found a Chi-Lites song 'Too Good To Be Forgotten'?

Answers to page 163
NINETIES 4: 1. 'Stars' 2. Santana 3. 'Love Is The Drug' 4. R.E.M.
5. Dr Dre 6. Shaggy 7. Prince Naseem 8. Gabrielle 9. 'Train In Vain'
10. *The Butcher's Wife* 11. Madonna 12. M People 13. George Michael
14. 'I Will Always Love You' 15. 'World In Motion' 16. 'Fantasy'

Blues 1

Answers on page 160

1. Which blues guitarist had a UK hit with 'Boom Boom' when it was featured in a 1992 TV commercial for jeans nearly 30 years after its original release?

2. Which blues singer teamed up with U2 in 1989 for 'When Love Comes To Town'?

3. What was young blues pianist Billy Emerson's nickname?

4. Which guitarist's 1981 album was titled 'King Bee'?

5. Who was boogie-woogie piano player Peter Chatman better known as?

6. Which British blues king headed the Bluesbreakers?

7. Guitarist Morris Holt adopted which stage name?

8. Which band did Alexis Korner form initially?

9. Who released the 1974 album 'Burglar'?

10. Which slide guitarist's debut release was 'Dust My Broom'?

11. Which blues singer was born Jamesetta Hawkins?

12. In which year did Rory Gallagher die?

13. What was William Thomas Dupree's nickname?

14. Which blues giant reached number six in the UK charts in 1956 with his version of 'Blueberry Hill'?

15. Which city did The Climax Blues Band drop from their name?

16. Who had a 1961 hit with 'Hit The Road Jack'?

Answers to page 160
CHART TOPPERS 7: **1.** 'Two Little Boys' **2.** 'Hey Joe' (Frankie Laine)
3. 'Rose Marie' (Slim Whitman) **4.** 'Christmas Alphabet' (Dickie
Valentine) **5.** 'Poor People Of Paris' (Winifred Atwell) **6.** 'Singing The
Blues' **7.** 'Little Red Rooster' **8.** 'Mr Tambourine Man' **9.** 'January'
10. 'Turtle Power' **11.** 'She Wears Red Feathers' (Guy Mitchell)
12. 'Silence Is Golden' **13.** 'Paint It Black' **14.** 'Butterfly' (Andy Williams)
15. 'Running Bear' (Johnny Preston) **16.** 'Rat Trap'

Nineties 4

Answers on page 161

1. 'Something Got Me Started' was taken from which Simply Red album?

2. Whose 1999 hit 'Smooth' was his first UK chart entry for 19 years?

3. Which Roxy Music song was remixed by Rollo and Sister Bliss in 1996?

4. 'Bang And Blame' was a hit for which band?

5. Who featured on Eminem's 'Guilty Conscience'?

6. Whose 1995 number one was 'Boombastic'?

7. Which boxer teamed up with Kaliphz for the 1996 single 'Walk Like A Champion'?

8. Which solo artist joined East 17 on 'If You Ever'?

9. Which Clash single was sampled on Garbage's 'Stupid Girl'?

10. From which film was Julia Fordham's 'Love Moves (In Mysterious Ways)' taken?

11. Who released the 1992 album 'Erotica'?

12. Who conducted a 'Search For The Hero' in 1995?

13. Who had a number two hit in 1998 with 'Outside'?

14. Which film track was the best-selling UK single of 1992?

15. Which soccer song reached number one in 1990?

16. Which Mariah Carey single sampled Tom Tom Club's 'Genius Of Love'?

Answers to page 161
COVER VERSIONS 5: **1.** Billy Paul **2.** Brenda Lee **3.** B.A. Robertson and Maggie Bell **4.** 'Have You Seen Her' **5.** Bob and Earl **6.** 'Dedicated To The One I Love' **7.** 'Crying In The Chapel' **8.** 'Darlin'' **9.** Roy Orbison **10.** The Equals and Pato Banton **11.** Billy Idol **12.** Chuck Berry **13.** 'Stay' **14.** 'Summertime' **15.** 'Surfin' USA' **16.** Amazulu

Boyzone 1

Answers on page 166

1. On whose Irish TV show did Boyzone make their debut?

2. Which Louis was Boyzone's manager?

3. Which member of Boyzone took part in *Celebrity Big Brother*?

4. Which two members of the band used to be garage mechanics?

5. What was Shane Lynch studying before he joined Boyzone?

6. 'Love Me For A Reason' and 'Father And Son' were both tracks on which Boyzone album?

7. Which song gave Boyzone their second UK number one?

8. Which Boyzone single came from the musical *Whistle Down The Wind*?

9. Which was Boyzone's second cover version to reach number one in 1999?

10. What was the title of the band's third album?

11. Which member of Boyzone had his first solo number one in 1999?

12. What was the title of the track?

13. In which year did Boyzone release their debut single?

14. What did 'No Matter What' achieve that none of the band's three previous number ones had managed?

15. In which year did Boyzone release the album 'Where We Belong'?

16. Which former number one was removed from circulation at the request of Polydor while still in the charts at number 34?

Answers to page 166
EIGHTIES 5: **1.** 'Eat To The Beat' **2.** Bruce Foxton **3.** Dexy's Midnight Runners **4.** Olivia Newton-John **5.** Odyssey **6.** Major Tom **7.** Jason Donovan **8.** Fleetwood Mac **9.** 'January February' **10.** Katrina and The Waves **11.** ZZ Top **12.** 'Joan Of Arc' **13.** DeBarge **14.** Hazell Dean **15.** Aswad **16.** Tiffany

One-Hit Wonders 6

Answers on page 167

1. Whose only UK top twenty hit was 'That's Nice' in 1966?

2. Whose only hit was the 1972 instrumental 'Popcorn'?

3. Which UK band's one chart entry came with 'Making Up Again' in 1978?

4. What was the title of Crazy Elephant's 1969 hit?

5. Which South African girl band reached number two in 1978 with 'Substitute'?

6. Which French group had a number two hit in 1977 with 'Magic Fly'?

7. 'We Do It' was a 1976 hit for which duo?

8. Who asked 'Why Did You Do It?' in 1975?

9. Which Dutch group had a UK hit with 'Ding-A-Dong', their 1975 Eurovision Song Contest winner?

10. Which Jamaican artist had a 1970 top ten hit with his version of 'Love Of The Common People'?

11. Which cover of a Jerry Lee Lewis song gave Tiny Tim his only UK hit?

12. Which much-covered song gave The Tokens their only chart success in 1961?

13. Who ate cannibals in 1982 and never figured again in the UK top 50?

14. Which kiddies' classic soared to number four in the charts in 1984 for The Toy Dolls?

15. America's Toxic Two had a 1992 hit with which track?

16. Which star of *Bonanza* charted in 1964 with 'Ringo'?

Answers to page 167
NOVELTY NUMBERS 3: 1. *Tiswas* 2. 'Eh-Oh!' 3. 'Margate' 4. Adge Cutler 5. The Wombles 6. A dustman 7. The Barron Knights 8. Dick Emery 9. 'Monster Mash' 10. Bobby 'Boris' Pickett and The Crypt-Kickers 11. 'In The Brownies' 12. 'Black Pudding Bertha' 13. 'D.I.V.O.R.C.E.' 14. 1975 15. 'The Ying Tong Song' 16. 'Bloodnok's Rock 'n' Roll Call'

Eighties 5

Answers on page 164

1. The number one single 'Atomic' was taken from which Blondie album?

2. Who was the bassist with The Jam?

3. Big Jim Paterson played trombone with which Eighties band?

4. Who joined the Electric Light Orchestra on the 1980 number one 'Xanadu'?

5. Which disco band topped the charts with 'Use It Up And Wear It Out'?

6. In 'Ashes To Ashes', who was revealed as 'a junkie...hitting an all-time low'?

7. 'Every Day (I Love You More)' was a 1989 hit for which soap star?

8. 'Oh Diane' and 'Big Love' were hits for which band in the Eighties?

9. Which two months did Barbara Dickson sing about in 1980?

10. Who were 'Walking On Sunshine' in 1985?

11. 'Gimme All Your Lovin'' and 'Sharp Dressed Man' were hits for which US rockers?

12. Which 15th-century French maid provided Orchestral Manoeuvres In The Dark with a 1981 top five hit?

13. Who had a 1985 hit with 'Rhythm Of The Night'?

14. Who was 'Searchin'' in 1984?

15. Which band's name means 'black' in Arabic?

16. As whom was American teenager Ms Darwisch better known?

Answers to page 164
BOYZONE 1: 1. Gay Byrne 2. Louis Walsh 3. Keith Duffy 4. Mikey Graham and Keith Duffy 5. Architecture 6. 'Said And Done' 7. 'A Different Beat' 8. 'No Matter What' 9. 'You Needed Me' 10. 'Where We Belong' 11. Ronan Keating 12. 'When You Say Nothing At All' 13. 1994 14. It stayed at number one in the UK for more than a week 15. 1998 16. 'No Matter What'

Novelty Numbers 3

Answers on page 165

1. The presenters of which Saturday morning TV show unleashed 'The Bucket Of Water Song'?

2. What did Teletubbies say in 1997?

3. About which seaside resort did Chas and Dave wax lyrical in 1982?

4. Who led The Wurzels on their 1967 hit 'Drink Up Thy Zider'?

5. 'Minuetto Allegretto' was a 1974 hit for which furry creatures?

6. What was Lonnie Donegan's old man by profession?

7. 'Call Up The Groups' and 'Pop Go The Workers' were Sixties hits for which comedy band?

8. Who used his catchphrase 'You Are Awful' in a 1973 hit?

9. Which monster hit began: 'I was working in the lab late one night'?

10. And which group sang it?

11. What was Billy Connolly's answer to The Village People's 'In The Navy'?

12. According to The Goodies, who was the Queen of Northern Soul?

13. Which Billy Connolly parody achieved a higher chart placing than the original?

14. In which year did Jasper Carrott ride into town on his 'Funky Moped'?

15. Which song gave The Goons top ten hits in 1956 and 1973?

16. Which track formed a double A-side on the Goons' hit of 1956?

Answers to page 165
ONE-HIT WONDERS 6: 1. Neil Christian 2. Hot Butter 3. Goldie
4. 'Gimme Gimme Good Lovin'' 5. Clout 6. Space 7. R and J Stone
8. Stretch 9. Teach-In 10. Nicky Thomas 11. 'Great Balls Of Fire'
12. 'The Lion Sleeps Tonight' 13. Toto Coelo 14. 'Nellie The Elephant'
15. 'Rave Generator' 16. Lorne Greene

Pot Luck 26

Answers on page 170

In which years were the following tracks top ten hits in the UK?

1. 'Far Far Away' (Slade)

2. 'Best Years Of Our Lives' (Modern Romance)

3. 'Material Girl' (Madonna)

4. 'As Tears Go By' (Marianne Faithfull)

5. 'Elected' (Alice Cooper)

6. 'The Universal' (Blur)

7. 'Zabadak!' (Dave Dee, Dozy, Beaky, Mick and Tich)

8. 'Whole Lotta Shakin' Goin' On' (Jerry Lee Lewis)

9. 'Rio' (Duran Duran)

10. 'Like Clockwork' (The Boomtown Rats)

11. 'Blue Eyes' (Elton John)

12. 'Daydream Believer' (The Monkees)

13. 'Old Before I Die' (Robbie Williams)

14. 'My Eyes Adored You' (Frankie Valli)

15. 'Happy Jack' (The Who)

16. 'Calendar Girl' (Neil Sedaka)

Answers to page 170
LYRICS 6: 1. 'You're So Vain' (Carly Simon) 2. 'Maggie May' (Rod Stewart) 3. 'Green Green Grass Of Home' (Tom Jones) 4. 'Substitute' (The Who) 5. 'Wishing Well' (Free) 6. 'Vincent' (Don McLean) 7. 'Chance' (Big Country) 8. 'Crocodile Rock' (Elton John) 9. 'Life On Mars' (David Bowie) 10. 'Radio Ga Ga' (Queen) 11. 'Breakfast In America' (Supertramp) 12. 'Don't Look Back In Anger' (Oasis) 13. 'Love Is All Around' (Wet Wet Wet) 14. 'Let It Be' (The Beatles) 15. 'You Keep It All In' (The Beautiful South) 16. 'Australia' (Manic Street Preachers)

Soul 2

Answers on page 171

1. Which duo had a 1969 hit with 'Soul Sister Brown Sugar'?

2. Who boarded the 'Love Train' in 1973?

3. Which group released 'Doctor My Eyes' as a single in 1973?

4. Which northern soul band were 'Skiing In The Snow' in 1975?

5. For which group was 'Na-Na The Saddest Word'?

6. 'You Little Trustmaker' was a 1974 hit for which group?

7. Which soul singer was invited to dinner at the White House after appealing on TV for calm in the wake of the assassination of Martin Luther King?

8. Which female singer enjoyed 31 US chart singles in the Sixties?

9. For whom was Michael Jackson's hit 'Ben' originally written?

10. Which event shook the soul world on 1 April 1984?

11. Eddie Levert, Walter Williams and William Powell made up which group?

12. Who had a 1970 hit with 'Farewell Is A Lonely Sound'?

13. In 1964, which soul star was shot dead by the manageress of a Los Angeles motel he had just booked into?

14. Who wanted to 'Blame It On The Boogie' in 1978?

15. Which Jimmy Ruffin song was a UK top ten record twice in the space of eight years?

16. In which year did Aretha Franklin record 'I Say A Little Prayer'?

Answers to page 171
CHER 1: 1. 'All I Really Want To Do' 2. 'Bang Bang (My Baby Shot Me Down)' 3. *Chastity* 4. 'Gypsies, Tramps And Thieves' 5. 1974 6. Gregg Allman 7. David Bowie 8. *Silkwood* 9. 'I Found Someone' 10. Time ('If I Could Turn Back Time') 11. 'Believe' 12. All the tracks were written and performed originally by men 13. Memphis 14. Bonnie Jo Mason 15. He was elected Mayor of Palm Springs 16. 'Sonny Side Of Cher'

Lyrics 6

Answers on page 168

From which songs are the following lyrics taken?

1. 'You walked into the party like you were walking on to a yacht'

2. 'It's late September and you really should be back at school'

3. 'The old home town looks the same as I step down from the train'

4. 'I was born with a plastic spoon in my mouth'

5. 'You've always been a good friend of mine but you're always saying farewell'

6. 'Starry starry night, paint your palette blue and grey'

7. 'All the rain came down on a cold new town as he carried you away'

8. 'I remember when rock was young, me and Susie had so much fun'

9. 'It's a god-awful small affair to the girl with the mousy hair'

10. 'So don't become some background noise, a backdrop for the girls and boys'

11. 'Take a look at my girlfriend she's the only one I got'

12. 'Slip inside the eye of your mind, don't you know you might find a better place to play'

13. 'I feel it in my fingers, I feel it in my toes'

14. 'When I find myself in time of trouble Mother Mary comes to me'

15. 'Just like that murder in '73, just like that robbery in '62'

16. 'I want to fly and run till it hurts, sleep for a while and speak no words'

Answers to page 168
POT LUCK 26: **1.** 1974 **2.** 1982 **3.** 1985 **4.** 1964 **5.** 1972 **6.** 1995
7. 1967 **8.** 1957 **9.** 1982 **10.** 1978 **11.** 1982 **12.** 1967 **13.** 1997 **14.** 1975
15. 1966 **16.** 1961

Cher 1

Answers on page 169

1. Which Bob Dylan song gave Cher her first solo success?

2. Which track, produced by husband Sonny, reached number three in the UK in 1966?

3. Cher appeared in which 1969 film named after her and Sonny's daughter?

4. What was Cher's first US solo number one?

5. In which year did Sonny and Cher get divorced?

6. From whom did Cher seek a divorce in 1975, just ten days after their wedding?

7. Which UK artist made his US TV debut on Cher's show in 1975, singing a duet with her?

8. For which film was Cher nominated for an Oscar as Best Supporting Actress in 1984?

9. Which 1987 single was Cher's first UK chart entry for nearly 14 years?

10. What did Cher wish she could turn back in 1989?

11. In 1998, which song gave Cher her second UK number one?

12. Why was her album 'It's A Man's World' aptly titled?

13. Where was Cher walking in the title of a 1995 hit?

14. Under what pseudonym did Cher sing on the 1964 Phil Spector novelty number 'Ringo I Love You'?

15. What happened to Sonny in the same week in April 1988 that Cher won an Oscar for *Moonstruck*?

16. What was the corny title of Cher's second solo album?

Answers to page 169
SOUL 2: 1. Sam and Dave 2. The O'Jays 3. The Jackson Five 4. Wigan's Ovation 5. The Stylistics 6. The Tymes 7. James Brown 8. Aretha Franklin 9. Donny Osmond 10. Marvin Gaye was shot dead by his father 11. The O'Jays 12. Jimmy Ruffin 13. Sam Cooke 14. The Jacksons 15. 'What Becomes Of The Broken Hearted' 16. 1968

Film Tracks 3

Answers on page 174

1. Geri Halliwell's 'It's Raining Men' came from which film?
2. Which film featured The Cranberries' 1995 hit 'Ridiculous Thoughts'?
3. Which singer's daughter reached number 11 in the UK charts in 1967 with the theme from the Bond film *You Only Live Twice*?
4. Which group sang the title track from *Car Wash*?
5. Doris Day's 'Secret Love' was from the soundtrack of which Western?
6. 'Moon River' from *Breakfast at Tiffany's* provided which singer with his only UK number one?
7. 'A Certain Smile' from the film of the same name was a top five UK hit for which American singer in 1958?
8. Johnny Ray's 1955 hit 'If You Believe' came from which film?
9. Queen's 'Another One Bites The Dust' was re-released in 1998 following its inclusion in which film?
10. Part of which Queen track featured memorably in *Wayne's World*?
11. Paul McCartney's 'No More Lonely Nights' featured in which film?
12. 'Will You?' from *Breaking Glass* was a 1981 hit for which female artist?
13. 'I'm Every Woman' and 'I Have Nothing' were Whitney Houston tracks from which movie?
14. Which number from *Carousel* has been sung on football grounds across the land?
15. Adam Faith's top five hit 'The Time Has Come' featured in which film?
16. Who had a 1973 hit with the title track from *Take Me High*?

Answers to page 174
POT LUCK 27: **1.** Paul Anka ('I Confess' and 'Diana') **2.** Björk **3.** Perry Como **4.** Take That had just announced their split **5.** Andy Fairweather-Low **6.** Georgie Fame and Alan Price **7.** 'Bridget The Midget' **8.** The Young Rascals **9.** Neil Young **10.** Blue **11.** The Smiths **12.** 'Money For Nothing' (Dire Straits) **13.** Phil Collins **14.** The Eagles **15.** Paul Carrack **16.** Mickie Most

Albums 6

Answers on page 175

Who released the following albums?

1. 'The Raven' (1979)

2. 'Captain Fantastic And The Brown Dirt Cowboy' (1975)

3. 'Heroes' (1977)

4. 'Calling All Stations' (1997)

5. 'Touch' (1984)

6. 'A New Flame' (1989)

7. 'Human Touch' (1992)

8. 'Pop' (1997)

9. 'Rock 'n' Roll Juvenile (1979)

10. 'Dancing On The Ceiling' (1986)

11. 'Ommadawn' (1975)

12. 'Get Ready' (2001)

13. 'Close To The Edge' (1972)

14. 'Ironfist' (1982)

15. 'Time' (1981)

16. 'Shepherd Moons' (1991)

Answers to page 175
PUNK 2: **1.** Johnnie Fingers **2.** The Buzzcocks (*Never Mind the Buzzcocks*)
3. Dave Vanian **4.** Jon Moss **5.** Sham 69 **6.** The Skids **7.** Tenpole Tudor
8. The Clash **9.** 'Something Better Change' **10.** The Boomtown Rats
11. The Adverts **12.** Tony James **13.** 'Kiss Me Deadly' **14.** X-Ray Spex
15. X-Ray Spex **16.** 'Dear Prudence'

Pot Luck 27

Answers on page 172

1. Whose first single in the Fifties sold 3,000 copies and his second over nine million?

2. Which singer used to be in an Icelandic band called Tappi Takarrass which translates as 'cork that bitch's arse'?

3. Which crooner was often known as 'The Singing Barber'?

4. Why were Childline and the Samaritans besieged with calls from distraught teenage girls on 13 February 1996?

5. Which former Amen Corner singer was 'Wide Eyed And Legless' in 1975?

6. Which two pop pianists joined forces in 1971 for 'Rosetta'?

7. Who was The Queen of the Blues according to Ray Stevens?

8. Who were 'Groovin'' in 1967?

9. A lyric from one of whose songs did Kurt Cobain quote in his suicide note?

10. Who reached number one in 2001 with their single 'Too Close'?

11. Which band played their farewell gig at Wolverhampton Civic Hall on 22 December 1988?

12. Which was the first music video to be broadcast on MTV Europe?

13. Which superstar drummer guested in place of the late John Bonham when Led Zeppelin reunited for the US branch of Live Aid?

14. After an acrimonious split, which band vowed not to work together until 'hell freezes over'?

15. Who links Ace, Roxy Music, Squeeze, and Mike and The Mechanics?

16. Which record producer was born Michael Hayes?

Answers to page 172
FILM TRACKS 3: **1.** *Bridget Jones's Diary* **2.** *Butterfly Kiss* **3.** Frank Sinatra (Nancy Sinatra) **4.** Rose Royce **5.** *Calamity Jane* **6.** Danny Williams **7.** Johnny Mathis **8.** *There's No Business Like Show Business* **9.** *Small Soldiers* **10.** 'Bohemian Rhapsody' **11.** *Give My Regards To Broad Street* **12.** Hazel O'Connor **13.** *The Bodyguard* **14.** 'You''ll Never Walk Alone' **15.** *What a Whopper!* **16.** Cliff Richard

Punk 2

Answers on page 173

1. What did John Moylett change his name to when joining The Boomtown Rats?

2. Which punk band lent their name to a BBC rock quiz?

3. Who was working as a gravedigger in Hemel Hempstead when he was asked to join The Damned?

4. Which future member of Culture Club temporarily replaced Rat Scabies in The Damned during 1977?

5. Which band's first hit single was 'Angels With Dirty Faces'?

6. 'Masquerade' was a 1979 hit for which Scottish band?

7. Who had a 1981 hit with 'Wünderbar'?

8. 'Tommy Gun' and 'I Fought The Law' were hits for which band?

9. What was The Stranglers' second UK top ten record?

10. For which band was everything going 'Like Clockwork' in 1978?

11. Who reckoned it was 'No Time To Be 21' in 1978?

12. Who was in Generation X before setting up Sigue Sigue Sputnik?

13. What was the title of Generation X's final album?

14. Poly Styrene was the singer with which punk band?

15. Which punk band recorded 'Germ Free Adolescents'?

16. Which Beatles song gave Siouxsie and The Banshees their biggest hit?

Answers to page 173
ALBUMS 6: 1. The Stranglers 2. Elton John 3. David Bowie 4. Genesis 5. The Eurythmics 6. Simply Red 7. Bruce Springsteen 8. U2 9. Cliff Richard 10. Lionel Richie 11. Mike Oldfield 12. New Order 13. Yes 14. Motorhead 15. Electric Light Orchestra 16. Enya

Chart Toppers 8

Answers on page 178

1. Which workman kept Eminem off the top of the UK singles chart in 2000?

2. On what date in 1975 did Pilot's 'January' reach number one?

3. Which 1966 number one was inspired by the Fifties film *The Asphalt Jungle* in which a gangster dreams of returning home to his farm?

4. Which 1968 hit was 'most efficacious in every way'?

5. Which single was UK number one from 13 July to 2 November 1991?

6. What was The Kinks' second UK number one?

7. Who was 'Starry Eyed' in 1960?

8. Which 1977 song from a musical was the 400th UK number one?

9. Who backed Ian Dury on his 1979 chart topper?

10. What nationality were 1982 chart toppers The Goombay Dance Band?

11. '99 Luftballons' was the German title of which 1984 UK number one?

12. How many weeks did Lionel Richie spend at number one in 1984 with 'Hello'?

13. With which act had Lionel Richie previously topped the chart?

14. What is Lionel Richie's middle name?

15. Gabriele Kerner was the singer with which number one band of the Eighties?

16. Which Seventies number one had just two letters in the title?

Answers to page 178
NUMBER TWOS 6: **1.** Frankie Vaughan **2.** Four Non-Blondes **3.** 'When A Man Loves A Woman' **4.** 'What's Love Got To Do With It' **5.** Will Smith **6.** 1966 **7.** Terrorvision **8.** 'Streets Of Philadelphia' **9.** 'Stayin' Alive' **10.** Nat King Cole **11.** 'Perfect 10' **12.** Duane Eddy **13.** Donny and Marie Osmond **14.** MN8 **15.** The Pet Shop Boys **16.** Steps

Seventies 6

Answers on page 179

1. In 1978, which young band won a talent contest sponsored by Guinness Harp Lager at Limerick Civic Week?

2. What role did Sven-Olof Walldoff play in the story of Abba?

3. In what year was 'Tiger Feet' a UK number one for Mud?

4. Who had two successive number ones ending in 'O'?

5. In 1972, which singer couldn't keep it in?

6. John Coghlan was the drummer with which band?

7. 'When', 'You Got What It Takes' and 'Dancin' Party' were all top five hits for Showaddywaddy in which year?

8. How many UK top ten hits did Showaddywaddy have in the Seventies?

9. Which two female solo singers topped the UK charts in 1970?

10. For whom did nothing rhyme in 1970?

11. Which brother and sister had a 1974 hit with 'Morning Side Of The Mountain'?

12. 'With A Little Luck' charted in 1978 for which band?

13. Who released the album 'The Six Wives Of Henry VIII'?

14. What was Robin Scott better known as?

15. And what was his biggest hit in that guise?

16. Which theme from *The Sting* was a hit for Marvin Hamlisch?

Answers to page 179
DANCE 3: 1. Kosheen 2. Lionrock 3. *The X Files* 4. Dutch 5. 'The Launch' 6. Louise Gard 7. DJ Misjah and DJ Tim 8. Tricky 9. DJ Shadow 10. Fatboy Slim 11. DJ Krush 12. Farley Jackmaster Funk 13. Nester 14. Turkish 15. 'For The Love Of A Princess' 16. DJ Luck and MC Neat

Number Twos 6

Answers on page 176

1. Whose 1956 number two with 'Green Door' was bettered by Shakin' Stevens 25 years later?

2. Which band of brunettes got to number two in 1993 with 'What's Up'?

3. Which Percy Sledge classic got to number two on its re-release in 1987?

4. Warren G took which Tina Turner hit to number two in 1996?

5. 'Wild Wild West' stopped short at number two for which artist in 1999?

6. In which year did The Troggs' 'Wild Thing' miss out on the top spot?

7. Who got to number two in 1999 with 'Tequila'?

8. Which Bruce Springsteen track made it to number two in 1994?

9. N-Trance made it second spot in 1995 with their revival of which Bee Gees song?

10. Who had to 'Pretend' in 1953?

11. Which 1998 song from The Beautiful South received top marks even though it only got to number two?

12. 'Pepe' was a 1961 runner-up for which guitarist?

13. Who both said 'I'm Leaving It All Up To You' in 1974?

14. Who promised in 1995: 'I've Got A Little Something For You'?

15. Who were eager to 'Go West' in 1993?

16. Which band got to number two in 2001 with 'Chain Reaction'?

Answers to page 176
CHART TOPPERS 8: **1.** Bob The Builder **2.** 1 February **3.** 'Green Green Grass Of Home' **4.** 'Lily The Pink' **5.** '(Everything I Do) I Do It For You' **6.** 'Tired Of Waiting For You' **7.** Michael Holliday **8.** 'Don't Cry For Me Argentina' **9.** The Blockheads **10.** German **11.** '99 Red Balloons' **12.** Six **13.** The Commodores **14.** Brockman **15.** Nena **16.** 'If'

Dance 3

Answers on page 177

1. Who wanted to 'Hide U' in 2001?

2. As whom is Manchester DJ/remixer Justin Robertson better known?

3. DJ Dado got into the charts in 1996 with a dance version of the theme to which TV sci-fi series?

4. What nationality are DJ Jean and Alice Deejay?

5. And which dance track did DJ Jean take to number two in the UK charts in 1999?

6. Who was the vocalist on DJ Miko's 1994 hit 'What's Up'?

7. Which two DJs combined on 'Access' in 1996?

8. Who released 'The Hell' EP in 1995?

9. Josh Davis is more usually known as which Californian DJ who scored a 1997 hit with 'High Noon'?

10. Who was 'Gangsta Trippin'' in 1998?

11. Which Japanese hip-hop artist released the album 'Strictly Turntablized' in 1994?

12. Which Chicago DJ had a hit in 1986 with a cover version of 'Love Can't Turn Around'?

13. What is Haddaway's first name?

14. What nationality is DJ Quicksilver, resident of 'Planet Love' in 1998?

15. Which track from the film *Braveheart* was sampled on 'Protect Your Mind', a 1999 hit for DJ Sakin and Friends?

16. Which pair had a 1999 dance hit with 'A Little Bit Of Luck'?

Answers to page 177
SEVENTIES 6: 1. U2 2. He was the conductor who dressed as Napoleon when the group performed 'Waterloo' at the 1974 Eurovision Song Contest 3. 1974 4. The Brotherhood Of Man ('Angelo' and 'Figaro') 5. Cat Stevens ('I Can't Keep It In') 6. Status Quo 7. 1977 8. Ten 9. Dana and Freda Payne 10. Gilbert O'Sullivan ('Nothing Rhymed') 11. Donny and Marie Osmond 12. Wings 13. Rick Wakeman 14. M 15. 'Pop Muzik' 16. 'The Entertainer'

Pot Luck 28

Answers on page 182

1. Police in which Canadian city offered to 'review' Madonna's SkyDome show in 1990 following complaints about lewdness?

2. On which birthday did Prince announce that he was changing his name to a symbol?

3. Which legendary band took their name from a Muddy Waters song?

4. Who played his own version of 'The Star Spangled Banner' at Woodstock?

5. Which Eighties fashion icon was the son of a boxing club manager?

6. Which Sixties trio comprised sisters Barbara Ann and Rosa Lee Hawkins and their cousin Joan Johnson?

7. What was the name of Adam Faith's backing group?

8. Which Sixties R & B singer was 6ft 7in tall?

9. What was deceptive about the Canadian band Barenaked Ladies?

10. What is the real Christian name of Pink Floyd recluse Syd Barrett?

11. The theme from which BBC series about a boating family gave the Simon May Orchestra a 1985 hit?

12. Which tragic fate befell both singers of Badfinger?

13. Alice Nutter was a member of which anarchic group which had a number two hit in 1997?

14. Who wrote 'Downtown' for Petula Clark?

15. How many Fine Young Cannibals were there?

16. Which Beatle released the solo album 'All Things Must Pass'?

Answers to page 182
CLASSICAL GAS 2: **1.** 'The Military' **2.** Vivaldi **3.** Mendelssohn **4.** French **5.** Hamburg **6.** 'Brahms' Lullaby' **7.** Worcestershire **8.** Sibelius **9.** Puccini **10.** Liszt **11.** Dmitri **12.** Elgar **13.** 'The Clock' **14.** 'All women are the same' **15.** Beethoven **16.** Berlioz

The Rolling Stones 1

Answers on page 183

1. Which future Kinks drummer played with the Stones on their live debut in 1962?
2. In 1962, which Stone advertised in *Jazz News* under the name of Elmo Lewis for R & B musicians to form a band?
3. Which song did the Stones perform when making their TV debut on ITV's *Thank Your Lucky Stars*?
4. In which Gloucestershire town was Brian Jones born?
5. In which year did '(I Can't Get No) Satisfaction' top both the UK and US singles charts?
6. Which song kept '19th Nervous Breakdown' off the top of the UK charts after five successive number ones?
7. To promote which single did the Stones appear in drag?
8. Which song's lyrics did the Stones have to change when singing on America's *Ed Sullivan Show* in 1967?
9. What did the Stones refuse to do when appearing on *Sunday Night at the London Palladium* in 1967?
10. Which 1968 track gave the Stones their first UK number one for two years?
11. Which Stones album of 1972 was called 'obscene' by Mary Whitehouse?
12. In which year was 'Fool To Cry' released as a single?
13. What was the title of the Stones' number one album of 1980?
14. Which Stone bought a part-share in US soccer team Philadelphia Furies?
15. Which Bob and Earl song did the Stones cover in 1986?
16. Which Mick Jagger solo album featured 'Let's Work'?

Answers to page 183
ROCK 'N' ROLL 2: **1.** Johnny Cash **2.** Cliff Richard **3.** He was pilot of the plane in which Buddy Holly, Ritchie Valens and The Big Bopper were killed **4.** The Valiants **5.** 'Long Tall Sally' **6.** Jerry Lee Lewis **7.** Adam Faith **8.** 1956 **9.** Five **10.** 30 **11.** He had been involved in a car crash **12.** 'Tutti Frutti' **13.** Lionel Bart **14.** 'Mr Parnes Shillings and Pence' **15.** 'Maybe Tomorrow' **16.** Jerry Lee Lewis

Classical Gas 2

Answers on page 180

1. What is the nickname of Haydn's Symphony No. 100?

2. Which Italian composer became a priest for a year in 1703?

3. Who composed A *Midsummer Night's Dream*?

4. What nationality was Chopin's father?

5. In which German city was Brahms born?

6. As what is the song 'Wiegenlied' better known?

7. In which English county was Sir Edward Elgar born?

8. Who composed *Finlandia*?

9. *La Bohème* was an operatic work by which composer?

10. Who composed the *Faust Symphony*?

11. What was Shostakovich's first name?

12. Who wrote the *Enigma Variations*?

13. What is Haydn's Symphony No 101 more commonly known as?

14. What does the title of Mozart's opera *Cosi Fan Tutte* mean in English?

15. Which composer was born in Bonn on 15 December 1770?

16. Who composed the symphony *Harold In Italy*?

Answers to page 180
POT LUCK 28: 1. Toronto 2. 35th 3. The Rolling Stones 4. Jimi Hendrix 5. Boy George 6. The Dixie Cups 7. The Roulettes 8. Long John Baldry 9. They were all men 10. Roger 11. *Howard's Way* 12. Both committed suicide 13. Chumbawamba 14. Tony Hatch 15. Three 16. George Harrison

Rock 'n' Roll 2

Answers on page 181

1. Who had to leave Elvis Presley, Jerry Lee Lewis and Carl Perkins at their famous impromptu Sun recording session in 1956 because his wife wanted to go shopping?
2. Which 18-year-old singing hopeful began a four-week residency at Butlins Holiday Camp, Clacton, in 1958?
3. What role did Roger Peterson play in the history of rock 'n' roll?
4. Who recorded the original version of 'Good Golly Miss Molly'?
5. Which statuesque girl gave Little Richard a number three hit in the UK in 1957?
6. Who recorded the title track from the film *High School Confidential*?
7. Which rock 'n' roller acquired his stage name from a book of boys' and girls' names?
8. In which year did 'Don't Be Cruel' become a US number one for Elvis?
9. At what age did Buddy Holly make his stage debut?
10. How old was Bill Haley when 'Rock Around The Clock' first became number one?
11. Why was Carl Perkins unable to promote 'Blue Suede Shoes'?
12. Which rock classic gave Little Richard his first mainstream hit in the USA?
13. Which songwriter discovered Marty Wilde?
14. What was manager Larry Parnes's nickname?
15. What was Billy Fury's debut single?
16. Which rock 'n' roller was arrested in 1976 for waving a gun outside Elvis's home?

Answers to page 181
THE ROLLING STONES 1: **1.** Mick Avory **2.** Brian Jones **3.** 'Come On' **4.** Cheltenham **5.** 1965 **6.** 'These Boots Are Made for Walkin'' **7.** 'Have You Seen Your Mother, Baby, Standing In The Shadow'? **8.** 'Let's Spend The Night Together' became 'Let's Spend Some Time Together' **9.** They refused to stand and wave on the famous revolving stage at the end of the show **10.** 'Jumpin' Jack Flash' **11.** 'Exile On Main Street' **12.** 1976 **13.** 'Emotional Rescue' **14.** Mick Jagger **15.** 'Harlem Shuffle' **16.** 'Primitive Cool'

Football

Transfer Trail 1

Answers on page 188

1. Which Premiership club signed Norwegian defender John Arne Riise in summer 2001?

2. Which diminutive Coventry City striker joined Manchester United for £650,000 in 1986?

3. Which Italian club signed Alexei Mikhailichenko from Dynamo Kiev in 1990?

4. From which club did Port Vale sign midfielder Dave Brammer?

5. Which Italian striker joined Derby County in July 2001?

6. Which Norwegian joined Liverpool from Rosenborg for £3.5 million in 1998?

7. Which Algerian joined Spurs from Valencia for £2.3 million?

8. Which Stockport midfielder joined Wolves for £700,000 in 2000–1?

9. Who was the only Chilean player in English League football in season 1997–8?

10. From which club did Aston Villa sign Mark Delaney?

11. Which Australian forward joined Notts County from Manchester City in 2000–1?

12. Which English club ended Kevin Keegan's German exile in 1980?

13. Which long-serving full-back did Chelsea sign from St Mirren for £400,000 in 1987?

14. From which club did Crewe Alexandra sign Rodney Jack?

15. Which Grasshopper hopped to Coventry City for £3.25 million in 1997?

16. Who moved from Paris St Germain to Newcastle for £4.75 million in 1999?

Answers to page 188
STOCKPORT COUNTY 1: 1. Alun Armstrong 2. Gary Megson 3. 1997
4. Autoglass Trophy 5. Stoke City 6. Port Vale 7. Bury 8. 1937–8
9. Peterborough United 10. Ian Moore 11. Robert Murray 12. Burnley
13. Sheffield United 14. Asa Hartford 15. David Herd 16. Andy Thorpe

Livingston 1

Answers on page 189

1. In which year did Meadowbank Thistle relocate to Livingston?

2. What were Meadowbank previously known as?

3. Which title did the club win at the end of their first season as Livingston?

4. In which season did they win the Second Division Championship?

5. Who were runners-up to Livingston that year?

6. Which former Forfar and Dunfermline player weighed in with 11 goals that season?

7. In which season did Meadowbank reach the semi-finals of the Scottish League Cup?

8. For which games was Meadowbank's stadium built?

9. On which former Scottish League side's ground did the club play in their early days?

10. What are Livingston's club colours?

11. Who made 446 League appearances for the club from 1979 to 1989?

12. Who scored 64 goals for Meadowbank between 1986 and 1993?

13. Who succeeded Terry Christie as manager?

14. From which club did Meadowbank sign David Roseburgh?

15. Which Premier League team did Livingston beat 1–0 on their own ground in the third round of the Scottish FA Cup in 1999?

16. Who did Livingston beat 2–1 in their first-ever Premier Division match following their promotion in 2001?

Answers to page 189
THE WORLD GAME 1: 1. Finland 2. Sporting Lisbon 3. Anderlecht
4. Grasshoppers 5. Zurich 6. Westerlo 7. Luxembourg 8. Rio de Janeiro
9. Japan 10. Marco Van Basten 11. Ronaldo 12. Silkeborg 13. All light blue
14. Belgium 15. Slovenia 16. George Weah

Stockport County I

Answers on page 186

1. Which striker did Stockport sell to Middlesbrough for £1.6 million in 1998?

2. Who was County manager before Andy Kilner?

3. In which year did County reach the semi-finals of the League Cup for the first time?

4. In which competition were County beaten finalists in both 1992 and 1993?

5. Who beat them in the 1992 final?

6. And who defeated County in 1993?

7. Behind whom were County Second Division runners-up in 1997?

8. Before 1997–8, when was the last season when County had played in the top two divisions of the League?

9. Who beat Stockport in the 1992 Second Division play-off final?

10. Which striker did County sign from Nottingham Forest for £800,000 in 1998?

11. Who made 465 League appearances for the club from 1952 to 1963?

12. Who beat Stockport in the 1994 Second Division play-off final?

13. From which club did County sign Jim Gannon?

14. Which former Manchester City and Scotland midfielder became County manager in 1987?

15. Which future Manchester United star made his League debut for County at the age of 17 against Hartlepool United in 1951?

16. Who played 489 League games for County from 1978 to 1992?

Answers to page 186
TRANSFER TRAIL 1: **1.** Liverpool **2.** Terry Gibson **3.** Sampdoria
4. Wrexham **5.** Fabrizio Ravanelli **6.** Vegard Heggem **7.** Moussa Saib **8.** Tony Dinning **9.** Javier Margas (West Ham) **10.** Cardiff City **11.** Danny Allsopp
12. Southampton **13.** Steve Clarke **14.** Torquay United **15.** Viorel Moldovan
16. Alain Goma

The World Game 1

Answers on page 187

1. In which country do Haka play?

2. Who won the Portuguese League in 2000?

3. Who completed the Belgian League and Cup 'double' in 2000?

4. Who won their 26th Swiss League title in 2001?

5. In which city are they based?

6. In 2001, which team won the Belgian Cup for the first time?

7. F91 Dudelange retained which country's League Championship in 2001?

8. In which city do Brazilian club Fluminense play?

9. Which Asian team guested at the 1999 Copa America?

10. Who scored 128 goals for Ajax in 133 League games before moving to Milan for £1.5 million in 1987?

11. Which Brazilian scored 55 goals in 56 League games for PSV Eindhoven between 1994 and 1996?

12. Who won the Danish Cup in 2001?

13. What are the national colours of San Marino?

14. In which country was Tomasz Radzinski the leading League goalscorer in 2000–1?

15. In which country do Publikum and Rudar play?

16. Which Liberian international was named World Player of the Year for 1995?

Answers to page 187
LIVINGSTON 1: **1.** 1995 **2.** Ferranti Thistle **3.** Third Division **4.** 1998–9 **5.** Inverness Caledonian Thistle **6.** David Bingham **7.** 1984–5 **8.** The Commonwealth Games **9.** Edinburgh City **10.** Black and yellow **11.** Walter Boyd **12.** David Roseburgh **13.** Michael Lawson **14.** Hamilton Academicals **15.** Aberdeen **16.** Hearts

Scotland 1

Answers on page 192

1. Which gangling winger won 17 caps for Scotland from 1974 while a player with Coventry City?

2. Who were the only country to defeat Scotland in their qualifying group for the 1978 World Cup?

3. Which other country made up that group?

4. Who was Scotland's goalkeeper at the 1974 World Cup finals?

5. When did Colin Hendry win his first cap?

6. Who topped Scotland's qualifying group for the 1970 World Cup?

7. How many Scotland caps did Alan Hansen win?

8. Which Aberdeen player won his first cap against England in 1989 and went on to make 40 international appearances?

9. With which other team did Scotland qualify from Group Six at the 1982 World Cup?

10. Who did Scotland beat 5–2 in their opening match at the 1982 finals?

11. Who scored twice for Scotland in that match?

12. How many caps did Ron Yeats win?

13. With whom did Scotland qualify for Italia 90?

14. Which visitors held Scotland to a 2–2 draw in a World Cup qualifier in March 2001?

15. Who were Scotland's first opponents in the qualifying group for the 2002 World Cup?

16. In which city did Scotland defeat Sweden at Italia 90?

Answers to page 192
LIVERPOOL 1: 1. Millwall 2. £15,000 3. Patrik Berger 4. Three 5. Ian Rush
6. Dean Saunders 7. Glenn Hysen 8. West Ham 9. Gordon Hodgson
10. Sheffield Wednesday 11. Kenny Dalglish 12. Alun Evans 13. Peter
Cormack 14. Ian Callaghan 15. 1994 16. 224

Football League 1

Answers on page 193

1. Which team collected just eight points from 34 matches in 1904–5?

2. Which Liverpool full-back won eight League Championship medals?

3. Who played in four successive Championship-winning teams in the 1990s?

4. Who replaced Doncaster Rovers in the Football League in 1998?

5. In 1994, who were promoted from the Third Division via the play-offs in their first season in the Football League?

6. Who won their first 13 Third Division games at the start of season 1985–6?

7. Who went 30 games without a win in Division Three (North) in 1956–7?

8. Which are the only two clubs to have won the Championships of the old Divisions One, Two, Three and Four?

9. Who won their opening 11 First Division matches in 1992–3?

10. Which Reading player was the League's top scorer with 36 goals in 1983–4?

11. Of Ernie Moss's 749 League appearances between 1968 and 1988, over half were for which club?

12. Which club went from the Fourth Division to the First and back again from 1964 to 1987?

13. Which team were relegated in 1937–8 despite being the highest scorers in the First Division?

14. Who beat Bolton in the 1999 First Division play-off final?

15. With which two clubs did John McGovern win League Championships in the 1970s?

16. In which year did Accrington Stanley resign from the League?

Answers to page 193
GILLINGHAM 1: 1. Robert Taylor 2. Wigan Athletic 3. John Simpson
4. Keith Peacock 5. 1964 6. Plymouth Argyle 7. Brian Yeo 8. Gorleston
9. Tony Cascarino 10. Swindon Town 11. Sunderland 12. Peter Beadle
13. Reading 14. Robert Taylor 15. Nicky Forster 16. Peterborough United

Liverpool 1

Answers on page 190

1. As a youngster, Phil Babb was released by which London club before playing a first-team game?

2. How much did Ray Clemence cost from Scunthorpe United?

3. Which star of the Czech Republic team at Euro 96 was snapped up by Liverpool at the end of the tournament?

4. How many times have Liverpool been relegated?

5. Which £300,000 striker made his Liverpool debut in 1980 but failed to score in his first seven games?

6. Who was the first Liverpool player to score four in a European tie?

7. Which Swedish international defender joined Liverpool from Fiorentina in 1989?

8. With which League club did Ray Houghton begin his footballing career?

9. Which South African scored 232 goals for Liverpool before the war?

10. Against whom did Michael Owen score his first Premiership hat-trick?

11. Which Liverpool manager signed Nigel Spackman from Chelsea?

12. Who became the most expensive teenager in English football when he joined Liverpool from Wolves for £100,000 in 1968?

13. Which Scottish international half-back moved to Anfield from Nottingham Forest for £110,000 in 1972?

14. Who made his debut against Rotherham in 1960 and went on to play 843 games for Liverpool in a 21-year career?

15. When did Roy Evans become Liverpool manager?

16. How many League goals did Ian Rush score for Liverpool?

Answers to page 190
SCOTLAND 1: **1.** Tommy Hutchison **2.** Czechoslovakia **3.** Wales **4.** David Harvey **5.** 1993 **6.** Italy **7.** 26 **8.** Stewart McKimmie **9.** Northern Ireland **10.** New Zealand **11.** John Wark **12.** Two **13.** Yugoslavia **14.** Belgium **15.** Latvia **16.** Genoa

Gillingham 1

Answers on page 191

1. Who scored a hat-trick in seven minutes for Gillingham at Burnley in 1999?

2. Who did Gillingham beat in the 2000 Second Division play-off final to reach the top two divisions for the first time in their history?

3. Who made 571 League appearances for the club between 1957 and 1972?

4. Which former Charlton player became Gillingham manager in 1981?

5. When were Gillingham crowned Fourth Division champions?

6. From which club did Gillingham sign Mark Saunders?

7. Who scored 135 League goals for Gillingham from 1963 to 1975?

8. Who did Gillingham hammer 10–1 in a first-round FA Cup tie in 1957?

9. Which Republic of Ireland striker did Gillingham sell to Millwall for £225,000 in 1987?

10. Who beat Gillingham in the 1987 Second/Third Division play-off final?

11. Which team did Gillingham beat in the semi-finals of the play-offs that year to consign them to the Third Division for the first time ever?

12. Which striker did Gillingham sell to Spurs for £300,000 in 1992?

13. From which club did Gillingham sign Carl Asaba?

14. Who did Gillingham sell to Manchester City for £800,000 in 1999–2000?

15. Who was Gillingham's top scorer in 1993–4?

16. To whom did Gillingham finish Fourth Division runners-up in 1974?

Answers to page 191
FOOTBALL LEAGUE 1: **1.** Doncaster Rovers **2.** Phil Neal **3.** Eric Cantona (Marseille 1991, Leeds 1992, Manchester United 1993 and 1994) **4.** Halifax Town **5.** Wycombe Wanderers **6.** Reading **7.** Crewe Alexandra **8.** Wolves and Burnley **9.** Newcastle United **10.** Trevor Senior **11.** Chesterfield **12.** Carlisle United **13.** Manchester City **14.** Watford **15.** Derby County and Nottingham Forest **16.** 1962

World Cup 1

Answers on page 196

1. Which country has never progressed beyond the first round in nine World Cup finals?

2. Which two players appeared for Italy at both the 1934 and 1938 finals?

3. Which Peruvian player scored a hat-trick against Iran at the 1978 finals?

4. Which city staged the opening match at the 1994 finals?

5. A 2–0 World Cup defeat in 1993 meant that which country had still yet to score against England in eight internationals?

6. Which two countries reached the last four in their first appearance at the finals?

7. Which African nation qualified for their first finals in 1970?

8. Against whom had France gained their solitary point at the 1966 finals?

9. Who was Holland's first choice goalkeeper at the 1994 finals?

10. Which is the only country to have played a World Cup qualifier in five different continents?

11. Who coached the victorious Uruguayan team in 1930?

12. Who has made a record 25 appearances in World Cup finals?

13. How many times have Romania qualified for the World Cup finals?

14. Which French player was sent off against Saudi Arabia in the 1998 World Cup finals?

15. Who scored twice for Chile against Italy at the 1998 finals?

16. Who did England play in their opening match of the 2002 World Cup Finals?

Answers to page 196
SHEFFIELD UNITED 1: 1. Harry Johnson 2. Four 3. Brian Gayle 4. Marcelo 5. Steve Bruce 6. 1898 7. 1994 8. Jimmy Dunne 9. Leicester City 10. Alan Cork 11. Wembley 12. Notts County 13. Argentinian 14. Brian Deane 15. Oxford United 16. 1981–2

Who Said That? 1

Answers on page 197

1. Who said of 39-year-old Gordon Strachan: 'There's nobody fitter at his age, except maybe Raquel Welch'?

2. Which Wimbledon boss said: 'The only hooligans here are the players'?

3. Of whom was Sir Matt Busby speaking when he said: 'He's never hurt anyone. Mind you, he's frightened a few'?

4. Which player did Bill Shankly say 'could start a riot in a graveyard'?

5. Who, according to Sir Alex Ferguson, 'could start a row in an empty house'?

6. Which manager said: 'Hartson's got more previous than Jack the Ripper'?

7. Who said of Sheffield United goalkeeper Simon Tracey: 'He's got the brains of a rocking horse'?

8. Of which goalkeeper did former Wales boss Terry Yorath say: 'I wouldn't go so far as to say he is a complete nutcase, but he comes very close to it'?

9. Who called Poland's 1973 goalkeeper Jan Tomaszewski 'a clown'?

10. Which Liverpool boss said: 'Mind, I've been here during the bad times too. One year we came second'?

11. Of whom did Bill Shankly once say: 'He's deceptive – he's slower than you think'?

12. Who did Ron Atkinson call 'The Crab – because he only plays sideways'?

13. Which player did Sir Alex Ferguson call 'a big-time Charlie'?

14. Of which Newcastle player did Kenny Dalglish say: 'He does more in celebrations than he does in a week's training'?

15. Of which team's goal famine did Ron Atkinson say: 'Devon Loch was a better finisher'?

16. Who confessed in 1988: 'I'd kick my own brother if necessary'?

Answers to page 197
NAME THE YEAR 1: **1.** 1967 **2.** 1935 **3.** 1965 **4.** 1990 **5.** 1912 **6.** 1977
7. 1923 **8.** 1956 (Stanley Matthews) **9.** 1976 **10.** 1982 **11.** 1994 **12.** 1885
13. 1994 **14.** 1953 **15.** 1997 **16.** 1959

Sheffield United 1

Answers on page 194

1. Who scored 205 League goals for United from 1919 to 1930?

2. How many times have United won the FA Cup?

3. Which defender did United sign from Ipswich for £750,000 in 1991?

4. Who was United's top scorer in 1998–9?

5. Who became United manager in 1998?

6. When did United win the League Championship for the only time?

7. When were United last in the Premiership?

8. Who scored 41 League goals for United in 1930–1?

9. Who beat United in the semi-finals of the 1961 FA Cup?

10. Who scored United's goal in the 1993 FA Cup semi-final against Sheffield Wednesday?

11. Where was that match played?

12. What was Paul Devlin's first League club?

13. What nationality was 1970s star Alex Sabella?

14. Who was United's top scorer in 1990–1?

15. From whom did United sign Bobby Ford?

16. When did United spend their only season in Division Four?

Answers to page 194
WORLD CUP 1: **1.** Scotland **2.** Giovanni Ferrari and Giuseppe Meazza
3. Teofilo Cubillas **4.** Chicago **5.** Turkey **6.** Portugal (1966) and Croatia
(1998) **7.** Morocco **8.** Mexico **9.** Ed De Goey **10.** Israel **11.** Alberto Supicci
12. Lothar Matthäus **13.** Seven **14.** Zinedine Zidane **15.** Marcelo Salas
16. Sweden

Name the Year 1

Answers on page 195

1. When did Jimmy Hill quit as Coventry City manager?

2. In which year did Arsenal provide seven members of the England team?

3. In which year did Northampton Town become the first club to rise from the Fourth to the First Division?

4. When was Roberto Baggio transferred from Fiorentina to Juventus for a then world record fee of £7.7 million?

5. When did Britain last win the gold medal in the Olympic soccer tournament?

6. When did Terry Paine make the last of his 824 Football League appearances?

7. In which year was the 'White Horse' Cup final?

8. When was an Englishman first named European Footballer of the Year?

9. When did Liverpool win their first League title under Bob Paisley?

10. When did Bobby Robson become England manager?

11. When did Jürgen Klinsmann join Tottenham?

12. When did Arbroath beat Bon Accord 36–0 in the Scottish FA Cup?

13. When was Pele appointed Brazil's Minister for Sport?

14. When did Hungary crush England 6–3 at Wembley?

15. When was Ronaldo named World Player of the Year?

16. When did Billy Wright become the first man to win 100 England caps?

Answers to page 195
WHO SAID THAT? I: **1.** Ron Atkinson **2.** Dave Bassett **3.** Nobby Stiles **4.** Tommy Smith **5.** Dennis Wise **6.** Harry Redknapp **7.** Dave Bassett **8.** Neville Southall **9.** Brian Clough **10.** Bob Paisley **11.** Pat Crerand **12.** Ray Wilkins **13.** Paul Ince **14.** Temuri Ketsbaia **15.** Aston Villa **16.** Steve McMahon

Sunderland 1

Answers on page 200

1. When were Sunderland first relegated from the top division?

2. Which forward did Sunderland sign from West Bromwich Albion for £900,000 in 1991?

3. Who did Sunderland beat in the 1937 FA Cup final?

4. Which Sunderland player won 34 caps for Northern Ireland?

5. When did Sunderland drop into Division Three for one season?

6. Who did Sunderland sell to Crystal Palace for £1.5 million in 1991?

7. From which club did Sunderland sign Niall Quinn?

8. Which beanpole striker joined Sunderland from Italian club Lecce?

9. For which Middlesbrough striker did Sunderland pay £42,000 in 1961?

10. On which ground did Niall Quinn score the only goal of a 1999 Premiership game before being forced to play in goal?

11. Who was Sunderland's leading scorer in 2000–1?

12. Who defeated Sunderland in the 1999 League Cup final?

13. To whom were Sunderland Second Division runners-up in 1964?

14. Which Division Three team took Sunderland to a third-round replay in their Cup-winning year of 1973?

15. Who captained Sunderland in the 1973 final?

16. With which club did Andy Melville make his League debut?

Answers to page 200
THE WORLD GAME 2: **1.** France **2.** Japan **3.** Australia **4.** Innsbruck
5. Colombia **6.** Argentinian **7.** Belgium **8.** Boavista **9.** Henrik Larsson
10. Hernan Crespo **11.** Spain **12.** Daniel Passarella **13.** Herfolge **14.** Bosnia-Herzegovina **15.** Roma **16.** Niko and Robert Kovac

Football League 2

Answers on page 201

1. For which club did Andy Davidson make 511 League appearances from 1947 to 1967?

2. For which former League club did Dixie McNeil score 85 goals in the 1970s?

3. Which club used to be known as Headington United?

4. For whom did Terry Harkin score 35 Fourth Division goals in 1964–5?

5. In 1921, which London club marked their first season in the Football League by gaining promotion from Division Three?

6. What is the name of Stockport County's ground?

7. In 1959, who became the first champions of Division Four?

8. Which other three clubs were promoted with them?

9. For which former League club did John Dungworth score 26 goals in 1978–9?

10. Which north-east club won their first-ever promotion in 1968?

11. Who was Brighton's leading scorer in 2000–1?

12. Who beat Stoke City in the semi-finals of the 2001 Second Division play-offs?

13. For which club did Geoff Bradford make 245 League appearances from 1949 to 1964?

14. In which season were both Sheffield clubs in the Third Division?

15. Which club's highest League position was finishing runners-up to Liverpool in the First Division in 1983?

16. And who finished a best-ever second to Liverpool in 1984?

Answers to page 201
REPUBLIC OF IRELAND 1: **1.** Paddy Moore **2.** Aberdeen **3.** Alan McLoughlin **4.** John Sheridan **5.** Noel Cantwell **6.** Manchester United **7.** 19 **8.** Paul McGee **9.** Kevin Sheedy **10.** England **11.** Roy Keane **12.** Shay Given **13.** Czechoslovakia and Scotland **14.** Liam Tuohy **15.** Austria **16.** Jimmy Conway

The World Game 2

Answers on page 198

1. Which country won the 2001 Confederations Cup?

2. Who did they beat in the final?

3. Which country's team are known as 'The Socceroos'?

4. Which club won the Austrian League in 2000?

5. Which country staged the 2001 Copa America?

6. What nationality is Kily Gonzalez?

7. For which country did Paul Van Himst score 30 international goals?

8. Who won the Portuguese League in 2000–1?

9. Which Swede won the Golden Shoe for 2001 after scoring 35 League goals for Celtic?

10. Which Lazio player was runner-up?

11. Emilio Butragueno played for which country?

12. Which Argentine defender scored 20 goals in 65 internationals?

13. Which Danish club won their first League title in 2000?

14. Zeljeznicar won the League and Cup double of which country in 2001?

15. With which Italian club was the Brazilian Cafu a player in 2000–1?

16. Which Croat international brothers joined Bayern Munich in summer 2001?

Answers to page 198
SUNDERLAND 1: **1.** 1958 **2.** Don Goodman **3.** Preston North End
4. Martin Harvey **5.** 1987 **6.** Marco Gabbiadini **7.** Manchester City
8. Daniele Dichio **9.** Brian Clough **10.** Valley Parade (Bradford City)
11. Kevin Phillips **12.** Leicester City **13.** Leeds United **14.** Notts County
15. Bobby Kerr **16.** Swansea City

Republic of Ireland 1

Answers on page 199

1. Who scored four goals for Ireland in their first-ever World Cup match, against Belgium in 1934?

2. With which Scottish League club was he a player at the time?

3. Who scored the Republic's goal in their 1993 World Cup qualifier in Belfast?

4. Which Sheffield Wednesday player was a member of Ireland's 1990 World Cup squad?

5. Which West Ham full-back won the first of his 36 Ireland caps in 1954?

6. With which club did Don Givens win his first Irish cap?

7. How many international goals did he score?

8. Which Preston player scored twice for the Republic as they won 3–2 in Cyprus in 1980?

9. Who scored the Republic's opening goal of the 1990 World Cup finals?

10. Who were their opponents?

11. Whose goal earned a 1–1 draw with Portugal at Lansdowne Road in June 2001?

12. Who played in goal for Ireland in that match?

13. Which two countries were in Ireland's qualifying group for the 1962 World Cup?

14. Who was Republic manager from 1971 to 1972?

15. Who inflicted a 10–1 double on the Republic in qualifiers for the 1972 European Championship?

16. Which Fulham forward won his first cap against Spain in 1967?

Answers to page 199
FOOTBALL LEAGUE 2: 1. Hull City 2. Hereford United 3. Oxford United
4. Crewe Alexandra 5. Crystal Palace 6. Edgeley Park 7. Port Vale
8. Coventry City, York City and Shrewsbury Town 9. Aldershot
10. Hartlepool United 11. Bobby Zamora 12. Walsall 13. Bristol Rovers
14. 1979–80 15. Watford 16. Southampton

Managers 1

Answers on page 204

1. Who took Roma to Italy's Serie 'A' title in 2001?

2. Which manager guided Peterhead into the Scottish League?

3. Which former England defender quit as Bolton Wanderers manager in 1999?

4. Who was sacked in March 2000 after just seven months at West Bromwich Albion?

5. Fatih Terim was appointed national coach of which country in 1993?

6. Which Englishman quit FC Copenhagen for Udinese in 2001?

7. Who was appointed Chesterfield manager in May 2000?

8. Which former England striker was sacked as manager of Macclesfield in December 2000?

9. Who became manager of Southampton in 1985?

10. Which Uruguayan managed Rochdale in 1988?

11. Frenchman Robert Corfou was appointed coach of which African nation in 2001?

12. Which Spanish team did Luis Aragones take to third place in the Spanish League in 2000–1?

13. Who was appointed Spain's coach in 1992?

14. Which club did Norman Hunter manage from 1985 to 1987?

15. Who was Portsmouth manager from 1961 to 1970?

16. When did Peter Taylor become Gillingham boss?

Answers to page 204
ON THE SPOT 1: **1.** Antonin Panenka **2.** Holland **3.** David Batty **4.** Paul Ince **5.** Gary Lineker **6.** Kanu **7.** Gareth Southgate **8.** Andreas Möller **9.** Jaap Stam **10.** Frank De Boer **11.** Corinthians **12.** Darren Purse **13.** Andrew Johnson **14.** Miguel Nadal **15.** Nigel Martyn **16.** Gaizka Mendieta

Manchester United 1

Answers on page 205

1. Victory over which team in 1999 made United the first British side to be crowned World Club Champions?

2. In which city was that game played?

3. Who scored the only goal of the match?

4. In which year did Peter Schmeichel join United?

5. Who was United's leading Premiership scorer in 1994–5?

6. Who knocked United out of the FA Cup in 1998?

7. In January 2000, which visiting team became the first in over six years to win a Premiership penalty at Old Trafford?

8. Who were the only two members of United's 1952 Championship side to play in the 1956 Championship-winning team?

9. From which Irish club did United buy Mick Martin?

10. Who scored the decisive goal for Chelsea in both League matches against United in 1993–4?

11. Who joined United in 1987 for £800,000 from Norwich City?

12. Which Brighton goalkeeper faced United in the 1983 FA Cup final?

13. Who scored twice for Vasco da Gama as they beat United 3–1 at the FIFA Club World Championship in January 2000?

14. Who scored twice against his old club to win the 1991 European Cup-Winners' Cup for United?

15. How many League goals did Denis Law score for United?

16. How many seasons did Martin Buchan spend at Old Trafford?

Answers to page 205
BARNSLEY 1: **1.** Gerry Taggart **2.** Twice **3.** Georgi Hristov **4.** Craig Hignett **5.** 1965 **6.** Ashley Ward **7.** Norman Hunter, Bobby Collins and Allan Clarke (twice) **8.** Rotherham United **9.** Danny Wilson **10.** Bolton Wanderers **11.** Watford **12.** Red **13.** David Currie **14.** Carl Tiler **15.** Johnny Steele **16.** Liverpool

On the Spot 1

Answers on page 202

1. Which Czech cheekily chipped German keeper Sepp Maier to win the penalty shoot-out at the end of the 1976 European Championship?

2. Which country have lost their last five penalty shoot-outs?

3. Which player who had never previously taken a penalty tried his luck for England in the shoot-out against Argentina at the 1998 World Cup?

4. Who missed England's first penalty against Argentina?

5. Who would have equalled Bobby Charlton's record total of England goals but for fluffing a penalty against Brazil?

6. Which Arsenal player missed a penalty for Nigeria in the shoot-out to decide the 2000 African Nations Cup final?

7. Whose 1993 penalty miss relegated Crystal Palace to Division One?

8. Who scored the decisive German penalty against England in the semi-final shoot-out at Euro 96?

9. Which Manchester United player blasted a penalty over the bar during Holland's shoot-out with Italy in the semi-finals of Euro 2000?

10. Who missed Holland's first penalty in that shoot-out?

11. Which team won the 2000 Club World Championship on penalties?

12. Whose late penalty took the 2001 Worthington Cup final to extra time?

13. Who then missed fatally for Birmingham City in the shoot-out?

14. Who missed Spain's last penalty against England at Euro 96?

15. Which England keeper saved a penalty against Spain in March 2001?

16. Who put Valencia ahead with a penalty in the 2001 UEFA Champions' League final?

Answers to page 202
MANAGERS 1: **1.** Fabio Capello **2.** Ian Wilson **3.** Colin Todd **4.** Brian Little **5.** Turkey **6.** Roy Hodgson **7.** Nicky Law **8.** Peter Davenport **9.** Chris Nicholl **10.** Danny Bergara **11.** Cameroon **12.** Mallorca **13.** Javier Clemente **14.** Rotherham United **15.** George Smith **16.** 1999

Barnsley 1

Answers on page 203

1. Which Leicester City and Northern Ireland international centre-back made 212 League appearances for Barnsley?

2. How many times have Barnsley reached the FA Cup final?

3. Who did Barnsley sign for a club record £1.5 million from Partizan Belgrade in 1997?

4. Who was Barnsley's top scorer in 1999–2000?

5. In which year did Barnsley fall into Division Four for the first time?

6. Who did Barnsley sell to Blackburn for £4.25 million in 1998?

7. Which three ex-Leeds players managed Barnsley in the 1980s?

8. Behind which South Yorkshire neighbours did Barnsley finish Third Division runners-up in 1981?

9. Which manager took Barnsley into the Premiership in 1997?

10. To whom did Barnsley finish First Division runners-up that year?

11. Which was Bruce Dyer's first League club?

12. In what colour shirts do Barnsley play?

13. Which forward did Barnsley sign from Oldham for £250,000 in September 1991?

14. Which centre-back did they sell to Nottingham Forest for £1.5 million in May 1991?

15. Who managed Barnsley from 1960 to 1971?

16. Who beat Barnsley 4–0 at Oakwell in the sixth round of the FA Cup in 1985?

Answers to page 203
MANCHESTER UNITED 1: **1.** Palmeiras **2.** Tokyo **3.** Roy Keane **4.** 1991 **5.** Andrei Kanchelskis **6.** Barnsley **7.** Middlesbrough **8.** Roger Byrne and Johnny Berry **9.** Bohemians **10.** Gavin Peacock **11.** Steve Bruce **12.** Graham Moseley **13.** Romario **14.** Mark Hughes **15.** 236 **16.** 12

World Cup 2

Answers on page 208

1. Up to January 2002, who is the only player to have scored in two successive World Cup finals?

2. In which World Cup final was one nation's ball used in the first half and the other's in the second after the two teams had been unable to agree?

3. In which year did Colombia first qualify for the World Cup finals?

4. Who scored two penalties in England's quarter-final victory over Cameroon at the 1990 World Cup?

5. Whose only England goal was enough to beat Egypt in Group F at the 1990 finals?

6. Within the space of two days in April 2001, which country beat Tonga 22–0 and American Samoa 31–0 in World Cup qualifiers?

7. Which country topped England's group at the 1986 finals?

8. Whose hat-trick against Poland in the 1986 finals saw England scrape through to the second round?

9. Who was Scotland's leading scorer with two goals at the 1974 finals?

10. Who were England's first opponents at the 1970 finals?

11. Which England player scored the only goal of the game?

12. Which Scot scored in five successive World Cup qualifiers in 1988–9?

13. On which racecourse did the England players train before leaving for the 1950 finals in Brazil?

14. Failure to beat which team in their last group match cost England a place in the quarter-finals of the 1958 tournament?

15. Who were the one country to win all three group matches at the 1978 finals?

16. Who did the Germans beat 5–0 in their first match at the 1966 finals?

Answers to page 208
THE WORLD GAME 3: 1. Levski Sofia 2. Parma 3. Valencia 4. San Moix Stadium 5. Raul 6. Maritimo 7. Venezuela 8. Honved 9. Bastia 10. Sepp Maier 11. Olympiakos 12. Peru 13. San Lorenzo 14. Feyenoord 15. Romario 16. Davide Xausa

Premiership 1

Answers on page 209

1. Which Premiership team won just one away game in 2000–1?

2. Which Arsenal player refuses to fly?

3. Which manager took Middlesbrough into the Premiership in 1992?

4. In which year did Sunderland sell Lee Clark to Fulham?

5. Which former Gunner was West Ham's top scorer in 1998–9?

6. Which three Blackburn players were chosen for the PFA Divisional Team of the Season for 1993–4?

7. To which animal did opposing supporters compare Tony Adams early in his career?

8. Which Arsenal player was voted African Footballer of the Year in 1999?

9. Who was Leeds United's top scorer in 1999–2000?

10. Which striker joined Everton on loan from Turkish club Trabzonspor in March 1999?

11. Of which Premiership club is Peter Ridsdale the chairman?

12. What colour are Sunderland's shirts?

13. Who were unbeaten in their first dozen Premiership games in 1997–8?

14. And who emulated that feat the following season?

15. Who topped the Charlton scoring charts in 2000–1?

16. Who was Leicester City's only ever-present in 1998–9?

Answers to page 209
PORTSMOUTH 1: **1.** Jack Tinn **2.** Peter Harris **3.** 1929 **4.** Colin Clarke **5.** Notts County **6.** Steve Claridge **7.** Milan Mandaric **8.** 1949 **9.** Leicester City **10.** Wolves **11.** Cliff Parker **12.** Reading **13.** Liverpool **14.** Darren Anderton **15.** Nottingham Forest **16.** Derby County

The World Game 3

Answers on page 206

1. Who won the Bulgarian League in 2000–1?

2. Against which club did Roma clinch Italy's Serie 'A' title in 2001?

3. Which Spanish club are known as the Ches?

4. What is the name of Mallorca's ground?

5. Whose 24 goals made him the leading scorer in the Spanish League in 2000–1?

6. Who did FC Porto beat to win the 2001 Portuguese Cup final?

7. In which South American country do Monagas and Carabobo play?

8. For which Hungarian army team did Ferenc Puskas play from 1948 to 1958?

9. Which Corsican club won the French Cup in 1981?

10. Which German international goalkeeper of the 1970s was famed for his long, baggy shorts?

11. Who were crowned League Champions of Greece in 2001?

12. In which country did 13-year-old Fernando Rafael Garcia make his League debut for Juan Aurich in May 2001?

13. Which club won the 2001 Closing Championship in Argentina to pick up their first title since 1995?

14. Who were runners-up in the Dutch League in 2001?

15. Which Brazilian star was transferred from PSV Eindhoven to Barcelona in 1993 after complaining bitterly about the Dutch weather?

16. Which Inverness Caledonian Thistle player was in Canada's squad for the 2001 Confederations Cup?

Answers to page 206
WORLD CUP 2: **1.** Vava (Brazil, 1958 and 1962) **2.** 1930 (Argentina v Uruguay) **3.** 1962 **4.** Gary Lineker **5.** Mark Wright **6.** Australia **7.** Morocco **8.** Gary Lineker **9.** Joe Jordan **10.** Romania **11.** Geoff Hurst **12.** Mo Johnston **13.** Ascot **14.** Austria **15.** Italy **16.** Switzerland

Portsmouth 1

Answers on page 207

1. Which Portsmouth manager was famous for wearing 'lucky spats'?

2. Who scored a record 194 League goals for the club between 1946 and 1960?

3. When did Portsmouth first reach the FA Cup final?

4. Which Northern Ireland striker did Pompey sign from Queens Park Rangers for £450,000 in 1990?

5. Who did Pompey beat 9–1 in a Second Division match in 1927?

6. Who briefly became player/manager of the club in 2000–1?

7. What is the name of Pompey's wealthy chairman?

8. In which year did Pompey first win the League Championship?

9. Who defeated them in the FA Cup semi-finals that year, thereby depriving them of a possible double?

10. Who did Pompey shock 4–1 to win the 1939 FA Cup final?

11. Who was Portsmouth's two-goal hero that day?

12. To whom did Portsmouth sell Sammy Igoe in 2000?

13. To whom did Portsmouth lose on penalties after a 1992 FA Cup semi-final replay?

14. Who had scored Pompey's goal in the first semi-final?

15. Which top flight team had Pompey beaten in the sixth round?

16. Behind whom did Portsmouth finish Second Division runners-up in 1986–7?

Answers to page 207
PREMIERSHIP 1: 1. Bradford City 2. Dennis Bergkamp 3. Lennie Lawrence
4. 1999 5. Ian Wright 6. Tim Flowers, David Batty and Alan Shearer
7. Donkey 8. Kanu 9. Michael Bridges 10. Kevin Campbell 11. Leeds United
12. Red and white stripes 13. Arsenal 14. Aston Villa 15. Jonatan Johansson
16. Steve Guppy

Millwall 1

Answers on page 212

1. On whose ground did Millwall seal promotion to the First Division in 1988?

2. Who put Millwall ahead at Anfield in 1988?

3. Which former Spurs striker did Bruce Rioch bring to The Den for £250,000?

4. Which future Scottish international striker joined Millwall from Bury?

5. In which year did Barry Kitchener make his Millwall debut?

6. Which lanky forward did Benny Fenton sign for Millwall from Darlington for £17,000 after he had terrorised them in a League Cup tie?

7. Which 18-year-old became the youngest Millwall player to score a League hat-trick when he bagged three against Shrewsbury Town in 1986?

8. When did Millwall first win the FA Youth Cup?

9. Which First Division team did Millwall knock out of the FA Cup in 1965?

10. How many times have Millwall reached the semi-finals of the FA Cup?

11. How many successive home League games without defeat did Millwall play up to January 1967?

12. Which legendary Lion scored 11 goals in 1970–1?

13. Who became Millwall manager in 1974?

14. Which Millwall goalkeeper went 787 minutes without conceding a goal in 1976?

15. With which two clubs were the Lions promoted that year?

16. Who did Millwall hammer 5–0 to clinch the Second Division title in May 2001?

Answers to page 212
MANAGERS 2: **1.** Dynamo Kiev **2.** Brazil **3.** Dave Stringer **4.** Monaco **5.** Jan Molby **6.** Jimmy Nicholl **7.** 1995 **8.** Oldham Athletic **9.** Bayern Munich **10.** Coventry City **11.** Chesterfield **12.** Terry Paine **13.** Guus Hiddink **14.** Norway **15.** Bobby Moore **16.** 1995

The World Game 4

Answers on page 213

1. Which team played in a record five consecutive French Cup finals between 1946 and 1955?

2. Which club won their first French League title in 1998?

3. Who won the 1998 French Cup final?

4. Which club completed the Spanish League and Cup double in 1975?

5. Which member of West Germany's 1966 World Cup final team played 409 League games for Cologne between 1961 and 1977 and won 81 international caps?

6. Who finished runners-up in Italy's Serie 'A' in 2000–1?

7. Which French club had an average attendance of over 28,000 in 1988 from a town population of 35,000?

8. Which European country beat Zambia 9–0 in 1994?

9. Which French World Cup winner joined Bordeaux from Cannes in 1992?

10. Who won the Italian League in 1997?

11. Who were runners-up in the Spanish League in 2000–1?

12. For which country did Toni Polster win a record number of caps?

13. Who lost on penalties to Uruguay in the final of the 1995 Copa America?

14. Birkirkara and Sliema are clubs in which country?

15. Which Brazilian keeper made his international debut against Switzerland in 1989 and played in Italy with Inter Milan, Parma and Reggina?

16. Which club did the Luxembourg League and Cup double in 1999?

Answers to page 213
PREMIERSHIP 2: **1.** Frederic Kanoute **2.** Swindon Town **3.** Barnsley **4.** Peter Swales **5.** Wimbledon **6.** Jan-Aage Fjørtoft **7.** Alex Ferguson and Alan Curbishley **8.** Michael Owen **9.** Ian Wright **10.** Freddy Shepherd and Douglas Hall **11.** Mauricio Taricco **12.** Roy Evans **13.** Nottingham Forest **14.** Manchester (United and City) **15.** Efan Ekoku **16.** Villa Park

Managers 2

Answers on page 210

1. Valery Lobanovsky guided which club to European Cup-Winners' Cup success in 1975 and 1986?

2. Luiz Felipe Scolari was coach of which country in 2001?

3. Which former player became manager of Norwich City in 1987?

4. Which French club did Jean Tigana manage in 1998–9?

5. Which Dane took charge of Swansea City in 1996?

6. Which former Manchester United full-back had two spells as manager of Raith Rovers?

7. When did Terry Fenwick become Portsmouth manager?

8. Which Lancashire club had just two managers between 1970 and 1994?

9. Ottmar Hitzfeld was coach of which German club in 2000–1?

10. Which club did Joe Mercer manage from 1972 to 1975?

11. Jimmy McGuigan, Joe Shaw and Frank Barlow all managed which English League club?

12. Which former Southampton and England winger managed Cheltenham Town in 1979?

13. Who did Frank Rijkaard succeed as national coach of Holland?

14. Nils Johan Semb became coach of which country in 1998?

15. Which England World Cup winner became manager of Southend United in 1984?

16. When did Dave Jones become manager of Stockport County?

Answers to page 210
MILLWALL 1: **1.** Hull City **2.** Paul Stephenson **3.** Mark Falco **4.** John McGinlay **5.** 1967 **6.** Bryan Conlon **7.** Michael Marks **8.** 1979 **9.** Fulham **10.** Three **11.** 59 **12.** Harry Cripps **13.** Gordon Jago **14.** Ray Goddard **15.** Hereford United and Cardiff City **16.** Oldham Athletic

Premiership 2

Answers on page 211

1. Who was West Ham United's leading Premiership scorer in 2000–1?

2. Which is the only team to concede 100 goals in a Premiership season?

3. In 1997–8, which club tasted their only season in the Premiership?

4. Who resigned as Manchester City chairman in November 1993?

5. A 4–2 defeat away to which London club confirmed Swindon Town's relegation in 1994?

6. Who was Swindon's leading scorer for that season?

7. Which two Premiership managers each won two Manager of the Month awards during 1998–9?

8. Who was Liverpool's top Premiership scorer in 2000–1?

9. Which Premiership player was banned for three matches in 1999 for trashing a referee's room?

10. Which controversial pair returned to the Newcastle United board in 1998?

11. Who was George Graham's first signing for Tottenham?

12. Who left his partnership with Gerard Houllier in 1998?

13. In December 1994, against which club did Manchester United concede their first Premiership goal at Old Trafford for 1,135 minutes?

14. Two clubs from which city were the only teams to win at Blackburn in their 1994–5 Championship season?

15. Who was Wimbledon's leading scorer in 1994–5?

16. Where did Blackburn pick up their only away League win in 1998–9?

Answers to page 211
THE WORLD GAME 4: **1.** Lille **2.** Lens **3.** Paris St. Germain **4.** Real Madrid **5.** Wolfgang Overath **6.** Juventus **7.** Lens **8.** Belgium **9.** Zinedine Zidane **10.** Juventus **11.** Deportivo La Coruña **12.** Austria **13.** Brazil **14.** Malta **15.** Claudio Taffarel **16.** Jeunesse d'Esch

Leeds United 1

Answers on page 216

1. Who beat Leeds in the semi-finals of the 2000 UEFA Cup?

2. What nationality is Eirik Bakke?

3. Which Lucas is South African?

4. When did David O'Leary become Leeds manager?

5. Who did he succeed?

6. From which club did Leeds sign Johnny Giles?

7. In imitation of which famous European club did Don Revie change Leeds' strip to all white?

8. Who were promoted to the First Division with Leeds in 1964?

9. On which ground did Leeds beat Manchester United 1–0 in a 1965 FA Cup semi-final replay?

10. Who scored the only goal of the game?

11. Which two Leeds players in their 1965 FA Cup final team had already won full England caps?

12. In which year did Alan Smith play his first game for Leeds?

13. And on which ground did he mark his debut with a goal in a 3–1 win?

14. In which city was Harry Kewell born?

15. From which Irish club did Leeds sign Gary Kelly?

16. Which Norwegian defender joined Leeds from Nottingham Forest?

Answers to page 216
FA CUP 1: **1.** Bury (in 1903) **2.** David Nish **3.** West Ham and Queens Park Rangers **4.** Pat Jennings, Pat Rice and Sammy Nelson **5.** Torquay United **6.** Marcel Desailly **7.** Roberto Di Matteo **8.** Gus Poyet **9.** Arsenal **10.** Gretna **11.** Bill Brown **12.** Bobby Moore and Alan Mullery **13.** Five **14.** Tranmere Rovers **15.** Lawrie Sanchez **16.** Luton Town

England 1

Answers on page 217

1. Which two players from England's opening match in the 1966 World Cup finals did not play in the final itself?

2. Which member of the 1966 World Cup final team did not make his first appearance in the tournament until the quarter-final stage?

3. Which Wolves defender scored England's first-ever goal in the European Championship – a penalty in 1962?

4. Which Nottingham Forest forward won his only England cap as a substitute against the Republic of Ireland In 1985?

5. Which Derby County defender won the first of his 28 England caps in 1971?

6. At which venue did England play their group matches at Italia 90?

7. Who scored England's goal when they lost 3–1 to West Germany in the first leg of the 1972 European Championship quarter-finals?

8. Against whom was England's sole victory in the qualifying group for the 1974 World Cup?

9. Which other home country was in England's qualifying group for the 1986 World Cup?

10. Which Swede became the England team's first foreign manager in 2001?

11. Who did England beat 2–0 in a World Cup qualifier in June 2001?

12. Who scored England's goals?

13. When did Alan Shearer win his first England cap?

14. How many England goals did Martin Peters score?

15. When did England last score ten goals in an international?

16. And who were their opponents that day?

Answers to page 217
FOOTBALL LEAGUE 3: 1. Crewe Alexandra 2. Hull City 3. Wrexham
4. Oxford United 5. Notts County 6. Trevor Steven (in Scotland with
Rangers and in France with Marseille) 7. Huddersfield Town 8. Torquay
United 9. Marco Gabbiadini 10. Hull City 11. Shrewsbury Town 12. West
Ham United and Notts County 13. Merthyr Town 14. Jamie Forrester
15. Crystal Palace 16. Blackpool

FA Cup 1

Answers on page 214

1. Who recorded the biggest win in an FA Cup final?

2. Who was just 21 when he captained Leicester's 1969 Cup final team?

3. Which two Second Division clubs reached the Cup final in the 1980s?

4. Which three Northern Ireland internationals were members of Arsenal's Cup final teams of 1978 and 1979?

5. Which West Country club equalled their best-ever Cup run by reaching the fourth round in 1989–90?

6. Who became the first player to earn Cup winners' medals from three countries after Chelsea beat Aston Villa in the 2000 FA Cup final?

7. Who scored Chelsea's winning goal in the 2000 final?

8. Who had scored twice for Chelsea in their semi-final victory over Newcastle in 2000?

9. Who knocked Chelsea out of the Cup in 2001?

10. In 1991 which club became the first Scottish team to play in the FA Cup proper for 105 years?

11. Which Scottish international kept goal for Spurs in the 1961 and 1962 finals?

12. Which two England internationals played for Fulham in the 1975 final?

13. How many matches did it take to settle the third-round tie between Arsenal and Sheffield Wednesday in 1979?

14. Who came from 3–0 down to defeat Southampton 4–3 in 2001?

15. Who scored Wimbledon's winner in the 1988 Cup final?

16. Which First Division team did Wimbledon beat in the semi-finals that year?

Answers to page 214
LEEDS UNITED 1: **1.** Galatasaray **2.** Norwegian **3.** Lucas Radebe **4.** 1998 **5.** George Graham **6.** Manchester United **7.** Real Madrid **8.** Sunderland **9.** City Ground, Nottingham **10.** Billy Bremner **11.** Jack Charlton and Alan Peacock **12.** 1998 **13.** Anfield **14.** Sydney **15.** Home Farm **16.** Alf-Inge Haaland

Football League 3

Answers on page 215

1. Which club are nicknamed 'The Railwaymen'?

2. Who did Leyton Orient beat in the Third Division play-off semis in 2001?

3. For which club did Tom Bamford score 175 League goals from 1928 to 1934?

4. Who were the one Nationwide League team to concede 100 goals in 2000–1?

5. Mark Stallard was leading scorer for which club in 2000–1?

6. Which member of Everton's title-winning sides of 1985 and 1987 went on to capture League Championship medals in two other countries?

7. Which Yorkshire team fielded an ever-present defence for the 42 Second Division matches of 1952–3?

8. Who were the last team to finish bottom of the Fourth Division before relegation to the Conference was introduced?

9. Who was Darlington's leading scorer in 1999–2000?

10. Which club were locked out of their own ground in May 2000?

11. In 1979 which club were promoted to Division Two for the first time?

12. With which two clubs were Swansea City promoted to Division One in 1981?

13. Which former League club went 61 away League games without a win from 1922 to 1925?

14. Who was Northampton Town's leading marksman in 2000–1?

15. Whose 2–0 victory over Chelsea in 1973 was their first success against another London club in 32 attempts?

16. Which club failed to gain re-election in 1899 but returned to the League a year later and have been members ever since?

Answers to page 215
ENGLAND 1: **1.** Jimmy Greaves and John Connelly **2.** Geoff Hurst **3.** Ron Flowers **4.** Peter Davenport **5.** Roy McFarland **6.** Cagliari **7.** Francis Lee **8.** Wales **9.** Northern Ireland **10.** Sven Goran Eriksson **11.** Greece **12.** Paul Scholes and David Beckham **13.** 1992 **14.** 20 **15.** 1964 **16.** USA

Whistle Happy 1

Answers on page 220

1. What was referee Andy Hall's blunder in September 2000?

2. Why was referee David Syme locked in his dressing room after a 1988 match between Hearts and Rangers?

3. How many penalties did Dutch referee Dick Jol award in the 2001 Champions' League final?

4. Which Newcastle player was fined £1,500 in 1998 for 'laying hands' on referee David Elleray?

5. Which Barnsley official refereed the 1997 FA Cup final?

6. In which year did Clive Thomas referee the FA Cup final?

7. What was referee Peter Willis's claim to fame?

8. Which Scottish referee officiated at two matches in Euro 2000?

9. Who was Britain's first senior woman referee?

10. How did Karl Josef Assenmacher upset Graham Taylor in 1993?

11. Which country's goalkeeper was suspended indefinitely in 1981 for kicking referee Tor Moeien?

12. Which Rangers full-back had to leap out of the bath and run back on to the pitch after referee Arthur Ellis realised he had blown for time five minutes early in a 1956 European Cup tie?

13. Which referee allowed the infamous West Brom 'offside' goal at Elland Road which cost Leeds the 1971 League Championship?

14. Which referee came from the Surrey village of Great Bookham?

15. Whose decision that the ball had not crossed the line robbed Chesterfield of an historic FA Cup final place in 1997?

16. What was Mr A Stair's claim to fame?

Answers to page 220
MOTHERWELL 1: **1.** Rodger Hynd **2.** 1991 **3.** Dundee United **4.** Tommy McLean **5.** Celtic **6.** Willie Pettigrew **7.** Brian McLaughlin **8.** 1932 **9.** PSV Eindhoven **10.** Tommy Coyne **11.** Bill McFadyen **12.** Tom Boyd **13.** Brian Martin **14.** Hugh Ferguson **15.** Dundee United **16.** Dundee

Wales 1

Answers on page 221

1. Behind which country did Wales finish in Group Three at the 1958 World Cup finals?

2. Who scored for Wales against Hungary in that tournament?

3. And who got Wales's goal in the 1–1 draw with Mexico?

4. Which Manchester United player won his first Wales cap in 1985 against Norway?

5. With which club was Mike England a player when he won his first Wales cap in 1962?

6. Which country knocked Wales out of the 1964 European Championship?

7. Which country did Wales beat twice in the 1972 European Championship qualifiers?

8. Defeat at home to whom stopped Wales going to the 1994 World Cup finals?

9. Which other home country was in Wales's qualifying group for the 1986 World Cup?

10. Which Arsenal goalkeeper won 41 Welsh caps from 1954 to 1962?

11. When did Ian Rush win his first cap?

12. How many caps did he win in total?

13. Who topped Wales's qualifying group for the 1966 World Cup?

14. For which Italian club did John Charles play?

15. Who scored a hat-trick against Malta in 1978 but won a total of just four caps?

16. Whose goal earned Wales a 1–1 draw in Ukraine in June 2001?

Answers to page 221
SHARPSHOOTERS 1: **1.** Marian Pahars **2.** Steve Butler **3.** Bristol City **4.** Nigeria **5.** Chris Kiwomya **6.** Bristol City **7.** Barrie Thomas **8.** Valencia **9.** Mateja Kezman **10.** Leo Fortune-West **11.** Geoff Hurst **12.** David Platt **13.** Toto Schillaci **14.** Eusebio **15.** 23 **16.** Mario Kempes

Motherwell 1

Answers on page 218

1. Who did Ally MacLeod succeed as manager of Motherwell?

2. When did Motherwell last win the Scottish FA Cup?

3. Who did they beat after extra time in the final?

4. Which manager led Motherwell to that triumph?

5. Who beat Motherwell in the 1931 Scottish FA Cup final after a replay?

6. Who was Motherwell's top scorer in 1975–6 and 1976–7?

7. Which Motherwell man was voted Scottish First Division Player of the Year in 1981–2?

8. In which year did Motherwell win the Scottish League title?

9. From which Dutch club did Motherwell sign Mitchell Van der Gaag for £400,000 in 1995?

10. Who was Motherwell's top scorer in 1994–5?

11. Who scored 52 League goals for Motherwell in 1931–2?

12. Which full-back did Motherwell sell to Chelsea for £800,000 in 1991?

13. Who joined Motherwell from St Mirren for a then club record fee of £175,000 in 1991?

14. Who scored 283 goals for the club between 1916 and 1925?

15. Who did Motherwell beat 12–1 in a Second Division match in 1954?

16. Who did Motherwell defeat 4–0 in the 1952 Scottish FA Cup final?

Answers to page 218
WHISTLE HAPPY 1: **1.** He forgot to send off Barnsley's Mitch Ward after giving him two yellow cards **2.** Hearts director Douglas Park locked him in because he was angry about his handling of the match **3.** Three **4.** David Batty **5.** Stephen Lodge **6.** 1976 **7.** He was the first referee to send someone off in a Wembley Cup final (Kevin Moran, 1985) **8.** Hugh Dallas **9.** Wendy Toms **10.** He failed to send off Ronald Koeman for a professional foul, thus allowing him to score the decisive goal in a crucial World Cup qualifier with England **11.** Norway **12.** Eric Caldow **13.** Ray Tinkler **14.** Ray Lewis **15.** David Elleray **16.** He refereed the first FA Cup Final

Sharpshooters 1

Answers on page 219

1. Which Latvian striker was Southampton's top scorer in 1999–2000?

2. Who scored five times in a Second Division match for Cambridge United against Exeter City in 1994?

3. For which English League club did Don Clark score 36 goals in 1946–7?

4. In which country was Dele Adebola born?

5. Which former Ipswich and Arsenal striker was Queens Park Rangers' top scorer for 1999–2000?

6. From which club did Manchester City sign Shaun Goater?

7. Which Scunthorpe United player scored 31 League goals in 1961–2?

8. For which Spanish club did Argentine striker Claudio Lopez play in 2001?

9. Which PSV Eindhoven player was the leading scorer in the Dutch League in 2000–1?

10. Who was Rotherham United's top scorer in 1999–2000?

11. Who scored six goals for West Ham in an 8–0 hammering of Sunderland in 1968?

12. Who scored England's goal in their 2–1 defeat to Italy in the third place match at the 1990 World Cup?

13. Whose goal for Italy put the Republic of Ireland out of the 1990 World Cup?

14. Who scored 316 goals in 294 League games for Benfica?

15. How old was Jimmy Greaves when he scored his 200th League goal?

16. Which Argentine ace scored nine times to help Valencia reach the 1980 European Cup-Winners' Cup final?

Answers to page 219
WALES 1: **1.** Sweden **2.** John Charles **3.** Ivor Allchurch **4.** Clayton Blackmore **5.** Blackburn Rovers **6.** Hungary **7.** Finland **8.** Romania **9.** Scotland **10.** Jack Kelsey **11.** 1980 **12.** 73 **13.** USSR **14.** Juventus **15.** Ian Edwards **16.** Mark Pembridge

Manchester City 1

Answers on page 224

1. Who holds City's record for most League appearances?

2. How many England caps did Colin Bell win?

3. Who did City sell to Tottenham in 1988 for £1.7 million?

4. Who lasted only 32 days as City manager in 1996?

5. Which City player made his League debut in 1961 at just 15 years of age?

6. Who joined City from Bolton Wanderers for £60,000 in 1967?

7. Whose five goals made him leading scorer in City's 1981 FA Cup run?

8. Where did City play their home games from 1887 to 1923?

9. Which Third Division team did City beat on their way to winning the FA Cup in 1969?

10. Who captained City in the 1969 Cup final?

11. What nationality is Danny Tiatto?

12. From which club did City sign him?

13. Which three managers were in charge of City during 1973?

14. When did Joe Mercer become City boss?

15. How many times did City change divisions in the 1980s?

16. From which London club did City buy Terry Phelan?

Answers to page 224
MANAGERS 3: **1.** Jupp Heynckes **2.** Romania **3.** Oxford United **4.** Tony Waddington **5.** Bruce Rioch **6.** Mansfield Town **7.** Chile **8.** United Arab Emirates **9.** Fulham **10.** Mick Halsall **11.** France **12.** Guus Hiddink **13.** George Curtis and John Sillett **14.** 1991 **15.** Bulgaria **16.** Scunthorpe United

European Championship 1

Answers on page 225

1. Which country's victory over Malta in 1995 was their first in a European Championship match for 32 years?

2. Who knocked reigning European champions Italy out of the 1972 tournament in the quarter-finals?

3. When did Holland first reach the quarter-finals of the European Championship?

4. Whose two goals for Holland decided a play-off against the Republic of Ireland in 1995?

5. In which city was that game played?

6. Which country lost all three matches in Group Two at the 1988 finals?

7. Who did France beat in the semi-finals of the 1984 tournament?

8. Which country conceded most goals at Euro 2000?

9. Against whom did co-hosts Belgium pick up their only win at Euro 2000?

10. Who scored England's only goal at the 1992 finals?

11. Who got Sweden's winning goal in their 2–1 victory over England at the 1992 finals?

12. Who lost to the Czech Republic on penalties in the semi-finals of Euro 96?

13. Which award did England win at Euro 96?

14. Whose solo goal clinched victory for England against Scotland at Euro 96?

15. Goals by John Jensen and Kim Vilfort secured the European Championship title for which country?

16. Which two countries lost all ten games in the Euro 96 qualifiers?

Answers to page 225
ASTON VILLA 1: 1. 1987–8 2. Millwall 3. Mark Walters 4. Nottingham Forest 5. Five 6. Spurs 7. Dynamo Berlin 8. Nigel Callaghan 9. Newcastle United 10. Wolves 11. Czechoslovakia 12. Stan Collymore 13. George Ramsay 14. 1998 15. Savo Milosevic 16. Ian Ormondroyd

Managers 3

Answers on page 222

1. Which German coach took over for the second time at Athletic Bilbao in summer 2001?

2. Anghel Iordanescu was appointed coach of which country in 1993?

3. Of which English League club did Malcolm Shotton become manager in 1998?

4. Who was Stoke City manager from 1960 to 1977?

5. Who quit as Norwich City boss in March 2000?

6. Danny Williams, Stuart Boam and George Foster have all been managers of which Third Division club?

7. Pedro Garcia was coach of which country in 2001?

8. Which Middle East country fired Frenchman Henri Michel as national coach in 2001?

9. Bedford Jezzard was manager of which London club from 1958 to 1964?

10. Who did Barry Fry follow as Peterborough United manager?

11. Raynald Denoueix coached the League champions of which country in 2001?

12. Who was appointed coach of Holland in 1994?

13. Which management duo led Coventry City to FA Cup success in 1987?

14. When was Arrigo Sacchi made coach of Italy?

15. Dimitar Penev was coach of which nation at the 1994 World Cup?

16. Ron Ashman managed which English League club from 1976 to 1981?

Answers to page 222
MANCHESTER CITY 1: **1.** Alan Oakes **2.** 48 **3.** Paul Stewart **4.** Steve Coppell **5.** Glyn Pardoe **6.** Francis Lee **7.** Paul Power **8.** Hyde Road **9.** Luton Town **10.** Tony Book **11.** Australian **12.** Stoke City **13.** Malcolm Allison, Johnny Hart and Ron Saunders **14.** 1965 **15.** Four (twice relegated to Division Two and twice promoted back) **16.** Wimbledon

Aston Villa 1

Answers on page 223

1. In which season were Villa last out of the top flight?

2. Behind whom did they finish Second Division runners-up that year?

3. Which winger did Villa sell to Rangers for £550,000 in 1987?

4. From which club did Villa sign Steve Stone?

5. How many times did Villa win the League Championship between 1893–4 and 1899–1900?

6. Who beat Villa in the 1971 League Cup final?

7. Which East German team did Villa beat on the away goals rule en route to the 1982 European Cup final?

8. Which former Watford winger joined Villa from Derby for £525,000 in 1989?

9. From which club did Villa sign Peter Withe?

10. Which Midlands rivals did Villa lose to in the semi-finals of the 1960 FA Cup?

11. Which country did Dr Jozef Venglos take to the quarter-finals of the 1990 World Cup?

12. Which £7 million buy scored just six goals in his first season with Villa?

13. Which manager led Villa to six FA Cup triumphs?

14. In which year did John Gregory become Villa boss?

15. Which player joined Villa for £3.5 million in 1995 although manager Brian Little had only seen him in action on a video?

16. Which beanpole striker was recruited from Bradford City for £650,000 in 1989?

Answers to page 223
EUROPEAN CHAMPIONSHIP 1: **1.** Luxembourg **2.** Belgium **3.** 1976 **4.** Patrick Kluivert **5.** Liverpool **6.** England **7.** Portugal **8.** Yugoslavia **9.** Sweden **10.** David Platt **11.** Tomas Brolin **12.** France **13.** Fair Play Award **14.** Paul Gascoigne **15.** Denmark **16.** Estonia and San Marino

Wolverhampton Wanderers 1

Answers on page 228

1. Which former Millwall player did Wolves sell to Crystal Palace for £2 million in 1997?

2. When did Stan Cullis become Wolves manager?

3. Who scored twice for Wolves in the 1960 FA Cup final?

4. Who was in goal for Wolves that day?

5. When did Steve Bull make his Wolves debut?

6. Which full-back made 501 League appearances for the club between 1967 and 1982?

7. Which manager bought Andy Gray from Aston Villa?

8. Who did Wolves sign from Birmingham City for £500,000 in 1990?

9. Who beat Wolves in the semi-finals of the 1981 FA Cup?

10. Which much-travelled manager had a spell in charge at Molineux from 1984–5?

11. From which German club did Wolves sign Havard Flo?

12. Who was Wolves' leading scorer for 1998–9?

13. Which Finnish forward joined Wolves from Bolton and was sold to Hibernian in September 1998?

14. What nationality is Kevin Muscat?

15. From which London club did Wolves sign him?

16. With which club did Keith Curle make his League debut?

Answers to page 228
SCOTTISH SCENE 1: **1.** Elgin City **2.** Greenock Morton and Alloa Athletic **3.** Clydebank **4.** Kilmarnock **5.** Rangers **6.** St Mirren and St Johnstone **7.** Steve Crawford **8.** Peterhead **9.** Black and white **10.** Raith Rovers **11.** Stenhousemuir **12.** 1987 **13.** Dundee United **14.** Alan Rough **15.** Ken Eadie **16.** 1922

Oddballs 1

Answers on page 229

1. Golfer Colin Montgomerie is a big fan of which Premiership club?

2. Which team won the Irish League six seasons in a row either side of the war between 1936 and 1948?

3. Which club won the Auto Windscreens Shield in 2000?

4. In which year did Scotland fans tear down the goalposts at Wembley?

5. Which star of the 1970s TV show *The Comedians* was a hard man with Doncaster Rovers In the 1950s?

6. Which member of Spurs' 1981 Cup final squad had a musical dream?

7. Which song did the England World Cup Squad take to number one in the charts in 1970?

8. Who were Wimbledon's first opponents in a Football League game?

9. Which club were thrown out of the 1999 Irish Cup for fielding an ineligible player in the semi-finals?

10. Who were awarded the Cup in their place?

11. Who won the League of Wales in 2001?

12. Who finished runners-up?

13. Which former Everton player was nicknamed 'Inchy'?

14. In what colour shirts do the Australian national team play?

15. For kicking which Argentinian player was David Beckham sent off at the 1998 World Cup?

16. Which manager moved from the Norwegian fjords to South London in June 1999?

Answers to page 229
EUROPEAN CHAMPIONSHIP 2 1. Azerbaijan 2. Eight 3. Belgium
4. Hungary 5. Holland 6. Bobby Charlton and Geoff Hurst 7. Holland
8. Denmark 9. Portugal 10. Republic of Ireland 11. Luther Blissett 12. 1994
13. Poland 14. Greece 15. Richard Moller Nielsen 16. Italy

Scottish Scene 1

Answers on page 226

1. Who propped up Scottish Division Three in 2001 at the end of their first season in the League?

2. Who were relegated to the Second Division in 2001?

3. Which team drew a crowd of just 29 for a Scottish League Cup tie with East Stirlingshire in 1999?

4. Which club had a Scottish FA Cup tie with Inverness Caledonian Thistle abandoned because of a frozen pitch in February 2001 after they had been forced to switch off their undersoil heating early the previous night following complaints about the noise from local residents?

5. Which club did Claudio Caniggia join in summer 2001?

6. A pre-season friendly between which two clubs in 2001 saw four men sent off?

7. Who was Dunfermline Athletic's top scorer in 1999–2000?

8. Which League newcomers lost 13–0 to Aberdeen in a 1923–4 Scottish FA Cup tie?

9. In what colour shirts do Elgin City play?

10. For which club did Donald Urquhart make 387 League appearances?

11. Which club gained their first-ever promotion in 1994?

12. When did St Mirren last win the Scottish FA Cup?

13. Who did they beat in the final?

14. Which goalkeeper was named Scotland's Player of the Year for 1981?

15. Which Clydebank player was Scotland's leading scorer in 1990–1?

16. When did Morton win the Scottish FA Cup for the only time?

Answers to page 226
WOLVERHAMPTON WANDERERS 1: 1. Neil Emblen 2. 1948 3. Norman Deeley 4. Malcolm Finlayson 5. 1986 6. Derek Parkin 7. John Barnwell 8. Kevin Ashley 9. Spurs 10. Tommy Docherty 11. Werder Bremen 12. Robbie Keane 13. Mixu Paatelainen 14. Australian 15. Crystal Palace 16. Bristol Rovers

European Championship 2

Answers on page 227

1. Who lost 10–0 to France in a qualifier for Euro 96?

2. How many French players scored in that match?

3. Who were beaten finalists in 1980?

4. Which nation finished third in the 1964 tournament?

5. Who did Czechoslovakia beat in the semi-finals of the 1976 European Championship?

6. Who scored England's goals in their 2–0 win over USSR in the third place match at the 1968 finals?

7. To whom did Cyprus lose 8–0 in a 1987 qualifier, only for the game to be declared void due to an attack on the Cypriot goalkeeper?

8. Who defeated Holland on penalties in the 1992 semi-finals?

9. Who did France beat in the 1984 semi-finals?

10. Against which country did Liechtenstein gain their first European Championship point?

11. Who scored a hat-trick for England as they mauled Luxembourg 9–0 in a 1982 qualifier?

12. When did Israel play their first European Championship matches?

13. Who did they beat in their opening group game?

14. Which country refused to face Albania in a 1962 qualifier because they were technically still at war with them?

15. Who was Denmark's coach at Euro 96?

16. Who beat Bulgaria in the quarter-finals of the 1968 tournament?

Answers to page 227
ODDBALLS 1: **1.** Leeds United **2.** Belfast Celtic **3.** Stoke City **4.** 1977
5. Charlie Williams **6.** Osvaldo Ardiles **7.** 'Back Home' **8.** Halifax Town
9. Cliftonville **10.** Portadown **11.** Barry Town **12.** Cwmbran **13.** Adrian
Heath **14.** Gold with green trim **15.** Diego Simeone **16.** Egil Olsen

Brazil 1

Answers on page 232

1. Which country sensationally knocked Brazil out of the Copa America in July 2001?

2. Who scored twice against Uruguay in September 1993 to confirm Brazil's place at the 1994 World Cup finals?

3. How many goals did Ronaldo score at the 1998 World Cup finals?

4. Who put Brazil out of the 1974 World Cup?

5. Who beat Brazil in the third place play-off for the 2001 Confederations Cup?

6. Who was replaced as national coach following that disappointing show?

7. By what name was Edwaldo Isidio Neto better known?

8. What were Brazil allowed to keep in 1970?

9. Who holds the Brazilian record of 77 international goals?

10. For which Spanish club did Denilson play in 2001?

11. Which free-kick specialist made his international debut in 1975 and was named South American Footballer of the Year two years later?

12. Who beat Brazil 3–0 in a World Cup qualifier in August 2000?

13. Which exponent of the 'banana shot' made his international debut in 1965 and went on to score 26 goals in 94 internationals?

14. Which team literally kicked Brazil out of the 1966 World Cup?

15. Who did Brazil beat in the semi-finals of the 1970 World Cup?

16. Who scored seven times for Brazil at the 1988 Olympics?

Answers to page 232
THE WORLD GAME 5: **1.** Nantes **2.** Dan Eggen **3.** Jordi Cruyff **4.** Levski Sofia **5.** Denmark **6.** Inter Milan **7.** Cagliari **8.** Sonny Anderson **9.** Wisla Krakow **10.** Tele Santana **11.** Mickey Walsh **12.** Al Kuwait **13.** Osvaldo Ardiles **14.** Numancia **15.** Azerbaijan **16.** Boca Juniors

Oddballs 2

Answers on page 233

1. Which team's fans are 'forever blowing bubbles'?

2. 'Goodnight Irene' is the song of which club's supporters?

3. Which club's fans belt out a rousing chorus of 'Delilah'?

4. In 1998, which punk-loving England full-back introduced the Sex Pistols on stage?

5. Which club does Simple Minds frontman Jim Kerr support?

6. Whose fans sing 'No one likes us, we don't care' to the tune of 'Sailing'?

7. Which team recorded 'Blue is the Colour' in 1972?

8. Which Manchester band joined forces with the England World Cup Squad in 1990 for 'World in Motion'?

9. Who was Liverpool's main man rapper?

10. Which rock star teamed up with the 1978 Scotland World Cup Squad for 'Ole Ola'?

11. Which club's fans sing 'When the Saints Go Marching In'?

12. 'Glory, Glory Hallelujah' became the anthem of which team in the 1960s?

13. Which club's fans sing 'The Wheelbarrow Song'?

14. Which club's fans were the first to adopt 'You'll Never Walk Alone'?

15. Whose fans rejoiced in their ability to win 1–0?

16. Which team does Spice Girl Mel B support?

Answers to page 233
CRYSTAL PALACE 1: 1. Terry Venables 2. Jim Cannon 3. Alan Pardew
4. Villa Park 5. Mikael Forssell 6. 1969 7. Derby County 8. Stuart Hall
9. Peter Taylor 10. Juventus 11. Phil Hoadley 12. Peter Simpson 13. 1924
14. Everton 15. Valerien Ismael 16. None

The World Game 5

Answers on page 230

1. Who won the French Cup in 2000 and the League in 2001?

2. Which Norwegian played for a Spanish team in the 2001 UEFA Cup final?

3. And which former Manchester United player was a member of the same team?

4. Which Bulgarian team did the League and Cup double in 2000?

5. Viborg won which country's Cup competition in 2000?

6. In 1989, which club won the Italian League title for the first time in nine years?

7. Who were Italian League champions in 1970 for the only time in their history?

8. Which Lyon player was the leading marksman in the French League in season 2000–1?

9. Who won the Polish League in 2001?

10. Who was Brazil's coach at the 1982 World Cup?

11. Who was the first British footballer to join a Portuguese club?

12. In 2001, which club won the Kuwaiti League for the first time in 22 years?

13. Which former Newcastle United manager was sacked as boss of Japanese team Yokohama F Marinos in 2001?

14. Who finished bottom of Spain's top division in 2001?

15. Shafa won which country's Cup final in May 2001?

16. Which Argentinian team beat Cruz Azul 1–0 in the final of the 2001 Copa Libertadores?

Answers to page 230
BRAZIL 1: **1.** Honduras **2.** Romario **3.** Four **4.** Holland **5.** Australia
6. Emerson Leao **7.** Vava **8.** The Jules Rimet Trophy after winning their third
World Cup **9.** Pele **10.** Real Betis **11.** Zico **12.** Chile **13.** Roberto Rivelino
14. Hungary **15.** Uruguay **16.** Romario

Crystal Palace 1

Answers on page 231

1. Who returned as head coach of Crystal Palace in 1998, 18 years after the end of his previous reign?

2. Which defender made 571 League appearances for Palace from 1973 to 1988?

3. Which current Football League manager scored Palace's extra-time winner against Liverpool in the 1990 FA Cup semi-finals?

4. Where was that game played?

5. Which Chelsea striker was on loan at Selhurst Park in 2000–1?

6. In which year were Palace first promoted to the top division?

7. With which club were they promoted?

8. Which eccentric voice of radio sport once played for Palace Reserves in 1953?

9. Which current Premiership manager scored four goals in Palace's 1975–6 Cup run?

10. From which Italian club did Palace sign Attilio Lombardo and Michele Padovano?

11. Which 16-year-old made his Palace League debut against Bolton in 1968?

12. Who scored 46 League goals for Palace in 1930–1?

13. In which year did the club move to Selhurst Park?

14. Who did Palace beat 4–1 in the 1991 Zenith Data Systems Cup final?

15. For whom did Palace pay RC Strasbourg a club record £2.75 million in 1998?

16. How many of Palace's 1990 Cup final team were already full internationals?

Answers to page 231
ODDBALLS 2: 1. West Ham United 2. Bristol Rovers 3. Stoke City
4. Stuart Pearce 5. Celtic 6. Millwall 7. Chelsea 8. New Order 9. John
Barnes 10. Rod Stewart 11. Southampton 12. Spurs 13. Notts County
14. Liverpool 15. Arsenal 16. Leeds United

European Cups 1

Answers on page 236

1. Which French club – the only one to win the European Cup – were stripped of the crown in 1993?

2. Which Croatian team did Aston Villa beat in the InterToto Cup in July 2001?

3. Which Belgian team were beaten in the 1982 European Cup-Winners' Cup final?

4. Who defeated them?

5. Who won the 2001 Champions' League?

6. In which year was the European Cup final first played at Wembley?

7. Which two teams contested that final?

8. Who were the second English club to reach a European Cup final?

9. Which Welsh club have played most seasons in Europe?

10. Which two Italian teams fought out the 1995 UEFA Cup final?

11. Which Italian team lost the 1992 UEFA Cup final on the away goals rule?

12. In 1969, who became the first Czech team to reach the European Cup-Winners' Cup final?

13. Who did they beat 3–2 in the final?

14. In 1967–8, which Irish club were the first team to lose out in a European Cup tie on away goals?

15. Which Portuguese giants progressed at their expense?

16. Which Swiss team did Liverpool beat in the semi-finals of the 1977 European Cup?

Answers to page 236
HIBERNIAN 1: **1.** Alex McLeish **2.** John Leslie **3.** 'The Hibees' **4.** Easter Road **5.** Ecuadorian **6.** Pat Stanton **7.** Eddie Turnbull **8.** 1887 **9.** Dumbarton **10.** Celtic **11.** Steve Crawford **12.** Joe Baker **13.** Jim Duffy **14.** Four **15.** Rangers **16.** 1949

Norwich City 1

Answers on page 237

1. What is Norwich City's nickname?

2. Which television cook became a director of the club?

3. In which year did Norwich first reach the semi-finals of the FA Cup?

4. In which division were they playing at the time?

5. Who beat Norwich in the semi-finals of the FA Cup in 1989?

6. From which club did City sign Mark Bowen?

7. In which year were Norwich promoted to the top division for the first time?

8. Which defender, bought from Leeds in 1994, was Norwich's first million-pound signing?

9. Who scored 31 League goals for City in 1955–6?

10. Who were Norwich's three managers in 1995?

11. Who made 592 League appearances for the club from 1947 and became manager in 1962?

12. Who joined Norwich for £925,000 from Port Vale in 1991?

13. Which Scot did City sell to Chelsea for £2.1 million in 1992?

14. With which club did Iwan Roberts make his League debut?

15. In which year did Norwich move to Carrow Road?

16. Which former Northern Ireland boss was sacked as Norwich manager in 2000?

Answers to page 237
WHOSE HOME? 1: **1.** San Siro Stadium **2.** Montrose **3.** Hearts **4.** Swansea City **5.** Fir Park **6.** West Ham United **7.** Nottingham Forest **8.** Mansfield Town **9.** Chelsea **10.** Wimbledon **11.** Bristol Rovers **12.** Birmingham City **13.** Manchester United **14.** Tannadice Park (Dundee United) **15.** Dumbarton **16.** Abbey Stadium (Cambridge United)

Hibernian 1

Answers on page 234

1. Who was manager of Hibernian at the start of the 2001–2 season?

2. Which former *Blue Peter* presenter is a keen Hibernian fan?

3. What is Hibernian's nickname?

4. What is the name of their home ground?

5. What nationality is the club's record signing, Ulises de la Cruz?

6. Which Hibs' player was voted the Scottish Football Writers' Player of the Year in 1970?

7. Which future Hibs' manager made 348 League appearances for the club as a player?

8. In which year did Hibs first win the Scottish FA Cup?

9. Who did they beat in the final?

10. Who did Hibs defeat in the 1972–3 Scottish League Cup final?

11. Who was Hibs' top scorer in 1998–9?

12. Who scored 42 League goals for Hibs in 1959–60 before furthering his career in Italy and England?

13. Who followed Alex Miller as Hibs' manager?

14. How many times have Hibs been crowned Scottish League champions?

15. Who were runners-up to Hibs in their last three Championship years?

16. In which year did Lawrie Reilly win his first Scottish international cap?

Answers to page 234
EUROPEAN CUPS 1: **1.** Marseille **2.** Slaven Belupo **3.** Standard Liege
4. Barcelona **5.** Bayern Munich **6.** 1963 **7.** AC Milan and Benfica **8.** Leeds
United (in 1975) **9.** Cardiff City **10.** Parma and Juventus **11.** Torino
12. Slovan Bratislava **13.** Barcelona **14.** Glentoran **15.** Benfica **16.** Zurich

Whose Home? 1

Answers on page 235

1. Where do Inter Milan play?

2. Which Scottish club play at Links Park?

3. Who plays at Tynecastle?

4. Whose home ground is the Vetch Field?

5. Where do Motherwell play their home matches?

6. Who plays at Upton Park?

7. The City Ground is home to which First Division club?

8. Who plays at Field Mill?

9. Which London club play at Stamford Bridge?

10. Which club used to play at Plough Lane?

11. Whose home is the Memorial Ground?

12. Whose home is St Andrews?

13. Which Premiership club once had a home ground called Bank Street?

14. Which Scottish ground used to be called Clepington Park?

15. Which Scottish club first played at Boghead Park in 1879?

16. Which English League ground used to be called The Celery Trenches?

Answers to page 235
NORWICH CITY 1: **1.** 'The Canaries' **2.** Delia Smith **3.** 1959 **4.** Three **5.** Everton **6.** Tottenham Hotspur **7.** 1972 **8.** Jon Newsome **9.** Ralph Hunt **10.** John Deehan, Martin O'Neill and Gary Megson **11.** Ron Ashman **12.** Darren Beckford **13.** Robert Fleck **14.** Watford **15.** 1935 **16.** Bryan Hamilton

Coventry City 1

Answers on page 240

1. Who served as manager of Coventry City from 1972 to 1981?

2. Which tough-tackling centre-half made 486 League appearances for the Sky Blues from 1956 to 1970?

3. Who joined Coventry for £4 million from Deportivo La Coruña in 1999?

4. Who scored a record 171 League goals for Coventry from 1931 to 1937?

5. From which club did Coventry sign Steve Ogrizovic?

6. Who did Coventry beat in the semi-finals of the 1987 FA Cup?

7. Who scored City's goal in their 1–0 fourth-round victory at Old Trafford in 1987?

8. Which Welsh international was a member of City's 1987 Cup final team?

9. Who finished Third Division runners-up to City in 1964?

10. Which former England international became Coventry manager in 1990?

11. Who was Coventry's chairman prior to Mike McGinnity?

12. Which City forward of the 1990s won international caps for Zimbabwe?

13. Which Scottish international joined Coventry from Leeds for £3 million in 1996?

14. Which Welsh international forward joined Coventry from Norwich in 2000?

15. When did Gordon Strachan become City manager?

16. How many League games did Darren Huckerby play for Newcastle before going to Coventry?

Answers to page 240
NAME THE YEAR 2: **1.** 1953 **2.** 1968 **3.** 1954 **4.** 1967 (Celtic) **5.** 1996
6. 1999 **7.** 1989 (Littlewoods Cup and Simod Cup) **8.** 1995 **9.** 1949
10. 1891 **11.** 1930 **12.** 1892 **13.** 1992 **14.** 1888 **15.** 1982 **16.** 1961

Goalkeepers 1

Answers on page 241

1. Which Australian goalkeeper moved from Manchester United to Chelsea in 2001?

2. Ricardo Tavarelli and Aldo Bobadilla were the goalkeepers in which country's squad for the 2001 Copa America?

3. For which country does Middlesbrough's Mark Schwarzer play?

4. Which goalkeeper saved three penalties in the shoot-out at the 2001 Champions' League final?

5. Who started his playing career with Chesterfield in 1955 and went on to win 73 England caps?

6. Which two goalkeepers have captained Italy to victory in the World Cup?

7. For which club side were they both playing at the time?

8. Who was Argentina's goalkeeper in the 1990 World Cup final?

9. For which Italian club does Brazil's international keeper Dida play?

10. What nationality is Preston keeper Teuvo Moilanen?

11. Steve Phillips was the regular goalkeeper for which Second Division team in 2000–1?

12. For which country has Bernard Lama played international football?

13. Which Canadian keeper is on West Ham's books?

14. Who kept goal for Northern Ireland in their World Cup qualifier away to the Czech Republic in June 2001?

15. In which year did Peter Shilton win his record-breaking 109th cap for England?

16. Who were England's opponents in that game?

Answers to page 241
PREMIERSHIP 3: **1.** Newcastle United **2.** One **3.** Coventry City **4.** Jimmy Floyd Hasselbaink **5.** 23 **6.** James Beattie **7.** Charlton Athletic **8.** Tottenham Hotspur **9.** Stanic **10.** Leicester City **11.** Arsenal **12.** Alex Rae **13.** Graeme Le Saux **14.** Chelsea **15.** Claudio Ranieri **16.** George Boateng

Name the Year 2

Answers on page 238

1. In which year was the 'Matthews Cup final'?

2. In which year did Manchester United first win the European Cup?

3. When was the World Cup staged in Switzerland?

4. When did a British team first contest the World Club Cup final?

5. In which year did Manchester United become the first English club to do the double twice?

6. In which year did France gain their first victory at Wembley?

7. In which year did Nottingham Forest become the first team to win two Wembley finals in the same season?

8. When did Bolton Wanderers reach their first League Cup final?

9. When did Yeovil Town famously knock Sunderland out of the FA Cup?

10. When did Everton win their first League Championship?

11. When was the first World Cup?

12. When were Liverpool FC founded?

13. In which year did Aldershot drop out of the Football League?

14. In which year was the Football League formed?

15. When did Kevin Keegan win his last England cap?

16. When did Denis Law score six goals in an FA Cup tie, only for the match to be abandoned?

Answers to page 238
COVENTRY CITY 1: **1.** Gordon Milne **2.** George Curtis **3.** Mustapha Hadji **4.** Clarrie Bourton **5.** Shrewsbury Town **6.** Leeds United **7.** Keith Houchen **8.** David Phillips **9.** Crystal Palace **10.** Terry Butcher **11.** Bryan Richardson **12.** Peter Ndlovu **13.** Gary McAllister **14.** Craig Bellamy **15.** 1996 **16.** One

Premiership 3

Answers on page 239

1. Defeat at Charlton in February 2001 extended which team's run without a win in London to 25 matches?

2. How many home League games did Arsenal lose in 2000–1?

3. Who were relegated in 2001 after losing 3–2 at Aston Villa?

4. Who was the top Premiership scorer in 2000–1?

5. How many goals did he get?

6. Who was Southampton's leading scorer for 2000–1?

7. Who signed England Under-21 defender Luke Young from Tottenham for £3 million in July 2001?

8. Yugoslav Goran Bunjevcevic joined which Premiership team in 2001?

9. Which Mario is Chelsea's Croatian midfielder?

10. Tony Cottee was which club's leading Premiership goalscorer in 1999–2000?

11. Who won the 1999 FA Charity Shield?

12. Which Sunderland midfielder was admitted to a clinic in 1998 for alcohol-related reasons?

13. Which Chelsea player clashed with Liverpool's Robbie Fowler in 1999?

14. Which London club did French defender William Gallas join in summer 2001?

15. Who succeeded Gianluca Vialli as Chelsea manager?

16. Which Dutch midfielder did Aston Villa sign from Coventry in 2000?

Answers to page 239
GOALKEEPERS 1: 1. Mark Bosnich 2. Paraguay 3. Australia 4. Oliver Kahn
5. Gordon Banks 6. Gianpiero Combi (1934) and Dino Zoff (1982)
7. Juventus 8. Sergio Goycochea 9. Milan 10. Finnish 11. Bristol City
12. France 13. Craig Forrest 14. Maik Taylor 15. 1989 16. Denmark

Arsenal 1

Answers on page 244

1. Who moved to Highbury in 1976 and scored 42 League goals in 84 games for the Gunners before retiring through injury?

2. Which London club knocked Arsenal out of the FA Cup in 1989?

3. Which were the only teams to win at Highbury in the League during season 1997–8?

4. In 1970, which tournament gave Arsenal their first major trophy for 17 years?

5. Who was captain of Arsenal's 1971 'double' team?

6. Who joined Arsenal from Southampton in 1934 and went on to score 136 goals for the Gunners?

7. From which club did Arsenal sign Perry Groves?

8. Which Arsenal striker moved to Anfield in 1974 as Bill Shankly's last purchase for Liverpool?

9. Which full-back joined Arsenal from Huddersfield Town in 1966?

10. Which Arsenal manager signed David Platt?

11. In which year did Ian Wright make his Arsenal debut?

12. Who was Arsenal's top scorer in 2000–1?

13. What nationality was Anders Limpar?

14. Who scored Arsenal's goal in the 2001 FA Cup final?

15. Who kept goal for Arsenal in the 1930 FA Cup final?

16. Which Scottish international inside-forward joined Arsenal from Preston in 1929 and won four League Championships and two FA Cups at Highbury?

Answers to page 244
NON-LEAGUE 1: 1. Hayes 2. Kidderminster Harriers 3. Lancaster City
4. Cheltenham Town 5. Kettering Town 6. Scarborough 7. Ryman Premier
8. St Albans City 9. Altrincham 10. Boreham Wood 11. Watford
12. Unibond Premier League 13. Nuneaton Borough 14. Matthew Hanlan
15. Ricky George 16. Bishop Auckland

European Cups 2

Answers on page 245

1. In 2000, who became the first Turkish club to win a European trophy?
2. Who did they beat in a penalty shoot-out in that year's UEFA Cup final?
3. Which ex-Tottenham defender converted the Turks' match-winning penalty?
4. Which Spanish club did Bayern Munich defeat in the semi-finals of the 2001 Champions' League?
5. And which Spanish team did they beat in the final?
6. Which Scottish team did Leeds beat in the semis of the 1968 UEFA Cup?
7. In which city did Everton win the 1985 European Cup-Winners' Cup final?
8. Which English side did Nottingham Forest knock out of the 1978–9 European Cup?
9. Which Northern Ireland team were Liverpool's first European Cup victims in the 1977–8 competition?
10. Which Arsenal striker missed the 1994 European Cup-Winners' Cup final through suspension?
11. Which Turkish side stunned Manchester City in the first round of the 1968–9 European Cup?
12. Who went on to win the 1986 UEFA Cup despite losing 5–1 away to Borussia Moenchengladbach in the first leg of their third-round tie?
13. Which team had to take part in a European Cup play-off against Leeds in 1992 because they had exceeded the number of permitted 'foreigners'?
14. Who scored 15 goals for Bayern Munich in their 1995–6 UEFA Cup run?
15. Which was the only East German team to win the Cup-Winners' Cup?
16. Who did they beat 2–0 in the 1974 final?

Answers to page 245
ODDBALLS 3: **1.** Kidderminster Harriers **2.** Kilmarnock **3.** Total Network Solutions **4.** Glentoran **5.** Linfield **6.** Shelbourne **7.** Bournemouth **8.** Ayr United **9.** Sunderland **10.** Lazio **11.** RC Strasbourg **12.** Bill Nicholson (Spurs, 1961) and Alf Ramsey (Ipswich Town, 1962) **13.** Graham Kelly **14.** Millwall **15.** Queens Park Rangers **16.** Bert Trautmann (1956)

Non-League 1

Answers on page 242

1. Which Conference club used to be known as Botwell Mission?

2. Ian Foster's goals in 1999–2000 helped which Conference club gain Football League status?

3. Which Unibond team play at the Giant Axe?

4. Who won the Conference in 1999?

5. Who finished Conference runners-up in 1999 but were relegated from it two years later?

6. Which Conference team play at the McCain Stadium?

7. In what League do Aldershot currently play?

8. Which Hertfordshire club's plans to redevelop their ground in the 1990s foundered because of an ancient oak tree behind one goal?

9. Which Northern Premier League side held Everton to a draw at Goodison Park in the third round of the 1974–5 FA Cup?

10. Which Ryman League club were formed in 1948 following a merger of a local team and the exotically named Royal Retournez?

11. Who beat Harlow Town 4–3 in a 1980 fourth-round FA Cup tie?

12. In which League do Barrow play?

13. Who won the Dr Martens League Premier Division in 1999?

14. Who scored Sutton United's winner in their 1989 FA Cup giant-killing of Coventry City?

15. Which substitute scored Hereford United's Cup winner against Newcastle in 1972?

16. Which Northern Leaguers beat Ipswich Town 3–0 in the FA Cup in 1955?

Answers to page 242
ARSENAL 1: **1.** Malcolm Macdonald **2.** West Ham United **3.** Liverpool and Blackburn **4.** European Fairs (UEFA) Cup **5.** Frank McLintock **6.** Ted Drake **7.** Colchester United **8.** Ray Kennedy **9.** Bob McNab **10.** Bruce Rioch **11.** 1991 **12.** Thierry Henry **13.** Swedish **14.** Freddy Ljungberg **15.** Charlie Preedy **16.** Alex James

Oddballs 3

Answers on page 243

1. Which Midlands team were originally formed to play rugby?

2. And which west of Scotland club were so accustomed to rugby that outfield players kept picking the ball up during early soccer matches?

3. Which snappily named outfit won the League of Wales in 2000?

4. Who won the Irish Cup four years in a row from 1985 to 1988?

5. Who captured the Northern Irish League in 2000?

6. Which Republic of Ireland team did the Irish League and Cup 'double' in 2000?

7. In 1961 which English seaside club's first game under floodlights was delayed for an hour after the lights failed just before kick-off?

8. Jimmy Smith scored a record 66 Scottish League goals for which club in 1927–8?

9. Which Premiership club used to play at Blue House Field, Hendon?

10. For which Italian club did Marcelo Salas play in 2000–1?

11. Which club finished bottom of the French League in 2001?

12. Which two members of Spurs' 1951 League Championship side went on to manage League Championship-winning teams?

13. Who resigned as chief executive of the FA in 1998?

14. Whose 2–0 victory at Nottingham Forest in 1994 made them the first team to win a League Cup tie at the City Ground for 18 years?

15. In 1908, which London club contested the first-ever FA Charity Shield?

16. Who was the first foreign player to be voted Footballer of the Year?

Answers to page 243
EUROPEAN CUPS 2: 1. Galatasaray 2. Arsenal 3. Gheorghe Popescu
4. Real Madrid 5. Valencia 6. Dundee 7. Rotterdam 8. Liverpool
9. Crusaders 10. Ian Wright 11. Fenerbahce 12. Real Madrid 13. VfB
Stuttgart 14. Jürgen Klinsmann 15. Magdeburg 16. AC Milan

Wimbledon 1

Answers on page 248

1. Who scored 145 League goals for Wimbledon from 1977 to 1992?

2. Which manager took the Dons into the Football League?

3. Who replaced him a year later?

4. Who were Wimbledon's first victims in their epic 1988 Cup run?

5. Who did Wimbledon buy from Port Vale for £775,000 in 1991?

6. From which non-League club did Jon Goodman enter League football?

7. Which full-back did Wimbledon sell to Newcastle for £4 million in 1995?

8. In which year did the Dons gain promotion from Division Four?

9. Behind whom were they Third Division runners-up the following year?

10. Of Wimbledon's starting line-up at the 1988 FA Cup final, who was the only international?

11. And for which country had he been capped?

12. From which club did Wimbledon sign Gareth Ainsworth?

13. Which Brentford forward moved to Wimbledon after making 156 League appearances for the Bees?

14. Who scored Wimbledon's first FA Cup goal as a Football League club?

15. Who were Wimbledon's first opponents in a Football League match?

16. When did Joe Kinnear become Wimbledon manager?

Answers to page 248
MANAGERS 4: **1.** Marseille **2.** 1974 **3.** Roy Hodgson **4.** Aberdeen **5.** Uganda **6.** Bristol City **7.** John Reames **8.** Sunderland and Liverpool **9.** Willie Bell **10.** FC Porto **11.** Bertie Mee **12.** Jimmy McIlroy **13.** San Lorenzo **14.** Northampton Town **15.** Joe Mercer **16.** Danny Wilson

Whose Home? 2

Answers on page 249

1. Which Scottish League club play at Balmoor Stadium?

2. Thousands of worms were scattered on which Football League ground in 1999–2000 in an effort to improve the pitch?

3. Where do Hednesford Town play?

4. Which Scottish team play at Dens Park?

5. Whose home is Saltergate?

6. Christie Park is the home ground of which Conference team?

7. Which Scottish team play at the Shyberry Excelsior Stadium?

8. Which Ryman League team play at Clarence Park?

9. In which city is the Azadi Stadium?

10. Which English League club play at Vale Park?

11. Craven Cottage is home to which club?

12. Which Conference club play at The Lawn?

13. Where do Farnborough Town play their home games?

14. Which Scottish club used to play at Broomfield Park?

15. In which country is the Castelao Stadium?

16. What is the name of Elgin City's home ground?

Answers to page 249
EVERTON 1: 1. Duncan Ferguson 2. Aston Villa 3. Bill Kenwright 4. Graeme Sharp and Andy Gray 5. Gary Lineker 6. Francis Jeffers 7. 1998 8. Partick Thistle 9. Tommy Wright 10. George Wood 11. Four 12. Kevin Ratcliffe 13. Derek Temple 14. Kevin Sheedy 15. Bob Latchford 16. University College Dublin

Managers 4

Answers on page 246

1. Tomislav Ivic resigned as coach of which French club in July 2001?

2. In which year did Bill Nicholson step down as Tottenham manager?

3. Who succeeded Ray Harford as Blackburn Rovers' boss in 1997?

4. Ebbe Skovdahl was manager of which Scottish club in 2000–1?

5. Harrison Okagbue was fired as coach of which African country following a 2001 Nations Cup defeat by Togo?

6. Russell Osman was player/manager of which English League club from 1993–4?

7. Which Lincoln City chairman took on the dual role of manager in November 1998?

8. Which two clubs did Tom Watson steer to the League Championship?

9. Which Lincoln City boss resigned in 1978 to join an American religious sect?

10. Which Portuguese club did Tommy Docherty manage?

11. Which double-winning manager's playing career was restricted to a brief spell as a winger with Mansfield Town before retiring through injury at 27?

12. Who was manager of Bolton Wanderers for 16 days in 1970?

13. Oscar Ruggeri resigned as coach of which Argentine club in 2001?

14. Kevin Wilson was manager of which League club in 2000–1?

15. Who won three League Championships as a player with Everton and Arsenal (twice) before managing Manchester City to the title?

16. Which former Barnsley boss became manager of Bristol City in 2000?

Answers to page 246
WIMBLEDON 1: **1.** Alan Cork **2.** Allen Batsford **3.** Dario Gradi **4.** West Bromwich Albion **5.** Robbie Earle **6.** Bromley **7.** Warren Barton **8.** 1983 **9.** Oxford United **10.** Lawrie Sanchez **11.** Northern Ireland **12.** Port Vale **13.** Marcus Gayle **14.** Alan Cork **15.** Halifax Town **16.** 1992

Everton 1

Answers on page 247

1. Which striker joined Everton from Rangers for £4 million in 1994?

2. Who beat Everton in the 1977 League Cup final?

3. Which former *Coronation Street* actor bought the club?

4. Who were Everton's two goalscorers in the 1984 FA Cup final victory over Watford?

5. Who put Everton ahead in the 1986 Cup final against Liverpool?

6. Which forward did Everton sell to Arsenal in summer 2001?

7. In which year did Walter Smith become manager?

8. From which Scottish club did Everton sign Sandy Brown?

9. Which Everton defender gave away two first-minute own goals within the space of four days in 1972?

10. Which goalkeeper signed from Blackpool in the 1970s went on to win four caps for Scotland?

11. How many times did Everton reach the FA Cup final in the 1980s?

12. Who was captain on each occasion?

13. Who famously profited from Gerry Young's clanger to win the Cup for Everton?

14. Who was Everton's leading scorer with four goals in their 1985 FA Cup run?

15. Which Everton and former Birmingham City striker won the first of his 12 England caps in 1978?

16. Against which Irish part-timers did Everton scrape through 1–0 on aggregate before going on to win the 1984–5 European Cup-Winners' Cup?

Answers to page 247
WHOSE HOME? 2: **1.** Peterhead **2.** Feethams (Darlington) **3.** Keys Park
4. Dundee **5.** Chesterfield **6.** Morecambe **7.** Airdrie **8.** St Albans City
9. Tehran **10.** Port Vale **11.** Fulham **12.** Forest Green Rovers
13. Cherrywood Road **14.** Airdrie **15.** Brazil **16.** Borough Briggs

Who Said That? 2

Answers on page 252

1. Which noted angler said in 1993: 'If Kevin Keegan fell into the Tyne, he'd come up with a salmon in his mouth'?

2. Of which legendary manager did Graeme Souness say: 'He ruled with a rod of iron, an iron fist without a velvet glove'?

3. Which fellow manager called Sir Alf Ramsey 'a stubborn bugger'?

4. Who did Bob Stokoe want castrating 'for the way he left England'?

5. Of which rival manager did Kenny Dalglish say in 1988: 'You might as well talk to my (baby) daughter. You'll get more sense out of her'?

6. Who described Kenny Dalglish as 'the moaningest minnie I've ever known'?

7. Who said of his shock 1974 resignation: 'When I went to see the chairman to tell him, it was like walking to the electric chair'?

8. Who said of his time at Rotherham: 'I made a promise to the chairman that I would take the club out of the Second Division. I did. I took it straight into the Third'?

9. Who said of Jimmy Hill: 'If there's a prat in the world, he's the prat'?

10. Which German national coach lamented in 1996: 'If I walked on water, my accusers would say it is because I can't swim'?

11. Who said he was looking forward to seeing 'some sexy football'?

12. Who said: 'Football is a simple game and should be kept simple'?

13. Who said in 1970: 'We have nothing to learn from Brazil'?

14. Who said: 'If Everton were playing in my garden, I'd draw the curtains'?

15. Which Aston Villa boss said in 1994: 'It looks as though we are going to be happy just to stay on the same page of Ceefax as Manchester United'?

Answers to page 252
ITALY 1: 1. Austria 2. Toto Schillaci 3. Paolo Rossi 4. 1974 5. Giovanni Trapattoni 6. USSR 7. Norway 8. Giacinto Facchetti 9. Argentina 10. South Korea 11. Middlesbrough (Ayresome Park) 12. Chile 13. West Germany 14. Russia 15. Paolo Maldini 16. 1986

Transfer Trail 2

Answers on page 253

1. Which Bradford City forward joined Newcastle for £500,000 in 1988?

2. Which Norwegian defender moved to Blackburn from Old Trafford for £1.75 million?

3. Which international defender did Coventry buy from Rangers for £450,000 in 1990?

4. Which Dutchman joined Arsenal from Rangers in summer 2001?

5. From which Portuguese club did Middlesbrough sign Emerson?

6. Which Brazilian defender joined Arsenal from Corinthians for £4 million in 1999?

7. Which Queens Park Rangers striker joined Kilmarnock in summer 2001?

8. Which England goalkeeper did Arsenal sign in summer 2001?

9. Who did Everton sell to Lens for £6.5 million in 1999?

10. Which German international moved from Newcastle to Liverpool for £8 million in summer 1999?

11. Which striker joined Nottingham Forest from Millwall for £2 million in 1991?

12. Which Cameroon star did West Ham sign from Lens for £3.5 million in 1999?

13. From which club did Huddersfield Town sign Kenny Irons?

14. With which club did Des Lyttle make his League debut?

15. Which was Marco Gabbiadini's first League club?

16. Which Croatian defender moved from West Ham to Everton for £4.5 million in 1997?

Answers to page 253
DUNFERMLINE ATHLETIC 1: **1.** 1962–3 **2.** Valencia **3.** Norrie McCathie **4.** 1968 **5.** Hearts **6.** Istvan Kozma **7.** Celtic **8.** Jim Leishman **9.** 1968–9 **10.** Slovan Bratislava **11.** Hibernian **12.** Charlie Dickson **13.** Bobby Robertson **14.** Black and white stripes **15.** Bobby Skinner **16.** Charlie Dickson

Italy 1

Answers on page 250

1. Who were Italy's first opponents at the 1990 World Cup finals?

2. Which substitute scored Italy's winning goal in that match?

3. Whose hat-trick put Brazil out of the 1982 World Cup?

4. When did Italy last fail to progress beyond the first round in the World Cup finals?

5. Who is Italy's coach for the 2002 World Cup finals?

6. Who knocked Italy out of the 1964 European Championship?

7. Defeat by which country eliminated Italy from the 1992 European Championship?

8. Who was Italy's captain at the 1970 World Cup?

9. Who topped Italy's first-round group at the 1978 World Cup finals?

10. Who were the only team Italy beat in that group?

11. On whose ground did Italy lose 1–0 to North Korea at the 1966 World Cup finals?

12. Which country beat Italy in the group matches at the 1962 World Cup finals?

13. Who did Italy defeat 4–3 in the semi-finals of the 1970 World Cup?

14. Who did Italy beat in a play-off to reach the 1998 World Cup finals?

15. Who captained Italy at the 1998 World Cup?

16. In which year did Paolo Rossi play his last international?

Answers to page 250
WHO SAID THAT? 2: **1.** Jack Charlton **2.** Jock Stein **3.** Brian Clough **4.** Don Revie **5.** Sir Alex Ferguson **6.** John Bond **7.** Bill Shankly **8.** Tommy Docherty **9.** Sir Alex Ferguson **10.** Berti Vogts **11.** Ruud Gullit **12.** Bill Shankly **13.** Sir Alf Ramsey **14.** Bill Shankly **15.** Ron Atkinson

Dunfermline Athletic 1

Answers on page 251

1. In which season's Fairs Cup were Dunfermline eliminated despite winning the second leg 6–2?

2. Who were their opponents?

3. Who made 497 League appearances for the club between 1981 and 1996?

4. When did Dunfermline last reach the Scottish FA Cup final?

5. Who did they beat 3–1 on that occasion?

6. Which Hungarian forward joined Dunfermline in 1989?

7. Who defeated Dunfermline in the 1965 Scottish Cup final?

8. Which larger-than-life manager began Dunfermline's revival in the 1980s?

9. In which season did Dunfermline reach the semi-finals of the European Cup-Winners' Cup?

10. Which eventual winners of the competition knocked out Dunfermline 2–1 on aggregate?

11. Who beat Dunfermline in the 1991–2 Scottish League Cup final?

12. Who scored 154 League goals for the club from 1955 to 1964?

13. Who made 360 League appearances for Dunfermline between 1977 and 1988?

14. In what colour shirts do Dunfermline play?

15. Who scored 53 League goals for Dunfermline in 1925–6?

16. Who scored Dunfermline's second goal in their 2–0 win over Celtic in the 1961 Scottish FA Cup final replay?

Answers to page 251
TRANSFER TRAIL 2: **1.** John Hendrie **2.** Henning Berg **3.** Terry Butcher **4.** Giovanni van Bronckhorst **5.** FC Porto **6.** Silvinho **7.** Michel Ngonge **8.** Richard Wright **9.** Olivier Dacourt **10.** Dietmar Hamann **11.** Teddy Sheringham **12.** Marc-Vivien Foe **13.** Tranmere Rovers **14.** Swansea City **15.** York City **16.** Slaven Bilic

Premiership 4

Answers on page 256

1. Which Northern Ireland international goalkeeper did Manchester United buy in summer 2001?

2. Who led 3–0 at Leeds after 33 minutes in November 1997 but ended up losing 4–3 to a last-minute goal?

3. Which 17-year-old netted for Spurs against Everton in 1992 to become the youngest Premiership scorer?

4. Which club conceded just four home League goals in 1994–5?

5. Which club lost eight Premiership games on the trot in 1998–9?

6. From which club did Derby County sign Igor Stimac?

7. From which non-League club did Matt Elliott enter League football?

8. Behind Arsenal, which club have the longest current unbroken run in the top division?

9. Who became Britain's costliest goalkeeper in 1993 after his £2 million move from Southampton to Blackburn?

10. Which Manchester United player was sent off in two successive matches in March 1994?

11. Who beat Liverpool at Anfield in 1994 in the last match for standing spectators on the Kop?

12. Who avoided Premiership relegation on goal difference in 1992–3?

13. Who lost 13 home games to finish bottom of the Premiership in 1994–5?

14. From which French club did Arsenal sign Gilles Grimandi?

15. With which country is Leicester's Muzzy Izzet an international?

16. Which goalkeeper moved from Liverpool to Millwall in 1999?

Answers to page 256
GRIMSBY TOWN 1: 1. 1939 2. Wolverhampton Wanderers
3. Northampton Town 4. Kevin Donovan 5. Chelsea 6. Blackburn Rovers
7. Keith Jobling 8. Alan Buckley 9. Bournemouth 10. Shaun Cunnington
11. Sheffield United 12. Arsenal 13. Pat Glover 14. Wales 15. Lee Ashcroft
16. Bill Shankly

Scottish Scene 2

Answers on page 257

1. Which club lost two Cup finals in 1999–2000?

2. Who beat them in the Scottish League Cup final?

3. And who beat the same team in the Scottish FA Cup final?

4. Who won the Third Division title in 2000, only to be relegated the following year?

5. Who Joined Rangers from Hamburg for £4 million in 1996 and was the top scorer at Ibrox in 1999–2000?

6. Which club won all 18 League games in 1898–9?

7. Which Celtic player was sent off in the 1984 Scottish FA Cup final?

8. Who was the first player to score 200 goals in the Premier Division?

9. Who scored five times for Dundee United against Morton in 1984?

10. What was introduced to the Scottish Premier Division in January 1999?

11. Who were Second Division champions in 1999–2000?

12. Which club's only Scottish FA Cup triumph came in 1922?

13. For which club did Alec Hair score 41 First Division goals in 1926–7?

14. For whom did Tony Fitzpatrick make 351 League appearances from 1973 to 1988?

15. Which club sold Kevin McAllister to Chelsea for £225,000 in 1991?

16. Billy Little, John Brownlie and Hugh McCann have all managed which Scottish League club?

Answers to page 257
EUROPEAN CUPS 3: **1.** NK Maribor **2.** Rangers **3.** Sporting Lisbon **4.** José Altafini **5.** Ajax **6.** Villa Park **7.** Marseille **8.** Trelleborgs **9.** Celtic **10.** Roma **11.** Johan Cruyff **12.** Sampdoria **13.** Alfredo di Stefano **14.** Benfica **15.** Nottingham Forest **16.** Wembley

Grimsby Town 1

Answers on page 254

1. When did Grimsby last reach the semi-finals of the FA Cup?

2. To whom did they lose 5–0 in the semi-final in that year?

3. Who did Grimsby beat in the 1998 Second Division play-off final?

4. Who scored the Mariners' winning goal?

5. From which club did Grimsby sign Steve Livingstone?

6. Who finished Third Division runners-up to Grimsby in 1980?

7. Who made 448 League appearances for Grimsby from 1953 to 1969?

8. Who was Grimsby manager from 1988 to 1994 and returned for a second spell in 1997?

9. Who did Grimsby overcome 2–1 in the 1998 Auto Windscreens final?

10. Which midfielder did Grimsby sell to Sunderland for £650,000 in 1992?

11. From which club did Grimsby sign Clive Mendonca?

12. Who beat Grimsby in the 1936 FA Cup semi-finals?

13. Who scored 42 League goals for the Mariners in 1933–4?

14. For which country did he win seven international caps?

15. Who did Grimsby sign from Preston for £400,000 in 1998?

16. Which managerial great spent two years in charge of Grimsby, from 1951 to 1953?

Answers to page 254
PREMIERSHIP 4: 1. Roy Carroll 2. Derby County 3. Andy Turner
4. Manchester United 5. Charlton Athletic 6. Hajduk Split 7. Epsom & Ewell
8. Everton (since 1954) 9. Tim Flowers 10. Eric Cantona 11. Norwich City
12. Oldham Athletic 13. Ipswich Town 14. Monaco 15. Turkey 16. Tony Warner

European Cups 3

Answers on page 255

1. Which Slovenian team did Rangers play in a Champions' League second qualifying round tie in July 2001?

2. Which Scottish team did Spurs defeat 8–4 on aggregate on their way to winning the 1963 European Cup-Winners' Cup?

3. Which Portuguese side routed Appel Nicosia 16–1 in the first leg of a 1963–4 European Cup-Winners' Cup tie?

4. Which AC Milan player scored eight times against US Luxembourg in a 1962–3 European Cup tie?

5. Who did Arsenal beat in the semi-finals of the 1970 UEFA Cup?

6. Which English ground staged the 1999 European Cup-Winners' Cup final?

7. Which French club lost 3–0 to Parma in the 1998–9 UEFA Cup final?

8. Which Scandinavian minnows ousted big-spending Blackburn in the first round of the 1994–5 UEFA Cup?

9. Which Scottish club crashed out of the 1964 Cup-Winners' Cup to MTK Budapest after winning the first leg 3–0?

10. Which Italian club knocked Leeds out of the 1998–9 UEFA Cup?

11. Who coached Barcelona to their 1992 European Cup triumph?

12. Which Italian team did Barcelona beat in the final?

13. Who is the only player to have scored in five successive European Cup finals?

14. Who were the first team to beat Real Madrid in a major European final?

15. Which English club did Anderlecht beat in the 1984 UEFA Cup semi-finals?

16. In which stadium did Manchester United win the 1968 European Cup?

Answers to page 255
SCOTTISH SCENE 2: 1. Aberdeen 2. Celtic 3. Rangers 4. Queen's Park
5. Jörg Albertz 6. Rangers 7. Roy Aitken 8. Ally McCoist 9. Paul Sturrock
10. A three-week winter shutdown 11. Clyde 12. Morton 13. Partick
Thistle 14. St Mirren 15. Falkirk 16. East Stirlingshire

FA Cup 2

Answers on page 260

1. Who were the last team to retain the FA Cup?

2. Who were the last Fourth Division club to reach the quarter-finals of the Cup?

3. Which team won the FA Cup in 1901 when still in the Southern League?

4. Which Third Division team knocked Arsenal out of the Cup in 1965?

5. Who was the first player to lose Wembley FA Cup finals with three different clubs?

6. In which year was a Cup semi-final first played at Wembley?

7. Which two London teams were involved in that match?

8. Which team – no relation to a present League club of the same name – entered the very first FA Cup in 1871?

9. Which 1980s Cup winners did so without a solitary Englishman in their final line-up?

10. Who captained Southampton's 1976 Cup-winning team?

11. Which 1999 FA Cup tie was replayed following a controversial goal?

12. Who was the only 20th-century player to pick up four FA Cup-winners' medals?

13. Who is the only player to have captained Scottish and English FA Cup-winning teams?

14. Which manager took Everton to the 1995 Cup final?

15. Who is the only player to earn FA Cup-winners' medals either side of the Second World War?

16. What was special about the 1986–7 FA Cup quarter-finals?

Answers to page 260
EUROPEAN CHAMPIONSHIP 3: **1.** Romania **2.** 1992 **3.** Hungary **4.** Ronnie Whelan **5.** Florence **6.** Tony Woodcock **7.** Spain **8.** France, Italy, Portugal and Holland **9.** Patrick Kluivert and Savo Milosevic **10.** Peter Schmeichel **11.** Spain **12.** Czechoslovakia **13.** Turkey **14.** Denmark **15.** Karel Poborsky **16.** Dennis Bergkamp and Glenn Helder

Manchester United 2

Answers on page 261

1. Who led out the United team at the 1958 FA Cup final?

2. In their Cup-winning season of 1963, what position did United finish in the First Division?

3. On whose ground did United clinch the 1967 League Championship with a 6–1 win?

4. Which goalkeeper ended his United career with the 'treble' in 1999?

5. Which unsung hero destroyed Benfica in the 1968 European Cup final with a brilliant display on the left-wing?

6. Who scored Benfica's goal in that final?

7. And who scored twice for United?

8. Who scored 32 League goals for United in 1959–60?

9. From which club did United sign Quinton Fortune?

10. Which goalkeeper returned to Old Trafford in 1999?

11. Which £40,000 buy from Tranmere made his United debut as a substitute against Cardiff City in 1975?

12. Which experienced Scot was Tommy Docherty's first signing for United?

13. Which United manager signed Ray Wilkins?

14. Against which club did Bobby Charlton make his final League appearance for United in 1973?

15. Who was the first United player to pick up three FA Cup-winners' medals?

16. On whose ground did Steve Bruce make his United debut in 1987?

Answers to page 261
NICKNAMES 1: 1. Emile Heskey 2. Tony Brown 3. Dundee 4. Dennis Bergkamp 5. Ian Hamilton 6. Ron Harris 7. Reading 8. Dunfermline Athletic 9. Malcolm Macdonald 10. 'The Pitmen' 11. Preston North End 12. Teddy Sheringham 13. Leyton Orient 14. Halifax Town 15. Brighton & Hove Albion 16. 'The Cherries'

European Championship 3

Answers on page 258

1. Against whom did San Marino score their first goal in the European Championship?

2. In which year did Scotland reach the final stages for the first time?

3. Who finished third in the 1964 tournament?

4. Who scored the Republic of Ireland's goal in the 1–1 draw with USSR at the 1988 finals?

5. In which city did England lose to Yugoslavia in the semi-finals of the 1968 tournament?

6. Who scored England's winning goal against Spain at the 1980 finals?

7. Which country defeated Denmark on penalties in the semi-finals of the 1984 European Championship?

8. Who were the four semi-finalists at Euro 2000?

9. Which two players were joint top scorers at Euro 2000?

10. Who was Denmark's goalkeeper in the 1992 final?

11. Which country withdrew from the quarter-finals in 1960 after political pressure, allowing the USSR a walk over into the last four?

12. Who topped England's qualifying group for the 1976 tournament?

13. Who did Portugal beat in the quarter-finals of Euro 2000?

14. Which country failed to score at Euro 2000?

15. Whose spectacular chip against Portugal at Euro 96 won him a move to Old Trafford and earned the Czech Republic a place in the semi-finals?

16. Which two Arsenal players were in the Dutch squad for Euro 96?

Answers to page 258
FA CUP 2: 1. Tottenham Hotspur (1982) 2. Cambridge United (1990) 3. Tottenham Hotspur 4. Peterborough United 5. John Barnes (Watford 1984, Liverpool 1988 and 1996, Newcastle United, 1998) 6. 1991 7. Tottenham and Arsenal 8. Crystal Palace 9. Liverpool (1986) 10. Peter Rodrigues 11. Arsenal v Sheffield United 12. Mark Hughes 13. Martin Buchan (Aberdeen 1970 and Manchester United 1977) 14. Joe Royle 15. Raich Carter (Sunderland 1937 and Derby County 1946) 16. For the first time, all were won by the away team

Nicknames 1

Answers on page 259

1. Which powerful Liverpool striker is known as 'Bruno'?

2. Which West Bromwich Albion forward of the 1970s was nicknamed 'Bomber'?

3. Which Scottish club are called 'The Dark Blues'?

4. Which Arsenal player is known as 'The Ice Man'?

5. Which Chelsea and Aston Villa forward of the 1960s was known as 'Chico'?

6. 'Chopper' was the nickname of which tough-tackling Chelsea defender?

7. Who are 'The Royals'?

8. Which Scottish club are nicknamed 'The Pars'?

9. Which 1970s striker was known as 'Supermac'?

10. What is the nickname of Hednesford Town?

11. Which Lancashire club are called 'The Lilywhites'?

12. Which Premiership striker have fans christened 'Superted'?

13. Who are 'The O's'?

14. Who are known as 'The Shaymen' in honour of their ground?

15. Who are 'The Seagulls'?

16. What is AFC Bournemouth's nickname?

Answers to page 259
MANCHESTER UNITED 2: 1. Jimmy Murphy (Matt Busby was still recovering from the Munich air crash) 2. 19th 3. West Ham 4. Peter Schmeichel 5. John Aston 6. Jaime Gruça 7. Bobby Charlton 8. Dennis Viollet 9. Atletico Madrid 10. Mark Bosnich 11. Steve Coppell 12. George Graham 13. Dave Sexton 14. Chelsea 15. Arthur Albiston 16. Portsmouth

League Cup 1

Answers on page 264

1. In 1991, who became the first Division Two club to win the League Cup for 16 years?

2. Which was the last London team to win the League Cup?

3. Whose two goals won the League Cup for Aston Villa in 1977?

4. Who beat Manchester United in the 1964 final?

5. Which club reached their only major Cup semi-final when getting to the last four of the League Cup in 1970?

6. Who knocked them out of the competition at that stage?

7. Which Third Division team did Manchester City beat in the semi-finals of the 1974 League Cup?

8. Who did Liverpool defeat 10–0 on their way to the 1987 final?

9. Who scored Luton's goal in the 1989 final against Nottingham Forest?

10. But who scored twice for Forest to make his father's day?

11. Who did Oxford United defeat in the semi-finals of the 1986 League Cup?

12. Whose extra-time goal in the 1984 final replay took the League Cup to Anfield?

13. Who beat Arsenal 5–0 in the 1998–9 competition?

14. Who scored the only goal in each leg of Liverpool's 1995 semi-final?

15. Who did Liverpool beat in that semi?

16. Who scored the first goal of the 1994 final?

Answers to page 264
TRANSFER TRAIL 3: **1.** Claudio Caniggia **2.** Liverpool **3.** Vicenza **4.** Andy Gray **5.** Bradford City **6.** Dean Richards **7.** Paul Kitson **8.** Fabrizio Ravanelli **9.** Foggia **10.** Colin Foster **11.** Stuart Pearce **12.** Derby County **13.** Hereford United **14.** Borussia Dortmund **15.** Coventry City **16.** Crystal Palace

European Championship 4

Answers on page 265

1. Which country knocked England out of the 1972 European Championship?

2. When did Scotland first qualify for the European Championship finals?

3. How many times have they qualified in total?

4. By what score did England beat Holland at Euro 96?

5. Who scored two of England's goals?

6. With whom did England draw their opening match at Euro 96?

7. Who made amends for missing his previous England penalty by scoring in the shoot-out against Spain at Euro 96?

8. Who was Italy's coach at Euro 96?

9. An 8–0 victory over which country was insufficient to get the Republic of Ireland to the 1984 European Championship finals?

10. Who missed a last-minute penalty for Spain against France in the quarter-finals of Euro 2000?

11. Who fought back to draw 3–3 with Slovenia at Euro 2000 after going three goals down?

12. Which Tottenham player scored for Norway at Euro 2000?

13. How many countries originally entered Euro 2000?

14. Which two countries were new to European competition?

15. Who was England's captain at the 1992 European Championship?

16. In which city did England draw 0–0 with Denmark at the 1992 European Championship?

Answers to page 265
FA CUP 3: 1. Derby County 2. Walley Barnes 3. Brighton & Hove Albion 4. 32 5. Lee Sinnott 6. Crystal Palace and Arsenal 7. Sheffield United 8. Bill Perry 9. George Farm 10. 1970 11. Manchester United 12. Swansea City 13. 1887 14. Aston Villa and West Bromwich Albion 15. David Webb (Chelsea, 1970) 16. Sunderland (1992)

Transfer Trail 3

Answers on page 262

1. Which Argentine World Cup star played for Dundee in 2000–1?

2. From which neighbours did Tranmere sign Andy Parkinson?

3. From which Italian club did Inter Milan sign Alessandro Pistone in 1996?

4. Which Scottish international striker joined Wolves from Aston Villa for £1.4 million in 1979?

5. From which club did Oldham Athletic sign Lee Duxbury?

6. Which defender moved from Valley Parade to Molineux for £1.3 million in 1995?

7. Which former Derby County forward joined West Ham from Newcastle for £2.3 million in 1997?

8. Which ex-Riverside Italian joined Lazio from Marseille in 2000?

9. From which Italian side did Nottingham Forest sign Bryan Roy in 1994?

10. Which Nottingham Forest centre-back joined West Ham for £750,000 in 1989?

11. Which 39-year-old former England stalwart moved to Maine Road in summer 2001?

12. From which club did Ipswich sign midfielder Geraint Williams in 1992?

13. Who sold Darren Peacock to Queens Park Rangers in 1990?

14. Following his spell with Lazio, for which club did Karlheinz Riedle sign in 1993 on his return to Germany?

15. Which Midlands club paid Arsenal £1 million for youth team player Jay Bothroyd in 2000?

16. Which London club signed two Chinese players in 1998?

Answers to page 262
LEAGUE CUP 1: 1. Sheffield Wednesday 2. Tottenham 3. Brian Little
4. Aston Villa 5. Carlisle United 6. West Bromwich Albion 7. Plymouth
Argyle 8. Fulham 9. Mick Harford 10. Nigel Clough 11. Aston Villa
12. Graeme Souness 13. Chelsea 14. Robbie Fowler 15. Crystal Palace
16. Dalian Atkinson (Aston Villa)

FA Cup 3

Answers on page 263

1. Which Midlands club have lost nine out of 13 FA Cup semi-finals?

2. Which Arsenal player who went on to become a TV commentator was carried off injured in the 1952 FA Cup final?

3. Which League club had to play in the qualifying rounds of the 1932–3 competition because they had forgotten to claim exemption?

4. How many goals did they score in those four qualifying rounds?

5. Who was Watford's 18-year-old in their 1984 Cup final team?

6. For which two teams did Ian Wright score Cup final goals?

7. Which Second Division side reached the 1936 Cup final?

8. Which South African-born player was a member of the Blackpool Cup final teams of 1951 and 1953?

9. Which Scot kept goal for Blackpool in those two finals?

10. In which year did a third place play-off match first take place on the eve of the Cup final?

11. Who were the first winners?

12. Which team were awarded a bye into round two in 1992–3 after Maidstone United went into liquidation?

13. When was the first Cup final 'derby'?

14. Which two teams met in that final?

15. Which Cup winner was unable to collect his medal because he had swapped shirts with an opponent and was refused admission to the directors' box?

16. Which Cup final losers were given the winners' medals by mistake?

Answers to page 263
EUROPEAN CHAMPIONSHIP 4: 1. West Germany 2. 1992 3. Two 4. 4–1
5. Teddy Sheringham 6. Switzerland 7. Stuart Pearce 8. Arrigo Sacchi
9. Malta 10. Raul 11. Yugoslavia 12. Steffen Iversen 13. 51 14. Andorra and
Bosnia-Herzegovina 15. Gary Lineker 16. Malmo

On the Spot 2

Answers on page 268

1. Who missed a penalty for Bayern Munich in normal time at the 2001 Champions' League final?

2. But who later scored Bayern's equaliser from the penalty spot?

3. Which two Arsenal players hit the woodwork in the penalty shoot-out with Galatasaray in the 2000 UEFA Cup final?

4. In which World Cup were both semi-finals decided on penalties?

5. Len Davies's missed penalty in the final minute of the last match of the 1923–4 season cost which club the League Championship?

6. Who scored a penalty for Spurs against Burnley in the 1962 FA Cup final?

7. When was the first time the European Cup was decided on penalties?

8. Who went rubber-legged in goal to help Liverpool win that shoot-out?

9. Who was the first man to miss a spot kick in a World Cup final?

10. For which country did Manuel Rosas become the first man to convert a penalty in the World Cup?

11. Which Polish player missed a penalty against Argentina in the 1978 World Cup finals on his 100th international appearance?

12. In 1974, which competition produced the first penalty shoot-out at Wembley?

13. Who won that shoot-out?

14. Which English team lost out in the first European Cup-Winners' Cup final to be decided on penalties?

15. Who beat them in that final?

16. Who beat Marseille on penalties in the 1991 European Cup final?

Answers to page 268
NON-LEAGUE 2: 1. Tiverton Town 2. Grantham Town 3. Unibond League 4. Aylesbury United 5. Burton Albion 6. Nigel Clough 7. Gainsborough 8. Slough Town 9. Pegasus 10. Green and white 11. Accrington Stanley, Barrow and Gateshead 12. Dagenham & Redbridge 13. Hoddesdon Town 14. Hendon 15. Woking 16. Pickering Town

England 2

Answers on page 269

1. Who was England's caretaker manager following the end of Sir Alf Ramsey's reign?

2. By what score did England beat Spain in March 2001?

3. When did Rob Lee make his England debut?

4. Who were the first team to score against England at the 1966 World Cup?

5. Who did England beat in the second round at the 1986 World Cup?

6. Who scored England's goals in that game?

7. Who scored England's only goal from open play in the quarter-final victory over Cameroon at Italia 90?

8. How many England caps did Frank Lampard senior win?

9. Who scored three goals in his first five games under Sven Goran Eriksson after previously netting just one England goal?

10. Which West Ham pair won their first caps against Mexico in 2001?

11. Which Leeds youngster also made his England debut in that match?

12. Which sturdy Liverpool, Tottenham, West Ham and Crystal Palace defender won his only England cap against Nigeria in 1995?

13. Behind whom did England qualify for the 1982 World Cup finals?

14. Who were England's opening opponents in the 1982 finals?

15. Who scored twice for England in that match?

16. Who got England's winning goal against Kuwait in Group Four at the 1982 World Cup finals?

Answers to page 269
RANGERS 1: 1. Mark Hateley 2. Terry Butcher and Chris Woods 3. Eric Caldow 4. The Iron Curtain 5. William Struth 6. Basile Boli 7. Bob McPhail 8. Jörg Albertz 9. Derek Johnstone 10. Juventus 11. Stockholm 12. Paul Gascoigne 13. John Greig 14. Jim Bett 15. Gordon Durie 16. Aberdeen

Non-League 2

Answers on page 266

1. Which Devon club won the FA Challenge Vase in 1998 and 1999?

2. Which Lincolnshire team are nicknamed 'The Gingerbreads'?

3. In which League do Bamber Bridge play?

4. From which Ryman League team did Jermaine Darlington join Queens Park Rangers?

5. Who were runners-up in the Dr Martens Premier Division in 2000–1?

6. Which son of a famous manager is their boss?

7. Which Unibond League team have the suffix 'Trinity'?

8. From which Ryman League team did striker Lloyd Owusu move to Brentford?

9. Which student team won the FA Amateur Cup twice in the 1950s?

10. What are Yeovil Town's colours?

11. Which three former League clubs played in the Unibond League Premier Division in season 2000–1?

12. Who won the Ryman League Premier Division in 1999–2000?

13. Which Hertfordshire club won the first-ever FA Challenge Vase final?

14. Which Ryman League team won 1–0 at Leyton Orient in a 1998 FA Cup first-round tie?

15. Which Conference team won an FA Cup replay at Millwall in 1997?

16. From which Yorkshire team did Craig Short enter League football?

Answers to page 266
ON THE SPOT 2: 1. Mehmet Scholl 2. Steffen Effenberg 3. Davor Suker and Patrick Vieira 4. 1990 5. Cardiff City 6. Danny Blanchflower 7. 1984
8. Bruce Grobbelaar 9. Antonio Cabrini of Italy in 1982 10. Mexico
11. Kazimierz Deyna 12. FA Charity Shield 13. Liverpool, 6–5 against Leeds
14. Arsenal 15. Valencia 16. Red Star Belgrade

Rangers 1

Answers on page 267

1. Whose two goals against Aberdeen clinched the Scottish League Championship for Rangers in 1991?

2. Which two Rangers 'Anglos' were sent off along with Celtic's Frank McAvennie during a tempestuous Old Firm fixture in 1987?

3. Which Rangers defender broke his leg in the 1963 England–Scotland international at Wembley?

4. What was Rangers' impenetrable defence of the 1950s popularly known as?

5. Who managed Rangers from 1920 to 1954?

6. Which international defender did Rangers sign from Marseille for £2.7 million in 1994?

7. Whose club scoring record did Ally McCoist break in 1995?

8. Which Rangers favourite returned to his old club, Hamburg, in summer 2001?

9. Which 16-year-old headed Rangers' winning goal against Celtic in the 1970–1 Scottish League Cup final?

10. From which Italian club did Rangers sign Sergio Porrinio in 1997?

11. In which city was Richard Gough born?

12. Which Rangers recruit of the 1990s was booked in 16 of his first 32 matches for the club?

13. Which stalwart player became Rangers manager in 1978?

14. Who joined Rangers from Lokeren of Belgium for £180,000 in 1980?

15. Which former Spurs player was Rangers' top scorer in 1995–6?

16. Who did Rangers beat 3–0 on the opening day of the 2001–2 season?

Answers to page 267
ENGLAND 2: 1. Joe Mercer 2. 3–0 3. 1995 4. Portugal 5. Paraguay
6. Gary Lineker (2) and Peter Beardsley 7. David Platt 8. Two 9. David
Beckham 10. Joe Cole and Michael Carrick 11. Alan Smith 12. Neil
Ruddock 13. Hungary 14. France 15. Bryan Robson 16. Trevor Francis

Whose Home? 3

Answers on page 272

1. At which ground did St Johnstone play before moving to McDiarmid Park?

2. In which city do St Johnstone play?

3. Where do Barry Town play?

4. In their Football League days, what was the name of Workington's ground?

5. Who plays at The Hawthorns?

6. Where do Tranmere Rovers play?

7. Which London club's traditional home is Loftus Road?

8. In which country is the Arrudao Stadium?

9. Kenilworth Road is home to which English League club?

10. Which Scottish team play at Dens Park?

11. The Bosuil Stadium is the home ground of which Belgian club?

12. Who plays at Oakwell?

13. Which former League club play at Underhill?

14. What is the name of Queen of the South's home ground?

15. Which English League club's ground was the only one to be bombed during the First World War?

16. At which Scottish League ground would you find the Cemetery End?

Answers to page 272
GERMANY 1: **1.** Franz Beckenbauer **2.** Five **3.** Gerd Müller **4.** Belgium **5.** Rudi Völler **6.** Switzerland **7.** Lothar Matthäus **8.** Gunter Netzer **9.** Charleroi **10.** Northern Ireland **11.** Sepp Maier **12.** Jürgen Klinsmann **13.** Helmut Haller **14.** Uwe Seeler **15.** 103 **16.** Wales

Goalkeepers 2

Answers on page 273

1. How old was Peter Shilton when he kept goal for Leicester City in the 1969 FA Cup final?

2. What was keeper Maik Taylor's first League club?

3. Which Scottish club had a goalkeeper called Ray Charles in 1990?

4. Which goalkeeper became manager of Birmingham City in 1960?

5. Which goalkeeper had spells as manager of Dundee, Coventry City, Blackburn Rovers and Fulham?

6. Which former Hartlepool goalkeeper was Brian Clough's sidekick?

7. Who kept goal for Sunderland in the 1992 FA Cup final?

8. Which Leeds goalkeeper once famously threw the ball into his own net?

9. And which Leeds goalkeeper helped the ball into his own net during a 1992 European Cup tie with Rangers?

10. Which country has Alan Fettis played for?

11. What nationality is Bodo Illgner?

12. Which French goalkeeper did Millwall sign in 2000?

13. What nationality is Hans Segers?

14. From which club did Southampton sign Paul Jones?

15. Who kept goal for Berwick Rangers in their shock 1967 Scottish FA Cup victory over Rangers and went on to manage both clubs?

16. From which Scottish club did Norwich City recruit Bryan Gunn?

Answers to page 273
NEWCASTLE UNITED 1: 1. Robert Lee 2. Nottingham Forest 3. Leicester City 4. Barnsley 5. Bristol City 6. Joe Harvey 7. Malcolm Macdonald 8. Tony Green 9. Northern Ireland 10. 1998 11. Kenny Dalglish 12. Jackie Milburn 13. Bayern Munich 14. Andy Cole 15. Gary Speed 16. Didier Domi

Germany 1

Answers on page 270

1. Who captained West Germany at the 1974 World Cup?

2. In how many World Cup finals tournaments has Lothar Matthäus played?

3. Who scored 68 goals in just 62 internationals for West Germany?

4. Who did Germany beat 3–2 in the second round at the 1994 World Cup finals?

5. Who scored two of the German goals in that match?

6. Against whom did West Germany play their first-ever international, in 1908?

7. Who played with a broken wrist in the 1986 World Cup final?

8. Who converted a penalty against England in the quarter-finals of the 1972 European Championship?

9. In which town did Germany meet England at Euro 2000?

10. Which country surprisingly remained unbeaten against Germany for 20 years, from 1977 to 1997, covering five matches?

11. Which German goalkeeper made his international debut against the Republic of Ireland in 1966?

12. Which striker made his international debut against Brazil in 1987?

13. Who scored West Germany's first goal in the 1966 World Cup final?

14. Which veteran striker's back-header looped over Peter Bonetti to stun England in the quarter-finals of the 1970 World Cup?

15. How many international caps did Franz Beckenbauer win?

16. Which home nation held West Germany to a goalless draw in a World Cup qualifier in 1989?

Answers to page 270
WHOSE HOME? 3: **1.** Muirton Park **2.** Perth **3.** Jenner Park **4.** Borough Park **5.** West Bromwich Albion **6.** Prenton Park **7.** Queens Park Rangers **8.** Brazil **9.** Luton Town **10.** Dundee **11.** Royal Antwerp **12.** Barnsley **13.** Barnet **14.** Palmerston Park **15.** Hartlepool United **16.** Glebe Park (Brechin City)

Newcastle United 1

Answers on page 271

1. Who played 298 League matches for Charlton before moving to St James' Park?

2. Who did Newcastle beat in a sixth-round FA Cup second replay in 1974 after a crowd invasion at St James' Park had halted the first match with United losing 3–1?

3. With whom were United relegated from Division One in 1978?

4. Who did Newcastle beat in the 1910 FA Cup final?

5. From which club did Newcastle sign Andy Cole?

6. Which manager took Newcastle to the 1974 FA Cup final?

7. Who left Newcastle for Arsenal for £333,000 in 1976?

8. Which Scottish international midfielder joined Newcastle from Blackpool for £150,000 in 1971?

9. For which country did Alf McMichael win 40 international caps?

10. When did Ruud Gullit become United manager?

11. Who did he succeed?

12. Who scored in the first minute for Newcastle at the 1955 FA Cup final?

13. From which German club did United sign Dietmar Hamann?

14. Who scored 34 League goals in 40 matches for United in 1993–4?

15. Who was Newcastle's only ever-present in 1998–9?

16. Which defender moved from Paris St Germain to Newcastle in 1998?

Answers to page 271
GOALKEEPERS 2: **1.** 19 **2.** Barnet **3.** East Fife **4.** Gil Merrick **5.** Don Mackay **6.** Peter Taylor **7.** Tony Norman **8.** Gary Sprake **9.** John Lukic **10.** Northern Ireland **11.** German **12.** Willy Gueret **13.** Dutch **14.** Stockport County **15.** Jock Wallace **16.** Aberdeen

Southampton 1

Answers on page 276

1. With which club did Chris Marsden make his League debut?

2. Which Third Division team did Southampton beat in the semi-finals of the 1976 FA Cup?

3. Who converted a penalty in that match?

4. Who was the only Scottish international in Southampton's line-up for the 1976 FA Cup final?

5. Who pipped Southampton for the Second Division title in 1978?

6. Who succeeded Alan Ball as Saints' manager in 1995?

7. Which player made a record 713 League appearances for the club?

8. Which Wallace brother moved from The Dell to Old Trafford for £1.2 million in 1989?

9. From which Italian club did Saints sign Paul Rideout?

10. Who scored 39 League goals for the club in 1959–60?

11. In which year did Saints reach their first FA Cup final?

12. Who beat them 4–0 in the final?

13. Which Arsenal Cup final hero joined Southampton from Derby in 1978?

14. Which future England international striker did Saints sell to Tottenham for £125,000 in 1968?

15. From which club did Southampton sign Phil Boyer?

16. How many League games did James Beattie play for Blackburn Rovers?

Answers to page 276
TRANSFER TRAIL 4: **1.** Gaizka Mendieta **2.** Inter Milan **3.** Wim Jonk **4.** Derek Dougan **5.** Juan Pablo Angel **6.** Gary Breen **7.** Bradford Park Avenue **8.** Charlton Athletic **9.** Christian Karembeu **10.** Alan McLoughlin **11.** Kilmarnock **12.** Leeds United **13.** Olof Mellberg **14.** Racing Santander **15.** Alan Ball **16.** John Jensen

Sharpshooters 2

Answers on page 277

1. Which Doncaster Rovers' player topped the League scoring charts in 1964–5?

2. Which Fiorentina player was the top scorer in Italy's Serie 'A' in 1994–5?

3. Which Milan player was leading marksman in Serie 'A' five times in six years in the early 1950s?

4. Which Portuguese striker was Walsall's leading scorer in 2000–1?

5. Which Gillingham player scored a hat-trick in two minutes against Leyton Orient in 1952?

6. Who was rejected as a goalkeeper by Newcastle before returning as a striker?

7. Which forward was Liverpool's record signing at £35,000 in 1961?

8. In 1994, which 42-year-old became the oldest player to appear in the World Cup finals?

9. Which England player scored the first of his five international hat-tricks against Turkey in 1985?

10. From which club did Rushden & Diamonds sign Duane Darby?

11. Who was the first player to score four goals for England in an international?

12. Against which club was Kenny Dalglish's final match as Liverpool manager?

13. Who was Sunderland's leading scorer in 1999–2000?

14. In which year did John Charles make his Leeds United debut?

15. Which Arsenal star is anything but a flying Dutchman?

16. Against which club did George Best score six times in a 1970 FA Cup tie?

Answers to page 277
ENGLAND 3: 1. Italy 2. Egypt 3. 1974, 1978 and 1994 4. Andy Cole (Terry Venables, Glenn Hoddle, Howard Wilkinson and Kevin Keegan) 5. Mick Channon 6. G.O. Smith 7. Tony Woodcock 8. 1984 9. Chorzow 10. Gary Neville 11. Jamie Redknapp 12. David Beckham 13. Bobby Robson 14. 26 15. Alan Shearer 16. 1996

Transfer Trail 4

Answers on page 274

1. Who moved from Valencia to Lazio for £29.5 million in July 2001?

2. From which Italian club did Liverpool sign Paul Ince?

3. Which Dutch international moved from PSV to Sheffield Wednesday for £2.5 million in 1998?

4. Which charismatic Northern Ireland centre-forward joined Wolves from Leicester for £50,000 in 1967?

5. Who went from River Plate to Villa Park for £9.5 million in 2000–1?

6. Which defender left Birmingham City for Coventry for £2.5 million in 1997?

7. From which ill-fated Yorkshire club did Wolves recruit Kenny Hibbitt?

8. Bulgarian Radostin Kishishev joined which London club in 2001?

9. Before eventually ending up at Middlesbrough, which player joined Sampdoria from Nantes for £5 million in 1995?

10. Which Republic of Ireland midfielder was Southampton's first £1 million signing?

11. From which Scottish club did Reading sign Jim McIntyre?

12. What was Jamie Forrester's first League club?

13. Which Swedish international defender joined Aston Villa in summer 2001?

14. From which Spanish club did they sign him?

15. Which World Cup winner was a British record signing when moving from Everton to Arsenal in 1971 for £220,000?

16. Which European Championship hero did Arsenal buy from Brøndby for £1.1 million in 1992?

Answers to page 274
SOUTHAMPTON 1: 1. Sheffield United 2. Crystal Palace 3. David Peach
4. Jim McCalliog 5. Bolton Wanderers 6. Dave Merrington 7. Terry Paine
8. Danny 9. Bari 10. Derek Reeves 11. 1900 12. Bury 13. Charlie George
14. Martin Chivers 15. Norwich City 16. Four

England 3

Answers on page 275

1. In 1997, which country inflicted England's first-ever home defeat in a World Cup qualifier?

2. Against whom did England gain their only victory at the group stage in the 1990 World Cup finals?

3. For which three World Cups have England failed to qualify?

4. Which England striker won his first four caps under four different managers?

5. Which Southampton player made his England debut against Yugoslavia in 1973?

6. Which England captain of the 1890s refused to head the ball because he believed that the game should be played on the ground?

7. Which Nottingham Forest, Cologne and Arsenal striker scored 16 international goals in 42 starts?

8. In which year did John Barnes score his magical goal in Rio?

9. In which city did England play their last game before the 1966 World Cup?

10. Which Manchester United defender had played just 19 games at club level when he won his first England cap?

11. Which England player's shot produced the famous 'scorpion save' in 1995?

12. Which captain made his England debut against Moldova in 1997?

13. Which future England manager scored twice in his international debut against France in 1957?

14. How many goals did Bryan Robson score for England?

15. Which striker had not scored for 12 internationals prior to Euro 96?

16. In which year did Sol Campbell win his first cap?

Answers to page 275
SHARPSHOOTERS 2: **1.** Alick Jeffrey **2.** Gabriel Batistuta **3.** Gunnar Nordahl **4.** Jorge Leitao **5.** Jimmy Scarth **6.** Alan Shearer **7.** Ian St John **8.** Roger Milla **9.** Gary Lineker **10.** Notts County **11.** Tommy Lawton **12.** Everton **13.** Kevin Phillips **14.** 1949 **15.** Dennis Bergkamp **16.** Northampton Town

Sheffield Wednesday 1

Answers on page 280

1. Which Sheffield Wednesday goalkeeper won 33 England caps?

2. When did Wednesday win the FA Cup for the first time?

3. Who did they beat in the final?

4. Who became Wednesday manager in 1969?

5. From which Italian club did Wednesday sign Des Walker?

6. Which member of the Monty Python team is a dedicated Wednesday fan?

7. Who was Wednesday's top scorer in 1993–4?

8. Who moved from Wednesday to Preston in 1949 for a British record fee of £26,000?

9. Which shaggy-haired full-back left Wednesday for Rangers in 1989?

10. Who did Wednesday beat 2–1 in the semi-finals of the 1993 FA Cup?

11. Who scored the Wednesday goals?

12. In which year were Wednesday relegated to Division Three for the first time?

13. In 1959, who finished runners-up to Wednesday in Division Two?

14. Which Wednesday player scored in every round of the 1934–5 FA Cup?

15. Who did they defeat in the final that year?

16. Who did Wednesday buy from Oldham Athletic for £750,000 in 1991?

Answers to page 280
DUNDEE UNITED 1: 1. 1987 2. Maurice Malpas 3. Steven Pressley 4. 1984
5. AS Roma 6. Lorraine Kelly 7. Billy McKinlay 8. Rangers 9. Aberdeen
10. Billy McKinlay 11. John Coyle 12. Ivan Golac 13. Paul Sturrock
14. Aberdeen 15. Willie Pettigrew 16. Paul Sturrock

Managers 5

Answers on page 281

1. Which manager left Carlisle United in July 2001?

2. When was Matt Busby named Manager of the Year?

3. Who steered Dunfermline Athletic to the club's first major trophy – the 1961 Scottish FA Cup?

4. Who was manager of Oldham Athletic from 1970 to 1982?

5. Which manager has had spells in charge of Notts County, Plymouth Argyle, Oldham Athletic and Sheffield United?

6. Which former Newcastle United captain became Plymouth manager in 1981?

7. Who replaced Tommy McLean as Dundee United boss in 1998?

8. Of which country was Mansour Pourheidari named national coach in 1998?

9. Who was manager of Oxford United from 1969 to 1975?

10. Which former Arsenal stalwart became manager of Watford in 1948?

11. With which two clubs did Tom Watson win the Football League Championship?

12. In which year was Brian Flynn appointed Wrexham manager?

13. Which Spanish club had three different managers before a ball had been kicked at the start of the 1998–9 season?

14. Which Sheffield Wednesday boss – a former goalscoring hero with the club – was sacked on Christmas Eve 1973?

15. Who had two stints as manager of Chesterfield in the last 20 years?

16. Who succeeded Alan Mullery as Charlton boss in 1982?

Answers to page 281
THE WORLD GAME 6: 1. Bayern Munich 2. Schalke 04 3. Wynton Rufer
4. Andoni Zubizarreta 5. Paolo Maldini 6. Olympique Lyon 7. AS Monaco
8. Liechtenstein 9. Romania 10. Cyprus 11. Alfredo di Stefano 12. Berti
Vogts 13. Norway 14. Edgar Davids 15. Uruguay 16. Bergamo

Dundee United 1

Answers on page 278

1. In which year did United lose the UEFA Cup final and the Scottish FA Cup final in the space of two days?

2. Who was named Scotland's Player of the Year in 1991?

3. Who moved to Tannadice from Coventry for a club record £750,000 in 1995?

4. When did United reach the European Cup semi-finals?

5. Who beat them 3–2 on aggregate?

6. Which female breakfast television presenter is a United fan?

7. Who was named Scotland's Young Player of the Year in 1989?

8. Who beat United in the 1981–2 Scottish League Cup final?

9. Who defeated United in the 1990 Scottish FA Cup final?

10. Which United forward made his Scotland debut against Malta in 1994?

11. Who scored 41 Second Division goals for United in 1955–6?

12. Who succeeded Jim McLean as United manager?

13. Who scored twice for United in their 1980–1 League Cup final victory over Dundee?

14. Who did United beat in the previous year's final?

15. Who scored two goals for United in that match?

16. Which former United favourite was appointed manager of Plymouth Argyle in 2000–1?

Answers to page 278
SHEFFIELD WEDNESDAY 1: **1.** Ron Springett **2.** 1896 **3.** Wolverhampton Wanderers **4.** Danny Williams **5.** Sampdoria **6.** Michael Palin **7.** Mark Bright **8.** Eddie Quigley **9.** Mel Sterland **10.** Sheffield United **11.** Chris Waddle and Mark Bright **12.** 1975 **13.** Fulham **14.** Ellis Rimmer **15.** West Bromwich Albion **16.** Paul Warhurst

The World Game 6

Answers on page 279

1. In 2000–1, who won the Bundesliga for the third year in a row?

2. Who finished runners-up?

3. Who was voted Oceania's Player of the Century?

4. Which Spanish goalkeeper moved from Athletic Bilbao to Barcelona in 1986 for a then world record goalkeepers' fee of £1.2 million?

5. Which Italian international did Wales's Robbie Savage insult by throwing away his shirt during a TV interview?

6. Who won their first trophy for 28 years in 2001 by lifting the French League Cup?

7. Who did they beat in the final?

8. Who did Romania crush 7–0 in a qualifier for Euro 2000?

9. In which country do Universitatea Craiova and Otelul Galati play?

10. Which Mediterranean minnows shocked Spain 3–2 in a Euro 2000 qualifier?

11. Which Spanish star was kidnapped on a tour of Venezuela in 1963?

12. Who quit as German national coach in September 1998?

13. Nils Johan Semb was appointed boss of which national team in 1998?

14. Which combative Dutch international midfielder was banned by FIFA in 2001 for failing a drug test?

15. For which South American country was Hector Scarone a prolific goalscorer?

16. In which Italian city do Atalanta play?

Answers to page 279
MANAGERS 5: 1. Ian Atkins 2. 1968 3. Jock Stein 4. Jimmy Frizzell 5. Neil Warnock 6. Bobby Moncur 7. Paul Sturrock 8. Iran 9. Gerry Summers 10. Eddie Hapgood 11. Sunderland and Liverpool 12. 1989 13. Betis Sevilla 14. Derek Dooley 15. John Duncan 16. Ken Craggs

France 1

Answers on page 284

1. In which year did France reach the World Cup final for the first time?

2. Against whom did France draw 3–3 in their first international?

3. In which year was that match played?

4. How many goals did Michel Platini score for France?

5. Who scored twice in his international debut in 1994 against the Czech Republic?

6. Which nation thrashed France 17–1 in 1908?

7. Who was banned from the national team for a year after insulting manager Henri Michel?

8. Which home country's last two meetings with France have ended in goalless draws?

9. In what position did France finish at the 1982 World Cup?

10. In which year did they go one better?

11. When did Michel Platini retire from football?

12. Who scored both French goals in their 2–0 win at Wembley in 1999?

13. Which Arsenal player later came on as substitute for the goalscorer?

14. Which two French stars retired from international football after the friendly with England in 2000?

15. How many matches did France win in normal time during Euro 2000?

16. Who were France's first opponents at the 1998 World Cup?

Answers to page 284
WHO SAID THAT? 3: **1.** Glenn Hoddle **2.** Bobby Robson **3.** Jocky Scott **4.** Ron Atkinson **5.** Bill Shankly **6.** Joe Kinnear **7.** Sammy Chung **8.** Glenn Hoddle **9.** George Graham **10.** Bill Shankly **11.** Jock Stein **12.** Sir Alf Ramsey **13.** Brian Clough (the Nottingham Forest 'genius' was John Robertson) **14.** Don Revie **15.** Brian Clough **16.** Pele

FA Cup 4

Answers on page 285

1. In 1990, which club reached the semi-finals of the FA Cup for the first time in 77 years?

2. Who prevented them reaching the final?

3. Who won the 2000 FA Cup final?

4. And who did they beat?

5. In the 1993 Cup final replay against Sheffield Wednesday, which defender struck for Arsenal in the last minute of extra time?

6. Which club reached the semi-finals of the FA Cup for the first time in 1984?

7. Whose goal for Watford denied them a place in the final?

8. Which brothers played for Preston North End in the 1937 Cup final?

9. Who was the only member of Manchester United's beaten Cup final team of 1979 never to win an international cap?

10. Which current Premiership side were humbled 4–1 by Chelmsford City in 1939?

11. Which Southern League club knocked Norwich City out of the Cup in 1932?

12. Which club controversially withdrew from the 1999–2000 FA Cup?

13. As a result, which 'lucky losers' from an earlier round were reinstated?

14. Who were the last team to win the Cup without an international in their line-up?

15. How many times have Millwall reached the semi-finals of the FA Cup?

16. Which club's only appearance in an FA Cup semi-final was back in 1888?

Answers to page 285
ODDBALLS 4: **1.** Roma **2.** The Pope (who used to be a goalkeeper)
3. Darlington **4.** Middlesbrough **5.** Padova **6.** Dundee United **7.** Iraq **8.** John Sims **9.** San Marino **10.** Chris Hutchins **11.** Hendon **12.** Kevin Keegan
13. Meadowbank Thistle **14.** The corner kick **15.** 1952 **16.** 1982

Who Said That? 3

Answers on page 282

1. Who said of Gazza: 'Mentally, Paul has a few problems'?

2. Which England manager described Gazza as 'daft as a brush'?

3. Which former Dunfermline Athletic boss said: 'It's a great job, apart from Saturday afternoons'?

4. Which manager said: 'Women should be in the kitchen, the discotheque and the boutique, but not in football'?

5. Who said: 'Football is not a matter of life and death. It's much more important than that'?

6. Which Wimbledon manager described his transfer policy as 'buy in Woolworth's, sell in Harrods'?

7. Who predicted in 1994: 'Doncaster will reach the First Division by 1999'?

8. Which England boss warned: 'I do not get mad. I get even'?

9. Which manager described joining Millwall as 'a bit of a culture shock'?

10. Who said: 'I don't drop players, I make changes'?

11. Which manager said of Bobby Moore: 'He read the game twenty minutes before anybody else'?

12. Who described Martin Peters as being 'ten years ahead of his time'?

13. Who told Martin O'Neill: 'What's the point of giving you the ball when there's a genius on the other wing'?

14. Who said of Eddie Gray: 'When he plays on snow, he doesn't leave any footprints'?

15. Who said of Trevor Brooking: 'He floats like a butterfly and stings like one'?

16. Who said in 1966: 'A penalty is a cowardly way to score'?

Answers to page 282
FRANCE 1: 1. 1998 2. Belgium 3. 1903 4. 41 5. Zinedine Zidane
6. Denmark 7. Eric Cantona 8. Northern Ireland 9. Fourth 10. 1986
11. 1997 12. Nicolas Anelka 13. Patrick Vieira 14. Laurent Blanc and Didier Deschamps 15. Three 16. South Africa

Oddballs 4

Answers on page 283

1. Which Italian club won Serie 'A' in 2000–1?

2. To whom did they send the first football shirt bearing the word 'scudetta' and with a number one on the back?

3. Which English League club does Vic Reeves support?

4. And which club does Bob Mortimer follow?

5. Which Italian club's fans ran into trouble over a 1995 banner which read: 'Stop nuclear tests in Muroroa – do them in Naples instead'?

6. Which Scottish club's relegation in 1995 ended a 35-year unbroken run in the top flight?

7. From 1981 to 1983, Al Talaba completed a hat-trick of League titles in which country?

8. Who was manager at Torquay United for 33 days in 1985?

9. Which country scored after eight seconds against England in 1994?

10. Who succeeded Paul Jewell as Bradford City manager in 2000?

11. For which Ryman League outfit did former Bulgarian international Bontcho Guentchev turn out in 1999?

12. Which footballer advertised Brut with Henry Cooper in the 1970s?

13. Which Scottish club used to have a fanzine called *Mr Bismarck's Electric Pickelhaube*?

14. Which aspect of the game was introduced in 1872?

15. Which year's Cup final did the FA refuse to allow to be televised?

16. In which year did the Scotland World Cup Squad reach number five in the charts with 'We Have a Dream'?

Answers to page 283
FA CUP 4: 1. Oldham Athletic 2. Manchester United 3. Chelsea 4. Aston Villa 5. Andy Linighan 6. Plymouth Argyle 7. George Reilly 8. Frank and Hugh O' Donnell 9. Jimmy Greenhoff 10. Southampton 11. Folkestone 12. Manchester United 13. Darlington 14. Sunderland 15. Three 16. Crewe Alexandra

Bolton Wanderers 1

Answers on page 288

1. In which year did Bolton first win the FA Cup?

2. And when did they last reach the FA Cup final?

3. Which former Liverpool player was Bolton manager from 1985 to 1992?

4. With which club did Dean Holdsworth make his League debut?

5. Who scored 255 League goals for Bolton between 1946 and 1961?

6. In which year did Bolton first drop into Division Four?

7. From which Lancashire neighbours did Bolton sign John Byrom in the 1960s?

8. Who became Bolton manager in 1971?

9. Who scored 38 First Division goals for Bolton in 1920–1?

10. Which forward did Bolton sell to Birmingham City for £340,000 in 1981?

11. Who did Wanderers buy from West Bromwich Albion for £350,000 in 1979?

12. What is the highest position that Bolton have ever finished in the top division?

13. Who scored both Bolton goals in the 1958 FA Cup final?

14. Who did Bolton beat in that final?

15. Which two players scored the goals in Wanderers' shock 2–0 win at Anfield in the 1993 FA Cup?

16. Which centre-half joined Bolton from Leeds for £450,000 in 1995?

Answers to page 288
ON THE SPOT 3: 1. Barcelona 2. Steaua Bucharest 3. David Seaman 4. Mark Bosnich 5. Alan Slough 6. Jan Molby 7. Crystal Palace 8. Clive Walker 9. Arnold Muhren 10. Glenn Hoddle 11. Tony Parks 12. Ioan Ganea 13. Patrik Berger 14. Charlie Wallace (Aston Villa) 15. Italy 16. Mark Robins

Derby County 1

Answers on page 289

1. Who was Derby's leading Premiership marksman in 2000–1?

2. Which team inflicted an 11–2 FA Cup defeat on Derby in 1890?

3. What is Derby's nickname?

4. Which defender moved to Derby from Notts County for £2.5 million in 1992?

5. Which Welsh international forward did Derby sell to Liverpool for £2.9 million in 1991?

6. Who beat Derby in the 1993 Anglo-Italian Cup final?

7. Who were League runners-up to Derby in 1974–5?

8. Which manager took Derby to that League title?

9. Who had guided them to their other League Championship three years earlier?

10. Which Derby player moved to Southampton in summer 2001?

11. When did Jim Smith become Derby manager?

12. From which club did Derby sign Roy McFarland?

13. From which Italian club did Derby buy Francesco Baiano?

14. Who beat Derby in the semi-finals of the 1976 FA Cup?

15. How many England caps did Kevin Hector win?

16. Who scored 37 League goals for Derby in 1956–7?

Answers to page 289
WORLD CUP 3: 1. Mexico 2. Iceland 3. Hans Tilkowski 4. Scotland
5. Aimore Moreira 6. Gordon Strachan 7. Alan McLoughlin 8. Iran
9. Cordoba 10. Bebeto 11. Argentina 12. Dennis Bergkamp 13. Los
Angeles 14. Mexico 15. England and Uruguay 16. Czechoslovakia

On the Spot 3

Answers on page 286

1. Which club missed all four penalties in the shoot-out at the end of the 1986 European Cup final?

2. Who were their opponents?

3. Whose goalkeeping heroics enabled England to progress at the expense of Spain in Euro 96?

4. Which Aston Villa keeper saved four penalties in two consecutive matches in 1994 – two in a Coca-Cola Cup semi-final shoot-out against Tranmere, then two in the Premiership at Tottenham?

5. Who scored a hat-trick of penalties for Peterborough United at Chester in 1978 but still finished on the losing side?

6. Which Dane's only hat-trick in English football comprised three penalties against Coventry in 1986?

7. Which team missed three penalties against Brighton in 1989 but scored another and won 2–1?

8. Who missed a penalty for Sunderland in the 1985 Milk Cup final?

9. Who converted a penalty for Manchester United in the replay of the 1983 FA Cup final?

10. Whose penalty decided the outcome of the 1982 FA Cup final replay?

11. Whose save in a penalty shoot-out won the 1984 UEFA Cup for Tottenham?

12. Which Romanian scored a late penalty against England in Euro 2000?

13. Who converted a penalty in the Euro 96 final?

14. Who was the first man to miss a penalty in an FA Cup final?

15. Who were eliminated on penalties from the World Cup in 1990, 1994 and 1998?

16. Whose penalty miss cost Rotherham a draw at Watford in 2001–2?

Answers to page 286
BOLTON WANDERERS 1: **1.** 1923 **2.** 1958 **3.** Phil Neal **4.** Watford **5.** Nat Lofthouse **6.** 1987 **7.** Blackburn Rovers **8.** Jimmy Armfield **9.** Joe Smith **10.** Neil Whatmore **11.** Len Cantello **12.** Third **13.** Nat Lofthouse **14.** Manchester United **15.** John McGinlay and Andy Walker **16.** Chris Fairclough

World Cup 3

Answers on page 287

1. Against whom did England gain their first victory at the 1966 World Cup?

2. Failure to beat which country in Swansea denied Wales a place at the 1982 World Cup finals?

3. Who was in goal for West Germany in the 1966 World Cup final?

4. Which country were eliminated on goal difference in three consecutive World Cup finals – 1974, 1978 and 1982?

5. Who was coach of the victorious Brazil team at the 1962 World Cup?

6. Who scored Scotland's only goal at the 1986 World Cup finals?

7. Who was the only Portsmouth player in the Republic of Ireland's 1994 World Cup squad?

8. Who held Scotland to a draw in their second match at the 1978 finals?

9. In which city was that match played?

10. Who scored Brazil's winning goal in their second-round match against the USA in the 1994 finals?

11. Who did Holland defeat in the quarter-finals of the 1998 World Cup?

12. Who scored Holland's winner?

13. In which city was the 1994 final played?

14. Which country were banned from taking part in the 1990 World Cup?

15. Which two previous winners of the competition failed to make the 1994 World Cup finals?

16. Who defeated Argentina 6–1 at the 1958 finals?

Answers to page 287
DERBY COUNTY 1: 1. Malcolm Christie 2. Everton 3. 'The Rams' 4. Craig Short 5. Dean Saunders 6. Cremonese 7. Liverpool 8. Dave Mackay 9. Brian Clough 10. Rory Delap 11. 1995 12. Tranmere Rovers 13. Fiorentina 14. Manchester United 15. Two 16. Ray Straw

Manchester United 3

Answers on page 292

1. Which ex-Millwall winger was United's top scorer for 1977–8?

2. What nationality is United full-back Michael Silvestre?

3. Which United legend was knighted in 1994?

4. In which year did Brian Kidd make his United debut?

5. Who was United's leading scorer in their Championship-winning years of 1965 and 1967?

6. Which Scottish centre-half joined United from Leeds for £500,000 in 1978?

7. In the year that United first won the European Cup, who knocked them out of the FA Cup in the third round?

8. Who succumbed 7–1 at Old Trafford on April Fool's Day, 2000?

9. Who bagged a hat-trick for United that day?

10. To whom did United lose 4–0 in the 1994–5 Champions' League?

11. Which manager took United to their first League Championship?

12. In which year did they achieve that feat?

13. Who were United's first opponents in their Second Division season of 1974–5?

14. Which former Hull City player was United's top scorer that season?

15. In 1997–8, United scored a total of 13 goals in two successive home games. Who were on the receiving end?

16. Which London club knocked United out of the 1996–7 FA Cup?

Answers to page 292
PREMIERSHIP 5: **1.** Alen Boksic **2.** Six **3.** Sunderland **4.** Ken Bates
5. Everton **6.** Leicester City **7.** Gustavo Poyet **8.** Sunderland **9.** Paul Ince
10. Four **11.** 19 **12.** Brian Kidd **13.** West Ham United **14.** Jim Jefferies
15. Southampton **16.** Sergei Rebrov

European Cups 4

Answers on page 293

1. Which Portuguese international defender played in goal for Benfica in the second half of the 1965 European Cup final?

2. Who beat Benfica 1–0 in that match?

3. Which Northern Irish team lost to Torpedo Kutaisi of Georgia in the first qualifying round of the 2001–2 Champions' League?

4. Who did Manchester United beat in the 1967 European Cup final?

5. Who scored twice in that match?

6. Which Maltese team did United defeat in the first round of that year's competition?

7. Which English club won the 2000–1 UEFA Cup?

8. Who scored two of Rangers' goals in their 1972 European Cup-Winners' Cup triumph?

9. Who were the first Dutch team to reach the UEFA Cup final?

10. And who were the second Dutch team to get to the UEFA Cup final?

11. Which country supplied a UEFA Cup finalist for eight years in a row from 1967?

12. In 1989 who became the first Italian club to win the UEFA Cup for 12 years?

13. Which British club reached three European Cup semi-finals between 1970 and 1974?

14. Which Greek team put Rangers out of the 1994–5 Champions' League?

15. Whose penalty won the 1985 European Cup for Juventus?

16. Who were the first Greek club to reach the European Cup final?

Answers to page 293
BIRMINGHAM CITY 1: **1.** Port Vale **2.** Leeds United **3.** Joe Bradford
4. Dele Adebola **5.** Gil Merrick **6.** Ipswich Town **7.** Oxford United **8.** Geoff Vowden **9.** Ricky Otto **10.** 1993 **11.** 1995 **12.** Carlisle United **13.** Paul Tait **14.** Watford **15.** Walter Abbott **16.** Sixth in 1956

Premiership 5

Answers on page 290

1. Which Croatian was Middlesbrough's leading Premiership scorer in 2000–1?

2. How many goals did Pierre Van Hooijdonk score when Nottingham Forest were relegated in 1998–9?

3. 'Mackems' are followers of which Premiership club?

4. Who is Chelsea's controversial chairman?

5. Which Premiership team plays at Goodison Park?

6. Which club are nicknamed 'The Foxes'?

7. Who scored twice for Chelsea on the opening day of the 1999–2000 season?

8. Who did Chelsea beat 4–0 that day?

9. Who was Middlesbrough's Player of the Season for 1999–2000?

10. How many goalless draws were there on the first day of the 1998–9 Premiership season?

11. How many Premiership goals did Marcus Stewart score in 2000–1?

12. Who took over as Blackburn boss in December 1988?

13. Which London club launched an ill-fated bond scheme in 1992?

14. Which Scottish manager could not save Bradford City from relegation in 2000–1?

15. Which club finished one position above the relegation places in 1998–9?

16. Which Russian was Spurs' top scorer in 2000–1?

Answers to page 290
MANCHESTER UNITED 3: **1.** Gordon Hill **2.** French **3.** Bobby Charlton **4.** 1967 **5.** Denis Law **6.** Gordon McQueen **7.** Tottenham Hotspur **8.** West Ham United **9.** Paul Scholes **10.** Barcelona **11.** Ernest Mangnall **12.** 1908 **13.** Orient **14.** Stuart Pearson **15.** Barnsley and Sheffield Wednesday **16.** Wimbledon

Birmingham City 1

Answers on page 291

1. From which club did Birmingham sign Jon McCarthy?

2. Who beat Birmingham 3–0 in the 1972 FA Cup semi-final?

3. Who scored 249 League goals for the club between 1920 and 1935?

4. Which striker – joint top scorer in 1998–9 – was signed by Birmingham from Crewe Alexandra?

5. Who kept goal for Birmingham in the 1956 FA Cup final?

6. From which club did Birmingham sign Keith Bertschin?

7. To whom were Birmingham Second Division runners-up in 1985?

8. Who was Birmingham's top scorer in 1966–7?

9. Which winger did Birmingham buy from Southend United for £800,000 in 1994?

10. When did Barry Fry become Birmingham boss?

11. When did Birmingham win the Auto Windscreens Shield?

12. Who did they beat in the final?

13. Who scored the sudden-death winner but then got into trouble for revealing an offensive T-shirt during the celebrations?

14. Who beat Birmingham in the 1999 First Division play-off semi-finals?

15. Who scored 33 League goals in a season for the club in 1898–9?

16. What is Birmingham's highest-ever finishing position in the top division?

Answers to page 291
EUROPEAN CUPS 4: 1. Germano de Figureido 2. Inter Milan 3. Linfield 4. Benfica 5. Bobby Charlton 6. Hibernians Valletta 7. Liverpool 8. Willie Johnston 9. Feyenoord 10. Twente Enschede 11. England 12. Napoli 13. Celtic 14. AEK Athens 15. Michel Platini 16. Panathinaikos

Football League 4

Answers on page 296

1. For which club did Arfon Griffiths make a record 592 League appearances?

2. With whom did Adrian Viveash make his League debut?

3. Who finished bottom of Division Two in 1998–9?

4. Which team lost three successive First Division play-off semi-finals before finally gaining promotion in 2000?

5. Which Lancashire club signed Baichung Bhutia – the first Indian international to play in the Football League?

6. Which club mascot was sent off in 1998 for making obscene gestures during a players' brawl in a match with Lincoln City?

7. In September 2000, which club scored two goals in succession without opponents Peterborough touching the ball?

8. Which club sold Bryan Hughes to Birmingham City for £800,000 in 1997?

9. Who went 30 games without a win in Third Division (North) in 1956–7?

10. Which Crystal Palace player was capped by England in 1961 while still playing in Division Three?

11. Which club's players refused to do any more promotional work in 1997 as a protest against the lack of nappy-changing facilities at the ground?

12. Which club used to be known as Bristol South End?

13. Which former League champions were relegated to Division Four in 1975?

14. 1977–8 was which club's only season in the top two divisions?

15. What is Peterborough United's home ground?

16. Who spent 39 successive seasons in Division Three until they were relegated in 1966?

Answers to page 296
NAME THE YEAR 3: **1.** 1986 **2.** 1977 **3.** 1964 **4.** 1994 **5.** 1998 **6.** 1928 **7.** 1979 **8.** 1982 **9.** 1991 **10.** 1995 **11.** 1939 **12.** 1966 **13.** 1995 **14.** 1976 **15.** 1976 **16.** 1998

Leeds United 2

Answers on page 297

1. Who moved from Leeds to Blackburn for £2.7 million in October 1993?

2. Who scored 17 Premiership goals for Leeds in 2000–1?

3. Who scored Leeds' goals when they lost 3–2 at Colchester in the FA Cup in 1971?

4. In which year did Jack Charlton make his League debut?

5. How many League appearances did he make for the club in his 20-year career?

6. For which country did Johnny Giles play?

7. Which three former Leeds players managed the club in the 1980s?

8. Which full-back joined Leeds from Blackburn in 1979 for a club record £354,000?

9. Which striker moved from Burnley to Leeds for £200,000 in 1976?

10. From which club did Leeds sign Robert Molenaar?

11. Which young striker moved to Notts County in summer 2001 for £120,000?

12. In which year did Leeds first gain promotion to Division One?

13. Who beat Leeds in the semi-finals of the 1966–7 FA Cup?

14. Who replaced Gary Sprake in goal for the 1970 FA Cup final replay with Chelsea?

15. Which Leeds player won the first of his 20 England caps against Wales in 1969?

16. Who pipped Leeds on goal average for the League Championship in 1964–5?

Answers to page 297
ENGLAND 4: **1.** 35 **2.** David Beckham **3.** 1992 **4.** John Gidman **5.** Seven
6. Paul Mariner **7.** Austria **8.** None **9.** Sunderland **10.** Neil Webb **11.** None
12. Mexico **13.** Six **14.** Morocco **15.** Monterrey **16.** Graeme Le Saux

Name the Year 3

Answers on page 294

1. When did Maradona's 'Hand of God' knock England out of the World Cup?

2. In which year did Don Revie walk out on England?

3. In which year did Emlyn Hughes make his League debut?

4. In which year was Robbie Fowler fined £1,000 for mooning at Leicester City fans?

5. When was Tom Finney knighted?

6. In which year did Scotland's 'Wembley Wizards' destroy England 5–1?

7. In which year did Ray Wilkins join Manchester United?

8. In which year was Paolo Rossi voted European and World Footballer of the Year?

9. When did Ryan Giggs make his Manchester United debut?

10. When did Paul Gascoigne join Rangers?

11. When did Portsmouth win the FA Cup?

12. When did Johan Cruyff make his international debut?

13. When did Eric Cantona perform his famous karate kick at Selhurst Park?

14. When did Billy Bremner play his last game for Leeds United?

15. When did George Best join Fulham?

16. In which year was David Beckham sent off for England against Argentina?

Answers to page 294
FOOTBALL LEAGUE 4: **1.** Wrexham **2.** Swindon Town **3.** Macclesfield Town **4.** Ipswich Town **5.** Bury **6.** Macclesfield Town **7.** Wycombe Wanderers (who scored with the last kick of the first half and again straight from the kick-off of the second half) **8.** Wrexham **9.** Crewe Alexandra **10.** Johnny Byrne **11.** Bury **12.** Bristol City **13.** Huddersfield Town **14.** Mansfield Town **15.** London Road **16.** Southend United

England 4

Answers on page 295

1. How many clean sheets did Gordon Banks keep for England in his 73 internationals?

2. Who was the only England player to appear in all seven qualifying games for the 1998 World Cup?

3. When did Martin Keown make his England debut?

4. Which Aston Villa full-back won his only England cap in 1977 against Luxembourg?

5. In Trevor Brooking's 47 international games, how many times did he end up on the losing side?

6. Which Ipswich and Arsenal striker scored 13 England goals from 1977–85?

7. Who did England beat 7–0 at Wembley in 1973?

8. How many England caps did Steve Bruce win?

9. As a player with which club did Dave Watson make his England debut?

10. Which Nottingham Forest midfielder made his first England appearance in 1988 against West Germany?

11. How many goals did father and son Brian and Nigel Clough score between them for England?

12. Against whom did Robbie Fowler score his first England goal?

13. How many hat-tricks did Jimmy Greaves score for England?

14. Which African nation held England to a 0–0 draw at the 1986 World Cup?

15. Where did England play all three group matches at the 1986 World Cup?

16. Who was the first Channel Islander to play for England?

Answers to page 295
LEEDS UNITED 2: **1.** David Batty **2.** Mark Viduka **3.** Norman Hunter and Johnny Giles **4.** 1953 **5.** 629 **6.** Republic of Ireland **7.** Allan Clarke, Eddie Gray and Billy Bremner **8.** Kevin Hird **9.** Ray Hankin **10.** Volendam **11.** Tony Hackworth **12.** 1924 **13.** Chelsea **14.** David Harvey **15.** Terry Cooper **16.** Manchester United

Whose Home? 4

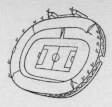

Answers on page 300

1. In which city do Fiorentina play?

2. On which London ground was the FA Cup final played from 1920 to 1922?

3. Which English League club left the County Ground in 1994?

4. Who used to play at the Goldstone Ground?

5. In which year was the Goldstone Ground demolished?

6. Whose ground is famous for having a pub in each corner?

7. What is the name of their ground?

8. Which club's former address was Cold Blow Lane?

9. Which club are planning a move from Filbert Street?

10. Which Northern Ireland club play at Mourneview Park?

11. Who plays at Boothferry Park?

12. Whose home is Priestfield Stadium?

13. Dean Court is associated with which south coast club?

14. In which city do Drumcondra play?

15. When did Oxford United move to the Manor Ground?

16. Which Scottish club play at Ochilview Park?

Answers to page 300
PRESTON NORTH END 1: **1.** 1998 **2.** Burnley **3.** 1946 **4.** 187 **5.** Luton Town **6.** Five **7.** Northampton Town **8.** Manchester United **9.** Swansea Town **10.** Bobby Charlton and Nobby Stiles **11.** Kurt Nogan **12.** Darlington **13.** Tommy Docherty **14.** Alex Dawson **15.** Deepdale **16.** Ted Harper

Tottenham Hotspur 1

Answers on page 301

1. Which Scottish striker did Spurs sign from Chelsea for £2.2 million in 1991?

2. How many times have Spurs been beaten FA Cup finalists?

3. Who were runners-up to Spurs when they won the League Championship in 1951?

4. Which TV inquisitor was the only Englishman to score for Spurs in the 1981 FA Cup final replay against Manchester City?

5. Which Chelsea midfielder did Spurs sign in summer 2001?

6. Who scored against Spurs in the 1982 FA Cup final and later moved to White Hart Lane?

7. Which former Charlton forward joined Spurs from Liverpool for £500,000 in 1988?

8. Who became Spurs' youngest player when he turned out against Manchester City at the age of 16 in 1982?

9. Which Scottish international forward did Spurs sign from Ipswich Town for £450,000 in 1983?

10. Which Scottish international was tragically killed by lightning in 1964?

11. Who were the two Welsh internationals in Spurs' 1962 FA Cup final team?

12. In which year did Gerry Francis become Tottenham manager?

13. From which Scottish club did Spurs sign winger Jimmy Robertson?

14. Which prodigal son returned to White Hart Lane as manager in 2001?

15. From which German club did Spurs sign Steffen Freund?

16. Which Spurs player won his first cap for the Republic of Ireland against Sweden in 1999?

Answers to page 301
TRANSFER TRAIL 5: **1.** Derek Whyte **2.** Celta Vigo **3.** Remi Moses
4. Hibernian **5.** Tranmere Rovers **6.** Simon Coleman **7.** Frank and Ronald De Boer **8.** Hermann Hreidarsson **9.** John Chiedozie **10.** Burnley
11. Gillingham **12.** David Tuttle **13.** Tomas Brolin **14.** Inter Milan **15.** Nigel Quashie **16.** Nico Claesen

Preston North End 1

Answers on page 298

1. When did David Moyes become Preston manager?

2. Who were Preston's first opponents in a Football League game?

3. When did Tom Finney make his Preston debut?

4. How many League goals did he score for the club?

5. From which club did Preston sign Graham Alexander?

6. How many times have Preston finished FA Cup runners-up?

7. Behind whom did Preston finish Fourth Division runners-up in 1987?

8. Who beat Preston in the FA Cup quarter-finals in 1966?

9. Which fellow Second Division team did Preston beat in the semi-finals that year?

10. Which two World Cup winners managed Preston in the 1970s?

11. Who was Preston's top scorer in 1998–9?

12. From which club did Preston sign Sean Gregan?

13. Which future much-travelled manager was transferred as a player from Preston to Arsenal for £29,500 in 1958?

14. Who scored six goals for Preston in their 1964 FA Cup run?

15. What is the name of Preston's ground?

16. Who scored 37 League goals for Preston in 1932–3?

Answers to page 298
WHOSE HOME? 4: **1.** Florence **2.** Stamford Bridge **3.** Northampton Town **4.** Brighton & Hove Albion **5.** 1997 **6.** Brentford **7.** Griffin Park **8.** Millwall **9.** Leicester City **10.** Glenavon **11.** Hull City **12.** Gillingham **13.** AFC Bournemouth **14.** Dublin **15.** 1925 **16.** Stenhousemuir

Transfer Trail 5

Answers on page 299

1. Which player did Middlesbrough sign from Celtic for £900,000 in 1992?

2. From which Spanish club did Ipswich Town sign Spanish Under-21 striker Pablo Gonzales Counago in summer 2001?

3. Which Moses found the promised land of Manchester in 1981 after a £500,000 move from West Bromwich Albion?

4. From which club did Rangers sign Russell Latapy in summer 2001?

5. Who sold Ronnie Moore to Cardiff City in 1979?

6. Which defender moved from Mansfield Town to Middlesbrough for £500,000 in 1989?

7. Which brothers joined Barcelona for a total fee of £14 million in 1999?

8. For which Icelandic defender did Brentford pay Crystal Palace a club record £850,000 in 1998?

9. Which Nigerian winger moved from Orient to Notts County for £480,000 in 1981?

10. Who paid £800,000 to re-sign Steve Davis from Luton Town in 1998?

11. Which club sold Ade Akinbiyi to Bristol City in 1998?

12. Which Barnsley centre-back moved to Millwall in 2000?

13. Which Swedish international joined Leeds United from Parma in 1996?

14. Which Italian club bought Marco Branca from Roma for £2 million in 1996?

15. Which former Queens Park Rangers midfielder moved from Nottingham Forest to Portsmouth in 2000?

16. Which Belgian forward joined Spurs from Standard Liege in 1986?

Answers to page 299
TOTTENHAM HOTSPUR 1: **1.** Gordon Durie **2.** Once **3.** Manchester United **4.** Garth Crooks **5.** Gustavo Poyet **6.** Terry Fenwick **7.** Paul Walsh **8.** Ally Dick **9.** Alan Brazil **10.** John White **11.** Cliff Jones and Terry Medwin **12.** 1994 **13.** St Mirren **14.** Glenn Hoddle **15.** Borussia Dortmund **16.** Stephen Carr

Sharpshooters 3

Answers on page 304

1. Which Chelsea player scored six First Division hat-tricks in 1960–1?

2. Ron Barnes, Wyn Davies and Roy Ambler all bagged hat-tricks for which club in a 10–1 demolition of Hartlepool in 1962?

3. Which future World Cup winner was Liverpool's top scorer with 41 League goals in 1961–2?

4. From which club did Norwich City sign Kevin Reeves?

5. Who scored six goals for Hull City in a 1996–7 FA Cup tie against Whitby?

6. Which Preston player scored in every round of the FA Cup in 1954?

7. Which player opened the scoring in the final of Euro 2000?

8. Who was Manchester United's top Premiership scorer in 2000–1?

9. For which country does David Trezeguet play?

10. Which striker did Bristol Rovers sell to Huddersfield for £1.2 million in 1996?

11. From which club did Bristol City sign Tony Thorpe?

12. In which country was Laurent D'Jaffo born?

13. Whose goal at Stockport kept Crystal Palace in Division One at the end of 2000–1?

14. From which club was he signed earlier in the season?

15. Which moustachioed striker moved from Ipswich to Liverpool for £200,000 in 1976?

16. Which striker cost Torquay United a club record £70,000 from Barry Town in 1999?

Answers to page 304
WATFORD 1: **1.** Mike Keen **2.** Yellow **3.** 1970 **4.** Chelsea **5.** Terry Garbett **6.** Liverpool **7.** Barry Endean **8.** 1982 **9.** Liverpool **10.** Gary Penrice **11.** Paul Furlong **12.** Andy Hessenthaler **13.** Gerard Lavin **14.** Duncan Welbourne **15.** 1976 **16.** Dave Bassett

Scotland 2

Answers on page 305

1. Which Scottish player was sent off in the Euro 2000 qualifier against the Faroe Islands in Toftir?

2. Who scored Scotland's goal in that 1–1 draw?

3. Who scored Scotland's winner in Germany in April 1999?

4. In which city was that friendly played?

5. How many Scottish caps did Bob Wilson win?

6. Which goalkeeper represented Scotland at both soccer and cricket?

7. With which club was Denis Law a player when he won his first Scotland cap?

8. In which year did Jim Leighton win his first cap?

9. Who were Scotland's opponents that day?

10. Who knocked Scotland out of Euro 2000?

11. In which city did Scotland lose 1–0 to Brazil at the 1990 World Cup finals?

12. Who scored Scotland's winning goal against Switzerland at Euro 96?

13. Where was that game played?

14. Which seasoned midfielder who starred with Liverpool in 2000–1 made his Scotland debut in 1990 against East Germany?

15. With which League club was he a player at the time?

16. Which Scottish international played his football in Germany in 1997?

Answers to page 305
ODDBALLS 5: **1.** Bolton Wanderers **2.** Perry Digweed **3.** Vinnie Jones
4. Paul Gascoigne **5.** Graeme Souness **6.** They defected to West Germany
by ferry **7.** Oxford United **8.** Stoke City **9.** Cowdenbeath **10.** Brazil
11. Nigeria **12.** Republic of Ireland **13.** Wimbledon's Sam Hammam
14. Everton **15.** Cheltenham Town **16.** Swansea City

Watford 1

Answers on page 302

1. Which former Queens Park Rangers captain became manager of Watford in 1973?

2. What is the predominant colour in Watford's shirts?

3. In which year did Watford first reach the semi-finals of the FA Cup?

4. To whom did they lose 5–1 that year?

5. Who scored Watford's goal that day?

6. Who had Watford beaten in the sixth round?

7. And who scored Watford's winning goal in that game?

8. In which year were Watford promoted to the top division for the first time in their history?

9. Behind whom did they finish First Division runners-up the following year?

10. Which forward did Watford sell to Aston Villa for £1 million in 1991?

11. Who was Watford's leading scorer in 1992–3?

12. Which former Watford player was manager of Gillingham in 2000–1?

13. Which Scottish full-back moved to Millwall for £500,000 in 1995?

14. Which former Grimsby Town full-back made 411 League appearances for Watford from 1963 to 1974?

15. When did Luther Blissett make his Watford debut?

16. Who followed Graham Taylor as Watford manager in 1987?

Answers to page 302
SHARPSHOOTERS 3: 1. Jimmy Greaves 2. Wrexham 3. Roger Hunt
4. Bournemouth 5. Duane Darby 6. Charlie Wayman 7. Marco Delvecchio
8. Teddy Sheringham 9. France 10. Marcus Stewart 11. Fulham 12. France
13. Dougie Freedman 14. Nottingham Forest 15. David Johnson 16. Eifion
Williams

Oddballs 5

Answers on page 303

1. A fan from which club was fined £60 and banned for three months in 1995 for throwing a turnip in front of Graham Taylor?

2. Which Brighton goalkeeper failed to turn up for a match in 1988 because nobody had remembered to tell him he was playing?

3. Who did Sam Hammam call a 'mosquito brain' in 1992?

4. Which Lazio player belched into a TV microphone in 1993?

5. Which Rangers manager reduced the width of the Ibrox Park pitch before a 1987 European Cup tie with Dynamo Kiev?

6. What happened to East German internationals Emil Poklithar and Rolf Stawost after a 1961 game in Copenhagen?

7. Which League club does Tim Henman support?

8. Which League club has a fanzine called *The Oatcake*?

9. In 1994, which Scottish club ended a run of 38 home League matches without a win?

10. Which country's League did Bangu win for the first time in 1967?

11. Fourteen members of which country's youth team went into hiding in 1993 during a tournament in Gothenburg?

12. Which country did Terry Mancini play for?

13. In 1993, which club owner landed in hot water after allegedly scrawling graffiti on the dressing room at West Ham?

14. Which club appeared in four successive Charity Shields from 1984 to 1987?

15. Which League club used to play at Grafton Cricket Ground?

16. Which club does Catherine Zeta-Jones follow?

Answers to page 303
SCOTLAND 2: 1. Matt Elliott 2. Allan Johnston 3. Don Hutchison
4. Bremen 5. Two 6. Andy Goram 7. Huddersfield Town 8. 1983 9. East Germany 10. England 11. Turin 12. Ally McCoist 13. Villa Park 14. Gary McAllister 15. Leicester City 16. Paul Lambert

Arsenal 2

Answers on page 308

1. In which year did Tony Adams make his Arsenal debut?

2. Which Welsh striker joined Arsenal from Luton Town in 1995?

3. Which midfielder made 110 appearances for Arsenal after signing from Watford in 1987?

4. Which FA Cup final hero came to Highbury from Wolves in 1977?

5. Behind whom did Arsenal finish First Division runners-up in 1925–6?

6. Arsenal's 1971 FA Cup triumph was their first for how many years?

7. Which opponents did they meet in the final on both occasions?

8. Which brother of an England cricket captain made 50 League appearances for Arsenal from 1978?

9. Which London club knocked Arsenal out of the 1994–5 FA Cup?

10. Which two clubs finished below Arsenal to save them from relegation to Division Two in 1925?

11. Which reliable defender played 353 League games for Arsenal from 1961–78?

12. With which country was Pat Rice an international?

13. Who was Arsenal's top scorer in 1974–5?

14. Who joined Arsenal for £1.3 million from Queens Park Rangers in 1990?

15. To whom were Arsenal First Division runners-up in 1931–2?

16. Who took Arsenal to penalties in the third round during the FA Cup-winning year of 1998?

Answers to page 308
FOOTBALL LEAGUE 5: **1.** Adam Buckley (son of Alan Buckley) **2.** Wolves **3.** Black and white stripes **4.** Barnsley **5.** Blackpool **6.** Jamie Cureton **7.** Rod Thomas **8.** Sunderland **9.** Bolton Wanderers **10.** Liverpool **11.** Rochdale **12.** Chester City **13.** Bristol City **14.** Crewe Alexandra **15.** 1997 **16.** Kidderminster Harriers

The World Game 7

Answers on page 309

1. In which South American country do Cerro Porteno and Olimpia play?

2. Who was voted German Footballer of the Year in 1998?

3. RBC Roosendaal finished bottom of which country's First Division in 2001?

4. Which Italian club are known as 'The Nerazzuri'?

5. Who was Spanish national coach from 1982 to 1988?

6. Cobreloa, Copa Libertadores winners in 1982, came from which country?

7. Which Uruguayan team were the first winners of the World Club Championship?

8. Who finished runners-up in the French League in 2000–1?

9. Which club has won most Swedish League titles?

10. Braga, Maritimo and Farense are clubs in which country?

11. Vardar won which country's Cup final in 1999?

12. Who were the first Argentinian winners of the Copa Libertadores?

13. With which Swedish club did Roy Hodgson begin his managerial career?

14. Who did Parma sign for £6.5 million from Juventus in 1994–5?

15. Whose injury-time equaliser at Hamburg earned his team the 2000–1 Bundesliga title by a solitary point?

16. Who won the Spanish League in 2000–1?

Answers to page 309
KILMARNOCK 1: **1.** 'Killie' **2.** 1920 **3.** 1997 **4.** Falkirk **5.** 1957 **6.** Bobby Williamson **7.** Ally McCoist **8.** Rotherham United **9.** Harry 'Peerie' Cunningham **10.** Alan Robertson **11.** Paul Wright **12.** Willie Watters **13.** 1965–6 **14.** Real Madrid **15.** Hearts **16.** Joe Nibloe

Football League 5

Answers on page 306

1. Which Lincoln City player is the manager's son?

2. Against whom did Scarborough play their first Football League game?

3. In what colour shirts do Notts County play?

4. Which club are nicknamed 'The Tykes'?

5. Which Lancashire club used to play at Raikes Hall Gardens?

6. Who was Reading's leading scorer in 2000–1?

7. Which Swindon Town player won 50 caps for Wales from 1967–78?

8. Who totalled 105 points in romping to the First Division title in 1999?

9. Which First Division team reached the FA Cup semi-finals in 2000?

10. Based on final League positions, which was the most successful team in the 1980s?

11. And which was the least successful team of the 1980s?

12. Which former League club paid a record £94,000 to buy Stuart Rimmer from Barnsley in 1991?

13. Which club won most titles of the old Division Three (South)?

14. Which current First Division team had to apply for re-election to the League on seven occasions?

15. In which year were Macclesfield Town promoted to the Football League?

16. Which club were promoted to the Football League in 2000?

Answers to page 306
ARSENAL 2: **1.** 1983 **2.** John Hartson **3.** Kevin Richardson **4.** Alan Sunderland **5.** Huddersfield Town **6.** 21 **7.** Liverpool **8.** Steve Gatting **9.** Millwall **10.** Preston North End and Nottingham Forest **11.** Peter Simpson **12.** Northern Ireland **13.** Brian Kidd **14.** David Seaman **15.** Everton **16.** Port Vale

Kilmarnock 1

Answers on page 307

1. What is Kilmarnock's unsurprising nickname?

2. In which year did Kilmarnock win the Scottish FA Cup for the first time?

3. When did they last win the Scottish Cup?

4. Who did Kilmarnock beat in the final?

5. In which year had the same two clubs previously met in the final?

6. Who succeeded Alex Totten as manager?

7. Which veteran striker was Kilmarnock's leading scorer in 1998–9?

8. To which English club did Kilmarnock pay £100,000 to sign Bobby Williamson as a player in 1990?

9. Who scored 34 League goals for Kilmarnock in 1927–8?

10. Who made 481 League appearances for the club between 1972 and 1988?

11. Who did Kilmarnock sign for £300,000 from St Johnstone in 1995?

12. Which Kilmarnock forward was voted Second Division Player of the Year for 1989–90?

13. In which season did Kilmarnock play in the European Cup?

14. Which Spanish aces knocked them out of that year's competition?

15. Who beat Kilmarnock 1–0 in the Scottish League Cup final of 1962–3?

16. Who won 11 Scottish caps as a Kilmarnock player from 1929 to 1932?

Answers to page 307
THE WORLD GAME 7: 1. Paraguay 2. Oliver Bierhoff 3. Holland 4. Inter Milan 5. Miguel Munoz 6. Chile 7. Peñarol 8. Olympique Lyon 9. IFK Gothenburg 10. Portugal 11. Macedonia 12. Independiente 13. Halmstad 14. Dino Baggio 15. Patrik Andersson (Bayern Munich) 16. Real Madrid

Early Baths 1

Answers on page 312

1. Which future England manager was sent off as a player in an Under-23 match against East Germany in 1972?

2. How many players were sent off when Gremio met Peñarol in a tempestuous South American Super Cup quarter-final in 1993?

3. Which Brentford player was sent off in the 1997 Second Division play-off final against Crewe?

4. Who was sent off against England in the 1966 World Cup quarter-finals?

5. Of which country was he the captain?

6. Which current Premiership manager missed the 1982 FA Cup final replay through suspension?

7. Who was booked after just five seconds and later sent off while playing for Sheffield United against Manchester City in 1991?

8. Which two Hearts players were suspended for ten matches for fighting each other during a pre-season friendly with Raith in 1994?

9. Which Arsenal player was given a three-match ban for pushing referee Paul Durkin after being sent off in 1997?

10. Giuseppe Lorenzo was sent off for striking an opponent after just ten seconds of an Italian League match with Parma in 1990. Who was he playing for?

11. Which Bury player scored a hat-trick in 1973 and was then sent off?

12. In 1973, who became the first Welsh international to be sent off?

13. Which Scottish international striker was sent off against Wales in 1981?

14. Which Northern Ireland player was sent off at the 1982 World Cup finals?

15. Which two Leeds players were sent off at Highbury in August 2001?

16. Who were sent off when Leicester visited Arsenal in August 2001?

Answers to page 312
BURNLEY 1: 1. Torquay United and Lincoln City 2. 1974 3. Newcastle United 4. Green 5. 30 6. Rotherham United 7. Harry Potts 8. Wolves 9. Spurs 10. Jimmy Robson 11. Adam Blacklaw 12. Glentoran 13. Ray Pointer 14. Stan Terrent 15. Andy Payton 16. Anglo-Scottish Cup

Goalkeepers 3

Answers on page 313

1. In which county was David Seaman born?

2. From which club did Bradford City sign Matt Clarke?

3. What nationality is Thomas Myhre?

4. From which club was he transferred to Everton?

5. Which England international kept goal for Sheffield Wednesday in the 1966 FA Cup final?

6. With which Italian club did Dino Zoff make his first League appearance in 1961?

7. How many goals did he let in on his debut?

8. For which club did Lev Yashin make 326 appearances?

9. What was Bob Wilson's profession before he became a goalkeeper?

10. Which 1999 FA Cup final goalkeeper began his career with Seaham Redstar?

11. Which was Bruce Grobbelaar's first English League club?

12. With which club did Frank Swift spend his entire career?

13. What nationality is Thomas Sorensen?

14. Which goalkeeper moved from Wimbledon to Tottenham in 2000?

15. For which country does he play at international level?

16. From which club did Charlton sign Dean Kiely?

Answers to page 313
LIVERPOOL 2: **1.** 1994 **2.** Rob Jones **3.** Phil Neal **4.** Preston North End
5. Steve McMahon **6.** 1965 **7.** Jason McAteer **8.** Alec Lindsay **9.** Norwegian
10. Jimmy Jackson **11.** Harry Bradshaw (England, 1897) **12.** Don Hutchison
13. Swiss **14.** Blackburn Rovers **15.** Steven Gerrard **16.** Howard Gayle

Burnley 1

Answers on page 310

1. Which were the only two clubs to finish below Burnley in the Football League in 1987?

2. When did Burnley last reach the semi-finals of the FA Cup?

3. Who beat them in that match?

4. What colour shirts did Burnley wear before copying Aston Villa's claret and blue?

5. How many games did Burnley go unbeaten on their way to winning the League Championship in 1921?

6. From which club did Burnley sign Frank Casper?

7. Who was Burnley manager from 1958 to 1970?

8. Who finished runners-up to Burnley when they won the League title in 1960?

9. Which team did Burnley meet for three successive years in the FA Cup between 1961 and 1963?

10. Who scored Burnley's goal when they lost 3–1 in the 1962 Cup final?

11. Who kept goal for Burnley in that match?

12. From which Irish club did Burnley sign Alex Elder and Jimmy McIlroy?

13. Which fair-haired centre-forward of the Cup final team went on to play for Coventry and Portsmouth?

14. Which manager steered Burnley into the First Division in 2000?

15. Who was their leading scorer in that promotion season?

16. Which Cup competition did Burnley win in 1979?

Answers to page 310
EARLY BATHS 1: **1.** Kevin Keegan **2.** Eight **3.** Brian Statham **4.** Antonio Rattin **5.** Argentina **6.** Glenn Roeder (as a player with Queens Park Rangers) **7.** Vinnie Jones **8.** Graeme Hogg and Craig Levein **9.** Emmanuel Petit **10.** Bologna **11.** John Murray **12.** Trevor Hockey **13.** Joe Jordan **14.** Mal Donaghy **15.** Lee Bowyer and Danny Mills **16.** Patrick Vieira and Dennis Wise

Liverpool 2

Answers on page 311

1. In which year was the Kop demolished?

2. Which full-back joined Liverpool from Crewe for £300,000 in 1991?

3. Who was Bob Paisley's first signing?

4. From which club did Liverpool sign Gordon Milne?

5. Who was Kenny Dalglish's first signing?

6. When did Liverpool first win the FA Cup?

7. Which Republic of Ireland international of the 1990s came from a boxing family?

8. Who moved to Liverpool from Bury for £67,000 in 1969?

9. What nationality is Oyvind Leonhardsen?

10. Which Liverpool hard man quit football in 1933 to become a church minister?

11. Who was the first Liverpool player to win an international cap?

12. Which future Scottish international joined Liverpool from Hartlepool United for £175,000 in 1990?

13. What nationality is Stephane Henchoz?

14. And which club did he leave to sign for Liverpool?

15. Which England midfielder made his Liverpool debut against Celta Vigo in a 1998 UEFA Cup tie?

16. Who was Liverpool's first black player?

Answers to page 311
GOALKEEPERS 3: 1. Yorkshire 2. Sheffield Wednesday 3. Norwegian
4. Viking Stavanger 5. Ron Springett 6. Udinese 7. Five 8. Moscow Dynamo
9. Teacher 10. Steve Harper 11. Crewe Alexandra 12. Manchester City
13. Danish 14. Neil Sullivan 15. Scotland 16. Bury

League Cup 2

Answers on page 316

1. Who scored Leicester City's last three goals in the 1999–2000 Worthington Cup?

2. Who did Tranmere Rovers beat in the semi-finals of the 1999–2000 Worthington Cup?

3. Which Leicester old boy scored Tranmere's goal in the final?

4. What was the League Cup competition called in 1990–1 and 1991–2?

5. Whose two goals won the 1963 League Cup final for Birmingham City against local rivals Aston Villa?

6. Who did Leicester City beat in the 1964 final?

7. How many times have Manchester United won the League Cup?

8. Which two London clubs did Aston Villa knock out of the 1976–7 competition?

9. Who did Birmingham City beat in the quarter-finals of the 1999–2000 Worthington Cup?

10. Which winger scored Manchester City's first goal in the 1976 final?

11. Where did the replay of the 1978 final between Nottingham Forest and Liverpool take place?

12. Including the 2001 final, which club have won the most League Cups?

13. Who were the two goalkeepers in the 1979 final between Nottingham Forest and Southampton?

14. Who beat Arsenal 6–2 at Highbury in a 1990 League Cup tie?

15. Who scored a hat-trick in that match?

16. Who did Chelsea beat 3–2 on aggregate in the 1965 final?

Answers to page 316
NAME THE YEAR 4: **1.** 1993 **2.** 1998 **3.** 1995 **4.** 1949 **5.** 1973 **6.** 1976 **7.** 1985 **8.** 1998 **9.** 1964 **10.** 1977 **11.** 1978 **12.** 1998 **13.** 1966 **14.** 1950 **15.** 1984 **16.** 1903

Argentina 1

Answers on page 317

1. Who won a record 98 caps for Argentina?
2. Whose goal in the quarter-finals of France 98 was Argentina's 100th in the World Cup?
3. Who did Argentina beat 6–0 in their last second-round match at the 1978 World Cup finals?
4. Who beat Argentina in their opening match at the 1982 World Cup finals?
5. Which was the only World Cup finals for which Argentina failed to qualify?
6. Which two countries finished above them in the South American group?
7. Which African nation shocked Argentina by defeating them 1–0 at Italia 90?
8. Who scored Argentina's goals in their 3–0 World Cup qualifying win over Colombia in June 2001?
9. Which former Arsenal defender played for Argentina in that match?
10. Which future White Hart Lane favourite starred in the 1978 World Cup final?
11. In which year did Diego Maradona win his first cap?
12. How many caps did Maradona win?
13. Who defeated Argentina in the first-round group at the 1994 World Cup finals?
14. Which European nation eventually knocked Argentina out of the 1994 tournament?
15. What piece of World Cup history did Pedro Monzon and Gustavo Dezotti make in 1990?
16. Who is Argentina's leading international goalscorer?

Answers to page 317
WEST BROMWICH ALBION 1: 1. Five 2. 1954 3. Tony Brown
4. Peterborough United 5. Jimmy Cookson 6. 1900 7. Australian
8. Blackpool 9. 1986 10. Four 11. William 'Ginger' Richardson 12. Johnny
Giles 13. Bryan Robson 14. Peter Barnes 15. Cambridge United 16. Alistair
Brown

Name the Year 4

Answers on page 314

1. When was Roberto Baggio voted World Player of the Year?

2. When did Chelsea win their second European Cup-Winners' Cup final?

3. When did Belarus beat Holland 1–0 in a European Championship qualifier?

4. When did Rangers complete their first 'treble'?

5. In which year did Italy gain their first win at Wembley?

6. When did East Germany win the Olympic soccer tournament?

7. When did Luton Town switch their pitch to plastic?

8. When did USA beat Brazil 1–0 in the Conacaf Gold Cup?

9. When did Bobby Moore become the youngest captain to lift the FA Cup?

10. In which year did Ally MacLeod become Scotland manager?

11. When did Frank Stapleton make the first of his five Cup final appearances?

12. When did Emley reach the fourth round of the FA Cup?

13. When did Peter Shilton play his first League match?

14. In which year did Colchester United join the Football League?

15. When did Liverpool complete a hat-trick of League Championships?

16. In which year did Bury win the FA Cup without conceding a goal?

Answers to page 314
LEAGUE CUP 2: **1.** Matt Elliott **2.** Bolton Wanderers **3.** David Kelly **4.** Rumbelows Cup **5.** Ken Leek **6.** Stoke City **7.** Once **8.** Millwall and Queens Park Rangers **9.** Sheffield Wednesday **10.** Peter Barnes **11.** Old Trafford **12.** Liverpool (five) **13.** Peter Shilton and Terry Gennoe **14.** Manchester United **15.** Lee Sharpe **16.** Leicester City

West Bromwich Albion 1

Answers on page 315

1. How many times have West Brom won the FA Cup?

2. In which year did Albion win the FA Cup and finish runners-up to Wolves in the League?

3. Who scored 218 League goals for Albion from 1963 to 1979?

4. From which club did Albion sign John Wile?

5. Who scored six goals against Blackpool in a Second Division match in 1927?

6. In which year did Albion move to The Hawthorns?

7. What nationality is Jason Van Blerk?

8. From which club did Albion sign James Quinn?

9. In which year were Albion last relegated from the top division?

10. How many League games did they win that season?

11. Who scored 39 League goals for Albion in 1935–6?

12. Who became Albion manager in 1975?

13. Which future England captain did Albion sell to Manchester United for £1.5 million in 1981?

14. Who did Albion sign from Manchester City for £748,000 in 1979?

15. From which club did Albion sign Brendan Batson?

16. Which Brown was Albion top scorer in 1978–9?

Answers to page 315
ARGENTINA 1: **1.** Oscar Ruggeri **2.** Claudio Lopez **3.** Peru **4.** Belgium **5.** 1970 **6.** Peru and Bolivia **7.** Cameroon **8.** Kily Gonzalez, Claudio Lopez and Hernan Crespo **9.** Nelson Vivas **10.** Osvaldo Ardiles **11.** 1977 **12.** 90 **13.** Bulgaria **14.** Romania **15.** They were the first players to be sent off in a World Cup final **16.** Gabriel Batistuta

Germany 2

Answers on page 320

1. Who was appointed German national coach in 1990?

2. Who scored West Germany's 90th-minute equaliser against England at the 1966 World Cup final?

3. In 1967, who did West Germany beat 6–0 in their first European Championship match?

4. Which country did the Germans crush 16–0 in 1912?

5. Who many caps did Franz Beckenbauer win?

6. Against whom did Germany come back from 2–0 down to snatch a priceless point in a June 2001 World Cup qualifier?

7. Which keeper won 95 caps for West Germany in a career spanning 11 years?

8. Who did the Germans beat in the quarter-finals of the 1990 World Cup?

9. Whose penalty proved decisive in that match?

10. Who scored West Germany's winner against England in the quarter-finals of the 1970 World Cup?

11. Who was voted Player of the Tournament at the 1990 World Cup?

12. In which year did the West and East German teams merge?

13. Who was the first East German to play for the new united Germany?

14. Who beat West Germany 2–0 in a group match at the 1986 World Cup finals?

15. Which African nation held the Germans to a 0–0 draw in Group Two at the 1978 World Cup finals?

16. Whose two goals beat Sweden in the semi-finals of the 1992 European Championship?

Answers to page 320
FOOTBALL LEAGUE 6: **1.** Preston North End **2.** Huddersfield Town **3.** Blackpool **4.** York City **5.** Chesterfield **6.** Peter Crouch **7.** 1920 **8.** It was expanded and regionalised **9.** Cardiff City **10.** Fulham **11.** Mansfield Town and Chester City **12.** Nelson **13.** Accrington Stanley **14.** Southend United **15.** No **16.** Newport County

Dundee 1

Answers on page 321

1. From whom did Jocky Scott take over as manager of Dundee?

2. Which Dundee striker scored 52 League goals in 1963–4 before moving to London?

3. When did Dundee win the Scottish FA Cup for the only time?

4. Who did they beat in the final?

5. Who was Dundee's leading goalscorer in 1998–9?

6. Who made 341 League appearances for the club between 1945 and 1961?

7. Which Italian was Dundee's manager in 2001?

8. When did Dundee last reach the Scottish FA Cup final?

9. When did Dundee win their only Scottish League Championship?

10. The centre-half in that team went on to win 11 Scotland caps and play for Arsenal. What was his name?

11. What nationality is Fabian Caballera?

12. Who was named Scottish First Division Player of the Year in 1977–8?

13. How many League goals did he score that season?

14. When were Dundee last promoted back to the Premier Division?

15. In which year did Dundee reach the semi-finals of the European Cup?

16. Who knocked them out of the competition?

Answers to page 321
ENGLAND 5: **1.** Chile **2.** Bobby Charlton **3.** Leon **4.** Argentina **5.** Gerry Hitchens **6.** Three (1958, 1962 and 1970) **7.** Spain **8.** Chris Powell **9.** Pride Park, Derby **10.** Naples **11.** Brian Labone **12.** Francis Lee **13.** Denmark and France **14.** Rio Ferdinand **15.** Nandor Hidegkuti **16.** Red

Football League 6

Answers on page 318

1. Which Nationwide League team won most away games in 1999–2000?

2. Which team were relegated after losing to Birmingham City on the last day of the 2000–1 season?

3. Who knocked Hartlepool United out of the 2001 Third Division play-offs?

4. Which club replaced Ashington as Football League members in 1929?

5. Which club's best-ever League season was finishing fourth in Division Two in 1946–7?

6. Which 6ft 7in striker joined Portsmouth from Queens Park Rangers in summer 2001?

7. When did the Football League introduce a Third Division?

8. And what happened to the Third Division the following year?

9. Which team were the highest Nationwide League scorers in 2000–1?

10. And which team had the best defensive record?

11. Which two clubs joined the Football League in 1931?

12. Which Lancashire club dropped out of the League that year, never to return?

13. Which former League members narrowly missed out on promotion to Division Two in 1955, 1956, 1957 and 1958?

14. Martin Carruthers was leading League goalscorer for which club in 1999–2000?

15. Have Rochdale ever played in the top two divisions?

16. Which club left the Football League in 1931, returned a year later and then dropped out again in 1988?

Answers to page 318
GERMANY 2: **1.** Berti Vogts **2.** Wolfgang Weber **3.** Albania **4.** Russia **5.** 103 **6.** Finland **7.** Sepp Maier **8.** Czechoslovakia **9.** Lothar Matthäus **10.** Gerd Müller **11.** Lothar Matthäus **12.** 1990 **13.** Matthias Sammer **14.** Denmark **15.** Tunisia **16.** Karlheinz Riedle

England 5

Answers on page 319

1. Which country gained their first-ever victory at Wembley in 1998?

2. Who broke Billy Wright's England appearances record in the 1970 World Cup quarter-final against West Germany?

3. In which city did that game take place?

4. Which South American country did England beat 3–1 in the group matches at the 1962 World Cup finals?

5. Who scored England's goal in their quarter-final defeat to Brazil at the 1962 World Cup finals?

6. How many times have England and Brazil met in World Cup matches?

7. Who were England's first opponents under Sven Goran Eriksson?

8. Which Charlton full-back won his first cap under Eriksson?

9. Where did England play Mexico in 2001?

10. In which city did England beat Cameroon in the quarter-finals of the 1990 World Cup?

11. Which Everton centre-half won the first of his 26 caps in 1963?

12. Which pugnacious Manchester City forward, who won his first cap in 1969, scored 10 goals in 27 international appearances?

13. Against which two teams did England gain goalless draws at the 1992 European Championship finals?

14. Which was the only Leeds player to start the July 2001 World Cup qualifier in Greece?

15. Which Hungarian scored a hat-trick against England at Wembley in 1953?

16. What colour shirts did England wear in the 1966 World Cup final?

Answers to page 319
DUNDEE 1: **1.** Archie Knox **2.** Alan Gilzean **3.** 1910 **4.** Clyde **5.** Eddie Annand **6.** Doug Cowie **7.** Ivano Bonetti **8.** 1964 **9.** 1962 **10.** Ian Ure **11.** Argentinian **12.** Billy Pirie **13.** 35 **14.** 1998 **15.** 1963 **16.** Benfica

FA Cup 5

Answers on page 324

1. Which Midlands club have reached eight FA Cup semi-finals without ever winning the competition?

2. How many Second Division teams reached the FA Cup final in the 1970s?

3. Which team lost the 1926 final and were relegated in the same season?

4. Who was the only Republic of Ireland international in Liverpool's victorious 1992 team?

5. Which future manager of the club scored twice for West Bromwich Albion in the 1954 Cup final?

6. Who did Albion beat in the final?

7. Who were the two Argentinians in Tottenham's 1981 Cup final team?

8. Who was the first Swedish international to play in an FA Cup final?

9. In which year did Southern Leaguers Wimbledon take Leeds United to a Cup replay?

10. Which Wimbledon keeper saved a Peter Lorimer penalty in that tie?

11. Who did Queens Park Rangers beat in the semi-finals of the 1982 FA Cup?

12. Who scored QPR's winning goal?

13. Which Fourth Division team put First Division Millwall out of the Cup in 1990?

14. Which London club knocked Aston Villa out of the 1998–9 FA Cup?

15. In 1997, which team were beaten in the Cup final and also relegated to Division One?

16. Who lost successive finals in 1985 and 1986?

Answers to page 324
THE WORLD GAME 8: **1.** St Etienne **2.** Javier Alvarez **3.** Las Palmas
4. Genoa **5.** Mexico **6.** Nuremberg **7.** Erich Ribbeck **8.** Athletic Bilbao
9. Barcelona **10.** Never **11.** CSKA Sofia **12.** Roberto Pruzzo **13.** Sardinia
14. 16 **15.** Argentinian **16.** Burkina Faso

Nicknames 2

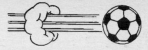

Answers on page 325

1. Which English League club are known as 'The Throstles' or 'The Baggies'?

2. Which English club are nicknamed 'The Dons'?

3. And which Scottish club are called 'The Dons'?

4. Who are 'The Hornets'?

5. What is Luton Town's nickname?

6. Which London club are known as 'The Eagles'?

7. Who are 'The Bluebirds'?

8. What is Exeter City's nickname?

9. Which Scottish club are called 'The Jags'?

10. Who are known as 'The Potters'?

11. Which Scottish club are nicknamed 'The Binos'?

12. Who are 'The Spireites'?

13. Which nickname is shared by Bristol City, Cheltenham Town, Swindon Town and Wrexham?

14. In Scotland, who are 'The Wee Rovers'?

15. What is Queen of the South's nickname?

16. Who are known as 'The Saddlers'?

Answers to page 325
MANAGERS 6: 1. Roy McFarland 2. John Beck 3. Ray Harford 4. Alan Cork
5. Carlos Alberto Parreira 6. Billy McNeill 7. Lawrie McMenemy
8. Millwall 9. Syd Owen 10. Brentford 11. Bulgaria 12. Frank Stapleton
13. Keith Burkinshaw 14. Bill McGarry 15. East Fife 16. 1981

The World Game 8

Answers on page 322

1. Which French League club were deducted seven points in 2000–1?

2. Who was appointed coach of Colombia in September 1998?

3. In 2000–1, which team played in the top division of the Spanish League for the first time in 12 years?

4. In which Italian city do Sampdoria play their home games?

5. In which country do Cruz Azul and Atletico Morelia play?

6. Which club won the German Second Division title in 2001?

7. Who was appointed German coach in September 1998?

8. Which is Spain's oldest club?

9. Which Spanish club sacked coach Ferrer after losing 3–1 to Osasuna in April 2001?

10. How many times have Olympique Lyon won the French League?

11. Which Bulgarian club play at the Bulgarska Armia Stadium?

12. Which Roma striker was Serie 'A''s leading marksman in 1981, 1982 and 1986?

13. On which island are Cagliari based?

14. How many times have PSV Eindhoven won the Dutch League?

15. What nationality is Gabriel Batistuta?

16. Didier Notheau was appointed coach of which African nation in 1998?

Answers to page 322
FA CUP 5: 1. Birmingham City 2. Three – Sunderland, Fulham and Southampton 3. Manchester City 4. Ray Houghton 5. Ronnie Allen 6. Preston North End 7. Osvaldo Ardlles and Ricardo Villa 8. Roland Nilsson (Sheffield Wednesday) 9. 1975 10. Dickie Guy 11. West Bromwich Albion 12. Clive Allen 13. Cambridge United 14. Fulham 15. Middlesbrough 16. Everton

Managers 6

Answers on page 323

1. Who was appointed manager of Torquay United in July 2001?

2. Which controversial figure managed Cambridge United from 1990 to 1992 and returned for a second spell in 2001?

3. Who succeeded Bobby Gould as Wimbledon manager?

4. Which former Wimbledon player took charge of Cardiff City in 2000–1?

5. Who was Brazil's victorious coach at the 1994 World Cup finals?

6. Who succeeded Jock Stein as Celtic manager?

7. Who was manager of Southampton from 1973 to 1985?

8. Which London club did Benny Fenton manage from 1966 to 1974?

9. Who captained Luton Town at the 1959 FA Cup final and became manager of the club in the same year?

10. At which London club did chairman Ron Noades become manager in 1998?

11. Dimitar Dimitrov was appointed coach of which nation in 1998?

12. Which former Arsenal and Manchester United striker became manager of Bradford City in 1991?

13. Which Tottenham manager took the club to two FA Cup triumphs in the 1980s?

14. Who was Ipswich Town manager from 1964 to 1968?

15. Roy Barry, Steve Archibald and Jimmy Bone have all managed which Scottish club?

16. In which year did Howard Kendall first become Everton boss?

Answers to page 323
NICKNAMES 2: **1.** West Bromwich Albion **2.** Wimbledon **3.** Aberdeen **4.** Watford **5.** 'The Hatters' **6.** Crystal Palace **7.** Cardiff City **8.** 'The Grecians' **9.** Partick Thistle **10.** Stoke City **11.** Stirling Albion **12.** Chesterfield **13.** 'The Robins' **14.** Albion Rovers **15.** 'The Doonhamers' **16.** Walsall

Bradford City 1

Answers on page 328

1. Who scored 34 League goals for Bradford City in 1961–2?

2. Which former Republic of Ireland international became City manager in 1991?

3. Which division were City in when they reached the FA Cup quarter-finals in 1976?

4. Which First Division club did they knock out in round five?

5. Which team put an end to City's Cup run that year?

6. Which inspirational leader returned to Valley Parade after spells with Everton and Rangers?

7. Which Brazilian did City sell to Dunfermline Athletic in November 1998?

8. From which club did City sign Dean Windass?

9. How many goals did Albert Whitehurst score against Tranmere Rovers in a Third Division (North) match in 1929?

10. Which Isaiah did City buy from Arsenal for £1.3 million in 1998?

11. Who did City sell to Newcastle for £2 million in 1997?

12. Who made 502 League appearances for the club from 1970 to 1984?

13. Which two teams were promoted with Bradford from Division Three in 1985?

14. Who scored 121 League goals for City between 1981 and 1986?

15. In which year was the horrific fire at Valley Parade?

16. Which City player won nine caps for Northern Ireland between 1911 and 1914?

Answers to page 328
THE WORLD GAME 9: **1.** Union Berlin **2.** Schalke **3.** Switzerland **4.** Lazio **5.** Nigeria **6.** Red Star Belgrade **7.** AEK Athens **8.** Azerbaijan **9.** Bolivia **10.** Nigeria **11.** Monaco **12.** Hungary **13.** Armenia **14.** Albania **15.** Adelaide City **16.** Steaua Bucharest

Nicknames 3

Answers on page 329

1. Which club are known as 'The Villans'?

2. Which Scottish club call themselves 'The Blue Toon'?

3. What is Bradford City's nickname?

4. Which Conference club are called 'The Railwaymen'?

5. Which African country's team are nicknamed 'The Elephants'?

6. Which Bradford City striker of the 1960s was nicknamed 'Bronco' after a character in a TV Western?

7. Which English League club are known as 'The Posh'?

8. Which club's nickname is 'The Merry Millers'?

9. Which Arsenal player was known as 'Chippy'?

10. Who are 'The Owls'?

11. Which Premiership team are called 'The Toffees'?

12. What is Manchester United's nickname?

13. Who are known as 'The Sky Blues' because of their playing strip?

14. Who are simply called 'The Dale'?

15. What is Scunthorpe United's nickname?

16. Which Scottish club are known as 'The Accies'?

Answers to page 329
FA CUP 6: 1. Mick Mills 2. Tooting & Mitcham 3. Scunthorpe United
4. Cardiff City and Blackpool 5. Dennis Wise 6. Norwich City 7. Bob
Wilson (Arsenal) and Ray Clemence (Liverpool) 8. Tottenham Hotspur
9. Bury 10. Manchester United (1957, 1958), Everton (1985, 1986) and
Newcastle United (1998 and 1999) 11. Blackpool 12. Brian Talbot 13. He
was the first Australian to play in an FA Cup final 14. Newcastle United
15. Jimmy Case 16. Millwall

The World Game 9

Answers on page 326

1. Which amateur team reached the 2001 German Cup final?

2. Who beat them 2–0 in the final?

3. Servette beat Yverdon in which country's 2001 Cup final?

4. Who did the Italian League and Cup double in 1999–2000?

5. Dutchman Thijs Libregts was appointed national coach of which African country in August 1998?

6. Who won the Yugoslavian League in 2001?

7. Which club won the Greek Cup in 2000?

8. Which country's League title did Shamkir win in 2000?

9. In which country do a team called 'The Strongest' play?

10. Which African country defeated Spain in their first match at the 1998 World Cup finals?

11. In 2000, which club captured their seventh French League title?

12. Dunaferr won which country's League for the first time in 2000?

13. Whose League title did Shirak win in 2000?

14. Which national team were forbidden from swapping shirts with opponents Spain at the end of a 1993 international because they couldn't afford replacements?

15. For which Australian team did Damian Mori score after just four seconds against Sydney United in 1995?

16. Which club have won most Romanian League Championships?

Answers to page 326
BRADFORD CITY 1: **1.** David Layne **2.** Frank Stapleton **3.** Division Four **4.** Norwich City **5.** Southampton **6.** Stuart McCall **7.** Edinho **8.** Oxford United **9.** Seven **10.** Isaiah Rankin **11.** Des Hamilton **12.** Cec Podd **13.** Millwall and Hull City **14.** Bobby Campbell **15.** 1985 **16.** Harry Hampton

FA Cup 6

Answers on page 327

1. Who was captain of the Ipswich Town side which lifted the FA Cup in 1978?

2. Which Isthmian League side reached the fourth round of the FA Cup in 1976 before losing 3–1 away to Bradford City?

3. Which current Third Division club reached the fifth round for the first time in 1958 but then went out to Liverpool?

4. Which two First Division teams did Port Vale knock out of the Cup on their way to the semi-finals in 1954?

5. Who was Chelsea's victorious captain in the 1997 Cup final?

6. Which Third Division team knocked Manchester United out of the FA Cup in 1959?

7. Who were the opposing goalkeepers in the 1971 Cup final?

8. Which club won the first seven FA Cup finals they contested?

9. Which Lancashire club has played in two FA Cup finals and won them both?

10. Which three clubs have lost successive FA Cup finals since the war?

11. Which are the only FA Cup winners to have played in tangerine shirts?

12. Who played against Arsenal in the 1978 final and for them in the 1979 and 1980 finals?

13. What was the claim to fame of Preston North End's Joe Marston in 1954?

14. Which club have failed to score in their last three Cup final appearances?

15. Who scored Liverpool's goal when they lost 2–1 to Manchester United in the 1977 final?

16. Which London club have played in three FA Cup semi-finals without ever reaching the final?

Answers to page 327
NICKNAMES 3: **1.** Aston Villa **2.** Peterhead **3.** 'The Bantams' **4.** Leigh RMI **5.** Ivory Coast **6.** David Layne **7.** Peterborough United **8.** Rotherham United **9.** Liam Brady **10.** Sheffield Wednesday **11.** Everton **12.** 'The Red Devils' **13.** Coventry City **14.** Rochdale **15.** 'The Iron' **16.** Hamilton Academicals

Oddballs 6

Answers on page 332

1. Which former members of the Scottish League were known as 'The Hi Hi's'?

2. Which Belfast club won the Irish League nine years out of ten from 1978 to 1987?

3. Who broke the sequence in 1981?

4. Which English League club does Nick Hancock support?

5. What colour shirts do Romania play in?

6. Which Arsenal star of the 1970s had the misfortune to cut off a big toe with a lawnmower?

7. Which club's fans registered their protest by waving pants?

8. Which team do the Chuckle Brothers support?

9. In 1994, which Scottish team banned a male fan for running on to the pitch and kissing the referee?

10. Which Dutchman was Huddersfield Town's leading scorer in 1999–2000?

11. Which Belarus forward turned out for Sheffield United in 1999?

12. Who beat Chelsea 7–6 on aggregate in the 1958 FA Youth Cup final despite losing the first leg 5–1?

13. Who followed Martin O'Neill as Wycombe Wanderers' manager in 1995?

14. Impressionist Mike Yarwood was an honorary vice-president of which English League club?

15. Which future England player made his debut against them for Wales in a wartime international?

16. Before taking over at Old Trafford in 1945, Matt Busby turned down the post as coach at which club?

Answers to page 332
WALSALL 1: 1. David Kelly 2. Alan Buckley 3. Carlisle United 4. 1984
5. Macclesfield Town 6. 1998 7. 1960 8. Andy Rammell 9. Sunderland and Brighton 10. Shrewsbury Town 11. Maatias 12. Millwall 13. Mick Kearns
14. Tony Richards 15. Colin Taylor 16. Allan Clarke

Whose Home? 5

Answers on page 333

1. Which Danish club play at the Parken?

2. Which team play at Crabble Athletic Ground?

3. Which club play at Church Road?

4. Which Scottish League team used to play at Shawfield?

5. Which Scottish League team play at Firhill?

6. Which team plays at the Beveree Stadium?

7. Where do Dunfermline Athletic play?

8. Cathkin Park was the home of which former Scottish League side?

9. Which club play at Broughinge Road?

10. Who plays at Gayfield?

11. Which Scottish League newcomers used to play at Milnfield Park?

12. Where do Irish club Dundalk play?

13. Where do Derry City play?

14. Which English League club used to play at East Ferry Road?

15. Which German club play at the Volksparkstadion?

16. Which Belgian team are based at the Bosuil Stadium?

Answers to page 333
MANAGERS 7: 1. Ottmar Hitzfeld 2. Terry Neill 3. Icelandic
4. Shrewsbury Town 5. Switzerland 6. Bohemians 7. Sam Allardyce
8. Fernando Santos 9. Bruce Rioch 10. Ron Greenwood 11. Greece
12. George Kay 13. 1974 14. Sunderland 15. Len Richley 16. Herbert
Chapman (Huddersfield Town 1922 and Arsenal 1930)

Walsall 1

Answers on page 330

1. Which Republic of Ireland forward did Walsall sell to West Ham for £600,000 in 1988?

2. Who was Walsall manager from 1979 to 1986?

3. To whom were Walsall Third Division runners-up in 1995?

4. In which year did Walsall reach the semi-finals of the League Cup?

5. Who did Walsall thrash 7–0 away from home in an FA Cup tie in 1997?

6. When did Ray Graydon become Walsall manager?

7. In which year were Walsall crowned Fourth Division champions?

8. Who was Walsall's leading scorer in 1998–9?

9. Behind which two clubs were Walsall promoted from Division Three in 1988?

10. From which club did Walsall sign Darren Wrack?

11. Which Pedro made an impact at the Bescot in 2000–1?

12. Who beat Walsall in the southern final of the Auto Windscreens Shield in 1999?

13. Which Walsall keeper of the 1970s won 18 caps with the Republic of Ireland?

14. Who scored 184 League goals for the club from 1954 to 1963?

15. And who equalled that record ten years later?

16. Which Leeds and England forward of the 1970s began his League career with Walsall?

Answers to page 330
ODDBALLS 6: 1. Third Lanark 2. Linfield 3. Glentoran 4. Stoke City
5. Yellow 6. Charlie George 7. Reading 8. Rotherham United 9. Arbroath
10. Clyde Wijnhard 11. Petr Katchuro 12. Wolves 13. Alan Smith
14. Stockport County 15. Stan Mortensen 16. Liverpool

Managers 7

Answers on page 331

1. Which manager has won the European Champions' League twice – with Borussia Dortmund (1997) and Bayern Munich (2001)?

2. Which manager steered Arsenal to FA Cup success in 1979?

3. What nationality was Stoke City's 2000–1 manager?

4. Fred Davies was manager of which English League club from 1994 to 1997?

5. Enzo Trossero quit as coach of which national team in June 2001?

6. Roddy Collins left which Irish club in summer 2001?

7. Who became manager of Notts County in 1997 and went on to take Bolton into the Premiership?

8. Who stepped down as coach of FC Porto after the club won the 2001 Portuguese Cup?

9. Who became Middlesbrough manager in 1986?

10. Which future England manager took West Ham to FA Cup success in 1964?

11. Vasilis Daniel was coach of which national team in 2001?

12. Who was Liverpool's first post-war manager?

13. When did John Lyall take over at West Ham?

14. Alan Brown managed which north-east club from 1957 to 1964?

15. Who was sacked as Darlington manager 12 days into the 1971–2 season?

16. Who was the first manager to win the FA Cup with two different clubs?

Answers to page 331
WHOSE HOME? 5: 1. FC Copenhagen 2. Dover Athletic 3. Hayes 4. Clyde
5. Partick Thistle 6. Hampton & Richmond 7. East End Park 8. Third Lanark
9. Boreham Wood 10. Arbroath 11. Elgin City 12. Oriel Park
13. Brandywell 14. Millwall 15. Hamburg 16. Royal Antwerp

Football League 7

Answers on page 336

1. Who were Third Division champions in 2000–1?
2. And who finished runners-up?
3. Which club managed to gain promotion despite having nine points deducted?
4. Who was Chester City's top scorer in the season they were relegated to the Conference?
5. Who did Northampton Town beat in the 1997 Third Division play-off final?
6. Which full-back grabbed the winning goal?
7. What was unusual about Newcastle's goalless draw with Portsmouth in December 1931?
8. How many home goals did Liverpool concede in Division One in 1978–9?
9. What was historic about Barnet's 5–4 victory over Torquay in December 1993?
10. Which is the only team to score six goals in a League match and lose?
11. Which innovative club of the 1960s were the first to erect a giant screen for televising an away match at their own ground?
12. Who was the first player-manager in England's top division?
13. Which father and son lined up together for Hereford United at Scunthorpe in 1990?
14. Who was Charlton Athletic's leading scorer as they clinched the First Division title in 2000?
15. Which club gained promotion from Division Four in 1982 – their fourth season in the Football League?
16. Who won the League Championship in 1967–8?

Answers to page 336
CHELSEA 1: 1. 1915 2. Graham 3. Peter Houseman 4. Five (Walter Winterbottom, Joe Mercer, Ron Greenwood, Terry Venables and Glenn Hoddle) 5. Tony Hateley 6. Three 7. Ian Hamilton 8. Atalanta 9. 1962 10. David Speedie 11. Gianluca Vialli 12. Carlisle United 13. Bobby Campbell 14. Dennis Wise 15. Roy Bentley 16. Arsenal

The World Game 10

Answers on page 337

1. Who won their 13th Russian League title in 1999?

2. In what colour shirts do Peru play?

3. Who took the Danish League title in 2001?

4. Which future Manchester United star helped Montpellier win the French Cup in 1990?

5. In 1996, which free-kick specialist became the first Brazilian to play for Real Madrid?

6. In which European country do Gravenmacher play?

7. Which Maldini was Italian national coach?

8. Who won the Polish League for only the second time in 2000?

9. And who won the Polish Cup in 2000?

10. For which Spanish club did Fernando Hierro play in 2001?

11. Which Birmingham City player was a member of the Australian squad at the 2001 Confederations Cup?

12. Who beat Corinthians 5–3 on aggregate to win the 2001 Brazilian Cup final?

13. Who was Roma's top scorer with 20 goals in 2000–1?

14. In 2001, Torpedo Kutaisi beat Lokomotiv Tbilisi in which country's Cup final?

15. Who beat Reggina in Italy's Serie 'A' relegation play-off in 2001?

16. With which German club did Uwe Seeler spend his entire playing career?

Answers to page 337
WORLD CUP 4: **1.** USA **2.** Gerd Müller **3.** It was the 1,000th goal in World Cup finals **4.** American Samoa **5.** Norway **6.** Bolivia **7.** Steve Bull **8.** Holland **9.** Spain **10.** Luigi Riva **11.** Jeff Astle **12.** Colin Bell **13.** Uruguay **14.** Tom Boyd **15.** Pontiac Silverdome **16.** Romario

Chelsea 1

Answers on page 334

1. When did Chelsea first reach the FA Cup final?

2. Which brother of Ray Wilkins played for Chelsea in the 1970s?

3. Which member of Chelsea's victorious 1970 Cup final team was killed in a car crash seven years later?

4. How many England managers have played for Chelsea?

5. Who scored Chelsea's winning goal against Leeds in the semi-finals of the 1967 FA Cup?

6. How many times did Jimmy Greaves score five goals in a League match for Chelsea?

7. Who was just 16 when making his Chelsea debut against Spurs in 1967?

8. From which Italian club did Chelsea secure Sam Dalla Bonna?

9. When did Tommy Docherty become Chelsea manager?

10. Which fiery forward did Chelsea sell to Coventry for £750,000 in 1987?

11. Who came on for Gianfranco Zola in the 1997 FA Cup final?

12. Who were the only team to finish below Chelsea in the First Division in 1974–5?

13. Who was Chelsea manager from 1988 to 1991?

14. In 1990, who joined Chelsea from Wimbledon for £1.6 million in what was then a British record transfer for a winger?

15. Who was Chelsea's leading scorer with five goals in their 1952 FA Cup campaign?

16. And which London rivals ended Chelsea's run at the semi-final stage that year?

Answers to page 334
FOOTBALL LEAGUE 7: **1.** Brighton & Hove Albion **2.** Cardiff City **3.** Chesterfield **4.** Luke Beckett **5.** Swansea City **6.** John Frain **7.** There wasn't one corner in the entire match **8.** Four **9.** It was the first time all four substitutes had scored in a Football League match **10.** Huddersfield Town (beaten 7–6 by Charlton in 1957) **11.** Coventry City **12.** Les Allen (Queens Park Rangers, 1968–9) **13.** Ian and Gary Bowyer **14.** Andy Hunt **15.** Wigan Athletic **16.** Manchester City

World Cup 4

Answers on page 335

1. Who did Argentina beat 6–1 in the semi-finals of the 1930 World Cup?

2. Who scored ten goals in the 1970 finals?

3. What was special about Robbie Rensenbrink's successful penalty for Holland against Scotland in the 1978 finals?

4. Which team conceded 57 goals in their four qualifying matches for the 2002 World Cup?

5. In 1994, which European country qualified for the World Cup finals for the first time since 1938?

6. Which South American country's appearance at the 1994 finals marked their first successful qualification since 1950?

7. Who came on for Gary Lineker during England's 1–1 draw with the Republic of Ireland at Italia 90?

8. Which country scored three times in the last four minutes to win 4–2 and avoid embarrassment in a June 2001 World Cup qualifier in Estonia?

9. Against whom did South Korea score their only goal at Italia 90?

10. Who scored twice for Italy in their 1970 quarter-final against Mexico?

11. Whose glaring miss cost England a draw with Brazil in 1970?

12. Who did Sir Alf Ramsey bring on for Bobby Charlton when England were leading West Germany 2–1 in the 1970 quarter-finals?

13. Who did West Germany beat 4–0 in the 1966 quarter-finals?

14. Who scored an own goal for Scotland against Brazil at the 1998 finals?

15. Which Detroit indoor stadium was used for the 1994 tournament?

16. Who was named best player in tournament at the 1994 finals?

Answers to page 335
THE WORLD GAME 10: **1.** Spartak Moscow **2.** White with a red stripe **3.** FC Copenhagen **4.** Eric Cantona **5.** Roberto Carlos **6.** Luxembourg **7.** Cesare **8.** Polonia Warsaw **9.** Amica Wronki **10.** Real Madrid **11.** Stan Lazaridis **12.** Gremio **13.** Gabriel Batistuta **14.** Georgia **15.** Verona **16.** Hamburg

Scottish Scene 3

Answers on page 340

1. Who were promoted to the Scottish Premier Division in 2000, only to be relegated the following season?

2. Which club shared Albion Rovers' Cliftonhill ground in 1999–2000?

3. Which two teams were promoted from Division Three in 2001?

4. Who was Scotland's Manager of the Year in 1989?

5. Which recent newcomers to the League reached the quarter-finals of the Scottish FA Cup in 1968?

6. Who eventually knocked them out of the competition?

7. Which club joined the Scottish League in 1974?

8. In 1929–30, which club reached the last eight of the Scottish FA Cup in their first season in the League?

9. Who was Hearts' top scorer in 1999–2000?

10. Who won the Scottish FA Cup in 2001?

11. Who did they beat 3–0 in the final?

12. Which Dutch goalkeeper was named Premier Division Player of the Year for 1988–9?

13. Which First Division team were twice beaten Scottish FA Cup finalists in the 1990s?

14. Which club tasted their only season of top division football in 1932–3?

15. Which Glasgow club last reached the Scottish FA Cup final in 1930?

16. How many times have Queen's Park won the Scottish FA Cup?

Answers to page 340
TRANSFER TRAIL 6: **1.** Don Rogers **2.** Craig Bellamy **3.** Wycombe Wanderers **4.** Vincenzo Montella **5.** Distillery **6.** Michael Bridges **7.** Jimmy Floyd Hasselbaink **8.** Lee Hughes **9.** Frank Leboeuf **10.** Ilie Dumitrescu **11.** Gheorghe Popescu **12.** Perugia **13.** Huddersfield Town **14.** Tottenham **15.** Neil Cox **16.** Earl Barrett

World Cup 5

Answers on page 341

1. Who were the first black African country to reach the World Cup finals?

2. Which two nations did Rudolf Vytlacil lead to the World Cup finals?

3. Which team played 15 qualifying matches in the 1982 World Cup?

4. Which Belgian appeared in three successive World Cup finals tournaments?

5. Who played for Hungary in the 1954 finals and for Spain in 1962?

6. For which two countries did Luisito Monti play in World Cup finals tournaments?

7. In 1990 which Italian goalkeeper went 517 minutes without conceding a goal in the World Cup finals?

8. Which Argentinian finally found a way past him?

9. Who did Italy beat 2–1 in Tbilisi in a June 2001 World Cup qualifier?

10. Which two players scored Italy's goals?

11. Which West German scored in both the 1974 and 1982 finals?

12. Who scored twice in the 1958 final and once in the 1970 final?

13. On which ground did Hungary defeat Brazil 3–1 at the 1966 finals?

14. What was Anatoly Puzach's claim to fame?

15. Who scored four times for Portugal against North Korea at the 1966 finals?

16. Who did Belgium crush 10–1 in a World Cup qualifier in February 2001?

Answers to page 341
NORTHERN IRELAND 1: **1.** Colin Clarke **2.** 1972 **3.** 37 **4.** Wales **5.** Sammy Morgan **6.** Italy and Portugal **7.** Switzerland **8.** Scotland **9.** Yugoslavia and Honduras **10.** Billy Hamilton **11.** Alan McDonald **12.** 12 **13.** Jimmy Nicholl **14.** Linfield **15.** 1961 **16.** 10

Transfer Trail 6

Answers on page 338

1. Which League Cup hero moved from Swindon Town to Crystal Palace for £150,000 in 1972?

2. Which Welsh international joined Newcastle from Coventry in summer 2001?

3. From which club did Notts County buy Mark Stallard?

4. Who moved from Sampdoria to Roma for £15.3 million in June 1999?

5. From which Northern Ireland club did Celtic sign full-back Anton Rogan?

6. Which forward moved from Sunderland to Leeds for £5 million in 1999?

7. Which Leeds striker joined Atletico Madrid for £12 million in 1999?

8. Which flame-haired striker joined West Bromwich Albion from Kidderminster Harriers for £380,000 in 1997?

9. Which French defender moved from Chelsea to Marseille in July 2001?

10. Which Romanian was transferred from Steaua Bucharest to Tottenham for £2.6 million in 1994?

11. Which Romanian joined Tottenham from PSV Eindhoven for £2.9 million in 1994?

12. From which Italian club did Rangers sign Marco Negri?

13. From which club did Everton sign World Cup winner Ray Wilson?

14. From which club did Ipswich Town sign Jamie Clapham?

15. Which full-back moved from Scunthorpe to Aston Villa for £350,000 in 1991?

16. Which full-back did Oldham sell to Aston Villa for £1.7 million in 1992?

Answers to page 338
SCOTTISH SCENE 3: **1.** St Mirren **2.** Dumbarton **3.** Hamilton Academicals and Cowdenbeath **4.** Graeme Souness **5.** Elgin City **6.** Morton **7.** Meadowbank Thistle **8.** Montrose **9.** Gary McSwegan **10.** Celtic **11.** Hibernian **12.** Theo Snelders **13.** Airdrie **14.** East Stirlingshire **15.** Partick Thistle **16.** 10

Northern Ireland 1

Answers on page 339

1. Who scored a hat-trick when Northern Ireland won 5–0 against the Faroe Islands in a 1991 European Championship qualifier?

2. In which year did Sammy McIlroy win his first cap as a player?

3. How many caps did George Best win?

4. Against which home country did he make his debut in 1964?

5. Which Port Vale, Aston Villa, Brighton and Sparta Rotterdam striker won 18 caps from 1972 to 1979?

6. Which two other countries were in the group which Northern Ireland topped to qualify for the 1958 World Cup finals?

7. Which country denied Northern Ireland qualification for the 1966 World Cup finals?

8. Who topped Northern Ireland's qualifying group for the 1982 World Cup?

9. Against which two teams did Northern Ireland earn draws in their group at the 1982 World Cup finals?

10. Who scored both Northern Ireland's goals as they drew 2–2 with Austria in the second round at the 1982 World Cup finals?

11. Which Queens Park Rangers centre-back won the first of his 52 caps in 1986?

12. How many goals did Gerry Armstrong score for Northern Ireland?

13. Whose only goal for Northern Ireland came in Bulgaria in a 1978 European Championship qualifier?

14. For which club was Billy Hamilton playing when he won his first cap?

15. When did Terry Neill win his first cap?

16. How many goals did Billy Bingham score for Northern Ireland?

Answers to page 339
WORLD CUP 5: 1. Zaire (1974) 2. Czechoslovakia (1962) and Bulgaria (1966) 3. New Zealand 4. Bernard Voorhof 5. Ferenc Puskas 6. Argentina (1930) and Italy (1934) 7. Walter Zenga 8. Claudio Caniggia 9. Georgia 10. Marco Delvecchio and Francesco Totti 11. Paul Breitner 12. Pele 13. Goodison Park 14. In 1970 he was the first substitute to be used in the World Cup finals 15. Eusebio 16. San Marino

Football League 8

Answers on page 344

1. Whose penalty in the 1992 play-off final against Leicester City won Blackburn Rovers a place in the Premiership?

2. After joining the League in 1928, when did Torquay United earn their first promotion?

3. Which team yo-yo'd between the First and Second Divisions four times in six years between 1977–8 and 1983–4?

4. Which TV soccer pundit was manager of Portsmouth from 1974–7?

5. Where did Huddersfield Town play before the McAlpine Stadium?

6. Who finished 14th in Division Two in three successive years between 1929 and 1931, each time totalling 39 points?

7. Which club moved to the Bescot Stadium in 1990?

8. Which club were replaced by Maidstone United in 1989?

9. Which Yorkshire club spent the first 30 seasons of their existence in Division Two before being relegated in 1932?

10. Which club nicknamed 'The U's' only turned professional in 1946?

11. Which club started out life as the Black Arabs?

12. Which club name used to bear the suffix 'Pelham'?

13. Which League club used to play at John O'Gaunt's?

14. Who was Wigan Athletic's top scorer for 1998–9?

15. Which club won their first divisional championship in 1984?

16. Which club achieved promotion via the Fourth Division play-offs in 1989 after lying 15th in the table on 1 March?

Answers to page 344
NAME THE YEAR 5: **1.** 1997 **2.** 1987 **3.** 1996 **4.** 1991 **5.** 1999 (Auto Windscreens Shield) **6.** 1996 **7.** 1987 **8.** 1977 **9.** 1974 **10.** 1948 **11.** 1991 **12.** 1994 **13.** 1926 **14.** 1929 **15.** 1997 **16.** 1909

The World Game 11

Answers on page 345

1. Which former Bundesliga champions were promoted back to Germany's top division in 2001 after two seasons in Division Two?

2. Which former Ipswich Town player was sacked as coach of Malmo in 1998?

3. Which Spanish giants did Chelsea beat in 1998 to win the European Supercup?

4. Which Italian legend was given a free transfer by Juventus early in his career?

5. Which club won the Bundesliga in 1992?

6. Who won the Danish League title in 1999?

7. As a player with which club did Mexico's Hugo Sanchez win the European Golden Boot?

8. Which Dynamo Kiev player was European Footballer of the Year in 1975?

9. Who was appointed coach of Brazil in summer 1998?

10. Which Brazilian team refunded money to supporters after a 1998 defeat?

11. With which French club did David Ginola make his League debut?

12. Who finished bottom of the German First Division in 2001?

13. Who won the Brazilian League in 1996?

14. Which Russian international striker spent half a season at Millwall?

15. Francesco Scoglio was named coach of which African country in August 1998?

16. Which team did the French League and Cup double in 1958?

Answers to page 345
LEAGUE CUP 3: **1.** Ronnie Whelan **2.** Garry Birtles **3.** Southampton **4.** Aston Villa and Everton **5.** Ron Atkinson (his Aston Villa team beat Manchester United in 1994 to follow Sheffield Wednesday's victory over United in 1991) **6.** Jeff Astle **7.** Steve McManaman **8.** Bolton Wanderers **9.** Queens Park Rangers (1967) **10.** Watford **11.** Chris Armstrong (for Tottenham) **12.** York City **13.** Luton Town **14.** Middlesbrough **15.** Aston Villa **16.** Leeds United

Name the Year 5

Answers on page 342

1. In which year was Gianfranco Zola voted Footballer of the Year?

2. When was Ruud Gullit named European Footballer of the Year?

3. In which year did Trevor Francis become manager of Birmingham City?

4. In which year did Notts County beat Brighton 3–1 in the Second Division play-off final?

5. In which year did Millwall reach Wembley for their first peacetime cup final?

6. In which year did Manchester United beat Newcastle 4–0 in the FA Charity Shield?

7. When did Everton last win the League title?

8. When did Manchester United and Liverpool first meet in the FA Cup final?

9. When did Bobby Moore win his last England cap?

10. When did Blackpool's Stan Mortensen score in every round of the FA Cup?

11. In which year did Gary Lineker score for England after just 42 seconds against Malaysia in Kuala Lumpur?

12. In which year did Manchester United achieve their first League and Cup double?

13. In which year did Huddersfield Town complete a hat-trick of League titles?

14. In which year did York City join the Football League?

15. When did Peter Shilton play his last League game?

16. When did Bristol City reach their only FA Cup final?

Answers to page 342
FOOTBALL LEAGUE 8: 1. Mike Newell 2. 1960 3. Leicester City 4. Ian St John 5. Leeds Road 6. Millwall 7. Walsall 8. Darlington 9. Barnsley 10. Cambridge United 11. Bristol Rovers 12. Grimsby 13. Lincoln City 14. Stuart Barlow 15. York City 16. Leyton Orient

League Cup 3

Answers on page 343

1. Who scored two goals for Liverpool in the 1982 League Cup final?

2. Who was Nottingham Forest's two-goal hero in the 1979 final?

3. Who did Forest beat in that final?

4. Which two teams contested the 1977 final which was only decided after extra time in the second replay?

5. In 1994, which manager achieved a second League Cup final triumph in four years against his old club?

6. Who scored West Bromwich Albion's goal when they lost 2–1 to Manchester City in the 1970 final?

7. Who scored both Liverpool goals in the 1995 final?

8. Who did they beat in the final?

9. Roger Morgan, Rodney Marsh and Mark Lazarus were the scorers for which League Cup winners?

10. Who came back from a 4–0 first leg deficit to Southampton in the 1980–1 League Cup to win 7–5 on aggregate?

11. Whose two goals put Manchester United out of the 1998–9 League Cup?

12. Which Second Division side knocked Manchester United out of the 1995–6 League Cup, winning 3–0 at Old Trafford?

13. Which club reached successive League Cup finals in 1988 and 1989?

14. Who lost successive finals in 1997 and 1998?

15. Who won the 1996 final?

16. Who did they beat?

Answers to page 343
THE WORLD GAME 11: **1.** Borussia Mönchengladbach **2.** Frans Thijssen
3. Real Madrid **4.** Paolo Rossi **5.** Vfb Stuttgart **6.** Aalborg **7.** Real Madrid
8. Oleg Blokhin **9.** Wanderley Luxemburgo **10.** Flamengo **11.** Toulon **12.** Vfl
Bochum **13.** Gremio **14.** Sergei Yuran **15.** Tunisia **16.** Rheims

Transfer Trail 7

Answers on page 348

1. Which German international defender moved from Liverpool to Tottenham in July 2001?

2. Which Italian club did Ray Wilkins join in 1984?

3. Which Aston Villa forward was sent to Coventry in 2001?

4. Which club did Tommy Johnson join on leaving Notts County in 1992?

5. From which club did Everton sign John Oster?

6. From which Dutch club did Ipswich Town sign Bobby Petta?

7. Which club signed Twente Enschede striker Jan Vennegaar af Hesselink for a Dutch record fee of £5.6 million in 2001?

8. Which London club brought Joe Baker back from Italian football in 1962?

9. Which ex-Watford striker did Notts County buy from Sheffield United for £685,000 in 1991?

10. Who sold Mark Lawrenson to Liverpool in 1981?

11. Which Premiership newcomers signed Tugay Kerimoglu from Rangers for £1.3 million in 2001?

12. From which club did Port Vale sign Tony Naylor?

13. From which Midlands club did Arsenal pick up Jermaine Pennant?

14. For which Dutch club did Pierre Van Hooijdonk sign in 2001?

15. And which club sold him?

16. Which extrovert forward moved from Carlisle United to Queens Park Rangers for £110,000 in 1972?

Answers to page 348
SCOTTISH SCENE 4: **1.** Dundee United **2.** Meadowbank Thistle **3.** 1984
4. Inverness Caledonian Thistle **5.** Aberdeen **6.** Stenhousemuir **7.** Stranraer
8. East Stirlingshire **9.** 1935 **10.** Rangers **11.** Berwick Rangers
12. Motherwell **13.** Dumbarton **14.** Berwick Rangers **15.** Inverness
Caledonian Thistle **16.** Elgin City

Fulham 1

Answers on page 349

1. Before 2001, when did Fulham last play top division football?

2. When did Fulham first reach the semi-finals of the FA Cup?

3. Who beat them 6–0 in that match?

4. Which comedian was Fulham chairman in the 1960s?

5. When did Mohamed Al Fayed buy the club?

6. In which division were Fulham at the time?

7. Which father and son managed the club at different times?

8. Which defender did Fulham sell to Liverpool for £333,333 in 1980?

9. When did Fulham first play top-flight football?

10. Who was Fulham's first £1 million signing?

11. From which club did Fulham sign Allan Clarke?

12. Which French manager took Fulham into the Premiership in 2001?

13. Which Fulham boss left the club to become England manager?

14. Who did Fulham beat in the semi-finals of the 1975 FA Cup?

15. Who scored Fulham's winning goal?

16. From which club did Fulham sign Barry Hayles?

Answers to page 349
THE WORLD GAME 12: 1. Brazil 2. PSV Eindhoven 3. 17 4. Argentina
5. Hristo Bonev 6. David Ginola 7. Borussia Mönchengladbach 8. Balaguer
9. Daniel Passarella 10. Mozambique 11. Hristo Stoichkov 12. Zico
13. Juventus 14. Romania 15. Lausanne 16. Tunisia

Scottish Scene 4

Answers on page 346

1. Which Scottish club sold Kevin Gallacher to Coventry City in 1990?

2. Which club changed their name after relocating from Edinburgh to Livingston?

3. In which year did Forfar Athletic gain promotion for the first time?

4. For which club did Ian Stewart score 27 League goals in 1996–7?

5. Which Scottish club sold Arthur Graham to Leeds United in the 1970s?

6. Who finished Third Division runners-up to Ross County in 1998–9?

7. Who were the only team to win at Hibernian in the First Division in 1998–9?

8. Who plays at Firs Park?

9. In which year did Hamilton Academicals last reach the Scottish FA Cup final?

10. Who beat them 2–1 in that year's final?

11. For which club did Eric Tait make 435 League appearances between 1970 and 1987?

12. Who sold Phil O'Donnell to Celtic for £1.2 million in 1994?

13. From which Scottish club did Everton buy Graeme Sharp?

14. Which Scottish League ground is in England?

15. Which club used to play at Telford Street Park?

16. Which is the most northerly Scottish club?

Answers to page 346
TRANSFER TRAIL 7: 1. Christian Ziege 2. AC Milan 3. Julian Joachim
4. Derby County 5. Grimsby Town 6. Feyenoord 7. PSV Eindhoven
8. Arsenal 9. Tony Agana 10. Brighton & Hove Albion 11. Blackburn Rovers
12. Crewe Alexandra 13. Notts County 14. Feyenoord 15. Benfica 16. Stan Bowles

The World Game 12

Answers on page 347

1. Which country won the Copa America in 2000?

2. Who won the Dutch League for the second successive year in 2001?

3. How many Bundesliga titles have Bayern Munich won?

4. Marcelo Bielsa became coach of which South American country after the 1998 World Cup?

5. Who resigned as Bulgarian national coach in September 1998?

6. Whose last-minute blunder in a 1994 World Cup qualifier put France out of the competition and allowed Bulgaria to go to the United States?

7. Which German club won the Bundesliga five times between 1970 and 1977?

8. Which Spanish Fourth Division team defeated mighty Barcelona in the final of the 2001 Catalan Cup?

9. Who was Argentina coach at the 1998 World Cup finals?

10. Seven of which African country's players were banned for life in 1998 after being caught shoplifting on overseas trips?

11. Which Bulgarian was named European Footballer of the Year in 1994?

12. Which former international was appointed Brazil's Sports Minister in 1992?

13. Who won Italy's Serie 'A' in 1995?

14. In which country did Recolta Laza lose goalkeeper Valentin Bargan to Stemnic Buda in 1998 for £8 and a stack of firewood?

15. Who won the 1999 Swiss Cup final?

16. In which African country do Esperance play?

Answers to page 347
FULHAM 1: **1.** 1968 **2.** 1908 **3.** Newcastle United **4.** Tommy Trinder
5. 1997 **6.** Division Two **7.** Bill Dodgin Snr and Bill Dodgin Jnr **8.** Richard
Money **9.** 1949 **10.** Paul Peschisolido **11.** Walsall **12.** Jean Tigana **13.** Kevin
Keegan **14.** Birmingham City **15.** John Mitchell **16.** Bristol Rovers

Transfer Trail 8

Answers on page 352

1. Which Israeli midfielder switched from Celtic to Manchester City for £1.5 million in summer 2001?

2. Which London club paid Luton Town £1 million for Roy Wegerle in 1989?

3. Which former France captain played for Nantes, Marseille, Bordeaux, Juventus, Chelsea and Valencia?

4. In July 2001, which £4 million man became the Premiership's first Japanese signing?

5. Which English club did he join?

6. Who did Millwall buy from Derby County for a club record £800,000 in 1989?

7. Which player, famed for his 'donkey' free kick, was transferred from Swindon Town to Wolves for £40,000 in 1965?

8. Which Midlands club signed Martin Foyle from Oxford United in 1991?

9. Who sold Darren Anderton to Tottenham in 1992?

10. Which Lancashire club bought striker Ian Olney from Aston Villa in 1992?

11. With which club did Dean Saunders begin his League career?

12. From which Highland League team did Scott Murray join Aston Villa before moving to Bristol City?

13. Which manager moved as a player from Southend United to Crystal Palace for £120,000 in 1973?

14. Which Coventry centre-half joined Arsenal for £200,000 in 1972?

15. From which Conference club did Macclesfield sign Efetobore Sodje?

16. Which was Roger Freestone's first League club?

Answers to page 352
NON-LEAGUE 3: 1. Barnet 2. Margate 3. David Kelly 4. Yeovil Town
5. Unibond League 6. Dean Windass 7. Kettering Town, Kingstonian and Hednesford Town 8. Dr Martens League 9. Matlock Town 10. Nuneaton Borough 11. Taunton 12. Berkhamsted Town 13. Andy Hessenthaler
14. 'The Gladiators' 15. Stalybridge Celtic 16. Emley

European Cups 5

Answers on page 353

1. Which Englishman helped knock Manchester United out of the 2001 Champions' League?

2. Who beat Leeds United in the semi-finals of the 2001 Champions' League?

3. Which Austrian team were the first to reach the final of the European Cup-Winners' Cup?

4. Which German team did Manchester City beat in the semi-finals of the 1970 Cup-Winners' Cup?

5. Who scored in both legs of Ipswich's 1981 UEFA Cup final success?

6. Which club did Liverpool defeat in the 1976 UEFA Cup final and the 1978 European Cup final?

7. Which Portuguese team beat Bayern Munich in the 1987 European Cup final?

8. Which Spanish club, who were playing in the Fourth Division 11 years ago, reached the 2001 UEFA Cup final?

9. To whom did they lose 5–4?

10. Whose 'golden' own goal decided the outcome?

11. Which German team beat Juventus in the 1997 Champions' League final?

12. In 1992, who became the first French club to reach the European Cup-Winners' Cup final?

13. Who beat them in the final?

14. Who were runners-up to Bayern Munich in the 1996 UEFA Cup?

15. Which club reached three successive European Cup finals from 1961 to 1963?

16. Which Scottish team did Spurs defeat en route to the 1974 UEFA Cup final?

Answers to page 353
ST JOHNSTONE 1: **1.** Ally McCoist **2.** None **3.** Jimmy Benson **4.** Callum Davidson **5.** John Brogan **6.** 1997 **7.** 20 **8.** Rangers **9.** Billy Dodds **10.** Paul Wright **11.** Rangers **12.** 2–1 **13.** Bertie Auld **14.** 1996–7 **15.** Sandy McLaren **16.** Partick Thistle

Non-League 3

Answers on page 350

1. From which non-League club did Wimbledon sign Andy Clarke?

2. Who won the Dr Martens League in 2000–1?

3. Which West Ham, Leicester, Newcastle, Tranmere and Republic of Ireland striker entered League football from Alvechurch?

4. Which Conference team knocked Blackpool out of the FA Cup in 2000–1?

5. In which league do Whitby Town play?

6. Which Middlesbrough and former Hull and Bradford City striker began his career with North Ferriby?

7. Which three teams were relegated from the Conference in 2001?

8. In which League did Newport County play in 2000–1?

9. Which Northern Premier League team won 5–2 at Mansfield in a 1976 FA Cup tie?

10. Which Conference team play at Manor Park?

11. Who won the FA Carlsberg Vase in 2001?

12. Who did they beat in the final?

13. Which midfielder did Watford sign from Redbridge Forest for £65,000 in 1991?

14. What is Matlock Town's nickname?

15. Who won the Unibond League Premier Division in 2000–1 by a single point?

16. Who finished runners-up?

Answers to page 350
TRANSFER TRAIL 8: **1.** Eyal Berkovic **2.** Queens Park Rangers **3.** Didier Deschamps **4.** Junichi Inamoto **5.** Arsenal **6.** Paul Goddard **7.** Ernie Hunt **8.** Port Vale **9.** Portsmouth **10.** Oldham Athletic **11.** Swansea City **12.** Fraserburgh **13.** Peter Taylor **14.** Jeff Blockley **15.** Stevenage Borough **16.** Newport County

St Johnstone 1

Answers on page 351

1. Which striker did St Johnstone sell to Sunderland for £400,000 in 1982?

2. How many times have St Johnstone reached the Scottish FA Cup final?

3. Who scored 36 League goals for Saints in 1931–2?

4. Which wing-back did Saints sell to Blackburn Rovers for £1.75 million in 1998?

5. Who scored 140 goals for the club between 1977 and 1983?

6. In which year were Saints last promoted to the Premier League?

7. How many points ahead of runners-up Airdrie did they finish that season?

8. Who beat Saints in the semi-finals of the Scottish FA Cup in 1989?

9. Who did Saints buy from Dundee for £300,000 in 1994?

10. Which player did Saints sign from Hibernian for £285,000 in 1991?

11. Who beat Saints in the final of the 1998–9 Scottish Coca-Cola Cup?

12. What was the score?

13. Whose goal for Celtic defeated Saints in the final of the 1969–70 Scottish League Cup?

14. In which season were Saints runners-up in the League Challenge Cup?

15. Which Saints player won five Scotland caps from 1929–33?

16. Which Glasgow club did Saints crush 8–1 in a 1969 Scottish League Cup tie?

Answers to page 351
EUROPEAN CUPS 5: **1.** Owen Hargreaves (Bayern Munich) **2.** Valencia **3.** Austria/WAC **4.** Schalke 04 **5.** John Wark and Frans Thijssen **6.** FC Bruges **7.** FC Porto **8.** Alaves **9.** Liverpool **10.** Delfi Celi **11.** Borussia Dortmund **12.** Monaco **13.** Werder Bremen **14.** Bordeaux **15.** Benfica **16.** Aberdeen

Aston Villa 2

Answers on page 356

1. In which year did the club move to Villa Park?

2. For which country did Peter McParland win 34 caps?

3. In which season did Villa first compete in Europe?

4. From which club did Villa sign goalkeeper Jimmy Rimmer?

5. When did Villa first win the FA Youth Cup?

6. Who became Villa manager in 1987?

7. Which Midlands neighbours did Villa beat in their first two FA Cup final triumphs?

8. Who defeated Villa 1–0 in the 1959 FA Cup semi-finals?

9. Who was Villa's leading scorer for 1990–1?

10. Which striker did Villa sign from Sheffield Wednesday for £450,000 in 1986?

11. Which Villa youngster won his first England cap against the Czech Republic in 1999?

12. Which club was involved in a wrangle with Villa over the signing of Gareth Barry?

13. How many League games did Ugo Ehiogu play for West Brom before moving to Villa?

14. Which former Derby County full-back did Villa sell to Benfica in January 1999?

15. Who did Villa sell to Nottingham Forest for £3 million in 1999–2000?

16. In which year did Villa gain promotion to the old First Division and reach the semi-finals of the FA Cup?

Answers to page 356
ODDBALLS 7: **1.** Aldershot Town **2.** Sturm Graz **3.** Linfield **4.** Newport County (1946–7) 133 **5.** Norwich City **6.** Blackpool **7.** 1970 **8.** Ghana **9.** Dumbarton **10.** Accrington Stanley **11.** Oxford United and Reading **12.** Glentoran **13.** Jamie Moralee **14.** Sergei Yuran and Vasili Kulkov **15.** Luxembourg **16.** Frank

France 2

Answers on page 357

1. Victory over which country secured France's qualification for Euro 96?

2. Which French player was felled by German goalkeeper Harald Schumacher's appalling challenge in the semi-finals of the 1982 World Cup?

3. In which city was that match played?

4. Who did France play first in the 2002 World Cup Finals?

5. Which defender in that tournament went on to win a record 82 caps for France?

6. With which other nation did France qualify for the 1986 World Cup?

7. Who did France defeat on penalties in the quarter-finals of the 1986 World Cup after the match had ended 1–1?

8. Who had scored France's goal in normal time?

9. Which two English-based players were in France's squad for Euro 96?

10. And who was the only German-based player in that French squad?

11. Zinedine Zidane was forced to sit out which two matches at the 1998 World Cup?

12. Who did France defeat 7–1 in their first-ever European Championship match?

13. Three of France's first four games in the Euro 96 qualifiers ended in goalless draws. Who were their opponents?

14. Who did France defeat 10–0 in a Euro 96 qualifier?

15. How many French players were on the scoresheet in that game?

16. Two of the scorers went on to play for Chelsea. Who were they?

Answers to page 357
MANAGERS 7: 1. Dick Advocaat 2. Terry Burton 3. Jim Smith 4. Dario Gradi 5. Paul Jewell 6. Billy Dearden 7. Peter Reid 8. Gianluca Vialli 9. Jimmy Calderwood 10. David Jones 11. Jocky Scott 12. Danny Wilson 13. Steve McMahon 14. Gary Megson 15. Mark McGhee 16. Tommy Taylor

Oddballs 7

Answers on page 354

1. Which Diadora League Division Three team averaged gates of over 2000 in 1992–3?

2. Who won the Austrian Cup in 2000?

3. Who won the first three Irish League titles from 1891 to 1893?

4. Which club conceded the most Football League goals in a season since the war?

5. Which current English First Division club that played in Europe in the 1990s previously had to make four applications for re-election to the League?

6. Which English First Division runners-up of 1955–6 have yet to win the League Championship?

7. When did Bradford Park Avenue leave the Football League?

8. Which African nation play in an all-yellow strip?

9. Which Scottish club does TV presenter Hazel Irvine support?

10. Of the 12 original clubs in the Football League, which is the only one that is no longer a member?

11. Which two clubs did Robert Maxwell want to merge into the Thames Valley Royals?

12. Who won the Irish Cup in 2000?

13. Which former Millwall player scored one of Barry Town's goals in their 2001 Welsh Cup final victory over Total Network Solutions?

14. Which two Russians came to the New Den in 1996?

15. Etzella Ettlebruck won which country's Cup in 2001?

16. Which of the de Boer twins made their international debut first?

Answers to page 354
ASTON VILLA 2: 1. 1897 2. Northern Ireland 3. 1975–6 4. Arsenal 5. 1972 6. Graham Taylor 7. West Bromwich Albion 8. Nottingham Forest 9. David Platt 10. Garry Thompson 11. Lee Hendrie 12. Brighton 13. Two 14. Gary Charles 15. Riccardo Scimeca 16. 1938

Managers 7

Answers on page 355

Who was manager of these clubs at the start of season 2001–2:

1. Rangers

2. Wimbledon

3. Derby County

4. Crewe Alexandra

5. Wigan Athletic

6. Mansfield Town

7. Sunderland

8. Watford

9. Dunfermline Athletic

10. Wolverhampton Wanderers

11. Notts County

12. Bristol City

13. Blackpool

14. West Bromwich Albion

15. Millwall

16. Leyton Orient

Answers to page 355
FRANCE 2: 1. Romania 2. Patrick Battiston 3. Seville 4. Senegal
5. Manuel Amoros 6. Bulgaria 7. Brazil 8. Michel Platini 9. Eric Cantona and
David Ginola 10. Jean-Pierre Papin (Bayern Munich) 11. Denmark and
Paraguay 12. Greece 13. Slovakia, Poland and Israel 14. Azerbaijan 15. Eight
16. Marcel Desailly and Frank Leboeuf

General Quiz

General Quiz 1

Answers on page 362

1. What does Volkswagen mean?

2. What part did Matthew Simmonds play in the history of Manchester United?

3. Into which sea does the River Jordan flow?

4. Which golfer completed the Grand Slam of the amateur and professional Opens of both the USA and Britain in 1930?

5. Which singer was 'Moonlighting' in 1975?

6. What is the zodiac symbol for Gemini?

7. Which town on the south coast of England became a city as part of the Millennium celebrations?

8. Which newsreader presented the first series of *The People Versus*?

9. Which Scottish rugby player married a TV sports presenter in 2001?

10. What is a garganey?

11. Which boxer was banned for taking a bite out of Evander Holyfield's ear in 1997?

12. In which English county would you find St Michael's Mount?

13. Whose wife was turned into a pillar of salt?

14. Which novelist is credited with the introduction of pillar boxes?

15. Who directed the film *Blow-Up*?

16. What was the maiden name of Jane Austen's heroine *Emma*?

Answers to page 362
GENERAL QUIZ 3: 1. Brian Lara 2. Time And Relative Dimension In Space
3. Dead Sea 4. David Lean 5. Dartmoor 6. George IV 7. *High Road*
8. Holland 9. Lennox Lewis and Frank Bruno 10. Kent 11. *Peyton Place*
12. Robert Carlyle 13. Carina 14. Kneecap 15. Terry Gilliam 16. Adrian Moorhouse

General Quiz 2

Answers on page 363

1. Who is the brains behind the band Gorillaz?

2. What is a pangolin also known as?

3. From which country does the lambada dance originate?

4. Where is the Kuril Trench?

5. The Murray Darling is the longest river in which country?

6. Which building is the principal residence of the Archbishop of Canterbury?

7. Which golfer lost a six-shot lead in the final round of the 1996 US Masters?

8. What size paper is half of an A4 sheet?

9. Who was Luke Skywalker's father?

10. What is a jansky a unit of?

11. Brian Bennett was the drummer with which instrumental group?

12. Who owned a dog called Cracker in *Brookside*?

13. Which American ice skater was accused of plotting to break her rival's legs?

14. Who would have been called the Biblical 'Orpah' had the midwife not spelt the name wrongly on the birth certificate?

15. Which South American country was named after an Italian city?

16. Who wrote *Treasure Island* and *Kidnapped*?

Answers to page 363
GENERAL QUIZ 4: **1.** Bram Stoker **2.** France **3.** Mick Taylor **4.** Colombia and Peru **5.** Neville Chamberlain **6.** Richard Harris **7.** Kevin **8.** Toothpaste **9.** Quick-drying ink **10.** Natalie Imbruglia **11.** Weymouth **12.** Eddie Edwards **13.** *Shooting Stars* **14.** Minnehaha **15.** 10ft **16.** Beau and Jeff

General Quiz 3

Answers on page 360

1. Which cricketer broke the world record for the highest individual Test score with 375 for West Indies against England in 1994?

2. What does TARDIS stand for?

3. Which sea is nearly 1,300ft. below sea level?

4. Who won an Oscar for his direction of *Lawrence of Arabia*?

5. In which national park is Yes Tor?

6. With which King of England did Caroline of Brunswick endure a loveless marriage?

7. Which TV soap is set in Glendarroch?

8. What nationality were Teach-In, winners of the 1975 Eurovision Song Contest?

9. In 1993, which two men took part in the first 20th century World Heavyweight Championship fight between two British boxers?

10. The Isle of Sheppey is part of which English county?

11. Which Grace Metalious novel became a successful TV series starring Mia Farrow and Ryan O'Neal?

12. Who played TV detective *Hamish Macbeth*?

13. Which constellation is represented as a ship's keel?

14. What part of the human body is the patella?

15. Which American animator was a member of the *Monty Python* team?

16. Which English swimmer won the 100 metres breaststroke at the 1988 Seoul Olympics?

Answers to page 360
GENERAL QUIZ 1: **1.** 'People's car' **2.** He was the Crystal Palace fan at whom Eric Cantona launched his infamous flying kick in 1995 **3.** The Dead Sea **4.** Bobby Jones **5.** Leo Sayer **6.** Twins **7.** Brighton **8.** Kirsty Young **9.** Kenny Logan **10.** A teal-like bird **11.** Mike Tyson **12.** Cornwall **13.** Lot **14.** Anthony Trollope **15.** Michelangelo Antonioni **16.** Woodhouse

General Quiz 4

Answers on page 361

1. Who created Dracula?

2. In 1778, which country introduced the first state-controlled brothels?

3. Who was the first replacement for Brian Jones in The Rolling Stones?

4. Which two South American countries have borders with Ecuador?

5. Which British Prime Minister returned from Munich in 1938 clutching a piece of paper and a promise of 'peace in our time'?

6. Which Irish actor played Oliver Cromwell in the 1970 film?

7. Which boy's name means 'handsome at birth'?

8. A Roman mixture of vinegar, honey and salt was the first known example of what?

9. For what was Quink an abbreviation?

10. Which former *Neighbours* actress was 'Torn' in 1997?

11. Portland Bill is connected by road to which resort?

12. Which British ski jumper was ironically nicknamed 'The Eagle'?

13. Which TV series featured the Dove from Above?

14. Who was married to Hiawatha?

15. How high is a basketball hoop from the floor?

16. Who are the actor sons of Lloyd Bridges?

Answers to page 361
GENERAL QUIZ 2: 1. Damon Albarn 2. Scaly anteater 3. Brazil 4. In the Pacific Ocean 5. Australia 6. Lambeth Palace 7. Greg Norman 8. A5 9. Darth Vader 10. Radiation 11. The Shadows 12. Jimmy Corkhill 13. Tonya Harding 14. Oprah Winfrey 15. Venezuela (Venice) 16. Robert Louis Stevenson

General Quiz 5

Answers on page 366

1. What was wrong with the film title *Krakatoa, East of Java*?

2. Which golfer's chances of winning the 2001 British Open vanished when he was penalised for carrying too many clubs in his bag?

3. Dublin is the capital of which Irish province?

4. Which French town has a reputation for miraculous cures?

5. Eternal's 1996 hit 'Someday' was taken from which film?

6. Which footballer was the first person to refuse to be the subject of *This Is Your Life*?

7. What breed of dog is a clumber?

8. Who contributed guest vocals on UB40's version of 'I Got You Babe'?

9. If you ordered 'moules' in a French restaurant, what would you expect to be served?

10. According to Scottish superstition, which two colours should never be worn together?

11. Which crime has a potential 324 different combinations?

12. The name of which Indonesian city means 'place of victory'?

13. According to Alaskan state law, what is it illegal to look at from the window of an aircraft?

14. Which European city staged the 1928 Olympics?

15. What is the common name for the plant *Impatiens*?

16. Who rowed through a storm with her father one night in 1838 to save nine shipwrecked souls off the Farne Islands?

Answers to page 366
GENERAL QUIZ 7: **1.** Lake Victoria **2.** Hippopotamus **3.** Sn **4.** William Congreve **5.** Four **6.** Jerry Lewis **7.** Real Madrid **8.** Mini cab driver **9.** Craig Douglas **10.** Sir Geoffrey Howe **11.** 'Turnip' **12.** Trent **13.** Isosceles triangle **14.** A cold soup **15.** Isle of Man **16.** *Uncle Remus*

General Quiz 6

Answers on page 367

1. In music, what is meant by the term 'legato'?

2. Why is a cheetah unlike other cats?

3. What is pumpernickel?

4. In 1983, what became the first a cappella song to top the UK singles chart?

5. Which South African golfer won the US Open twice in the 1990s?

6. Who was the Roman god of fire?

7. Which Spaniard conquered the Aztec empire in the 16th century?

8. What kind of hopefuls attend RADA?

9. In which continent is the River Plate?

10. In motor-racing, who was the first winner of the World Drivers' Championship?

11. The thylacine is another name for which carnivorous marsupial?

12. Who took 'Ma Baker' to number two in the charts in 1977?

13. What is the national emblem of Canada?

14. Who was known as 'The Girl With The Million Dollar Legs'?

15. Ed Koch, the Mayor of New York in 1984, played himself in which Muppet movie?

16. About which London street did Gerry Rafferty sing in 1978?

Answers to page 367
GENERAL QUIZ 8: 1. Jean-Claude Van Damme 2. Durex 3. The telephone answering machine 4. *Ben-Hur* 5. Rawlplug 6. Reita Faria 7. Pauline Collins 8. Norway 9. Texas 10. Fishing (for eels) 11. God of marriage 12. Australia 13. *Danger Man* 14. Robert Dudley 15. Left 16. Jack Lemmon

General Quiz 7

Answers on page 364

1. Which lake is the source of the White Nile?

2. Which animal has been responsible for more human deaths than any other?

3. What is the chemical symbol for tin?

4. Which playwright penned *The Way of the World* in 1700?

5. How many sides does a trapezium have?

6. Who starred in the original version of *The Nutty Professor*?

7. Which Spanish football team won the European Champions' League in 1998 and 2000?

8. What did *Coronation Street*'s Don Brennan do for a living?

9. Which former milkman had a number one hit with 'Only Sixteen'?

10. Of which fellow politician did Denis Healey say: 'Being attacked in the House by him is like being savaged by a dead sheep'?

11. What was the nickname of agricultural reformer Charles Townshend?

12. Which river – the third longest in England – rises in the South Pennines and flows through the Midlands to the Humber?

13. What is the name for a triangle where two sides and two angles are the same?

14. What is gazpacho?

15. Whose parliament is called the Tynwald?

16. Brer Rabbit was a character in which series of talk tales by Joel Chandler Harris?

Answers to page 364
GENERAL QUIZ 5: 1. Krakatoa is west of Java 2. Ian Woosnam 3. Leinster
4. Lourdes 5. *The Hunchback of Notre Dame* 6. Danny Blanchflower
7. Spaniel 8. Chrissie Hynde 9. Mussels 10. Red and green 11. The murder in *Cluedo* 12. Jakarta 13. A moose 14. Amsterdam 15. Busy Lizzie
16. Grace Darling

General Quiz 8

Answers on page 365

1. Who is known as 'The Muscles From Brussels'?

2. Which product takes its name from its three prime requisites – durability, reliability and excellence?

3. The Electronic Secretary was the prototype of which device?

4. For which movie did Charlton Heston win a Best Actor Oscar in 1959?

5. London building contractor John J. Rawlings was responsible for which 20th-century invention?

6. Which Miss India won the Miss World contest in 1966?

7. Which actress left *The Liver Birds* after just five episodes?

8. Which Scandinavian country extends the farthest north?

9. Whose 1999 album was titled 'The Hush'?

10. What are you doing if you are sniggling?

11. Which god was Hymen in Greek mythology?

12. Which country won the 1999 Cricket World Cup?

13. Who was John Drake otherwise known as on TV?

14. What was the name of the Earl of Leicester who was a prominent member of the court of Elizabeth I?

15. Anything 'sinister' refers to which side?

16. Which Hollywood actor was born John Uhler III?

Answers to page 365
GENERAL QUIZ 6: **1.** Smoothly **2.** It can't retract its claws **3.** A type of bread **4.** 'Only You' by The Flying Pickets **5.** Ernie Els **6.** Vulcan **7.** Hernán Cortés **8.** Actors **9.** South America **10.** Dr Giuseppe Farina **11.** Tasmanian wolf **12.** Boney M **13.** Maple leaf **14.** Betty Grable **15.** *The Muppets Take Manhattan* **16.** 'Baker Street'

General Quiz 9

Answers on page 370

1. How many property squares are there on a Monopoly board?

2. Which singer/actress has been married to Jim Kerr and Liam Gallagher?

3. Which English actress played Ross's wife in *Friends*?

4. Which 17-year-old American became the youngest winner of a Grand Slam tennis title when he captured the 1989 French Open?

5. What is the name for a ring-shaped coral reef enclosing a lagoon?

6. What did Aesop write?

7. Which mythical monster has the body, tail and hind legs of a lion and the head, forelegs and wings of an eagle?

8. Which country created the first national netball association?

9. Shere Khan was the villain in which Disney film?

10. Which Great Train Robber played himself in The Sex Pistols' film *The Great Rock 'n' Roll Swindle*?

11. Which actor/singer was plain David Cook before joining the county set?

12. The name of which city in the Middle East means 'warm place'?

13. In which country are the Slieve Bloom mountains?

14. What was Burke and Hare's gruesome pursuit?

15. Who did Brazil's footballers beat 4–1 in the 1970 World Cup Final?

16. What did Beryl call sex in the TV sitcom *The Lovers*?

Answers to page 370
GENERAL QUIZ 11: **1.** No word in the English language rhymes with them **2.** Noddy **3.** Sicily **4.** Cooking pot **5.** BRM **6.** Lancashire **7.** The Who **8.** St Vitus **9.** Catherine contracted dandruff and didn't want the news to spread **10.** Robin Williams **11.** Murray Walker **12.** Red and white **13.** Thin Lizzy **14.** Two **15.** Smeeta Smitten **16.** Ruud Gullit

General Quiz 10

Answers on page 371

1. Susan Sarandon and Geena Davis played which 1991 fugitives?

2. With what sport was David Broome associated?

3. The island of Capri is situated at the southern entrance to which bay?

4. Who performed a concert in the park at the end of each episode of *Trumpton*?

5. Which British political party was founded in 1934?

6. What name is given to the white ball in snooker?

7. What country produces the wine Valpolicella?

8. In which city is the Wailing Wall?

9. What bird can be marsh, coal or crested?

10. What name is given to the President's study in the White House?

11. What is the name of the Marquess of Bath's stately home?

12. Who was the donkey in *Winnie-the-Pooh*?

13. Cheyenne is the capital of which American state?

14. Which group were in the 'Car Wash' in 1976?

15. Who made snooker's first televised maximum break?

16. What is the favourite coffee shop of the Crane brothers in *Frasier*?

Answers to page 371
GENERAL QUIZ 12: **1.** 'Twelve plus one' **2.** Havana **3.** 'Mama' Cass Elliot **4.** Henry VI **5.** Set **6.** W.C. Fields **7.** Three **8.** Twiggy **9.** India **10.** Sally Gunnell **11.** Starkiller **12.** Ava Gardner **13.** Bright blue **14.** '19' **15.** Lincolnshire **16.** One

General Quiz 11

Answers on page 368

1. What do the words 'month', 'orange', 'silver' and 'purple' have in common?

2. Whose car goes 'parp parp'?

3. From which island does the wine Marsala come?

4. What is a skillet?

5. In what make of car did Graham Hill become Formula One World Champion in 1962?

6. In which English county is the Fylde peninsula?

7. Which band were originally known as The High Numbers?

8. Who is the patron saint of comedians and mental illness?

9. Why did Catherine the Great of Russia have her hairdresser imprisoned in an iron cage for three years?

10. Who played the fast-talking DJ in *Good Morning Vietnam*?

11. Which sports commentator described his last race in September 2001?

12. Which two colours feature on the Austrian flag?

13. Which band sang about 'Whiskey In The Jar' in 1973?

14. How many Duncans were Kings of Scotland?

15. Who is the 'showbiz kitten' from *Goodness Gracious Me*?

16. Who was the first foreign manager to lift the FA Cup?

Answers to page 368
GENERAL QUIZ 9: 1. 22 2. Patsy Kensit 3. Helen Baxendale 4. Michael Chang 5. Atoll 6. Fables 7. Griffin 8. New Zealand 9. *The Jungle Book* 10. Ronnie Biggs 11. David Essex 12. Teheran 13. Ireland 14. Body-snatching 15. Italy 16. 'Percy Filth'

General Quiz 12

Answers on page 369

1. Which sum is an anagram of 'Eleven plus two'?

2. What is the capital of Cuba?

3. Which heavyweight American singer reportedly choked to death on a sandwich in 1974?

4. Who became King of England in 1422 at the age of eight months?

5. Of all the words in the English language, which has the most definitions?

6. Which comedy actor's last words, after flicking through the Bible on his deathbed, were: 'I'm looking for a loophole'?

7. How many times did the superstitious Charles Dickens touch everything for luck?

8. Which model had a stint presenting *This Morning* in 2001?

9. The lotus flower is the national symbol of which country?

10. In 1992, which athlete became the first British woman to win an Olympic track gold medal for 28 years?

11. From what was Luke Skywalker's surname in *Star Wars* changed at the last minute because the original sounded too violent?

12. Which movie star, who died in 1990, left her pet corgi Morgan a monthly salary plus his own limo and maid?

13. One in every 5000 North Atlantic lobsters is born what colour?

14. What number did Paul Hardcastle take to the top of the charts in 1985?

15. In which English county is Louth?

16. How many points are scored for knocking the ball over the crossbar in hurling?

Answers to page 369
GENERAL QUIZ 10: **1.** *Thelma and Louise* **2.** Show-jumping **3.** Bay of Naples **4.** The fire brigade band **5.** Scottish National Party **6.** Cue ball **7.** Italy **8.** Jerusalem **9.** Tit **10.** The Oval Office **11.** Longleat House **12.** Eeyore **13.** Wyoming **14.** Rose Royce **15.** Steve Davis **16.** Café Nervosa

General Quiz 13

Answers on page 374

1. Which TV pundit played a womanising footballer in the 2001 film *A Shot at Glory* at the same time that revelations emerged about his own private life?

2. Which horse race was temporarily switched to Ayr in 1989 – the first time Scotland had staged a classic?

3. What were Parliamentary followers known as during the English Civil War?

4. What was the Roman symbol for 1,000?

5. What is the common name for the pyrite iron sulphide?

6. What was the currency of Austria before the introduction of the euro?

7. Which Czech tennis player won the 1998 Wimbledon women's singles title?

8. Who wanted to buy a copy of his book *Fly Fishing*?

9. Where did William the Conqueror land in England in 1066?

10. What is a harvestman?

11. Who wrote *A Brief History of Time*?

12. What was the chosen stage name of Margarita Carmen Cansino, a star of 1940s musicals?

13. Which Leicester City football manager was sacked in October 2001?

14. At which athletic event was singer Johnny Mathis once ranked joint 85th in the world?

15. What is a baobab?

16. Which British Olympic athlete was not allowed to run as a schoolboy because of a heart defect?

Answers to page 374
GENERAL QUIZ 15: **1.** Bear **2.** Jimi Hendrix **3.** Marilyn Monroe **4.** Cardinal Wolsey **5.** George **6.** 35 minutes **7.** Leonardo Di Caprio **8.** The Internet **9.** Any whole number **10.** Herbivore **11.** Hertfordshire **12.** Geranium **13.** Flamingo **14.** Tribe of Gaels **15.** Australia **16.** June

General Quiz 14

Answers on page 375

1. Barrow is the most northerly town in which country?

2. In 1999, which American fulfilled her classmates' prediction that she would be 'The Girl Most Likely To Get Her Name in Lights'?

3. Which 15th-century English monarch was king for such a short time that nobody had a chance to paint his portrait?

4. Which ITV soap did Patrick Mower join in 2001?

5. In which 1996 movie did Demi Moore play a stripper?

6. Who was King of England at the time of the Gunpowder Plot?

7. What don't women in Iceland do when they get married?

8. Which English football club won the 1998 European Cup Winners' Cup?

9. Who had a number one with 'Shaddap You Face'?

10. American Greg LeMond was a champion at which sport?

11. Which Jane Austen adaptation won the BAFTA Best Film Award for 1996?

12. When do all racehorses have their birthday?

13. Which national anthem has 158 verses?

14. Who is the question-master on *University Challenge*?

15. Of what was Hecate a Greek goddess?

16. Which comedian had a 1960s hit with 'Happiness'?

Answers to page 375
GENERAL QUIZ 16: **1.** Two (Catherine of Aragon, Catherine Howard)
2. Pakistan **3.** Mount Pleasant **4.** Simon Schama **5.** Big Ben **6.** Pacific **7.** Barnet
8. Brine **9.** Bullfinch **10.** Australia **11.** Cable News Network **12.** Edith Cavell
13. 1994 **14.** Chilterns **15.** Tears for Fears **16.** *Crackerjack*

General Quiz 15

Answers on page 372

1. What animal features in the state flag of California?

2. Which guitar legend's first album was titled 'Are You Experienced'?

3. Which actress was fired from the set of her 1962 film *Something's Got To Give* shortly before her death?

4. Whom did Thomas More replace as Henry VIII's Lord Chancellor?

5. In the world of TV commercials, what was the name of the Hofmeister bear?

6. How long is each half in a game of hockey?

7. Who was nominated for an Academy Award for Best Supporting Actor for the 1993 film *What's Eating Gilbert Grape*?

8. Which computer network was launched in 1984?

9. What is an integer?

10. What name is given to an animal that feeds on green plants or their products?

11. Bishop's Stortford is in which English county?

12. Herb Robert is a wild form of which garden plant?

13. Which bird eats with its bill upside down?

14. What does the name of the political party 'Fine Gael' mean in Gaelic?

15. Of which country's rugby team was Nick Farr-Jones a captain?

16. In which month of the year is Father's Day?

Answers to page 372
GENERAL QUIZ 13: **1.** Ally McCoist **2.** St Leger **3.** Roundheads **4.** M
5. Fool's gold **6.** Schilling **7.** Jana Novotna **8.** J. R. Hartley **9.** Pevensey **10.** An arachnid **11.** Stephen Hawking **12.** Rita Hayworth **13.** Peter Taylor **14.** High jump **15.** A species of tree **16.** Roger Black

General Quiz 16

Answers on page 373

1. How many women named Catherine (with a 'C') did Henry VIII marry?

2. In which country is Faisalabad?

3. What is the name of the airport on the Falkland Islands?

4. Who presented the TV series *A History of Britain* in 2000?

5. Which London landmark took its name from Works Commissioner Benjamin Hall?

6. In which ocean is Bikini atoll?

7. Which club were relegated from the Football League in 2001?

8. What is a solution of sodium chloride in water commonly known as?

9. Which fruit-eating finch has the Latin name *Pyrrhula pyrrhula*?

10. Which country were Burke and Wills the first to cross from south to north?

11. What does CNN stand for?

12. Which nurse of a Brussels Red Cross hospital was executed by the Germans in 1915 for helping allied soldiers to escape?

13. In which year did Eurostar begin operations?

14. Coombe Hill, near Wendover, is the highest point of which range of hills?

15. Which Eighties duo had hits with 'Pale Shelter' and 'Shout'?

16. Peter Glaze was resident comic on which children's TV show?

Answers to page 373
GENERAL QUIZ 14: 1. USA 2. Monica Lewinsky 3. Edward V 4. *Emmerdale* 5. *Striptease* 6. James I 7. Change their surname 8. Chelsea 9. Joe Dolce 10. Cycling 11. *Sense and Sensibility* 12. I January 13. Greek 14. Jeremy Paxman 15. The underworld and magic 16. Ken Dodd

General Quiz 17

Answers on page 378

1. Which continent was explored by English navigator Matthew Flinders?

2. What nationality was the jeweller Fabergé?

3. Who invented the Kodak box camera?

4. Who was the first woman to fly across the Atlantic?

5. Which Hindu festival means 'garland of lamps'?

6. A dab is a member of which family of fish?

7. Which city is located at the Western end of Hadrian's Wall?

8. Which fashion designer created the 'Space Age Collection' in the 1960s?

9. Who holds the record for the most tries scored in international rugby?

10. What type of insect does *Buddleia davidi* attract?

11. Who played the king in *The King and I*?

12. In which Australian state is the town of Ballarat?

13. What is an auricula?

14. Who wrote 'Auld Lang Syne'?

15. In 1960s music what were Unit Four Plus?

16. Which celebrated cook was born Isabella Mary Mayson?

Answers to page 378
GENERAL QUIZ 19: 1. Isle of Dogs 2. Cassius Clay 3. English Civil War
4. El Cid 5. A cheese 6. Cheviot 7. Walter Winterbottom 8. Mason-Dixon
Line 9. Francisco Pizarro 10. Massif Central 11. Glottis 12. Globe Theatre
13. Tito Gobbi 14. Marie Lloyd 15. Geoffrey Durham 16. Egypt

General Quiz 18

Answers on page 379

1. The cane toad was introduced into Australia to eradicate which creature?

2. Fredericton is the capital of which Canadian province?

3. Which famous footballer was uncle to Jack and Bobby Charlton?

4. Which band recorded the album 'Together Alone'?

5. In music, what is the term for a group of three or more notes sounded together?

6. In Greek mythology, which nymph was changed into a laurel tree?

7. Which tunnel, built in 1963, runs under the River Thames to Purfleet?

8. What does 'Duce' mean in Italian?

9. What is a duiker?

10. Which US actress made her first starring appearance in the movie *Bonnie and Clyde* and later won an Oscar for *Network*?

11. In which country is The Curragh racecourse?

12. What can be gold, green or zebra?

13. Rustavi and Batumi are towns in which country?

14. Who won his first Formula One Grand Prix in Hungary in 1993?

15. In which country is the Lena river?

16. What did Walter Matuschanskavasky choose as his stage name?

Answers to page 379
GENERAL QUIZ 20: **1.** *Mona Lisa* **2.** Perry **3.** Joe DiMaggio **4.** Mock Orange **5.** Way of living **6.** Ed Moses **7.** Bob Marley **8.** Conchita Martínez **9.** France **10.** Izaak Walton **11.** Type of deer **12.** Witham **13.** Swift **14.** Broom **15.** Compact Disc Read-Only Memory **16.** The Chair

General Quiz 19

Answers on page 376

1. On which island is Canary Wharf?

2. Who changed his name to Muhammad Ali?

3. Edgehill was the opening battle in which war?

4. What was the nickname of Spanish soldier Rodrigo Díaz de Vivar?

5. What is Cucciocavallo?

6. Which range of hills in Northumberland gave their name to a breed of sheep?

7. Who preceded Alf Ramsey as England football manager?

8. What is the name of the boundary line between Maryland and Pennsylvania?

9. Which Spanish conquistador conquered Peru?

10. What is the mountainous plateau region of southern central France?

11. What is the narrow opening at the upper end of the larynx that contains the vocal cords?

12. Which London theatre was burned down in 1613 after a fired cannon set light to the thatch during a performance of Shakespeare's *Henry VIII*?

13. Which Gobbi was an Italian baritone?

14. Which music-hall artist was born Matilda Alice Victoria Wood?

15. Which magician is Victoria Wood's husband?

16. Which country is immediately to the east of Libya?

Answers to page 376
GENERAL QUIZ 17: 1. Australia 2. Russian 3. George Eastman 4. Amelia Earhart 5. Diwali 6. Flounder 7. Carlisle 8. Pierre Cardin 9. David Campese 10. Butterflies 11. Yul Brynner 12. Victoria 13. A species of primrose 14. Robert Burns 15. Two 16. Mrs Beeton

General Quiz 20

Answers on page 377

1. Which painting is also known as *La Gioconda*?

2. Who is Kevin the teenager's best friend?

3. Which baseball star was Marilyn Monroe's second husband?

4. What sort of orange is a shrub with white scented flowers?

5. What does the Latin '*modus vivendi*' mean?

6. Which 400 metres hurdler went 122 races unbeaten from 1977–87?

7. Who recorded the 1972 album 'Catch A Fire'?

8. Who beat Martina Navratilova in the 1994 Wimbledon ladies' singles final?

9. In which country is the Var river?

10. Who wrote *The Compleat Angler*?

11. What is a wapiti?

12. On which river does the Lincolnshire town of Boston stand?

13. As in the breed of dog, what does the Russian word 'borzoi' mean?

14. What can be a flowering shrub or an implement for sweeping?

15. What does CD-ROM stand for?

16. What is the highest fence in the Grand National?

Answers to page 377
GENERAL QUIZ 18: **1.** The cane beetle **2.** New Brunswick **3.** Jackie Milburn **4.** Crowded House **5.** Chord **6.** Daphne **7.** Dartford Tunnel **8.** Leader **9.** A small antelope **10.** Faye Dunaway **11.** Ireland **12.** Finches **13.** Georgia **14.** Damon Hill **15.** Russia **16.** Walter Matthau

General Quiz 21

Answers on page 382

1. Where in the human body is the eustachian tube?

2. In which ocean is Christmas Island situated?

3. Which bird won an Academy Award with the 1942 film *Der Fuhrer's Face*?

4. Which film was the musical version of *Pygmalion*?

5. If you have myopia, what do you suffer from?

6. Which mountain was revered by the ancient Greeks as the home of Apollo and the Muses?

7. Przhevalsky's is a wild breed of which animal?

8. What did Red Riding Hood take to her sick grandmother?

9. What nationality was the polar explorer Robert Peary?

10. Which season begins with the vernal equinox?

11. Who had a 1964 number one single with 'Do Wah Diddy Diddy'?

12. In whose company was Hugh Grant when he was arrested in 1995?

13. What does a pedometer count?

14. What is a peccary?

15. What sport did Canadian Wayne Gretzky play?

16. Whose final TV series before his retirement was the sitcom *Clarence*?

Answers to page 382
GENERAL QUIZ 23: **1.** Meg Ryan **2.** The Scunner Campbell **3.** Aberdeen **4.** Blubber **5.** Brooklands **6.** Denver **7.** Stalactite **8.** Billy J. Kramer **9.** Family histories **10.** *David Copperfield* **11.** The eye **12.** At sea **13.** Dani Behr **14.** Croatian **15.** Honshu **16.** Wild arum

General Quiz 22

Answers on page 383

1. Which actor was reputedly the target of Carly Simon's 'You're So Vain'?

2. Who said: 'It's not that I'm afraid to die, I just don't want to be there when it happens'?

3. What mode of transport have Olivia Newton-John, Eric Clapton and Don Johnson all owned?

4. Which American form of croquet was one of the sports in the 1904 Olympics?

5. What household convenience item was invented by Mrs W.A. Cochran in 1889?

6. Maritimo are a football team from which country?

7. 'Encephalic' refers to which part of the body?

8. On which river does Monmouth stand?

9. Where does Rupert Bear live?

10. Wizzard and ELO were splinter groups from which band?

11. Which Premiership football club had an Angel playing for them in 2001?

12. Which Shakespeare play was said to have been written at the request of Elizabeth I?

13. In which American state is the Sierra Nevada mountain range?

14. Which of the *Friends* composed 'Smelly Cat'?

15. Who wrote *Saturday Night and Sunday Morning*?

16. What does a spa town have?

Answers to page 383
GENERAL QUIZ 24: 1. James I 2. Zero 3. 'Sergeant Pepper's Lonely Hearts Club Band' 4. A Flying Circus (it was one of the names rejected before Monty Python) 5. 78 6. Joseph Warren Stilwell 7. Tchaikovsky 8. Saul 9. American football 10. Grace Kelly 11. Speedway 12. A flatfish 13. Sweden 14. Italy 15. The *Hindenburg* 16. Rhodesia

General Quiz 23

Answers on page 380

1. Who split from husband Dennis Quaid in 2001 after having a fling with a Gladiator?

2. Who was the villain in *Supergran*?

3. Who were the first British football club to convert their ground to an all-seater stadium?

4. What can be whale fat or to weep uncontrollably?

5. Which famous old motor-racing circuit was built near Weybridge?

6. In which US city was *Dynasty* set?

7. What is the name for a limestone deposit which hangs from the roof of a cave?

8. Which Merseybeat artist turned down 'Yesterday'?

9. What is genealogy the study of?

10. Mr Murdstone is a character in which Dickens novel?

11. Where in the human body is the iris?

12. Where is Davy Jones's Locker?

13. Which former girlfriend of Ryan Giggs was one of the presenters on *The Word*?

14. What nationality is tennis player Goran Ivanisevic?

15. Which is the largest island in Japan?

16. Which wild flower is also known as cuckoo-pint or lords-and-ladies?

Answers to page 380
GENERAL QUIZ 21: **1.** The ear **2.** Indian Ocean **3.** Donald Duck **4.** *My Fair Lady* **5.** Short-sightedness **6.** Mount Parnassus **7.** Horse **8.** Cakes **9.** American **10.** Spring **11.** Manfred Mann **12.** Divine Brown **13.** Walking steps **14.** A pig-like mammal **15.** Ice hockey **16.** Ronnie Barker

General Quiz 24

Answers on page 381

1. Who united the English and Scottish crowns in 1603?

2. Which number cannot be expressed in Roman figures?

3. Which famous album cover was designed by Peter Blake?

4. What did Cynthia Fellatio almost have on TV in 1969?

5. How many Tarot cards are there?

6. Which US general was nicknamed 'Vinegar Joe'?

7. Who composed the ballet *Sleeping Beauty*?

8. In the Old Testament, who was the first King of Israel?

9. What sport do the Dallas Cowboys play?

10. Which American actress starred in *Rear Window* and *High Society*?

11. At what sport was New Zealander Barry Briggs a world champion?

12. What is brill in the sea?

13. Carl XVI Gustav became king of which country in 1973?

14. Soave and Frascati are wines from which country?

15. What blew up at Lakehurst, New Jersey, on 6 May 1937?

16. What was Britain's last colony in Africa?

Answers to page 381
GENERAL QUIZ 22: 1. Warren Beatty 2. Woody Allen 3. Harley-Davidson motorbikes 4. Roque 5. Automatic dishwasher 6. Portugal 7. The brain 8. Wye 9. Nut Wood 10. The Move 11. Aston Villa 12. *The Merry Wives of Windsor* 13. California 14. Phoebe 15. Alan Sillitoe 16. A spring

General Quiz 25

Answers on page 386

1. Which daughter of a former *Blue Peter* presenter sang on a number one hit in 2000?

2. In Greek mythology, which beautiful youth was the favourite of the goddess Aphrodite?

3. Which cord connects a foetus to the placenta?

4. What colour is the lignite jet?

5. Which TV inquisitor described herself as an 'ageing ex-drunk with bad ankles'?

6. How many world championship points are awarded to the driver who comes second in a Formula One Grand Prix?

7. Where on your body might you wear puttees?

8. Which Spice Girl teamed up with Truesteppers and Dane Bowers for the 2000 single 'Out Of Your Mind'?

9. Who was known as 'The Virgin Queen'?

10. What is the cube of four?

11. Who wrote the fantasy novel *The Colour of Magic*?

12. Which English actor played law firm boss Ed Masry in the movie *Erin Brockovich*?

13. The US city of Cleveland is on the shores of which Great Lake?

14. Which two colours feature in the Spanish national flag?

15. In which sport did teams contest the Regal Trophy between 1971 and 1996?

16. The Amazon flows into the sea in which country?

Answers to page 386
GENERAL QUIZ 27: 1. Victoria Beckham (Brooklyn) 2. Icarus 3. Michelle Pfeiffer 4. Antarctica 5. New South Wales 6. Billy Wilder 7. Berkshire 8. Bowls 9. Father Peter Clifford 10. Kenny Dalglish 11. Seven 12. Dock 13. Lord Grade 14. Double vision 15. Duke of Windsor 16. Thomas Hardy

General Quiz 26

Answers on page 387

1. What colour is given to the name of the room at a studios where actors rest?

2. Who was the first Tory Prime Minister of Britain?

3. What is a native of Manchester called?

4. Bernadotte is the family name of which country's royal house?

5. Where would you find a Bezier curve?

6. Which Football League manager parted company with his club in September 2001 after nearly 12 years in charge?

7. Which Pakistan premier was the first female leader of a Muslim state?

8. What does BFI stand for?

9. The dace is a member of which family of freshwater fish?

10. Which sports presenter was the subject of an expensive transfer from BBC to ITV in 1999?

11. 'Peaches' was the first UK top ten hit for which punk rockers?

12. Which Jonathan Kaplan film earned Jodie Foster an Academy Award for Best Actress in 1988?

13. In which city do visitors land at Marco Polo airport?

14. Which countries form the Iberian Peninsula?

15. Which *Brookside* character was gunned down by Ron Dixon in 2001?

16. Who romanced Renee Zellweger in the film *Jerry Maguire*?

Answers to page 387
GENERAL QUIZ 28: **1.** 1923 **2.** Stephen Fry **3.** Six **4.** Mushroom **5.** Sash! **6.** Darts **7.** Switzerland **8.** Guns 'N' Roses **9.** Deadly nightshade **10.** Adolf Eichmann **11.** Greenland **12.** Suzanne Charlton **13.** Esperanto **14.** CD **15.** Newcastle-upon-Tyne **16.** Yerevan

General Quiz 27

Answers on page 384

1. Which singer's baby son could be heard on her 2001 album?

2. In Greek mythology, who plunged to his death after flying too close to the Sun?

3. Who was 'Makin' Whoopee' in *The Fabulous Baker Boys*?

4. In which continent is the Weddell Sea?

5. The town of Newcastle is in which Australian state?

6. Which director, who famously said that Marilyn Monroe was the meanest woman he ever met, died in 2002?

7. In which county is Bracknell?

8. Which outdoor game is played on a grass area known as a rink?

9. What was the name of the priest played by Stephen Tompkinson in *Ballykissangel*?

10. Who was the first professional footballer to score 100 goals in both Scotland and England?

11. After how many games in a lawn tennis match are the players given new balls?

12. Which plant's leaves cure nettle stings?

13. Which TV chief said of his forthcoming production *Moses the Lawgiver*: 'It looks good in the rushes'?

14. What do you suffer from if you have diplopia?

15. What title was Edward VIII given following his abdication?

16. Which novelist revived the term 'Wessex' to describe the south-west counties of England?

Answers to page 384
GENERAL QUIZ 25: **1.** Sophie Ellis Bextor (daughter of Janet Ellis)
2. Adonis **3.** Umbilical cord **4.** Black **5.** Anne Robinson **6.** Six **7.** On your legs
8. Victoria Beckham **9.** Elizabeth I **10.** 64 **11.** Terry Pratchett **12.** Albert
Finney **13.** Lake Erie **14.** Red and yellow **15.** Rugby League **16.** Brazil

General Quiz 28

Answers on page 385

1. In which year was Wembley Stadium first opened?

2. Who played the troubled playwright in the 1997 biopic of Oscar Wilde?

3. How many times has Steve Davis been World Snooker Champion?

4. The death cap is the most poisonous type of what?

5. Whose first UK hit was 'Encore Une Fois' in 1997?

6. Leighton Rees and Bobby George are practitioners of which sport?

7. Helvetia is another name for which country?

8. Slash is the guitarist with which heavy rock band?

9. Which plant's proper name is belladonna?

10. Which Nazi was executed after being tried in Israel in 1961 for war crimes?

11. Eric the Red is said to have been the first European to discover which land?

12. Which daughter of a famous footballer has been a weather forecaster for the BBC?

13. Which international language was devised by Ludwig L. Zamenhof?

14. What musical medium is 400 in Roman numerals?

15. In which English city is the district of Byker?

16. What is the capital of Armenia?

Answers to page 385
GENERAL QUIZ 26: 1. Green 2. Earl of Bute 3. Mancunian 4. Sweden 5. On a graph 6. Brian Flynn (Wrexham) 7. Benazir Bhutto 8. British Film Institute 9. Carp 10. Des Lynam 11. The Stranglers 12. *The Accused* 13. Venice 14. Spain and Portugal 15. Clint Moffat 16. Tom Cruise

General Quiz 29

Answers on page 390

1. Which long-serving tennis commentator died in 1992?

2. If you were to spell out numbers (omitting the 'and'), what number would you have to go to before finding the letter 'a'?

3. In which country was Chris De Burgh born?

4. The anagram of which actress's name is 'evil lass in erotica'?

5. What pseudonym is used by author David Cornwell?

6. What is the name for an alloy of copper and tin?

7. Who founded Habitat?

8. What colours are the numbers on a roulette wheel?

9. In which English county is Althorp House?

10. Who played Dr Andrew Attwood in *Peak Practice*?

11. Who was sent off as England's footballers went out of the 1998 World Cup?

12. Donald McGill created 12,000 examples of what type of artwork?

13. Which band are led by Ian Broudie?

14. What does the *Venus de Milo* lack?

15. How many chambers are there in the human heart?

16. How many Football League teams are there in Kent?

Answers to page 390
GENERAL QUIZ 31: 1. Liverpool 2. Pluto 3. A phase of the Moon
4. Antarctica 5. Mike Rutherford 6. Viv Anderson 7. *Pingwings* 8. Walt
Disney 9. Spain 10. Fear of the left side 11. New Hampshire 12. The baht
13. A backbone 14. Roberts 15. July 16. Partition between the nostrils

General Quiz 30

Answers on page 391

1. How many hearts does an earthworm have?

2. Which superstar sang backing vocals on Rockwell's 'Somebody's Watching You'?

3. Which *Blue Peter* presenter played one of *Doctor Who*'s assistants?

4. A crop of which fruit dropped from the sky onto a Louisiana building-site in 1961?

5. The Flathead Lake Monster is said to exist in which American state?

6. Which racehorse named after a Russian dancer won the Two Thousand Guineas, Derby and St Leger in 1970?

7. Which swashbuckling trio were created by Alexandre Dumas?

8. Who played Crêpe Suzette in the film *Absolute Beginners*?

9. Durrës is the chief port of which country?

10. Which battle on British soil took place on 9 September 1513?

11. Who was the original presenter of the TV talent show *New Faces*?

12. What speed can a dragonfly reach?

13. What is unique about the Book of Esther in the Bible?

14. Which Thursday precipitated the worldwide Depression in 1929?

15. Who duetted with Peter Gabriel on 'Don't Give Up'?

16. Who composed the ballet *Swan Lake*?

Answers to page 391
GENERAL QUIZ 32: 1. Brian Clough 2. Cumbria and Northumberland
3. Van Morrison 4. Tom and Jerry 5. Donald Duck 6. *Tess of the D'Urbervilles*
7. Dorset 8. North 9. Motorcycle racing 10. London and Paris 11. Miss
Scarlett 12. West Indies 13. Trappist 14. Lemon and melon 15. Racehorses
16. China

General Quiz 31

Answers on page 388

1. Which is farthest west – Bristol, Liverpool or Cheltenham?

2. Which is the smallest planet?

3. What does the term gibbous describe?

4. Where is Queen Maud Land?

5. Who is the 'Mike' of Mike and the Mechanics?

6. Who was the first black player to appear for England in a full football international?

7. Who lived on Berrydown Farm?

8. Although he had one himself, which movie studio boss refused to allow any of his employees to grow a moustache?

9. Which country hosts an annual mass tomato fight?

10. What is levophobia?

11. Which American state is nicknamed the 'Granite State'?

12. What is the national currency of Thailand?

13. What does an invertebrate lack?

14. What was Margaret Thatcher's maiden name?

15. In which month of the year is the British Open golf tournament held?

16. What is a septum?

Answers to page 388
GENERAL QUIZ 29: **1.** Dan Maskell **2.** One thousand **3.** Argentina **4.** Alicia Silverstone **5.** John Le Carré **6.** Bronze **7.** Terence Conran **8.** Red and black **9.** Northamptonshire **10.** Gary Mavers **11.** David Beckham **12.** Saucy seaside postcards **13.** The Lightning Seeds **14.** Arms **15.** Four **16.** One (Gillingham)

General Quiz 32

Answers on page 389

1. Which football manager retired after leading Nottingham Forest to relegation in 1993?

2. Which two English counties border Scotland?

3. Which veteran Irish rock star used to be one of Them?

4. Which animated protagonists were condemned in the 1970s for their 'mindless violence'?

5. Who was translated as Donald Anus by the Vatican newspaper?

6. Angel Clare appeared in which Thomas Hardy novel?

7. Blandford Forum is in which county?

8. On which coast of France is Deauville?

9. In which sport do competitors go earholing?

10. Which are the two cities in *A Tale of Two Cities*?

11. Which *Cluedo* suspect is known as Fröken Röd in Scandinavia?

12. Leary Constantine played Test cricket for which country?

13. Which order of monks maintain a vow of silence?

14. Which two fruits are anagrams of each other?

15. What does Sir Michael Stoute train?

16. In which country were the Triads founded?

Answers to page 389
GENERAL QUIZ 30: 1. Ten 2. Michael Jackson 3. Peter Purves 4. Peaches
5. Montana 6. Nijinsky 7. *The Three Musketeers* 8. Patsy Kensit 9. Albania
10. Battle of Flodden 11. Derek Hobson 12. 25 mph 13. It is the only book
of the Bible that doesn't mention God by name 14. Black Thursday
15. Kate Bush 16. Tchaikovsky

General Quiz 33

Answers on page 394

1. How many tusks does an adult wart hog have?

2. Which American state is known as the 'Pine Tree State'?

3. How many jumps does each competitor have in an Olympic long jump final?

4. Which two Northern Ireland politicians won the 1998 Nobel Peace Prize?

5. Which Sydney landmark was opened in 1973?

6. Which pungent creature has the Latin name *Mephitis mephitis*?

7. Which footballer was transferred to Newcastle United for a then world record fee of £15 million in 1996?

8. What can be standard, miniature or toy?

9. Which band released the best-selling album 'Rumours'?

10. As whom was jazz pianist Ferdinand Joseph La Menthe Morton better known?

11. What nationality was cyclist Eddie Merckx?

12. In which English county is Mablethorpe?

13. Which Filipino politician was known as the 'Iron Butterfly'?

14. Which novelist wrote *Small World* and *Nice Work*?

15. Who succeeded Michael Foot as leader of the Labour Party?

16. In which country is the port of Jeddah?

Answers to page 394
GENERAL QUIZ 35: 1. James Callaghan 2. Ron Howard 3. *The Eagle Has Landed* 4. R.E.M. 5. Anita Brookner 6. St Pancras 7. Sue Devoy 8. Warren Beatty 9. Gianfranco Zola 10. New South Wales 11. Platypus 12. Red and white 13. *Turandot* 14. John Milton 15. Spain 16. A marsupial

General Quiz 34

Answers on page 395

1. What does Interpol stand for?

2. Which League was formed by the trading cities of northern Europe in the 12th century?

3. Which movie sex symbol of the 1930s changed her name from Harlean Carpentier?

4. Which mythological creatures had women's faces and vultures' bodies?

5. From which country do freesia plants originate?

6. Which actress split from Woody Allen in 1992?

7. What was launched in 11 EU states in 1999?

8. In which field event did American athlete Randy Barnes specialise?

9. Which weasel has dark brown fur and two yellow face patches?

10. Susan Stranks, Mick Robertson and Tommy Boyd all presented which children's TV show?

11. Which band was fronted by the grandson of Sir John Mills?

12. What instrument did Mrs Mills play?

13. Which boxer took the World Heavyweight title from Lennox Lewis in 1994?

14. How many feet are there in a fathom?

15. Which French royal house gave its name to a biscuit?

16. Which athletic competition combines cross-country skiing with rifle shooting?

Answers to page 395
GENERAL QUIZ 36: **1.** Nigella Lawson **2.** Kinshasa (Zaire) **3.** Antarctica **4.** Willie Ryan **5.** Rudolph Valentino **6.** U Thant **7.** Sundial **8.** Tina Charles **9.** Furniture **10.** 1900 **11.** Denzel Washington **12.** Kent **13.** American **14.** Germany **15.** Julie Christie **16.** An aluminium can with a ring-pull

General Quiz 35

Answers on page 392

1. Which British home secretary of 1967–70 went on to become Prime Minister?

2. Which star of *Happy Days* has become a successful movie director?

3. Which 1976 movie starring Michael Caine, Donald Sutherland and Robert Duvall was based on a Jack Higgins best seller?

4. Michael Stipe is the singer with which band?

5. Who wrote *Hotel du Lac*?

6. Near which London railway station is the British Library?

7. Which New Zealander recorded a hat-trick of world squash titles from 1990–2?

8. Which actor directed the 1981 Oscar-winning movie *Reds*?

9. Which footballer joined Chelsea from Parma in 1996?

10. In which Australian state is Wagga Wagga?

11. Which mammal was thought to be a fake when first discovered?

12. What two colours feature on the flag of Peru?

13. From which Puccini opera does 'Nessun Dorma' come?

14. Who wrote *Paradise Lost*?

15. The cream of which country's footballers play in the Primera Liga?

16. What is a yapok?

Answers to page 392
GENERAL QUIZ 33: **1.** Four **2.** Maine **3.** Six **4.** John Hume and David Trimble **5.** Opera House **6.** Skunk **7.** Alan Shearer **8.** Poodle **9.** Fleetwood Mac **10.** Jelly Roll Morton **11.** Belgian **12.** Lincolnshire **13.** Imelda Marcos **14.** David Lodge **15.** Neil Kinnock **16.** Saudi Arabia

General Quiz 36

Answers on page 393

1. Which TV cook is the daughter of a former Chancellor of the Exchequer?

2. Which capital city was seized by Tutsi rebels in 1997?

3. Where is the Ross Sea?

4. Who rode Benny the Dip to victory in the 1997 Epsom Derby?

5. Which screen idol's first starring role was in *The Four Horsemen of the Apocalypse*?

6. Which U was secretary general of the United Nations?

7. On what does a gnomon cast a shadow?

8. Which Tina had a Seventies hit with 'I Love To Love'?

9. What did Thomas Sheraton design?

10. In which year was the Queen Mother born?

11. Who played boxer Rubin 'Hurricane' Carter in the 1999 movie *The Hurricane*?

12. In which county is Brands Hatch motor-racing circuit?

13. What nationality was the poet Henry Wadsworth Longfellow?

14. Which country forms the western border of the Czech Republic?

15. Who starred in *Billy Liar*, *Darling* and *Dr Zhivago*?

16. What were Iron City Beer of Pittsburgh, Pennsylvania, the first to produce in 1962?

Answers to page 393
GENERAL QUIZ 34: 1. International Criminal Police Organisation
2. Hanseatic League 3. Jean Harlow 4. Harpies 5. South Africa 6. Mia Farrow
7. The Euro 8. Shot putt 9. Arum lily 10. *Magpie* 11. Kula Shaker 12. Piano
13. Oliver McCall 14. Six 15. Bourbon 16. Biathlon

General Quiz 37

Answers on page 398

1. In cookery what is cayenne?

2. In which American state is the town of Cedar Rapids?

3. Which English king's lover was Piers Gaveston?

4. What is an epigram?

5. Which 1998 film about a shy girl who can sing like her showbiz idols starred Jane Horrocks and Michael Caine?

6. At which sport do England and Scotland compete for the Calcutta Cup?

7. Which is the world's oldest football knockout competition?

8. In which year did Abba reach number one in the UK with 'Knowing Me, Knowing You'?

9. Where in the world has the busiest roads?

10. Which country lies immediately to the south of Belarus?

11. Which TV magician gave Basil Brush his big break?

12. Which Argentinian cruiser was controversially sunk by British forces during the Falklands conflict with the loss of nearly 400 men?

13. In May 1982, what happened in Britain for the first time for 450 years?

14. Which former dress-wearing member of Mud has co-written number one hits for Spiller and Kylie Minogue?

15. Which bird is noted for its boom?

16. In France, what would you buy from a boulangerie?

Answers to page 398
GENERAL QUIZ 39: **1.** Bob Hoskins **2.** *The Forsyte Saga* **3.** 1988 **4.** Panama Canal **5.** Portuguese **6.** 'The Divine Comedy' **7.** Melchester Rovers **8.** John Reginald Christie **9.** St Bernard **10.** The Faeroe Islands **11.** North America **12.** Sardinia **13.** Arsenal **14.** Field hockey **15.** Milkman **16.** Sharon Watts

General Quiz 38

Answers on page 399

1. Whose short story *The Birds* was made into a Hitchcock thriller?

2. Which Shakespeare play begins: 'Now is the winter of our discontent'?

3. What is a horsetail?

4. In the Old Testament, which daughter of the King of Sidon married King Ahab of Israel?

5. Which boy band had the first new UK number one single of the 1990s?

6. Zealand, Fyn, Lolland, Falster and Bornholm are the principal islands of which country?

7. Which American city was hit by an earthquake in 1994, killing 61 people?

8. Who starred with Tom Cruise in the 1983 comedy *Risky Business*?

9. On a golf course, what is the name of the close-cut grass around the edge of the green?

10. Which decade in the USA is commonly referred to as the Jazz Age?

11. Which popular grey horse won the Cheltenham Gold Cup in 1989?

12. What is the term for the sensation that something encountered for the first time has actually been seen before?

13. Which boxer succeeded Henry Cooper as British heavyweight champion?

14. What three colours appear on the flag of Bulgaria?

15. Which country has the busiest rail network in the world?

16. What did *Lovejoy* deal in?

Answers to page 399
GENERAL QUIZ 40: 1. Portugal 2. September 3. Jamaica 4. Vinnie Jones
5. Cheshire 6. Birdwatcher 7. Helen Baxendale 8. Brugge 9. Alberta
10. Citroën 11. Guy Fawkes 12. Rhythmic gymnastics 13. Two
14. Edinburgh 15. Herbert Asquith 16. George Michael

General Quiz 39

Answers on page 396

1. Who played London crime lord Harold Shand in *The Long Good Friday*?

2. *The Man of Property* was the first part of which series of novels?

3. In which year did Bros reach number one with 'I Owe You Nothing'?

4. Where is the only place in the world that you can see the sun rise over the Pacific and set over the Atlantic?

5. Estoril is the venue of which Formula One Grand Prix?

6. Neil Hannon took his band name from which epic poem by Dante Alighieri?

7. For which football club did Roy Race play for many years?

8. Who committed the murders on which the film *10 Rillington Place* was based?

9. What breed of dog was Beethoven in the film of the same name?

10. Which country's national dish is puffin stuffed with rhubarb?

11. The Porcupine river is in which continent?

12. On which island is the town of Cagliari?

13. Who did Liverpool defeat in the 2001 FA Cup Final?

14. Which game starts with a bully?

15. What was Ernie's occupation in the Benny Hill number one hit?

16. Who returned to *EastEnders* as co-owner of the Queen Vic in 2001?

Answers to page 396
GENERAL QUIZ 37: **1.** Pepper **2.** Iowa **3.** Edward II **4.** A short, witty saying **5.** *Little Voice* **6.** Rugby union **7.** FA Cup **8.** 1977 **9.** Hong Kong **10.** Ukraine **11.** David Nixon **12.** *General Belgrano* **13.** The Pope visited Britain **14.** Rob Davis **15.** Bittern **16.** Cakes or bread

General Quiz 40

Answers on page 397

1. Coimbra and Setubal are towns in which European country?

2. In which month of the year is the St Leger run?

3. Kingston is the capital of which island?

4. Which former footballer played Big Chris in *Lock, Stock and Two Smoking Barrels*?

5. In which English county Is Crewe?

6. What is a twitcher?

7. Who plays Rachel in *Cold Feet*?

8. What is the Flemish name for Bruges?

9. In which Canadian province is Calgary?

10. Which French motor company was bought by Peugeot in 1974?

11. Who was arrested in the cellar beneath the Houses of Parliament on 4 November 1605?

12. A ribbon, ball or hoop are accessories in which sporting floor exercise?

13. How many wheels does a hansom cab have?

14. Where is Arthur's Seat?

15. Who was British Prime Minister at the outbreak of the First World War?

16. Whose debut solo album was titled 'Faith'?

Answers to page 397
GENERAL QUIZ 38: 1. Daphne du Maurier 2. *Richard III* 3. A plant
4. Jezebel 5. New Kids on the Block 6. Denmark 7. Los Angeles 8. Rebecca De Mornay 9. Apron 10. 1920s 11. Desert Orchid 12. *Déjà vu* 13. Joe Bugner 14. White, green and red 15. Japan 16. Antiques

General Quiz 41

Answers on page 402

1. How many players from each team are allowed on the ice at the same time in a game of ice hockey?

2. In which year did *Annie Hall* pick up a hatful of Oscars?

3. What is petit point?

4. What are petits pois?

5. What do the five Olympic rings represent?

6. Which character was nicknamed 'Lofty' in *It Ain't Half Hot Mum*?

7. Who lost her head at Fotheringay Castle in 1587?

8. The children of which family did *Mary Poppins* look after?

9. Why would your moggy like *nepeta*?

10. Which woman was Prime Minister of Israel from 1969 to 1974?

11. Who was the Roman goddess of intelligence and handicrafts?

12. What is the common name for pertussis?

13. Duluth, Bloomington and Rochester are towns in which American state?

14. From which film did the Madonna hit 'Beautiful Stranger' come?

15. What is the Duke of Bedford's stately home?

16. Which sport played on sand made its Olympic debut at the Sydney Games in 2000?

Answers to page 402
GENERAL QUIZ 43: 1. A sea bird 2. 'Give Ireland Back To The Irish' 3. 24
4. 18th 5. Cat Deeley 6. Cockney Rebel 7. Manchester United 8. Chester
9. Goran Ivanesevic 10. An anchor 11. The Seventh Day Adventists
12. Malcolm McLaren 13. The Rose and The Globe 14. Michael Dukakis
15. Wrestling 16. Canine teeth

General Quiz 42

Answers on page 403

1. *Brighton Belles* was the UK version of which US sitcom?

2. Which Welsh singer witnessed a 'Total Eclipse Of The Heart' in 1983?

3. Who rode the show-jumping horse Doublet?

4. Frank Worrell played Test cricket for which country?

5. Which item of confectionery did a young Emma Bunton advertise on TV?

6. Which country produces the wine Hock?

7. Which group of rioters wrecked machinery in northern England in the 1810s?

8. What can a polyglot do?

9. With what was Trotsky butchered?

10. How many American colonies signed the Declaration of Independence from Britain in 1776?

11. What is the capital of Ukraine?

12. Which TV police series started out on the beat as *Woodentop*?

13. The Gulf of Tonkin is part of which sea?

14. The Basque Separatist movement operates in which country?

15. Who wrote the novel *Gone With The Wind*?

16. Which Scottish football ground name means 'dung heap'?

Answers to page 403
GENERAL QUIZ 44: 1. Victoria Beckham 2. 'The Wallabies' 3. Francis Wilson 4. *The English Patient* 5. None 6. Cross of Lorraine 7. Colin Chapman 8. Lauren Bacall 9. 240 10. A Latin American dance 11. Antonio 12. Dire Straits 13. Chatsworth 14. Mr Bayleaf 15. Mary Peters 16. Channel 4

General Quiz 43

Answers on page 400

1. What is a skua?

2. Which Paul McCartney song of 1972 was banned by the BBC for being too political?

3. How many teats does the female multimammate rat have?

4. In which century did wolves become extinct in the UK?

5. Which female co-presented *SM:TV Live* with Ant and Dec?

6. Which band backed Steve Harley?

7. Which football team used to be called Newton Heath?

8. In which city is *Hollyoaks* set?

9. Who won the Wimbledon men's singles title in 2001?

10. What is tattooed on Popeye's forearm?

11. Which religious sect originally expected the second coming in 1844?

12. Who was manager of The Sex Pistols?

13. The remains of which two 16th-century theatres were discovered in London in 1989?

14. Who did George Bush defeat in the 1988 US Presidential election?

15. In which sport can you catch a Boston crab?

16. What name is given to the four pointed teeth between incisors and molars?

Answers to page 400
GENERAL QUIZ 41: **1.** Six **2.** 1977 **3.** An embroidery stitch **4.** Peas
5. Continents of the world **6.** Gunner Sugden **7.** Mary Queen of Scots
8. The Banks family **9.** It's the Latin name for catmint **10.** Golda Meir
11. Minerva **12.** Whooping cough **13.** Minnesota **14.** *Austin Powers – The Spy Who Shagged Me* **15.** Woburn Abbey **16.** Beach volleyball

General Quiz 44

Answers on page 401

1. Who was 'Not Such An Innocent Girl' in 2001?

2. What is the nickname of the Australian rugby union team?

3. Which TV weather forecaster used to describe clouds as 'fluffy bits'?

4. Which Anthony Minghella film won the Oscar for Best Picture in 1996?

5. How many moons does Mercury have?

6. Which emblem was adopted by the Free French forces in World War Two?

7. Who founded the Lotus motor car company?

8. Which Hollywood actress was born Betty Joan Perske?

9. How many pennies were there in an old pound?

10. What is a merengue?

11. From whom did Shylock demand a pound of flesh in *The Merchant of Venice*?

12. Who were the 'Sultans Of Swing' in 1979?

13. What is the Derbyshire home of the Duke and Duchess of Devonshire?

14. Who was the gardener on *The Herbs*?

15. Which British athlete won the women's pentathlon at the 1972 Olympics?

16. What TV channel first aired on 2 November 1982?

Answers to page 401
GENERAL QUIZ 42: **1.** *The Golden Girls* **2.** Bonnie Tyler **3.** Princess Anne **4.** West Indies **5.** Milky Bar **6.** Germany **7.** The Luddites **8.** Speak or write in many languages **9.** An ice pick **10.** 13 **11.** Kiev **12.** *The Bill* **13.** South China Sea **14.** Spain **15.** Margaret Mitchell **16.** Pittodrie (Aberdeen)

General Quiz 45

Answers on page 406

1. Which little bird has the Latin name *Troglodytes troglodytes?*

2. Which TV series featured a computer-generated dancing baby named Mr Huggy?

3. On which river does the Argentine city of Corrientes stand?

4. Which island is situated due north of Sardinia?

5. What sport takes place at the Daytona circuit in the USA?

6. Paul Keating was Prime Minister of which country from 1991–6?

7. Which bird had a UK number one hit in 1972?

8. Which was the first frozen food to go on sale in Britain?

9. Which prototype took 12 minutes to boil?

10. What can be a colourful crow or a decorating tool?

11. A scene showing which naked area of Sylvia Sidney's body when she embraced Cary Grant was cut by the Japanese from the 1932 movie *Madame Butterfly* ?

12. Which actor was born Coy Luther Perry III but chose his stage name from his favourite movie, *Cool Hand Luke?*

13. Which venomous snake is thought to be responsible for more human deaths than any other?

14. Which world championships take place each year at the Corner Pin public house at Ramsbottom near Manchester?

15. How many degrees are there in a circle?

16. What nationality was the composer Delius?

Answers to page 406
GENERAL QUIZ 47: 1. It was composed entirely of Scots 2. A tropical vine
3. James Boswell 4. Duke of Gloucester 5. A seabird 6. His boomerang
7. Queen 8. Loganberry 9. Mountaineering 10. A fearless Viking warrior
11. The Alamo 12. Homer 13. Jonathan Aitken 14. Ken Matthews 15. John
Hurt 16. *Home to Roost*

General Quiz 46

Answers on page 407

1. The town of Llanberis is at the foot of which mountain?

2. In *This Sporting Life*, Richard Harris played a miner convinced that his future lay in which sport?

3. What is the opposite of an anode?

4. Cauliflower is a variety of which vegetable?

5. Which wild Northumberland family were distinguishable by the grey streak in their hair?

6. What is the capital of Brazil?

7. Which progressive rock band released the albums 'Fragile' and 'Close To The Edge'?

8. As what is sodium hydroxide otherwise known?

9. In which American state is Sacramento?

10. Which TV show features 'Dictionary Corner'?

11. Which French engineer was responsible for the construction of the Suez Canal?

12. Former Olympic marathon champion Abebe Bikila represented which country?

13. In 1997, which band appealed 'Help The Aged'?

14. Which Hollywood star changed his name from John Carter?

15. Which Argentine golfer lost out on the 1968 US Masters after his playing partner accidentally put down the wrong score for a hole?

16. Which card game was first played among members of the Indian Civil Service around 1900?

Answers to page 407
GENERAL QUIZ 48: **1.** Cockfosters **2.** *The Taming of the Shrew* **3.** West Indies **4.** Joe Meek **5.** Airdrie **6.** Chief Robert T. Ironside **7.** Blue and white **8.** France **9.** Nepal **10.** Andrew **11.** Snooker **12.** Plymouth **13.** Baseball **14.** Denmark **15.** Morecambe and Wise **16.** Anchorage

General Quiz 47

Answers on page 404

1. What was remarkable about the team fielded by Accrington Stanley for a 1955 Football League match?

2. What is bougainvillea?

3. Who was Dr Samuel Johnson's biographer?

4. What was Richard III's title before he became king?

5. What is a booby?

6. What wouldn't come back for Charlie Drake?

7. John Deacon and Roger Taylor were members of which band?

8. Which fruit is named after an American judge who crossed a wild blackberry with a cultivated raspberry?

9. What is Chris Bonington's favourite pursuit?

10. Who was berserker?

11. At which battle was Davy Crockett killed?

12. Who wrote the *Iliad*?

13. Which former Conservative minister was jailed for 18 months in 1999 for perjury and perverting the course of justice?

14. Which Briton won gold at the 1964 Olympics in the 20km walk?

15. Who starred in the film of *The Elephant Man*?

16. Which sitcom starred John Thaw as Henry Willows?

Answers to page 404
GENERAL QUIZ 45: 1. Wren 2. *Ally McBeal* 3. Parana 4. Corsica 5. Motor-racing 6. Australia 7. Lieutenant Pigeon 8. Asparagus 9. The electric kettle 10. Roller 11. Her left elbow 12. Luke Perry 13. Carpet viper 14. The World Black Pudding Knocking Championships 15. 360 16. English

General Quiz 48

Answers on page 405

1. Which station stands at the northern end of London Underground's Piccadilly Line?

2. The 1999 movie *10 Things I Hate About You* was an update of which Shakespeare play?

3. For which country does Brian Lara play Test cricket?

4. Which record producer shot himself dead on 3 February 1967, the anniversary of the death of his hero, Buddy Holly?

5. Which Scottish football club used to be known as Excelsior FC?

6. Which TV detective was confined to a wheelchair?

7. What two colours feature on the Greek national flag?

8. Which country is the most popular destination with foreign tourists?

9. In which country is Mount Everest?

10. What is the Christian name of the singer Roachford?

11. In which game would you use a 'spider'?

12. The River Tamar flows into the sea at which port?

13. At what sport was Babe Ruth a national hero?

14. Aalborg is a port in which country?

15. Bartholomew and Wiseman became better known as which duo?

16. What is the largest town in Alaska?

Answers to page 405
GENERAL QUIZ 46: **1.** Snowdon **2.** Rugby League **3.** Cathode **4.** Cabbage **5.** *The Mallens* **6.** Brasilia **7.** Yes **8.** Caustic soda **9.** California **10.** *Countdown* **11.** Ferdinand de Lesseps **12.** Ethiopia **13.** Pulp **14.** Charlton Heston **15.** Roberto De Vicenzo **16.** Bridge

General Quiz 49

Answers on page 410

1. A quarter of the bones in the human body are located in which area?

2. Who is Steve Coogan's Portuguese crooner?

3. Who wrote *Educating Rita* and *Shirley Valentine*?

4. What is a cotoneaster?

5. Blondel was a minstrel friend of which English king?

6. Which English city did the Romans call Venta Bulgarum?

7. How many dogs take part in a greyhound race?

8. A man with what appendage was hired in 1911 to assure passengers that the new escalators on the London Underground were safe to use?

9. Which English monarch reputedly shook hands with the branches of an oak tree in the belief that it was the King of Prussia?

10. What is pogonophobia?

11. Which US state is nicknamed the 'Bear State'?

12. Who were the first father and daughter to sing together on a UK number one?

13. Which war was the backdrop for Stanley Kubrick's 1987 movie *Full Metal Jacket*?

14. In music, how many quavers equal a crotchet?

15. In which sport do some participants wear sheepskin nosebands?

16. Which *Fawlty Towers* dragon is also the scourge of Tesco?

Answers to page 410
GENERAL QUIZ 51: 1. *The Catcher in the Rye* 2. Blue 3. Sindy 4. Postman
5. Feet 6. Romanian 7. Mollusc 8. Egypt 9. Bob Wilson 10. Renault
11. Sherlock Holmes 12. Rastafarianism 13. Richard II 14. Andy Williams
15. Roy Rogers 16. Sea lion

General Quiz 50

Answers on page 411

1. Which member of Emerson, Lake and Palmer went solo for a 1975 Christmas hit?

2. What was the pseudonym of playwright Jean-Baptiste Poquelin?

3. In *Brookside*, who married Emily Shadwick in 2001?

4. Which Bulgarian was named European Footballer of the Year in 1994?

5. In which country is Belo Horizonte?

6. Which country's flag features a white crescent and star on a red background?

7. Which is the first classic horse race of the British flat season?

8. Which animal produces 200 times more wind per day than the average human?

9. Which city's branch of Alcoholics Anonymous boasted just two members when it started up in 1948?

10. What followed Mary to school one day?

11. As whom was Julius Marx better known?

12. What mark indicates that a product has been approved by the British Standards Institute?

13. What nationality was suspected spy Mata Hari?

14. Ulan Bator is the capital of which country?

15. Which US President issued a detailed foreign policy doctrine in 1823?

16. Who had a hit with the theme song from *Friends*?

Answers to page 411
GENERAL QUIZ 52: **1.** St Alban **2.** Perseus **3.** Moroccan **4.** Lupe Velez **5.** Breathalyser **6.** Van Clomp **7.** Austin **8.** Italy **9.** East Grinstead **10.** The Mendips **11.** Wimbledon **12.** Goat **13.** Libel is written defamation, slander is spoken **14.** 1965 **15.** New York **16.** Florence

General Quiz 51

Answers on page 408

1. What book was Mark Chapman carrying when he shot John Lennon?

2. What colour Smartie replaced the light brown in 1989?

3. Which female icon didn't own a bath until 1972?

4. What was the job of *Cheers* regular Cliff Clavin?

5. Through which part of their bodies do butterflies taste?

6. What nationality was tennis player Ilie Nastase?

7. What type of creature is a clam?

8. Nefertiti was queen of which country in the 14th century BC?

9. Which male TV presenter's middle name is Primrose?

10. In which make of car did Alain Prost achieve his first Grand Prix win?

11. Basil Rathbone, Peter Cushing and Jeremy Brett have all played which character?

12. Which religion was originally based on the ideas of Marcus Garvey?

13. Which English king was the son of Edward, the Black Prince?

14. Which American singer had his first UK hit for 23 years in 1999?

15. Which TV cowboy had his horse Trigger stuffed and mounted after it died?

16. What animal is André in the 1994 film of that name?

Answers to page 408
GENERAL QUIZ 49: **1.** Feet **2.** Tony Ferrino **3.** Willy Russell **4.** A shrub **5.** Richard I **6.** Winchester **7.** Six **8.** A wooden leg **9.** George III **10.** Fear of beards **11.** Arkansas **12.** Frank and Nancy Sinatra **13.** Vietnam War **14.** Two **15.** Horse racing **16.** Prunella Scales

General Quiz 52

Answers on page 409

1. Who was Britain's first Christian martyr?

2. In Greek mythology, who rescued and married Andromeda?

3. What nationality is the distance runner Said Aouita?

4. Which Hollywood actress was known as 'The Mexican Spitfire'?

5. Which innovation was originally called the 'drunkometer'?

6. In *'Allo 'Allo*, who painted *The Fallen Madonna with the Big Boobies*?

7. What is the state capital of Texas?

8. Which country has a toe and a heel?

9. Heading due south along the meridian from Greenwich, what is the first town of any note outside Greater London?

10. Cheddar Gorge cuts a swathe through which hills?

11. Which Football League club used to play at Plough Lane?

12. If something is 'caprine', it is like which animal?

13. What is the difference between libel and slander?

14. In which year did Tom Jones reach number one with 'It's Not Unusual'?

15. In which city is the Holland road tunnel?

16. Fiorentina are a football team from which city?

Answers to page 409
GENERAL QUIZ 50: **1.** Greg Lake **2.** Molière **3.** Timothy O'Leary **4.** Hristo Stoichkov **5.** Brazil **6.** Turkey **7.** One Thousand Guineas **8.** Cow **9.** Luxembourg **10.** Her little lamb **11.** Groucho Marx **12.** Kite mark **13.** Dutch **14.** Mongolia **15.** James Monroe **16.** The Rembrandts

General Quiz 53

Answers on page 414

1. Who hit *The Big Time* after changing her name from Sheena Orr?

2. Which planet was first located in 1930?

3. Jacob's Creek is a brand name of wine from which country?

4. Which university did Prince William enrol at in 2001?

5. What is a satsuma?

6. Who won the Mr Universe contest in 1969?

7. Which church was founded in 1955 by L. Ron Hubbard?

8. Which sport has periods of play called chukkas?

9. The Tokens and Tight Fit both had hits with which tribal song?

10. In which fictitious village is the TV series *Peak Practice* set?

11. Of which fellow actor did Helena Bonham Carter say: 'His mouth is a no-go area. It's like kissing the Berlin Wall'?

12. Which is further east, Crete or Cyprus?

13. The town of Cairns is in which Australian state?

14. Where did Twizzle live?

15. Which group of birds collect in a charm?

16. Whose album was titled 'I've Been Expecting You'?

Answers to page 414
GENERAL QUIZ 55: **1.** Isle of Wight **2.** Tonic **3.** Canoeing **4.** Cher and B.A. Robertson **5.** Dudley Moore **6.** Baron **7.** Brownsea Island **8.** Sylvester **9.** Doug Digby **10.** North America **11.** 20 **12.** Mount Kosciusko **13.** Muriel Spark **14.** The Speaker **15.** Chelsea **16.** Quito (Ecuador)

General Quiz 54

Answers on page 415

1. *The Lancet* is the journal of which profession?

2. An appearance in which TV soap was the prize awaiting the winners in *Soapstars*?

3. At the 1984 Olympics which athlete took gold in the 100 and 200 metres, the long jump and the sprint relay?

4. In which English city is the Walker Art Gallery?

5. Which disco diva had a 1977 number one with 'I Feel Love'?

6. Who wrote *Watership Down*?

7. The Cambrian mountains are a range in which country?

8. In which sport is a drive prone to a shank or a slice?

9. Which city stages an annual Goose Fair?

10. Where was Ali G in his 2002 film?

11. Which singer's 2001 album was titled 'No Angel'?

12. In which continent is Eritrea?

13. Which American state is immediately south of South Dakota?

14. What are the administrative districts in France called?

15. Rockhopper and jackass are species of which bird?

16. What is a saluki?

General Quiz 55

Answers on page 412

1. Spithead is a safe anchorage between the coast of England and which island?

2. What can be a pick-me-up or the key note of music scale?

3. In which sport would you use an Eskimo roll?

4. Which two artists had UK top ten hits with songs titled 'Bang Bang'?

5. Which diminutive actor was nicknamed the 'Sex Thimble'?

6. Which is the lowest rank of the British peerage?

7. Which island off Dorset is one of the last British refuges of the red squirrel?

8. Who was Tweety Pie's arch enemy?

9. Who met his death by being impaled on one of his own javelins in *The Grimleys*?

10. The Jerusalem artichoke is a native of which continent?

11. How many times more sensitive are dogs' noses than humans'?

12. Which is the highest mountain in Australia?

13. Who wrote *The Prime of Miss Jean Brodie*?

14. Who keeps order in the House of Commons?

15. Which club won the FA Cup in 1997 and 2000?

16. Which capital city is nearest to the Equator?

Answers to page 412
GENERAL QUIZ 53: 1. Sheena Easton 2. Pluto 3. Australia 4. St Andrews
5. A fruit 6. Arnold Schwarzenegger 7. Church of Scientology 8. Polo
9. 'The Lion Sleeps Tonight' 10. Cardale 11. Woody Allen 12. Cyprus
13. Queensland 14. Stray Town 15. Goldfinches 16. Robbie Williams

General Quiz 56

Answers on page 413

1. Who was the only English pope?

2. Who played the 'alien' in the 2002 film *K-PAX*?

3. What sort of animal was the star of *My Friend Flicka*?

4. Which Latin phrase literally means 'from favour'?

5. Which sequel to *Porridge* saw Fletcher released from prison?

6. Bombay is on which coast of India?

7. Which West German swimmer won four gold medals at the 1976 Olympics?

8. What is an erg?

9. Which Australian Prime Minister was nicknamed 'The Prefect'?

10. What can be black-headed, herring or common?

11. On which river does the city of Indianapolis stand?

12. Who kissed the girls and made them cry?

13. Who created *The X Files*?

14. What is the name of the white ball in bowls?

15. Who directed *Interview with the Vampire* and *Michael Collins*?

16. Who is TV's 'Naked Chef'?

Answers to page 413
GENERAL QUIZ 54: 1. Medical 2. *Emmerdale* 3. Carl Lewis 4. Liverpool
5. Donna Summer 6. Richard Adams 7. Wales 8. Golf 9. Nottingham
10. Indahouse 11. Dido 12. Africa 13. Nebraska
14. Cantons 15. Penguin 16. A breed of dog

General Quiz 57

Answers on page 418

1. On which island of New Zealand is Wellington?

2. Which Swedish footballer won the Golden Shoe for 2001 after scoring 35 goals in Scotland?

3. On which river does Rome stand?

4. Who was the Maid of Orleans?

5. What was the Christian name of the 18th-century satirical poet Pope?

6. What was Alf Wight's pen name as an author?

7. Which colony reverted to Chinese control in 1997?

8. Which group backed Gladys Knight?

9. Who failed to heed the warning: 'Beware the Ides of March'?

10. What happens when you cross the International Date Line going east?

11. Where do the Inuit people live?

12. In what car did Michael Schumacher win the World Drivers' Championship in 1994 and 1995?

13. In which countries is the Gobi Desert?

14. Whose debut solo album was the 1997 release 'Open Road'?

15. Which TV series was inspired by the Clint Eastwood movie *Coogan's Bluff*?

16. As what was Jacobite leader James Edward Stuart popularly known?

Answers to page 418
GENERAL QUIZ 59: **1.** Supergrass **2.** THRUSH **3.** Singers castrated as boys to preserve their soprano voices **4.** Europa **5.** Dorothy **6.** Viscount Palmerston **7.** Both once worked as assistants in menswear shops **8.** Louis XIV **9.** Royal Birkdale **10.** Tiananmen Square **11.** Mali **12.** Bob Dylan **13.** Brenda Lee **14.** St Fiacre **15.** Adam Hart-Davis **16.** Hertfordshire

General Quiz 58

Answers on page 419

1. Which two cities in Japan are anagrams of each other?

2. From what figure does a championship game of darts start?

3. Which island in the western Pacific is the world's smallest republic?

4. On which Sixties TV series were Edward G. Robinson, George Raft and Sammy Davis Jnr all seen peering from windows?

5. In 2001, it was announced that Liverpool airport would be renamed in honour of whom?

6. Which future *Coronation Street* star appeared in *Carry On Cabbie*?

7. What garment did designer André Van Pier create that was adorned with 3,250 diamonds and cost £641,000?

8. In which island group is Iona?

9. Which sport was invented by James Naismith in 1892 by nailing two peach baskets to a balcony at a Massachusetts YMCA?

10. Who had a 1982 number one with 'Fame'?

11. Who was having a fling with Lilo Lil?

12. Which is the oldest university in Scotland?

13. The disease herpes zoster is more usually known as what?

14. In which national park is Dovedale?

15. Which Doctor was the title of a novel by Boris Pasternak?

16. Which fruit has the Latin name *Citrus sinensis*?

Answers to page 419
GENERAL QUIZ 60: **1.** Neptune **2.** Cave-dweller **3.** Scotland **4.** Kirsty MacColl **5.** The Monkees **6.** Humphrey Bogart **7.** Seven **8.** Adriatic **9.** Typewriter **10.** Michael Caine **11.** Mark Hughes **12.** *On Her Majesty's Secret Service* **13.** Oliver Goldsmith **14.** Isambard Kingdom Brunel **15.** Spain **16.** Shannon

General Quiz 59

Answers on page 416

1. Which band were 'In It For The Money' in 1997?

2. Who were the sworn enemies of UNCLE?

3. Who were the Italian *castrati*?

4. In Greek mythology, who was carried off by Zeus in the form of a bull?

5. What is actress Faye Dunaway's real first name?

6. Which British Prime Minister's last words were: 'Die, my dear doctor? That's the last thing I shall do'?

7. What did Norman Tebbit and Tony Hancock have in common?

8. Which French king hated washing so much that he took only three baths in his entire life?

9. Which Southport golf course has frequently staged the British Open?

10. In which Beijing square were over 1,000 protesters killed by government troops in 1989?

11. In which country is Timbuktu?

12. Which veteran performer entered the UK album charts in 2001 with 'Love And Theft'?

13. Which US singer of the Sixties was nicknamed 'Little Miss Dynamite'?

14. Who is the patron saint of venereal disease and taxi drivers?

15. Who sets off around Britain in search of *Local Heroes*?

16. Where is Ware?

Answers to page 416
GENERAL QUIZ 57: **1.** North Island **2.** Henrik Larsson **3.** Tiber **4.** Joan of Arc **5.** Alexander **6.** James Herriot **7.** Hong Kong **8.** The Pips **9.** Julius Caesar **10.** The date is put back a day **11.** In northern Canada and the Arctic **12.** Benetton **13.** Mongolia and China **14.** Gary Barlow **15.** *McCloud* **16.** 'The Old Pretender'

General Quiz 60

Answers on page 417

1. Triton is the largest of which planet's moons?

2. What is a troglodyte?

3. In which country are the Trossachs?

4. Who said: 'There's A Guy Works Down The Chipshop Swears He's Elvis'?

5. Which American pop group starred in the film *Head*?

6. Who starred in *The Maltese Falcon*?

7. What was motorcycle ace Barry Sheene's lucky number?

8. Which sea is situated off the east coast of Italy?

9. What did American William Burt invent in 1829?

10. Which future movie star made an early appearance as a convict in an episode of the TV series *The Adventures of William Tell*?

11. Which former Manchester United striker was nicknamed 'Sparky'?

12. In which film did George Lazenby make his only appearance as James Bond?

13. Who wrote *She Stoops To Conquer*?

14. Who designed the first steamship to cross the Atlantic?

15. In which country was the sitcom *Duty Free* set?

16. Which is the longest river in Ireland?

Answers to page 417
GENERAL QUIZ 58: 1. Tokyo and Kyoto 2. 501 3. Nauru 4. *Batman* 5. John Lennon 6. Amanda Barrie 7. A bra 8. Inner Hebrides 9. Basketball 10. Irene Cara 11. Freddie Boswell in *Bread* 12. St Andrews 13. Shingles 14. Peak District 15. *Doctor Zhivago* 16. Orange

General Quiz 61

Answers on page 422

1. Which TV presenter is married to *Pet Rescue*'s Matthew Robertson?

2. Where is Britain's first Champ Car track?

3. What was the name of Rocky Balboa's girlfriend played by Talia Shire in the film *Rocky*?

4. Which former US President survived an assassination attempt outside the Washington Hilton Hotel in 1981?

5. Which Scottish city is nicknamed 'Auld Reekie'?

6. At which sporting venue did Erika Roe streak?

7. The Maginot line was designed to protect which country?

8. The House of Grimaldi has ruled which state since 1297?

9. Which English king was the subject of a TV series by historian David Starkey in 2001?

10. Feargal Sharkey sang with which band before going solo?

11. On which island is the city of Jakarta?

12. What did black nationalist leader Malcolm Little call himself?

13. Who directed the films *Twelve Angry Men* and *Dog Day Afternoon*?

14. Which city was besieged for over four months in 1857 at the height of the Indian Mutiny?

15. Which English county disappeared in 1974 to become part of Cambridgeshire?

16. Which Hollywood actor was born William Franklin Beedle?

Answers to page 422
GENERAL QUIZ 63: 1. *Private Eye* 2. Ted Rogers 3. The Charlatans 4. Joan of Arc 5. Jodhpur 6. Malawi, Tanzania and Mozambique 7. Ryder Cup 8. Belgium 9. Elliott Gould 10. Monmouthshire 11. Oxford Committee for Famine Relief 12. Ross Kemp 13. Insects 14. Peppermint 15. Preposition 16. Scotland

General Quiz 62

Answers on page 423

1. In 2001, which symbol was removed from jars of Robertson's jams after 91 years?

2. Which sailing trophy was established in 1957 by the Royal Ocean Racing Club?

3. Which comedy duo were arrested while dressed as chickens in the film *Stir Crazy*?

4. Which cowboy was shot in the back by Bob Ford while hanging a picture?

5. What name is given to a region of total shadow during an eclipse?

6. In September 2001, which actress skipped the premiere of her new film *Enigma*?

7. What name for a day nursery is derived from the French for 'manger'?

8. How many points is the black ball worth at snooker?

9. Which novelist created Brother Cadfael?

10. What is the opposite of a spring tide?

11. Which Bevan introduced the National Health Service?

12. The Black Prince was the eldest son of which King of England?

13. Who had a 1993 number one with 'Oh Carolina'?

14. Who ran around in tight jumpsuits on *Treasure Hunt*?

15. Which rock star's stage personae have included Aladdin Sane and Ziggy Stardust?

16. In fencing, which is lighter – the foil or the épée?

Answers to page 423
GENERAL QUIZ 64: **1.** Corporal Klinger **2.** Walk on the Moon
3. Stoke-on-Trent **4.** Frank Bruno **5.** Sacramento **6.** Egypt **7.** France
8. Swansea City **9.** Jupiter **10.** Marianne Faithfull **11.** Fez **12.** 15 **13.** Jaguar
14. Milhous **15.** *Teenage Mutant Ninja Turtles* **16.** Mary

General Quiz 63

Answers on page 420

1. Which British publication carried the comic strip *The Adventures of Barry McKenzie*?

2. Who presented the TV game show *3-2=1*?

3. Which band released a 2001 album titled 'Wonderland'?

4. Who was burned at the stake in Rouen on 30 May 1431?

5. Which Indian city gave its name to a style of riding breeches?

6. Which three countries border Lake Malawi?

7. Which biennial sporting contest was postponed in 2001 following the 11 September terrorist attack on New York?

8. In which country is the industrial city of Mons?

9. Who played private eye Philip Marlowe in the 1973 movie *The Long Goodbye*?

10. Which old county formed the bulk of the new county of Gwent?

11. What does OXFAM stand for?

12. Who plays DC Jack Mowbray in the TV series *Without Motive*?

13. What does an oxpecker feed on?

14. What is the herb *Mentha piperita* more commonly known as?

15. 'In', 'on' and 'under' are all examples of what type of word?

16. For which international rugby team did Andy Irvine play?

Answers to page 420
GENERAL QUIZ 61: **1.** Davina McCall **2.** Rockingham **3.** Adrian **4.** Ronald Reagan **5.** Edinburgh **6.** Twickenham **7.** France **8.** Monaco **9.** Henry VIII **10.** The Undertones **11.** Java **12.** Malcolm X **13.** Sidney Lumet **14.** Lucknow **15.** Huntingdonshire **16.** William Holden

General Quiz 64

Answers on page 421

1. Who was a cross-dresser in *M*A*S*H*?

2. What was Charles Conrad the third person to do?

3. According to a 2001 survey, which city was named the least desirable place to live in Britain?

4. Who retired from boxing in 1996 after being warned by doctors that one more punch on the head could leave him blind?

5. What is the state capital of California?

6. Which country has the international vehicle index mark ET?

7. In which country was religious reformer John Calvin born?

8. Which football club plays at the Vetch Field?

9. Callisto is the second largest moon of which planet?

10. Which singer starred with Alain Delon in the cult movie *The Girl on a Motorcycle*?

11. What type of hat takes its name from a city in Morocco?

12. How many players are there in a hurling team?

13. Which British make of car won the Le Mans 24-Hour Race five times between 1951 and 1958?

14. What was the middle name of US President Richard Nixon?

15. Which cartoon strip was created by Kevin Eastman and Peter Laird in 1984?

16. What is the name of the wife of disgraced peer Lord Archer?

Answers to page 421
GENERAL QUIZ 62: 1. The golly 2. Admiral's Cup 3. Richard Prior and Gene Wilder 4. Jesse James 5. Umbra 6. Kate Winslet 7. Crèche 8. Seven 9. Ellis Peters 10. A neap tide 11. Aneurin Bevan 12. Edward III 13. Shaggy 14. Anneka Rice 15. David Bowie 16. Foil

General Quiz 65

Answers on page 426

1. What is the name for the end of a glacier?

2. What do bats use to stop them flying into things in the dark?

3. Don King is a leading promoter in which sport?

4. Who had a 1981 chart-topper with 'Japanese Boy'?

5. What was used for the first time at the Nevada State Prison, Carson City, on 8 February 1924?

6. Which was Britain's first national park?

7. In which continent is Graham Land?

8. At what sport did Walter Hagen win 11 major championships between 1914 and 1929?

9. At which London railway station would you arrive if you caught a direct train from Nottingham?

10. Why might Charlie Dimmock have a ha-ha?

11. Which animals conduct 'boxing matches' during the breeding season?

12. What is Karl Kennedy's profession in *Neighbours*?

13. Port Moresby is the capital of which country?

14. Which Welsh actor rejected the role of *Gandhi*?

15. What does a misogynist hate?

16. In which ocean are the Pitcairn Islands?

Answers to page 426
GENERAL QUIZ 67: 1. Borneo 2. Three 3. Anthony Burgess 4. Samantha Mumba 5. French 6. The Tremeloes 7. Horse racing 8. John Bunyan 9. New York 10. Edgar Bergen 11. Nena 12. Canis minor 13. Canute 14. 14th 15. Mike Tyson 16. Noel Murless

General Quiz 66

Answers on page 427

1. In which city do Linfield Football Club play?

2. What was Lady Chatterley's first name?

3. Which TV personality used to advertise Rice Krispies as a boy?

4. Which US Marine colonel was the central figure in the Irangate scandal?

5. Which city staged the Olympic Games in 1900 and 1924?

6. What did Levi Strauss make the first pair of?

7. Which country knocked England's footballers out of the 1998 World Cup?

8. What is the capital of the Lombardy region of Italy?

9. What does a manometer measure?

10. Who wrote The Catcher in the Rye?

11. Which Danny starred in the Lethal Weapon series of films?

12. What was Norwich the first British city to establish in 1608?

13. Which TV quiz was inspired by the Gestapo's grilling of prisoners-of-war?

14. Berlin's number one 'Take My Breath Away' came from which film?

15. Which horse profited from Devon Loch's misfortune at the 1956 Grand National?

16. What is a dunlin?

Answers to page 427
GENERAL QUIZ 68: 1. 1967 2. Roller skates 3. Absolutely Fabulous 4. 13
5. Boy Scouts' camp 6. Mont Blanc 7. Blue and yellow 8. 'It's Oh So Quiet'
9. John McEnroe 10. Big Daddy 11. Deciduous 12. Isle of Man 13. Speedwell
14. Top Cat 15. Vermont 16. East of Eden

General Quiz 67

Answers on page 424

1. Which of the Sunda Islands is the third largest island in the world?

2. How many fiddlers did Old King Cole have?

3. Who wrote the novel *A Clockwork Orange*?

4. 'Baby Come On Over' was a 2001 hit for which singer?

5. What nationality was the 19th-century novelist Balzac?

6. Chesney Hawkes' father was singer with which Sixties pop group?

7. In which sport do competitors battle for the Breeders' Cup?

8. Which author was imprisoned in Bedford jail for 12 years from 1660 for unlicensed preaching?

9. In which city is Carnegie Hall?

10. Which ventriloquist partnered Charlie McCarthy?

11. Gabriela Kerner was the singer with which German band who enjoyed a UK number one in 1984?

12. Procyon is the brightest star of which constellation?

13. Who became King of England in 1016, Denmark in 1018 and Norway in 1028?

14. In which century were *The Canterbury Tales* written?

15. In 1986, which boxer became the youngest ever World Heavyweight Champion?

16. Which horse racing trainer had a winner at Royal Ascot for 17 years in succession, from 1960–1976?

Answers to page 424
GENERAL QUIZ 65: 1. Snout 2. Sonar 3. Boxing 4. Aneka 5. Gas chamber
6. Peak District 7. Antarctica 8. Golf 9. St Pancras 10. It is the term for a
sunken boundary wall in landscape gardening 11. Hares 12. Doctor
13. Papua New Guinea 14. Anthony Hopkins 15. Women 16. Pacific

General Quiz 68

Answers on page 425

1. In which year did Foinavon win the Grand National at 100-1?

2. What mode of transport did instrument-maker Joseph Merlin invent in 1760?

3. Which BBC sitcom returned in 2001 after a five-year break?

4. How many are there in a baker's dozen?

5. What did Robert Baden-Powell hold for the first time at Brownsea Island in August 1907?

6. What is the highest mountain in Europe?

7. What two colours feature on the flag of Ukraine?

8. Which song originally recorded by Betty Hutton in 1948 gave Björk a 1995 hit?

9. Which tennis player did Clive James call 'as charming as a dead mouse in a loaf of bread'?

10. What was the professional name of wrestler Shirley Crabtree?

11. What is the opposite of evergreen?

12. On which island does a deemster hold jurisdiction?

13. Veronica is the cultivated name for which wild flower?

14. Who did close friends get to call TC?

15. Which American state is called the 'Green Mountain State'?

16. In which film did James Dean have his first starring role?

Answers to page 425
GENERAL QUIZ 66: 1. Belfast 2. Constance 3. Jonathan Ross 4. Oliver North 5. Paris 6. Jeans 7. Argentina 8. Milan 9. The pressure of liquids or gases 10. J.D. Salinger 11. Danny Glover 12. Public library 13. *Mastermind* 14. *Top Gun* 15. ESB 16. A bird

General Quiz 69

Answers on page 430

1. Which letter of the English alphabet hasn't changed shape since its introduction around 130 BC?

2. The pips of which fruit contain a minute measure of cyanide?

3. Why don't bulls see red?

4. Which former member of the band was the subject of Pink Floyd's 'Shine On You Crazy Diamond'?

5. What is the fourth letter of the Greek alphabet?

6. What is the highest that can be scored with a single dart?

7. What was the name of Lenny Henry's *Chef*?

8. What was the first name of the French philosopher and mathematician Descartes?

9. Who once wrote three symphonies in the space of six weeks?

10. Whose run of three successive UK number one singles was interrupted by St Winifred's School Choir with 'There's No One Quite Like Grandma'?

11. Which football manager tried to lead his team off the pitch before a penalty shoot-out in a play-off match at the end of the 2000–1 season?

12. What is the state capital of Australia's Northern Territory?

13. Who wrote the Barchester series of novels?

14. Which musical instrument has an inner sliding tube?

15. TB is an abbreviation for which disease?

16. Who did Mordred call 'uncle Arthur'?

Answers to page 430
GENERAL QUIZ 71: 1. The Cruisers 2. Berkshire 3. Dinar 4. Radius
5. Gulliver 6. 40 7. Germany, Austria, Liechtenstein, Italy and France
8. Sandy Lyle 9. Maplins 10. Peter Frampton 11. Sylvester Stallone 12. Syria
13. *Who Wants To Be A Millionaire* 14. Synonym 15. Lilac 16. It is the most northerly point on the British mainland

General Quiz 70

Answers on page 431

1. Whose film crew were accused of harassing Prince William at the start of his first university term?

2. What is the American equivalent of British Summer Time?

3. Which American golfer won the 2001 USPGA tournament?

4. Which English aircraft designer and manufacturer produced the Tiger Moth and the Mosquito?

5. From which continent do piranha fish come?

6. Which insect saw Cock Robin die?

7. Who started his acting career as *The Fresh Prince of Bel-Air*?

8. Which small stringed instrument takes its name from the Hawaiian for 'jumping flea'?

9. Which is the only Great Lake situated entirely within the United States?

10. Which song links Millie and Bad Manners?

11. In which English county is Launceston?

12. As whom is Steveland Judkins better known?

13. Which soldier, who conquered Sicily and Naples in 1860, gave his name to a type of biscuit?

14. What part of the body is affected by periodontal disease?

15. The Green Goblin is the arch enemy of which superhero?

16. Which Austrian skier won a record 25 World Cup downhill events from 1974–84?

Answers to page 431
GENERAL QUIZ 72: **1.** A type of cheese **2.** Climb trees **3.** Van Gogh
4. They are the only words in the English language where the five vowels are in alphabetical order **5.** Phil Neville **6.** The Yardbirds **7.** Iceland **8.** Tarzan (Lincoln stabbed a lion that attacked him) **9.** Japan **10.** Shinty **11.** Strasbourg **12.** Bay of Biscay **13.** Sarah-Jane Harvey **14.** Sylvester Stallone **15.** Both were once postmen **16.** 'It's Like That'

General Quiz 71

Answers on page 428

1. What was the name of Dave Berry's backing group?

2. In which English county is the Royal Military Academy, Sandhurst?

3. Which currency is used by Jordan, Iraq and Libya?

4. What is the name for a line drawn from the centre of a circle to the circumference?

5. Who visited Lilliput and Brobdingnag?

6. According to legend, for how many days is the weather on St Swithun's Day set to continue?

7. Which five countries border Switzerland?

8. In 1985, who became the first British golfer to win the Open for 16 years?

9. What was the name of the holiday camp in *Hi-De-Hi*?

10. Which ex-Humble Pie guitarist fronted a band called Camel?

11. Which Hollywood star is known as the 'Italian Stallion'?

12. Aleppo and Homs are towns in which Middle East country?

13. Major Charles Ingram's jackpot win on which TV quiz was investigated by the police?

14. What is the name for two words with the same meaning?

15. Which sweetly-scented tree has the Latin name *Syringa vulgaris*?

16. What is the geographical significance of Dunnet Head in Scotland?

Answers to page 428
GENERAL QUIZ 69: 1. O 2. Apples 3. They're colour-blind 4. Syd Barrett
5. Delta 6. 60 7. Gareth Blackstock 8. René 9. Mozart 10. John Lennon
11. Trevor Francis (Birmingham City) 12. Darwin 13. Anthony Trollope
14. Trombone 15. Tuberculosis 16. King Arthur

General Quiz 72

Answers on page 429

1. What is Blue Vinny?

2. What can robber crabs do that other crabs can't?

3. Which artist painted a picture a day for the last 70 days of his life?

4. What do the words 'abstemious', 'abstentious', 'arsenious', 'arteriosus' and 'facetious' have in common?

5. Who gave away a late penalty to put England out of the 2000 European Championship finals?

6. Keith Relf was lead singer with which Sixties band?

7. Which country publishes more books per head than any other in the world?

8. What role was Elmo Lincoln playing when he stabbed his co-star to death while filming a 1918 movie?

9. In which country is Mount Fuji?

10. Which game uses a curved stick called a caman?

11. Which French city stands on the River Ill?

12. Which stretch of water used to be called the Gulf of Gascony?

13. Which *Crossroads* character was unmasked as an impostor in 2001?

14. Who walked out on the 1985 movie *Beverly Hills Cop* after his demand for more action scenes was rejected?

15. What job links Abraham Lincoln and Rock Hudson?

16. What was the title of the 1998 number one for Run-DMC vs Jason Nevins?

Answers to page 429
GENERAL QUIZ 70: **1.** Prince Edward **2.** Daylight Saving Time **3.** David Toms
4. Geoffrey de Havilland **5.** South America **6.** The fly **7.** Will Smith
8. Ukelele **9.** Lake Michigan **10.** 'My Boy Lollipop' **11.** Cornwall **12.** Stevie
Wonder **13.** Garibaldi **14.** Gums **15.** Spiderman **16.** Franz Klammer

General Quiz 73

Answers on page 434

1. What happened if suspects drowned during trial by ordeal?

2. What was Napoleon in a George Orwell novel?

3. What do actors Anthony Newley, James Booth, Terence Stamp and Laurence Harvey have in common?

4. Which band was formed in 1989 by Johnny Marr and Bernard Sumner?

5. Who was Benton Fraser's first partner in *Due South*?

6. What type of creature is a painted lady?

7. Which actor's first name means 'cool breeze over the mountains' in Hawaiian?

8. Who succeeded Ruud Gullit as manager of Chelsea?

9. Of whom did Irving Layton once say: 'At last Canada has produced a political leader worthy of assassination'?

10. Who was England's goalkeeper in the 1966 World Cup Final?

11. Which boy band had a hit in 2001 with 'Let's Dance'?

12. Sarah Lancashire and Pam Ferris starred as nurses in which drama series?

13. Cirrhosis particularly attacks which organ of the body?

14. What can be electric or jellied?

15. May Hardman was the first death in which TV soap?

16. The lines of which army were drawn up by William Booth?

Answers to page 434
GENERAL QUIZ 75: **1.** C.S. Forester **2.** Helsinki **3.** New Zealand **4.** Red **5.** Ice skating **6.** Bill Grundy **7.** He was captain of the *Titanic* **8.** Red and white **9.** A US newspaper publisher **10.** Lambeth North **11.** Enzo Ferrari **12.** Brilliantine and cream **13.** Baghdad **14.** Rowley Birkin QC **15.** Equestrian three-day event **16.** Shropshire

General Quiz 74

Answers on page 435

1. Who played a character ageing from 17 to 121 in
   Little Big Man?

2. What was the sequel to *Naked Gun 2½: The Smell of Fear*?

3. As whom was Francis Morgan Thompson better known?

4. Which former All Saint appears in the 2002 film *Bend it Like Beckham*?

5. How many years are celebrated by a ruby anniversary?

6. Where in Britain would you find Robin Hood's Bay?

7. At what temperature Fahrenheit does water boil?

8. What does QC stand for?

9. Which planet was first located in 1846?

10. In *Great Expectations*, whose room had remained untouched for
    decades?

11. Maastricht is a town in which European country?

12. What shape is something that is falcate?

13. In what type of bowling does cricketer Shane Warne specialise?

14. What is the principal ingredient in a guacamole dip?

15. Which duck was guarded by Chopper the bulldog?

16. Which French couturier pioneered the mini skirt with Britain's Mary
    Quant?

Answers to page 435
GENERAL QUIZ 76: **1.** *Some Like It Hot* **2.** Five **3.** Benny Hill **4.** Malmö
5. World Snooker final **6.** The Mini **7.** Juggernaut **8.** Marie Antoinette
9. Madge Bishop **10.** H. G. Wells **11.** The Alps **12.** Canada **13.** Lord Byron
14. Malcolm and Donald Campbell **15.** P.D. James **16.** Electric guitar

General Quiz 75

Answers on page 432

1. Who created Horatio Hornblower?

2. What is the capital of Finland?

3. In which country was the 1993 film *The Piano* set?

4. What colour is the Central Line on maps of the London Underground?

5. In which sport might you perform a double axel and a lutz?

6. Who said to The Sex Pistols: 'Go on, you've got another ten seconds. Say something outrageous'?

7. What was Captain Edward Smith's principal role in nautical history?

8. What two colours feature on the Swiss national flag?

9. Who was Gordon Bennett?

10. Which London Underground station was called Westminster Bridge Road until 1917?

11. Which Enzo founded one of the world's leading car manufacturers?

12. Brylcreem is an amalgamation of which two ingredients?

13. The name of which Middle East capital means 'God's gift'?

14. Who was invariably 'very, very drunk' on *The Fast Show*?

15. The dressage is part of which Olympic event?

16. Ironbridge is in which English county?

Answers to page 432
GENERAL QUIZ 73: **1.** They were found innocent **2.** A pig **3.** They all turned down Michael Caine's role in *Alfie* **4.** Electronic **5.** Ray Vecchio **6.** Butterfly **7.** Keanu Reeves **8.** Gianluca Vialli **9.** Pierre Trudeau **10.** Gordon Banks **11.** Five **12.** *Where The Heart Is* **13.** Liver **14.** Eels **15.** *Coronation Street* **16.** The Salvation Army

General Quiz 76

Answers on page 433

1. In which 1959 film did Tony Curtis and Jack Lemmon appear in drag?

2. How many points is the letter 'K' worth in Scrabble?

3. Which comedian was born Alfred Hawthorne Hill?

4. Which is Sweden's most southerly city?

5. Which sporting event of 1985 attracted 18.6 million viewers in the early hours of the morning?

6. Which small car created a motoring revolution when it was introduced in 1959?

7. Which type of lorry is named after a Hindu god?

8. Who came out with the immortal line: 'Let them eat cake'?

9. Which *Neighbours* stalwart died in 2001?

10. Who wrote *The War of the Worlds*?

11. The Simplon tunnel runs beneath which range of mountains?

12. In which country is the Wood Buffalo national park?

13. Which English poet became a Greek national hero?

14. Which British father-and-son each held the world land and water speed records?

15. Who created the detective Adam Dalgliesh?

16. With which musical instrument is Duane Eddy associated?

Answers to page 433
GENERAL QUIZ 74: 1. Dustin Hoffman 2. *Naked Gun 33⅓: The Final Insult* 3. Daley Thompson 4. Shaznay Lewis 5. 40 6. North Yorkshire 7. 212 degrees 8. Queen's Counsel 9. Neptune 10. Miss Havisham 11. The Netherlands 12. Hooked 13. Leg spin 14. Avocado 15. Yakky Doodle 16. André Courrèges

General Quiz 77

Answers on page 438

1. What happened in 1971 while Calgary's KFSM radio station was playing Carole King's 'I Feel The Earth Move'?

2. In which English county is the Isle of Purbeck?

3. Who wrote the children's story *The Old Man of Lochnagar*?

4. In which year did Cliff Richard reach number one in the UK with 'We Don't Talk Anymore'?

5. Who was joint manager of Charlton Athletic with Alan Curbishley?

6. Which is the most easterly of the Balearic Islands?

7. Which river links St. Etienne and Nantes?

8. Charity Dingle is a character in which soap?

9. Fort Worth is a region of which American city?

10. According to legend, who saw above his head a sword suspended by a single hair?

11. What nationality was distance runner Emil Zátopek?

12. What is the term for the season when male deer become sexually aroused?

13. Who presented *Streetmate*?

14. Which stations lie at the ends of the Bakerloo Line on the London Underground?

15. Which is further north – Madrid, Valencia or Barcelona?

16. Who went solo after appearing in *The Partridge Family*?

Answers to page 438
GENERAL QUIZ 79: **1.** Greg Rusedski **2.** Rome **3.** George Sand **4.** San Marino **5.** Ballet **6.** Spain **7.** The Boo Radleys **8.** 1996 **9.** Birmingham **10.** The jawbone **11.** Lebanon **12.** A jiffy **13.** A parrot-like bird **14.** Bears **15.** Romania **16.** Berkshire

General Quiz 78

Answers on page 439

1. Which awards were made of wood to conserve metal during World War Two?

2. William Peter Blatty wrote which supernatural novel that became a 1973 box-office smash in the cinema?

3. In which year did Charles I become King of England?

4. Which new town in Buckinghamshire was created in 1967?

5. What were Bingo, Crossbow and Horlicks?

6. Which London racecourse closed in 1979?

7. What part of the body does a genuphobic fear?

8. How many hours are China ahead of the UK?

9. Which country was ruled by the House of Vasa from 1523–1654?

10. Who was Jimmy Carter's Vice-President?

11. What is the chemical symbol for aluminium?

12. What Latin phrase means 'time flies'?

13. What was Maigret's Christian name?

14. Who wrote *Volpone* and *The Alchemist*?

15. What country has the international vehicle index ROU?

16. What did Casey Jones drive?

Answers to page 439
GENERAL QUIZ 80: **1.** Hell's Angels **2.** *Emmerdale* **3.** St Christopher
4. Richmond **5.** Harry Chapin **6.** Derby County **7.** Headingley **8.** Australia
9. They are the longest words that can be typed with only the left hand in touch typing **10.** None **11.** Miss Piggy **12.** Po **13.** Tribbiani **14.** Mike Gatting
15. Champion **16.** Michael Foot

General Quiz 79

Answers on page 436

1. In 1997, who became the first British man to reach the world's top ten tennis rankings?

2. In which city is the Trevi fountain?

3. What was the pen name of Amandine Aurore Lucie Dupin?

4. Which tiny European country is divided up into nine castles?

5. What type of dancer is Lynn Seymour?

6. In which country is Santander?

7. Which indie band took their name from a character in the novel *To Kill A Mockingbird*?

8. In which year was football 'coming home' to England?

9. In which city is the Bull Ring Shopping Centre?

10. What is the hardest bone in the human body?

11. In which country was Keanu Reeves born?

12. What name is given to one-hundredth of a second?

13. What is a lory?

14. What can be spectacled, sun or black?

15. Carol I became the first king of which country in 1881?

16. Eton College is in which county?

Answers to page 436
GENERAL QUIZ 77: **1.** The studio collapsed **2.** Dorset **3.** Prince Charles **4.** 1979 **5.** Steve Gritt **6.** Minorca **7.** Loire **8.** *Emmerdale* **9.** Dallas **10.** Damocles **11.** Czech **12.** Rutting **13.** Davina McCall **14.** Harrow & Wealdstone and Elephant & Castle **15.** Barcelona **16.** David Cassidy

General Quiz 80

Answers on page 437

1. Which motorcycle gangs divide themselves into chapters?

2. In which soap did the pub owner marry the vicar in 2001?

3. Who is the patron saint of travellers?

4. What town name has a castle in North Yorkshire and a park near London?

5. Who sang about the morning DJ from 'W-O-L-D'?

6. Which Midlands football club are nicknamed the 'Rams'?

7. Which English cricket ground has the Kirkstall Lane end?

8. In which country is the Nullarbor Plain?

9. What is significant about the words 'stewardesses' and 'reverberated'?

10. How many living descendants does Shakespeare have?

11. Which Muppet was banned from Turkish TV during religious festivals so that viewers wouldn't be offended by the sight of an 'unclean' animal?

12. On which river does Turin stand?

13. What is Joey's surname in *Friends*?

14. Which England cricket captain was forced to apologise to umpire Shakoor Rana after a row that halted play for a day in Pakistan?

15. Which 'Wonder Horse' had his own TV series?

16. Who did Chris Patten call 'a kind of walking obituary for the Labour Party'?

Answers to page 437
GENERAL QUIZ 78: **1.** The Oscars **2.** *The Exorcist* **3.** 1625 **4.** Milton Keynes **5.** Operation code names from World War Two **6.** Alexandra Park **7.** Knees **8.** Eight **9.** Sweden **10.** Walter Mondale **11.** Al **12.** Tempus fugit **13.** Jules **14.** Ben Jonson **15.** Uruguay **16.** A railroad locomotive

General Quiz 81

Answers on page 442

1. How high is the net in a game of table tennis?

2. Who played the Duke of Edinburgh as a cowardly swine on TV in 1983?

3. Which band was fronted by David Byrne?

4. Tahiti is the largest of which group of Islands?

5. What was the name of the shaggy, piano-playing dog in *The Muppet Show*?

6. In which year did Bob Marley release 'No Woman No Cry'?

7. On which island is Margate?

8. What was the title of James Mason's final film?

9. Which judge looks after the baps?

10. What is the name of the chalk hill figure on the South Downs at Wilmington?

11. Which radio show featured Min and Henry Crun?

12. Which primrose opens at night?

13. Who won the 1995 Booker Prize with *The Ghost Road*?

14. What are roller, roman and venetian?

15. Which English explorer had the middle name Falcon?

16. Which river forms the eastern border between England and Scotland?

Answers to page 442
GENERAL QUIZ 83: 1. Arum lily 2. Very low temperatures 3. Cuckoo
4. 12th 5. Football 6. Adam Adamant 7. Salisbury Plain 8. Germany 9. Lord
Lucan 10. Peckham 11. Philip Larkin 12. Hale-Bopp comet 13. *Romeo And Juliet* 14. Spam 15. *Spitting Image* 16. A lemur-like creature

General Quiz 82

Answers on page 443

1. How many days of Christmas are there?

2. What was the surname of the Bros boys?

3. What can be a ballet dancer's skirt or the name of a South African cleric?

4. What was the pen name of author Samuel Langhorne Clemens?

5. Which policy of Mikhail Gorbachev meant literally 'reconstruction'?

6. As what was Percy Toplis better known?

7. Which singer, who topped the charts with Elton John in 1976, was born Pauline Matthews?

8. Which poet did Elizabeth Barrett marry?

9. What sporting activity takes place at Fairyhouse?

10. Which company was formed by Charlie Chaplin, Mary Pickford, Douglas Fairbanks and D. W. Griffith to distribute their films?

11. What is gneiss?

12. Who did the All Blacks play in a *Monty Python* rugby sketch?

13. Which English town houses the government surveillance centre, GCHQ?

14. Which boxer told his wife after losing his world heavyweight title in 1926: 'Honey, I just forgot to duck'?

15. Which French actor starred in the 1990 movie *Green Card*?

16. Which American state is known as the 'Centennial State'?

Answers to page 443
GENERAL QUIZ 84: 1. Government Communications Headquarters
2. *King Kong* 3. Japan 4. Axminster and Wilton 5. Chris Langham 6. January
7. George III 8. Glenn Close 9. *Family Affairs* 10. Federation Cup 11. Terence
12. Aries 13. A type of tree 14. Cerberus 15. Donald Bradman 16. Elton
John (Roy Dwight)

General Quiz 83

Answers on page 440

1. Which flower is also known as the calla lily?

2. What is cryogenics the science of?

3. What bird lays its eggs in the nests of other birds?

4. In which century did Saladin conquer Egypt?

5. What did George Bernard Shaw say was the only sport more boring than cricket?

6. Which TV superhero was played by Gerald Harper?

7. Westbury Down is the highest point of which stretch of English landscape?

8. The Ruhr Valley is a region of which country?

9. Whose car was found in Newhaven following his disappearance?

10. In which part of London did Del Boy and Rodney live?

11. Who wrote the 1964 poetry collection *The Whitsun Weddings*?

12. Which comet was discovered in 1995 by two American astronomers?

13. Which Shakespeare play was the title of a Dire Straits song?

14. Which tinned meat celebrated its 50th birthday in 1987?

15. Which TV show was created by Peter Fluck and Roger Law?

16. What is an aye-aye?

Answers to page 440
GENERAL QUIZ 81: **1.** Six inches **2.** Rowan Atkinson (the first Edmund Blackadder's title was Duke of Edinburgh) **3.** Talking Heads **4.** Society Islands **5.** Rowlf **6.** 1974 **7.** Isle of Thanet **8.** *The Shooting Party* **9.** Master of the Rolls **10.** The 'Long Man' **11.** *The Goon Show* **12.** Evening primrose **13.** Pat Barker **14.** Types of window blind **15.** Captain Scott **16.** Tweed

General Quiz 84

Answers on page 441

1. What does GCHQ stand for?

2. What was said to be Hitler's favourite film?

3. In which country might you be entertained by a geisha?

4. Which two English towns give their names to types of carpet?

5. Whom did Griff Rhys Jones replace in the *Not the Nine o'Clock News* team?

6. In which month does the Monte Carlo Rally traditionally take place?

7. In the reign of which King of England were the American colonies lost?

8. Who played the embittered mistress in *Fatal Attraction*?

9. Pete Callan is the resident villain in which TV soap?

10. In tennis, what is the women's equivalent of the Davis Cup?

11. What was Spike Milligan's real first name?

12. What is the first sign of the zodiac?

13. What is the bottlebrush?

14. In Greek mythology, what was the name of the three-headed dog guarding the entrance to the underworld?

15. Which Australian cricketer had a batting average of 99.94 from 52 Test matches?

16. Which singer had a cousin who scored an FA Cup final goal?

Answers to page 441
GENERAL QUIZ 82: 1. 12 2. Goss 3. Tutu 4. Mark Twain 5. Perestroika
6. 'The Monocled Mutineer' 7. Kiki Dee 8. Robert Browning 9. Horse racing
10. United Artists 11. A type of rock 12. Derby City Council
13. Cheltenham 14. Jack Dempsey 15. Gérard Depardieu 16. Colorado

General Quiz 85

Answers on page 446

1. Which distance runner was known as the 'Flying Finn'?

2. Whose 2001 album was titled 'Songs From The West Coast'?

3. Which rival TV cook labelled Jamie Oliver's shows 'tacky and gimmicky'?

4. What is the nickname of Northampton rugby club?

5. Who played showgirl Satine in the 2001 movie *Moulin Rouge*?

6. In which ocean is the Gulf of Ob?

7. Who starred as Lawrence of Arabia in the 1962 film of that title?

8. Who got in a basket with Teddy and Andy Pandy?

9. In which town is the ground of Grimsby Town Football Club?

10. In which city did the Peterloo massacre take place?

11. The ringgit is the currency of which country?

12. What number American President is George W. Bush?

13. Who played the devil in the remake of the film *Bedazzled*?

14. In 1996, who became the first British tennis player for 23 years to reach the quarter-finals of the men's singles at Wimbledon?

15. On which river does the Yorkshire town of Halifax stand?

16. Which Hollywood beauty made her film debut in *The Mask*?

Answers to page 446
GENERAL QUIZ 87: 1. Terrier 2. Tina Turner 3. Southern lights 4. Coventry City 5. Scarborough 6. The Proms 7. Bowls 8. Donna 9. Robbie Williams 10. George Patton 11. Pay-As-You-Earn 12. Eddie Murphy 13. Morrissey 14. Buckingham Palace 15. The Moby 16. Maastricht Treaty

General Quiz 86

Answers on page 447

1. Which singer married choreographer Cris Judd in 2001?

2. Which country borders Kenya to the south?

3. In 1994, who was sworn in as the first black President of South Africa?

4. Which Lancashire cricketer was appointed England captain in 1993?

5. Who did Boy George become on *Stars in Their Eyes* in 2001?

6. Which race traditionally ends at Mortlake?

7. Who created the Secret Seven?

8. Which actor wrote *A Short Walk From Harrods* in 1993?

9. Pablo Casals became famous for playing which musical instrument?

10. Who was 'Livin'' La Vida Loca'?

11. In which country did the Boxer Rebellion take place?

12. What did Dick Whittington achieve that Jeffrey Archer didn't?

13. Which flower became a craze in 17th-century Holland?

14. Which town provides the Scottish mainland terminus for the steamer service to the Orkneys?

15. Which river forms a long stretch of the border between Devon and Cornwall?

16. The Gulf of San Matias is off the coast of which country?

Answers to page 447
GENERAL QUIZ 88: 1. Cheshire 2. Flashing directional indicator lights
3. Denmark 4. Four 5. Maria Callas 6. Charles Dance 7. Boccaccio
8. Leonardo DiCaprio 9. Baha Men 10. Dry ice 11. Kew 12. Nigel Kennedy
13. Puck 14. Sarajevo 15. Swedish 16. Larry Grayson

General Quiz 87

Answers on page 444

1. Sealyham is a breed of which type of dog?

2. Which singer was born Annie Mae Bullock?

3. What is the common name for *aurora australis*?

4. Which Football League club plays at Highfield Road?

5. What is the home town of playwright Alan Ayckbourn?

6. Which series of concerts were founded by Henry Wood?

7. What game was Sir Francis Drake playing as the Spanish Armada approached?

8. What was the name of Dave Tucker's feisty wife in *Soldier, Soldier*?

9. 'Rock DJ' was a huge hit for which singer?

10. Which US general was known as 'Old Blood and Guts'?

11. What does PAYE stand for?

12. Who starred in *Vampire in Brooklyn* and *The Nutty Professor*?

13. Whose solo albums have included 'Viva Hate' and 'Your Arsenal'?

14. Marble Arch was constructed originally as a ceremonial entrance to which building?

15. What was the name of Ron Dixon's mobile shop in *Brookside*?

16. Which treaty was drawn up by European Community heads in 1991?

Answers to page 444
GENERAL QUIZ 85: **1.** Paavo Nurmi **2.** Elton John **3.** Antonio Carluccio **4.** 'The Saints' **5.** Nicole Kidman **6.** Arctic Ocean **7.** Peter O'Toole **8.** Looby Loo **9.** Cleethorpes **10.** Manchester **11.** Malaysia **12.** 43rd **13.** Liz Hurley **14.** Tim Henman **15.** Calder **16.** Cameron Diaz

General Quiz 88

Answers on page 445

1. In which county are Warrington and Widnes?

2. What were made compulsory on cars in Britain in 1954?

3. Which was the first country to introduce VAT?

4. How many Epsom Derby winners did Willie Carson ride?

5. Which singer was born Maria Kalogeropoulos?

6. Who played Guy Perron in *The Jewel in the Crown*?

7. Who wrote *The Decameron*?

8. Which actor made his movie debut as Tobias Wolff in *This Boy's Life*?

9. 'Who Let The Dogs Out' in 2000?

10. What is another name for solid carbon dioxide, often used in stage shows?

11. Where are London's Royal Botanic Gardens?

12. Whose 1986 recording of Vivaldi's 'Four Seasons' sold over a million copies?

13. What is used in place of a ball in ice hockey?

14. Where was Archduke Franz Ferdinand assassinated in 1914 – the event which sparked the First World War?

15. What nationality is tennis player Mats Wilander?

16. Who succeeded Bruce Forsyth in the Seventies as host of *The Generation Game*?

Answers to page 445
GENERAL QUIZ 86: **1.** Jennifer Lopez **2.** Tanzania **3.** Nelson Mandela **4.** Mike Atherton **5.** David Bowie's Ziggy Stardust **6.** The Boat Race **7.** Enid Blyton **8.** Dirk Bogarde **9.** Cello **10.** Ricky Martin **11.** China **12.** Lord Mayor of London **13.** Tulip **14.** Thurso **15.** Tamar **16.** Argentina

General Quiz 89

Answers on page 450

1. In which continent are the Atlas Mountains?

2. Which punk band were 'Turning Japanese' in 1980?

3. Which was the chosen event of British athlete Roger Black?

4. What colour were post boxes originally?

5. What form of transport was pioneered by Igor Sikorsky?

6. Which Russian novelist wrote *Crime and Punishment*?

7. What was Victoria Beckham's maiden name?

8. What product was Henry Doulton's speciality?

9. Jason Durr took over from Nick Berry in which TV series?

10. What did my true love give to me on the third day of Christmas?

11. Who gave birth to a baby girl – Holly Willow – in September 2001?

12. For what is ENT an abbreviation in medicine?

13. Who makes 'exceedingly good cakes'?

14. In what form of theatre did Ben Travers specialise?

15. What is a fata morgana?

16. Which Hollywood comic was born Joseph Levitch?

Answers to page 450
GENERAL QUIZ 91: 1. *Rebecca* 2. Côte d'Azur 3. Fred Trueman 4. Tom Cruise 5. Butterflies 6. Barney and Betty Rubble 7. Constantinople 8. Caspian Sea 9. 'The' 10. Amerigo Vespucci 11. Steve Cauthen 12. *Blade II* 13. Llandudno 14. A type of onion 15. Indiana 16. Concorde

General Quiz 90

Answers on page 451

1. Some 60,000 men were killed on the first day of which World War One battle?

2. Which actor's middle name is Columcille?

3. What number on the Beaufort Scale indicates a gale?

4. Varna is a port on which sea?

5. Which James Bond once advertised Big Fry chocolate bars?

6. Who was the Greek goddess of the Earth?

7. Who wrote *The Darling Buds of May*?

8. Which Football League team are nicknamed the 'Chairboys'?

9. Which Post Office executive invented adhesive stamps in the 19th century?

10. In which year did the Easter Rising take place in Dublin?

11. Which band released the album 'Automatic For The People'?

12. Rosencrantz and Guildenstern featured in which Shakespeare play?

13. Who painted *The Laughing Cavalier*?

14. Which English cricketer took a world record 19 wickets in a Test match against Australia in 1956?

15. The Barras is a market in which British city?

16. Who was Richie Rich's agent?

Answers to page 451
GENERAL QUIZ 92: 1. Dartmoor 2. Cardiff 3. Turin 4. John Cleese
5. Deirdre Rachid 6. *Riverdance* 7. Arthur C. Clarke 8. Canada 9. Pluto
10. 21% 11. Australia 12. Fatboy Slim 13. Both were called Eric 14. A joey
15. Chester 16. Japan

General Quiz 91

Answers on page 448

1. Which novel was set in a house called Manderley?

2. What is the name for the stretch of coastline which connects St Tropez, Cannes and Nice?

3. In 1964, which English cricketer became the first bowler to take 300 Test wickets?

4. Which Hollywood star enrolled to become a priest at 14, but dropped out after a year?

5. What are red admirals and swallow tails?

6. Who adopted Bam Bam?

7. Which city was the capital of the Byzantine Empire?

8. Astrakhan and Baku are the chief ports on which inland sea?

9. What is the most commonly used word in written English?

10. Which explorer gave his name to America?

11. Which American was UK champion jockey in 1984, 1985 and 1987?

12. In which 2002 film did Wesley Snipes reprise his role as a character who is half man, half vampire?

13. The Great Orme is near which Welsh resort?

14. What is a scallion?

15. Which American state wanted R. Dean Taylor in the title of a 1971 hit?

16. What was first tested by Brian Trubshaw?

Answers to page 448
GENERAL QUIZ 89: 1. Africa 2. The Vapors 3. 400 metres 4. Green
5. Helicopter 6. Dostoevsky 7. Adams 8. Pottery 9. *Heartbeat* 10. Three
French hens 11. Davina McCall 12. Ear, nose and throat 13. Mr Kipling
14. Farce 15. A mirage 16. Jerry Lewis

General Quiz 92

Answers on page 449

1. Which prison is located at Princetown?

2. In which city is the Millennium Stadium?

3. In which city do Juventus Football Club play?

4. Which comedy actor's middle name is Marwood?

5. Which *Coronation Street* character finally acquired a new pair of glasses in 2001?

6. Michael Flatley was associated with which Irish dance show?

7. Who wrote *2001: A Space Odyssey*?

8. In which country is the Great Slave Lake?

9. Which planet is farthest from the Sun?

10. What percentage of air is oxygen?

11. In which country is the Uluru national park?

12. Which man of many guises had a 1999 number one with 'Praise You'?

13. What did Hoss Cartwright have in common with the Stewart from 10cc?

14. What is a baby kangaroo called?

15. In which city was Michael Owen born?

16. In which country is the ski resort of Sapporo?

Answers to page 449
GENERAL QUIZ 90: 1. Battle of the Somme 2. Mel Gibson 3. Eight 4. Black Sea 5. George Lazenby 6. Gaia 7. H.E. Bates 8. Wycombe Wanderers 9. Rowland Hill 10. 1916 11. R.E.M. 12. *Hamlet* 13. Frans Hals 14. Jim Laker 15. Glasgow 16. Ralph Filthy

General Quiz 93

Answers on page 454

1. What was Corporal O'Reilly's nickname in *M*A*S*H* ?

2. Which stretch of water separates mainland Scotland from the Orkneys?

3. Who lamented about a 'Ghost Town' in 1981?

4. What colour are Bond Street, Regent Street and Oxford Street on a Monopoly board?

5. Who won a Best Actress Oscar for *Terms of Endearment* in 1983?

6. Who rebuilt Steve Austin as *The Six Million Dollar Man*?

7. In what sport may a crewman perform a trapeze?

8. Which European country is made up of around 500 islands?

9. What is the wild dog of Australia?

10. Who was George Gershwin's lyricist brother?

11. As what were the infamous Geheime Staatspolizei better known?

12. What does 'sotto voce' mean?

13. Which was 'the quiz of the week, from Norwich'?

14. After Old Etonians lifted the FA Cup in 1882, it was a further 19 years before which club became the next southern team to win the trophy?

15. Who wrote the *Ballad of Reading Gaol* from bitter personal experience?

16. In which country is Lake Neuchâtel?

Answers to page 454
GENERAL QUIZ 95: 1. Michael Crichton 2. *Daily Mirror* 3. Dorset
4. A cheese 5. Mike Myers 6. Grotbags 7. Luton Town 8. Antarctica
9. *A Midsummer Night's Dream* 10. Ptolemy 11. Tour de France 12. Sharon Stone 13. Everest 14. Terry Downes 15. Greenham Common 16. Bob Hoskins

General Quiz 94

Answers on page 455

1. What caused the Six Nations' Rugby Championship to be carried over into autumn 2001?

2. Which Morgan starred in the movie *Along Came a Spider*?

3. 'Spinning Around' enabled which singer to have number ones in three consecutive decades?

4. Who was *Dick Turpin*'s sidekick?

5. What does the horned toad squirt from its eyes to deter attackers?

6. Who designed the 'bouncing bomb'?

7. Who was christened Manchester United's 'baby-faced assassin'?

8. In which county is Alton Towers theme park?

9. What is the common name for tetanus?

10. What is a grackle?

11. The Reign of Terror was a period in which historical rebellion?

12. In television terms, what was the only case of a rat rescuing a sinking ship?

13. What kind of vegetable is a shallot?

14. Which comedian's real name is Bob Davis?

15. What number relates to the San Francisco American football team?

16. Whose 2001 album was titled 'No More Drama'?

Answers to page 455
GENERAL QUIZ 96: **1.** Prince Consort **2.** Cats **3.** Boston **4.** *Angel Eyes*
5. Richard Nixon **6.** Anthony Clare **7.** Leeds **8.** Gallagher and Lyle
9. Charles II **10.** Westminster Abbey **11.** Elizabeth **12.** Surinam **13.** Ethiopian
14. Yosser Hughes **15.** *The Others* **16.** Lord Mountbatten

General Quiz 95

Answers on page 452

1. Who wrote *Jurassic Park*?

2. In which newspaper did the cartoon strip *Andy Capp* first appear?

3. In which English county is the market town of Shaftesbury?

4. What is Roquefort?

5. Who was the voice of *Shrek*?

6. Who was the nasty green witch in *Emu's World*?

7. In 2001–2, which club played in the bottom division of the Football League for the first time since 1968?

8. Queen Maud Land is a region of which continent?

9. Cobweb and Mustardseed appeared in which Shakespeare play?

10. Which Egyptian astronomer's *Almagest* developed the theory that the Earth is the centre of the universe?

11. Which sporting event did Lance Armstrong win for the third consecutive year in 2001?

12. Who was the voice of Princess Bala in the movie *Antz*?

13. On which mountain did George Mallory die in 1924?

14. Which Terry became world middleweight boxing champion in 1961?

15. At which Common did CND supporters protest in the 1980s?

16. In a series of TV commercials, which cockney actor said: 'It's good to talk'?

Answers to page 452
GENERAL QUIZ 93: 1. 'Radar' 2. Pentland Firth 3. The Specials 4. Green 5. Shirley MacLaine 6. Dr Rudy Wells 7. Sailing 8. Denmark 9. Dingo 10. Ira 11. Gestapo 12. As an aside 13. *Sale of the Century* 14. Tottenham Hotspur 15. Oscar Wilde 16. Switzerland

General Quiz 96

Answers on page 453

1. In 1857, which title was conferred upon Queen Victoria's husband?

2. Which animals was Napoleon frightened of?

3. Which city is home to the world's oldest marathon?

4. Which film starred Jennifer Lopez and Jeremy Sisto?

5. Who was US President at the time of the Moon landings?

6. Who presented the radio programme *In The Psychiatrist's Chair*?

7. In which English city is Roundhay Park?

8. Which duo had a 1976 hit with 'Heart On My Sleeve'?

9. Which English king hid in a tree to escape capture following defeat at the Battle of Worcester?

10. Where was Britain's Unknown Soldier of the First World War buried?

11. What was the name of Captain Mainwaring's unseen wife in *Dad's Army*?

12. Which adjoining country forms the eastern border of Guyana?

13. What nationality is the distance runner Geta Wami?

14. Whose catchphrase was 'Gissa job'?

15. In what 2001 Nicole Kidman film did Eric Sykes appear?

16. Who was the last Viceroy of India?

Answers to page 453
GENERAL QUIZ 94: **1.** Foot and mouth disease **2.** Morgan Freeman **3.** Kylie Minogue **4.** Swiftnick **5.** Blood **6.** Barnes Wallis **7.** Ole Gunnar Solskjaer **8.** Staffordshire **9.** Lockjaw **10.** A bird **11.** French Revolution **12.** Roland Rat saving *TV-am* **13.** A small onion **14.** Jasper Carrott **15.** 49 (San Francisco 49ers) **16.** Mary J. Blige

General Quiz 97

Answers on page 458

1. Which actor quit making films with Francis the Talking Mule after learning that the mule received more fan mail than him?

2. Which birds are trained to catch and retrieve fish in China?

3. What can't an owl parrot do that other owls and parrots can?

4. Which grow faster – fingernails or toenails?

5. Which planet has daytime temperatures as high as 800 degrees Fahrenheit but has ice at its poles?

6. Which rap artist was born Robert Van Winkle?

7. In which country was Mel Gibson born?

8. What sport is played by the Sheffield Steelers and the Nottingham Panthers?

9. Which country boasts a Gold Coast?

10. In which city do *The Royle Family* live?

11. According to Ibiza superstition, it is bad luck to allow what on a fishing boat?

12. The Rye House Plot was a conspiracy against which English monarch?

13. What is siderophobia?

14. Which boxer was nicknamed 'Gentleman Jim'?

15. What was 8 May 1945 otherwise known as?

16. In which sport do European club sides play for the Heineken Cup?

Answers to page 458
GENERAL QUIZ 99: **1.** Ali G **2.** Ionian **3.** The Ivy League **4.** Copernicus **5.** Catherine Cookson **6.** 8,000 **7.** Prefab Sprout **8.** LXV **9.** Maryland **10.** Charlie Hungerford **11.** Tiger Woods **12.** Show-jumping **13.** Mecca **14.** Plaid Cymru **15.** Enya **16.** Pisces

General Quiz 98

Answers on page 459

1. Which Scottish island was evacuated on 29 August 1930?

2. Where did both Maria Muldaur and the Brand New Heavies spend Midnight?

3. What is the birthstone for November?

4. What sport do the Chicago Bulls play?

5. Who discovered the Victoria Falls?

6. Which comedians revived *Randall & Hopkirk (Deceased)*?

7. Who cut off Samson's hair?

8. Which American city is headquarters of the Mormon church?

9. On which golf course is the World Matchplay Championship held?

10. From which Dumfries and Galloway port would you catch a ferry to Larne in Northern Ireland?

11. In 1985, which two clubs became the first to regularly share a ground in the history of the Football League?

12. People with what colour hair have more hairs on their head than any other?

13. In which European country was cheese a form of currency in the 16th century?

14. How many brains does a leech have?

15. Who starred with Michelle Pfeiffer in *Frankie and Johnny*?

16. Who wrote *The Shining* and *Pet Sematary*?

Answers to page 459
GENERAL QUIZ 100: **1.** Western Australia **2.** *E.T.* **3.** Almond **4.** Pitcher **5.** One eye **6.** A coal fire **7.** Coatbridge **8.** Baron Greenback **9.** The Old Vic **10.** Missouri **11.** Eddie Irvine **12.** Ordnance Survey **13.** House of Orange **14.** Richard II **15.** Charles Laughton **16.** Bridge Street

General Quiz 99

Answers on page 456

1. Who is Sacha Baron Cohen's first famous creation?

2. In which sea is the island of Ithaca?

3. What league was originally made up of the American universities of Harvard, Yale, Columbia and Brown?

4. Who declared in 1543 that the Sun was at the centre of the Universe?

5. Which novelist wrote *Tilly Trotter* and *The Glass Virgin*?

6. What is the cube of 20?

7. Paddy McAloon is the singer with which band?

8. What is the Roman number for 65?

9. Annapolis is the capital of which American state?

10. Who was Jim Bergerac's father-in-law?

11. Which golfer won the 1997 US Masters by a record 12 shots?

12. Hickstead is synonymous with which sport?

13. Which city was the birthplace of Muhammad?

14. What is the name of the Welsh nationalist party?

15. Which Irish singer had a 1988 number one with 'Orinoco Flow'?

16. Which star sign follows Aquarius?

Answers to page 456
GENERAL QUIZ 97: **1.** Donald O'Connor **2.** Cormorants **3.** Fly
4. Fingernails **5.** Mercury **6.** Vanilla Ice **7.** USA **8.** Ice hockey **9.** Australia
10. Manchester **11.** A priest **12.** Charles II **13.** A fear of the stars **14.** James
J. Corbett **15.** V-E Day **16.** Rugby Union

General Quiz 100

Answers on page 457

1. In which Australian state is the town of Albany?

2. Which Steven Spielberg film was re-released in 2002 to celebrate its 20th anniversary?

3. What nuts are used to make marzipan?

4. What can be a large vessel, a carnivorous plant or a baseball thrower?

5. What part of Rex Harrison's anatomy was made of glass?

6. If there were French nuts in your lounge, what would you have?

7. In which Scottish town do the football team Albion Rovers play?

8. Which toad was the arch enemy of *Dangermouse*?

9. Which London theatre was home to the National Theatre from 1963–76?

10. On which river does Omaha stand?

11. Which British driver drove for Jaguar in Formula One in 2001?

12. Which body was previously known as the Trigonometrical Survey?

13. Which Dutch royal family took their name from a small principality in southern France?

14. Which English king was faced with the Peasants' Revolt?

15. Who starred in *Mutiny on the Bounty* and *The Hunchback of Notre Dame*?

16. In which street is the café in *EastEnders*?

Answers to page 457
GENERAL QUIZ 98: 1. St Kilda 2. At The Oasis 3. Topaz 4. Basketball
5. David Livingstone 6. Reeves and Mortimer 7. Delilah 8. Salt Lake City
9. Wentworth 10. Stranraer 11. Crystal Palace and Charlton 12. Blonde
13. Denmark 14. 32 15. Al Pacino 16. Stephen King

General Quiz 101

Answers on page 462

1. In which city is the University of East Anglia?

2. Which culinary term, popular in the late 1980s, means 'new cooking'?

3. Which wild flower is also known as heartsease?

4. Pérez de Cuéllar was secretary general of which body from 1982–91?

5. Which band wanted to 'Keep The Faith' in 1992?

6. What was Paddington Bear's favourite food?

7. Which planet has a moon named Charon?

8. How many playing cards are there in a standard pack?

9. Which American state is known as the 'Flickertail State'?

10. In which English county is Kettering?

11. Who played Scott Hastings in the Baz Luhrmann film *Strictly Ballroom*?

12. North Brabant is a province of which country?

13. Who sang about a 'Cornflake Girl'?

14. What is the singular of 'graffiti'?

15. What is unusual about Jane Austen's novel *Lady Susan*?

16. What is the name for a military morning wake-up call?

Answers to page 462
GENERAL QUIZ 103: **1.** Northamptonshire **2.** Steve McManaman **3.** 15
4. 49 **5.** French Guiana **6.** London **7.** Dance **8.** Doges **9.** Betty Grable
10. Holyrood House **11.** German **12.** Home Counties **13.** Khmer Rouge
14. Ireland **15.** Shirley MacLaine **16.** 'My lady'

General Quiz 102

Answers on page 463

1. What is Jude's surname in Thomas Hardy's novel *Jude the Obscure*?

2. Which Football League club plays at Sixfields Stadium?

3. Which ex-member of Bros had a role in the 2002 film *Blade II*?

4. Which bird took Manfred Mann to number one in 1966?

5. Which country lies immediately to the south of Angola?

6. Since 1066, which two English kings have been the only monarchs of that name?

7. Which chat show host was *All Talk*?

8. What statue stands in London's Piccadilly Circus?

9. What name is given to an area of open space surrounding a city?

10. In Greek mythology, what sprang up on the spot where Narcissus died?

11. In which American city does hip-hop music have its origins?

12. Opium is extracted from the unripe seeds of which plant?

13. In which century was Charlotte Brontë born?

14. To which body organ does the word hepatology relate?

15. What were the followers of 14th-century religious reformer John Wycliffe known as?

16. In which other country does London stand on the River Thames?

Answers to page 463
GENERAL QUIZ 104: 1. Mauritania 2. 95% 3. Melton Mowbray
4. Loudness 5. Michael Collins 6. November 7. Bird 8. Remus 9. Pete
Sampras 10. Maggie Smith 11. Norfolk 12. Gerald Durrell 13. Janus
14. Scottish country dances 15. Lillian Gish 16. Freetown

General Quiz 103

Answers on page 460

1. In which county was the Battle of Naseby fought in 1645?

2. Which footballing Steve moved from Liverpool to Real Madrid?

3. How many kings of Sweden were called Charles?

4. How many goals did Bobby Charlton score for England?

5. Off which country does Devil's Island lie?

6. In which English city is St Katherine's Dock?

7. In which field of the arts did Anton Dolin make his name?

8. What were the chief magistrates called in ancient Venice and Genoa?

9. Who starred in the musicals *Follow the Fleet* and *Pin Up Girl*?

10. What is the name of the royal residence in Edinburgh?

11. What nationality was the artist Hans Holbein?

12. What name is given to the counties closest to London?

13. Pol Pot was the leader of which guerrilla movement?

14. In which country is the River Liffey?

15. Which actress is the sister of Warren Beatty?

16. What does Madonna mean?

Answers to page 460
GENERAL QUIZ 101: **1.** Norwich **2.** Nouvelle cuisine **3.** Wild pansy
4. United Nations **5.** Bon Jovi **6.** Marmalade sandwiches **7.** Pluto **8.** 52
9. North Dakota **10.** Northamptonshire **11.** Paul Mercurio **12.** Netherlands
13. Tori Amos **14.** Graffito **15.** It is written in the form of letters
16. Reveille

General Quiz 104

Answers on page 461

1. The ouguiya is the currency of which country?

2. What percentage of a melon is water?

3. Which Leicestershire town is renowned for its pork pies?

4. A phon is a unit of what?

5. Which Irish nationalist leader was assassinated on 22 August 1922?

6. In which month is Remembrance Day?

7. What is a ring ouzel?

8. In Roman legend, who was Romulus's twin brother?

9. In 1990, which tennis player became the youngest winner of the US Open?

10. Who won an Academy Award for her role in *The Prime of Miss Jean Brodie*?

11. In which English county is Thetford?

12. Which naturalist founded Jersey Zoo?

13. Who was the Roman god of doorways and passageways?

14. What are The De'il Among The Tailors, Maxwell's Rant and Petronella?

15. As whom was the actress Lillian de Guiche better known?

16. What is the capital of Sierra Leone?

Answers to page 461
GENERAL QUIZ 102: 1. Fawley 2. Northampton Town 3. Luke Goss
4. 'Pretty Flamingo' 5. Namibia 6. Stephen and John 7. Clive Anderson
8. Eros 9. Green belt 10. A flower 11. New York 12. Opium poppy 13. 19th
14. Liver 15. Lollards 16. Canada

General Quiz 105

Answers on page 466

1. Which son of a Yorkshire Test cricketer made his England debut in 2001?

2. 'Someday My Prince Will Come' is a song from which Disney film?

3. Which radio show celebrated its 50th birthday on 1 January 2001?

4. What was King Arthur's legendary seat?

5. What unit of work and energy has replaced the calorie?

6. What is the common name for convolvulus?

7. In which county is Silverstone motor-racing circuit?

8. Meg Richardson ran which TV establishment?

9. With which musical instrument was John William Coltrane associated?

10. Which of the Seven Wonders of the World fell victim to an earthquake in 224BC?

11. Who starred in *Beau Geste* and *The Prisoner of Zenda*?

12. Which French philosopher said: 'I think, therefore I am'?

13. Which 1965 ballad was covered by 1,186 different performers in the first ten years?

14. Which is the largest moon in the solar system?

15. What is the capital of Bermuda?

16. Who played the drunken baseball coach in the 1992 movie *A League of their Own*?

Answers to page 466
GENERAL QUIZ 107: **1.** Norvell **2.** Bob Geldof **3.** Basketball **4.** Concertina **5.** Zloty **6.** Renault **7.** Roman Polanski **8.** Jennifer Aniston **9.** The Oval **10.** Owls **11.** Cornwall **12.** Glenn Miller **13.** Nell Gwynn **14.** Benny Goodman **15.** Anne Frank **16.** Iris

General Quiz 106

Answers on page 467

1. On which river does Hanoi stand?

2. Who cut off the tails of the Three Blind Mice?

3. Which rugby team won the Heineken Cup in 2000–1?

4. Which singer starred in *Memphis Belle*?

5. In Greek mythology, who was the daughter of Zeus and Leda?

6. What nationality was Henry the Navigator?

7. With what branch of music was John Lee Hooker associated?

8. Which English town has a tall church tower called a 'stump'?

9. Who was captain of Australia's cricket team from 1985–94?

10. Who was the subject of the film '*That Hamilton Woman*' – Emma Hamilton or Christine Hamilton?

11. Who does Amanda Burton play in *Silent Witness*?

12. Which Jesse founded a pharmacy chain?

13. Which English river has a bore?

14. Which jockey, who rode 21 classic winners, shot himself in a fit of depression in 1886?

15. For what was Anzac an acronym?

16. Which is the most northerly of the major Greek islands?

Answers to page 467
GENERAL QUIZ 108: 1. Epsom (salts) 2. *Cocktail* 3. Cycling 4. Blur 5. Greg Dyke 6. Frozen food 7. Blue Ridge Mountains 8. Czech Republic 9. Freshwater fish 10. Southampton 11. American 12. *Heathers* 13. Kingcup 14. Gary Lineker 15. Lammas 16. Illinois

General Quiz 107

Answers on page 464

1. What was Oliver Hardy's real Christian name?

2. Whose first album for almost a decade was the 2001 release 'Sex, Age And Death'?

3. What sport do the Harlem Globetrotters play?

4. Which musical instrument was invented by Charles Wheatstone?

5. What is the national currency of Poland?

6. Which motor manufacturing company was founded by the brothers Louis, Fernand and Marcel?

7. Who directed *Rosemary's Baby* and *Bitter Moon*?

8. Which of the *Friends* was 'worth it'?

9. Which ground was the venue for the Test match between England and Australia in 1880?

10. What can be barn, snowy or tawny?

11. In which county is the fishing port of Newlyn?

12. Who disappeared on a flight between England and France in 1944?

13. Who was the most famous orange-seller at London's Drury Lane Theatre?

14. Who was known as the 'King of Swing'?

15. Whose diary was finally published in full in 1989?

16. Which flower is also called a flag?

Answers to page 464
GENERAL QUIZ 105: **1.** Ryan Sidebottom (son of Arnie) **2.** *Snow White* **3.** *The Archers* **4.** Camelot **5.** Joule **6.** Bindweed **7.** Northamptonshire **8.** Crossroads Motel **9.** Saxophone **10.** Colossus of Rhodes **11.** Ronald Colman **12.** René Descartes **13.** 'Yesterday' **14.** Ganymede **15.** Hamilton **16.** Tom Hanks

General Quiz 108

Answers on page 465

1. What Surrey town gives its name to the common form of hydrated magnesium sulphate?

2. In which film did Tom Cruise play a slick bartender?

3. Chris Boardman won an Olympic gold medal in 1992 at which sport?

4. Dave Rowntree is the drummer with which band?

5. Who succeeded John Birt as director-general of the BBC?

6. What did Clarence Birdseye pioneer?

7. Which mountains extend from West Virginia to Georgia and were immortalised in a Laurel and Hardy song?

8. Bohemia is an area of which country?

9. What is a bleak?

10. Stuart Gray managed which Premiership football club at the start of season 2001–2?

11. What nationality was the painter Thomas Eakins?

12. Which 1989 movie starred Christian Slater and Winona Ryder as a pair of teenage murderers?

13. What is another name for the marsh marigold?

14. Which footballer moved to Japan in 1993 to play for Nagoya Grampus Eight?

15. Which harvest festival is celebrated on 1 August?

16. Which US state is nicknamed the 'Land of Lincoln'?

Answers to page 465
GENERAL QUIZ 106: **1.** Red River **2.** The farmer's wife **3.** Leicester Tigers **4.** Harry Connick Jnr **5.** Helen **6.** Portuguese **7.** Blues **8.** Boston **9.** Allan Border **10.** Emma Hamilton **11.** Sam Ryan **12.** Jesse Boot **13.** Severn **14.** Fred Archer **15.** Australian and New Zealand Army Corps **16.** Corfu

General Quiz 109

Answers on page 470

1. Which is the only breed of dog that can contract gout?

2. How many letters are there in the Cambodian alphabet?

3. In which English county is the seaside town of Hunstanton?

4. Which Radio 1 DJ married Fatboy Slim?

5. Who received an unprecedented nine sixes at the 1984 Winter Olympics?

6. What species of bird can be Dartford, grasshopper or reed?

7. Which *EastEnders* actress was one of *The Hello Girls*?

8. Which Spanish artist painted *The Transformation of Narcissus*?

9. What was the Mashed Potato?

10. Which London Underground line serves Heathrow Airport?

11. On which island is Las Palmas?

12. Which two English football clubs are nicknamed the 'Magpies'?

13. Which American state is immediately to the west of New Mexico?

14. Which soap celebrates its 30th birthday in 2002?

15. Which Julie Andrews film won the Best Picture Oscar for 1965?

16. Who wrote *The Camomile Lawn*?

Answers to page 470
GENERAL QUIZ 111: **1.** Kibbutz **2.** Jeanette Winterson **3.** Goodwood
4. Thursday **5.** Paula Radcliffe **6.** Errol Flynn **7.** Fear of train travel
(siderodromophobia) **8.** Alan Freeman **9.** Tchaikovsky **10.** James
11. Anastasia, daughter Of Russian Czar Nicholas II **12.** Louis XIV **13.** Isle of
Dogs **14.** Yemen **15.** Ice-T **16.** Generous

General Quiz 110

Answers on page 471

1. In which British town was Stan Laurel born?

2. Which Chris Morris TV programme landed in hot water in 2001?

3. According to a recent survey, seven per cent of Americans think who is still alive?

4. Which is the most westerly city on the African mainland?

5. Which Scottish football club plays in Cumbernauld?

6. Who had a US number one in 1974 with 'I Can Help'?

7. What is the world's best-selling book?

8. In which country is the Hekla volcano?

9. Who won a Best Actress Oscar in 1999 for *Boys Don't Cry*?

10. Who announced at the end of each episode of *The Magic Roundabout* that it was 'Time for bed'?

11. On which Mediterranean island is the port of Famagusta?

12. What does an aurist study?

13. On which sport is Alex Hay a TV commentator?

14. Whose album was titled 'Whoa Nelly'?

15. Fiver and Hazel were characters in which novel?

16. What in Britain are fallow, roe or red?

Answers to page 471
GENERAL QUIZ 112: 1. A tortoise 2. Utopia 3. Niger 4. Big Brother 5. Two by two 6. Norfolk 7. Kevin Kennedy (Curly Watts) 8. Saxophone 9. Jocky Wilson 10. Kent 11. Peak District 12. They are the same person 13. Sussex 14. Sizewell 15. Meat Loaf 16. Mark McManus

General Quiz 111

Answers on page 468

1. What is the name for a communal settlement in Israel?

2. Who wrote *Oranges Are Not the Only Fruit*?

3. The Stewards' Cup is run on which racecourse?

4. On which day of the week do British elections take place?

5. Who won the ladies' race at the 2002 London Marathon?

6. Which Hollywood swashbuckler once worked as a sheep-castrator?

7. What phobia did Sigmund Freud suffer from?

8. Which veteran DJ is known as 'Fluff'?

9. Which composer used to hold his chin with his left hand and conduct with his right because he was afraid his head would roll off his shoulders?

10. What is Paul McCartney's first name?

11. As whom did Anna Anderson pass herself off?

12. Which French monarch reigned for 72 years?

13. Which island is on the opposite side of the Thames from Greenwich Pier?

14. Which country owns the island of Socotra?

15. Which rap artist was born Tracy Marrow?

16. Which horse did Alan Munro ride to victory in the 1991 Derby?

Answers to page 468
GENERAL QUIZ 109: **1.** Dalmatian **2.** 74 **3.** Norfolk **4.** Zoë Ball **5.** Torvill and Dean **6.** Warbler **7.** Letitia Dean **8.** Salvador Dali **9.** A dance **10.** Piccadilly Line **11.** Gran Canaria **12.** Newcastle United and Notts County **13.** Arizona **14.** *Emmerdale* **15.** *The Sound of Music* **16.** Mary Wesley

General Quiz 112

Answers on page 469

1. What pet was re-named 'Wheely' after being fitted with a Lego leg in 1994?

2. Which ideal commonwealth was invented by Sir Thomas More?

3. Which is the third longest river in Africa?

4. Who ruled in *Nineteen Eighty-Four*?

5. In what formation did the animals enter Noah's Ark?

6. In which county in England would you find the Broads?

7. Which *Coronation Street* actor was a helper on *Cheggers Plays Pop*?

8. What instrument did Charlie Parker play?

9. Which Scotsman won the first World Professional Darts Championship?

10. Lydd airport is in which English county?

11. Kinder Scout is the highest point of which national park?

12. What links the authors Harry Patterson and Jack Higgins?

13. For which county cricket team did Ted Dexter play?

14. What is the name of the nuclear power station in Suffolk?

15. Whose biggest-selling album was 'Bat Out Of Hell'?

16. Who played *Taggart*?

Answers to page 469
GENERAL QUIZ 110: 1. Ulverston in England 2. *Brass Eye* 3. Elvis Presley 4. Dakar 5. Clyde 6. Billy Swan 7. The Bible 8. Iceland 9. Hilary Swank 10. Zebedee 11. Cyprus 12. Ears 13. Golf 14. Nelly Furtado 15. *Watership Down* 16. Deer

General Quiz 113

Answers on page 474

1. What is a cockchafer?

2. What nationality is author J. M. Coetzee?

3. The Arc de Triomphe stands at the head of which Paris thoroughfare?

4. Which is the second largest city in the Czech Republic?

5. Who wrote *Little Lord Fauntleroy* and *The Secret Garden*?

6. What do cricketers Tony Pigott, Mike Smith and James Whitaker have in common?

7. What appeared for only the third time on British soil in September 2001?

8. Who sang 'You Get What You Give' in 1999?

9. What is the smallest member of the flute family?

10. What is another name for the rowan tree?

11. What was Mick Dundee's nickname?

12. For which team did Damon Hill win the Formula One World Championship in 1996?

13. What is the name for the central part of the church?

14. Which US R&B group have the same name as a pair of Manchester United footballers?

15. Which sports manufacturing company is named after the Greek goddess of victory?

16. Which sports commentator was once responsible for the advertising slogan 'Trill makes budgies bounce with health'?

Answers to page 474
GENERAL QUIZ 115: 1. Britain, France and Russia 2. Forth 3. Sting 4. 48
5. Victor Meldrew 6. Sea Potato 7. Indianapolis 8. Pineapple 9. 3.14
10. Pennines 11. Ashley Judd 12. South America 13. T-shirt 14. 1994
15. David Attenborough 16. Dave Beasant

General Quiz 114

Answers on page 475

1. Whose debut novel was entitled *The Clematis Tree?*

2. Which British driver raced for the Benetton Formula One team in 2001?

3. In which English county is Ilkley Moor?

4. Between 901 and 1016 which was the only King of England whose name did not begin with an 'E'?

5. What nickname was given to the British 8th Army in North Africa during World War Two?

6. What game is played on ice with stones?

7. Who used to be backed by a band called the Revolution?

8. What is a pistil?

9. Which Scottish League football team plays in Perth?

10. What was the name of Frank Spencer's wife in *Some Mothers Do 'Ave 'Em?*

11. What is Denmark's currency?

12. Which country has the highest density of population?

13. Which British movie won the BAFTA award for Best Film in 1998?

14. Which writer immortalised Wigan Pier?

15. At which sport do players compete for the Wightman Cup?

16. Which London museum was originally called the Museum of Ornamental Art?

Answers to page 475
GENERAL QUIZ 116: 1. Ireland 2. Larry Adler 3. Canada 4. Chelsea Flower Show 5. Diana, Princess of Wales 6. John Braine 7. West Ham United 8. St Albans 9. Columbine 10. Dorset 11. Great White Shark 12. Flemington Park 13. Mercury 14. Sheep 15. Joe Mercer 16. Hayley and Juliet Mills

General Quiz 115

Answers on page 472

1. Which three countries formed the Triple Entente of 1907–17?

2. On which river does Stirling stand?

3. Whose 1993 album was titled 'Ten Summoner's Tales'?

4. In old money, how many farthings were there to a shilling?

5. Which TV character had a wife called Margaret and neighbours named Patrick and Pippa?

6. Which potato can burrow in sand?

7. In motor-racing where was the 2001 United States Grand Prix held?

8. Which fruit has the Latin name *Ananas comosus*?

9. To two decimal places, what is the value of pi?

10. Which range of mountains is known as the 'backbone of England'?

11. Which Ashley starred with Morgan Freeman in the 1997 movie *Kiss the Girls*?

12. In which continent is Patagonia?

13. Which garment was produced originally for the US Navy?

14. In which year was the National Lottery launched?

15. Whose 1995 TV series was called *The Private Life of Plants*?

16. Who saved a penalty in the 1988 FA Cup Final?

Answers to page 472
GENERAL QUIZ 113: **1.** A beetle **2.** South African **3.** Champs Elysées **4.** Brno **5.** Frances Hodgson Burnett **6.** All played just one Test for England **7.** An American green heron **8.** New Radicals **9.** Piccolo **10.** Mountain Ash **11.** 'Crocodile' **12.** Williams **13.** Nave **14.** The Neville Brothers **15.** Nike **16.** Murray Walker

General Quiz 116

Answers on page 473

1. Albert Reynolds became Prime Minister of which country in 1992?

2. Which harmonica maestro died in 2001?

3. In which country was tennis player Greg Rusedski born?

4. Which annual garden show is held on the grounds of the Royal Hospital, London?

5. Who died on French soil on 31 August 1997?

6. Who wrote *Room at the Top*?

7. Which club side was managed by former England football boss Ron Greenwood?

8. Which Roman city stands on the River Ver?

9. What is the common name for the plant aquilegia?

10. In which English county is Maiden Castle?

11. What large fish has the Latin name *Carcharadon carcharias*?

12. On which racecourse is the Melbourne Cup run?

13. On which planet is the Caloris Basin?

14. The merino is a breed of which animal?

15. Which former jockey shared the same name as a caretaker manager of the England soccer team?

16. Who are the two actress daughters of Sir John Mills?

Answers to page 473
GENERAL QUIZ 114: **1.** Ann Widdecombe **2.** Jenson Button **3.** West Yorkshire **4.** Athelstan **5.** Desert Rats **6.** Curling **7.** Prince **8.** The female part of a flower **9.** St Johnstone **10.** Betty **11.** Krone **12.** Monaco **13.** *The Full Monty* **14.** George Orwell **15.** Tennis **16.** Victoria and Albert Museum

General Quiz 117

Answers on page 478

1. Which country is immediately to the north of Belize?

2. What nationality were the band Golden Earring who had a Seventies hit with 'Radar Love'?

3. Which is the nearest Communist country to the United States?

4. What is the average duration of sexual intercourse for humans?

5. Who blink more – men or women?

6. Where is a shrimp's heart?

7. What were Cinderella's slippers originally made out of before the story was changed by a 17th-century translator?

8. What happened to Ronald Reagan's chimpanzee co-star the day before the premiere of *Bedtime for Bonzo*?

9. At which cricket ground do bowlers come in from the Radcliffe Road end?

10. Who was Warren's despatch rider lover on *This Life*?

11. What are auctioned at Tattersalls?

12. Which member of the Royal Family joined the Navy in 1971?

13. Lauryn Hill was singer with which Nineties band?

14. What materials did the three little pigs use to build their houses?

15. What was Stephanie Rahn's claim to fame in 1970?

16. What creature is sometimes called an eft?

Answers to page 478
GENERAL QUIZ 119: **1.** *The Adventures of Tom Sawyer* **2.** Sheffield **3.** A fruit **4.** Fulham **5.** Steven **6.** Austria **7.** Fiona Bruce **8.** New Guinea **9.** The Bodyline series **10.** 1997 **11.** New Mexico **12.** Spain **13.** Doris Day **14.** Canberra **15.** Harold Abrahams **16.** Julius Caesar

General Quiz 118

Answers on page 479

1. Who scored a hat-trick in the Matthews' Cup Final?

2. Who starred in *Roxanne* and *My Blue Heaven*?

3. Which were the first Olympic Games to be televised live in Britain?

4. Which is the most easterly state in the USA?

5. Which English town is famous for its crooked spire?

6. In which county is the Prime Minister's country home, Chequers?

7. Who had a number one album in 2001 with 'A Funk Odyssey'?

8. Where does a cow have its sweat glands?

9. At what age can a female lemming first become pregnant?

10. Who invented the motorists' aid, the cat's eye?

11. Which Dorset town is also the name of a city on the South Island of New Zealand?

12. What went down on 15 April 1912?

13. Which Seventies band were formed at Charterhouse School?

14. Who was the Roman god of the underworld?

15. Nuuk is the capital of which country?

16. Who wrote *Circle of Friends* and *The Glass Lake*?

Answers to page 479
GENERAL QUIZ 120: **1.** Toads **2.** In your eye **3.** Five **4.** Klondike and Yukon **5.** Ingrid Bergman **6.** Goat **7.** USA and Mexico **8.** Mr Hodges **9.** Mongooses **10.** Sunday **11.** Hampshire **12.** The movie *Space Jam* **13.** The Cranberries **14.** Red **15.** Scotland **16.** George

General Quiz 119

Answers on page 476

1. Which novel by Mark Twain was the first to be written on a typewriter?

2. In which English city is the Meadowhall Shopping Centre?

3. What is a wampee?

4. For which football club did 1966 World Cup hero George Cohen play?

5. What is Morrissey's first name?

6. Tirol is a province of which country?

7. Which Fiona co-presents *Crimewatch UK*?

8. The Torres Strait separates which country from Australia?

9. The controversial 1932 Test series between the cricketers of Australia and England became known as which series?

10. In which year did the charity single 'Perfect Day' reach number one?

11. Which American state is known as the 'Land of Enchantment'?

12. General Franco was dictator of which country from 1939?

13. Which Hollywood actress was nicknamed 'The Professional Virgin'?

14. The name of which Australian city means 'meeting-place'?

15. Which Olympic 100 metres champion was the subject of the film *Chariots of Fire* ?

16. Who said: 'I came, I saw, I conquered'?

Answers to page 476
GENERAL QUIZ 117: **1.** Mexico **2.** Dutch **3.** Cuba **4.** Two minutes **5.** Women **6.** In its head **7.** Fur **8.** It died **9.** Trent Bridge **10.** Ferdy **11.** Racehorses **12.** Prince Charles **13.** The Fugees **14.** Straw, sticks and bricks **15.** She was the first topless newspaper pinup **16.** Newt

General Quiz 120

Answers on page 477

1. What is bufonophobia a fear of?

2. Where would you find vitreous humour?

3. How old was Arran Fernandez when he sat a maths GCSE examination in 2001?

4. The Canadian city of Dawson lies at the confluence of which two rivers?

5. Which Swedish actress starred in *Casablanca*?

6. Saanen, Hongtong and Toggenburg are all breeds of which animal?

7. Which two countries are separated by the Rio Grande?

8. What was the name of the officious ARP warden in *Dad's Army*?

9. What is the plural of mongoose?

10. On what day of the week must a month start in order for there to be a Friday the 13th?

11. Hayling Island is part of which English county?

12. What brought Bugs Bunny and basketball star Michael Jordan together in 1996?

13. Dolores O'Riordan is the singer with which band?

14. What is the principal colour of the Moroccan flag?

15. The thistle is the emblem of which country?

16. What was Babe Ruth's real Christian name?

Answers to page 477
GENERAL QUIZ 118: **1.** Stan Mortensen **2.** Steve Martin **3.** The 1948 Olympics **4.** Maine **5.** Chesterfield **6.** Buckinghamshire **7.** Jamiroquai **8.** In its nose **9.** 14 days old **10.** Percy Shaw **11.** Christchurch **12.** The *Titanic* **13.** Genesis **14.** Pluto **15.** Greenland **16.** Maeve Binchy

General Quiz 121

Answers on page 482

1. Which actor wore nothing but black for the last 45 years of his life?

2. Who won a Grammy award for Best New Artist in 1999?

3. Whom did Anthony Eden succeed as British Prime Minister?

4. In which country is the Simpson Desert?

5. On which surface is the French Open tennis championship played?

6. Which Irish poet had the initials W.B.?

7. Which Goodie 'Goes Wild'?

8. Which rugby team shared Queens Park Rangers' ground in 2001?

9. Phil Oakey is the singer with which band?

10. Who wrote *Chips with Everything*?

11. What bird can be yellow, grey or pied?

12. Who was Secretary General of the United Nations from 1972–81?

13. Woodcote is a corner on which Grand Prix Circuit?

14. Which sport was played to train cavalrymen in ancient Persia?

15. To which city was the capital of Portugal moved between 1807 and 1821 while the country was at war with France?

16. What was Rigsby's first name in *Rising Damp*?

Answers to page 482
GENERAL QUIZ 123: 1. Davis Cup 2. Cookery 3. Aurora 4. Librarian
5. *Casualty* 6. Trumpet 7. Kenny Everett 8. Perthshire 9. Ralph Fiennes
10. Port Vale 11. The Bay City Rollers 12. Graham Hill 13. *Porridge*
14. Harry Houdini 15. Inverness 16. On an economics chart

General Quiz 122

Answers on page 483

1. What does the Russian word 'glasnost' mean?

2. Whose funeral was the biggest British televised event in history?

3. Which comedian's 2001 autobiography was titled *Close to the Edge*?

4. Which Dutch electronics company launched the compact cassette in Britain?

5. What were introduced to supermarkets in 1974?

6. Which Premiership club chairman is nicknamed 'Deadly Doug'?

7. What is a balalaika?

8. Shaun Ryder fronted which Manchester band?

9. What was the catchphrase of Janice Nicholls on the TV pop show *Thank Your Lucky Stars*?

10. In which English county is Belper?

11. Brother and sister Richard and Karen made up which Seventies singing duo?

12. Who starred in the 1998 movie *The Truman Show*?

13. What is 6 June 1944 popularly known as?

14. Who wrote the controversial book *Spycatcher*?

15. Casper and Laramie are towns in which US state?

16. Who was the first Briton to fly in space?

Answers to page 483
GENERAL QUIZ 124: **1.** Springfield **2.** Owen Hargreaves **3.** *Sex and the City* **4.** Eminem **5.** 'Great' **6.** Supertramp **7.** Fred Astaire **8.** Victoria **9.** Pacific **10.** Spine **11.** Beverley **12.** Morris **13.** Jack Nicklaus **14.** Five **15.** Australia **16.** Crown

General Quiz 123

Answers on page 480

1. Which sporting contest was first played in 1900 for a trophy donated by Dwight Filley Davis?

2. What type of books did Elizabeth David write?

3. Who was the Roman goddess of the dawn?

4. In what job did Casanova spend the last 13 years of his life?

5. *Holby City* is a spin-off from which TV series?

6. What instrument did Dizzy Gillespie play?

7. Whose characters included Sid Snot and Gizzard Puke?

8. In which county of Scotland is Gleneagles golf course?

9. Who starred in *Strange Days* and *The English Patient*?

10. Which Football League club has a home ground in the town of Burslem?

11. The Longmuir brothers were members of which teenybop band?

12. Which British driver won his second Formula One World Championship in 1968?

13. Ives and Lukewarm were characters in which classic TV sitcom?

14. As whom did Erich Weiss find fame?

15. Which Scottish town is positioned at the head of the Moray Firth?

16. Where would you find a J-curve?

Answers to page 480
GENERAL QUIZ 121: **1.** Yul Brynner **2.** Lauryn Hill **3.** Sir Winston Churchill **4.** Australia **5.** Clay **6.** Yeats **7.** Bill Oddie **8.** Wasps **9.** Human League **10.** Arnold Wesker **11.** Wagtail **12.** Kurt Waldheim **13.** Silverstone **14.** Polo **15.** Rio de Janeiro **16.** Rupert

General Quiz 124

Answers on page 481

1. In which town do *The Simpsons* live?

2. Which German-based footballer played for England in 2001?

3. Which TV series set in New York stars Sarah Jessica Parker?

4. Which artist's real name is Marshall Mathers III?

5. What does the Russian 'bolshoi' mean, as in the Bolshoi Ballet?

6. Which Seventies band recorded the album 'Breakfast in America'?

7. Which Hollywood star was born Frederick Austerlitz?

8. Melbourne is the capital of which Australian state?

9. Oceania is the name for a group of islands in which ocean?

10. Where in the human body are the lumbar bones?

11. Which Yorkshire town was named after the number of beavers that once lived in the area?

12. Lord Nuffield was the driving force behind which English motor car?

13. Who was voted Golfer of the Century in 1988?

14. How many boroughs are there in New York City?

15. In which country is the Murrumbidgee river?

16. What can be the cap of a tooth or a coin worth 25p?

Answers to page 481
GENERAL QUIZ 122: **1.** 'Openness' **2.** Diana, Princess of Wales **3.** Jim Davidson **4.** Philips **5.** Bar codes **6.** Doug Ellis (Aston Villa) **7.** Russian musical instrument **8.** The Happy Mondays **9.** 'Oi'll give it foive' **10.** Derbyshire **11.** The Carpenters **12.** Jim Carrey **13.** D-Day **14.** Peter Wright **15.** Wyoming **16.** Helen Sharman

General Quiz 125

Answers on page 486

1. Who played Young Jolyon Forsyte in ITV's 2002 adaptation of *The Forsyte Saga*?

2. Which Tomb Raider won an Oscar for Best Supporting Actress in the film *Girl, Interrupted*?

3. Which motor-racing circuit has a corner called Bus Stop?

4. Which country was controlled by the fascist Iron Guard in the 1930s?

5. What is hyperbole?

6. In military terms, what is the opposite of a hawk?

7. What was Louis Balfour's favourite type of music in *The Fast Show*?

8. Where in Britain would you find Lewis with Harris?

9. What is the next prime number after 37?

10. In which country is the Snake river?

11. Which city in the world has the largest population?

12. Where was the Store Baet suspension bridge opened in 1997?

13. What is Australia's equivalent of the County Cricket Championship?

14. What animals are affected by scrapie?

15. Who was elected President of the NUM in 1981?

16. Joshua Reynolds was an English painter in which century?

Answers to page 486
GENERAL QUIZ 127: **1.** Donnie Wahlberg **2.** Eddystone **3.** Spain and USA
4. Shrews **5.** English parliament **6.** Kate Winslet **7.** European bison
8. Brazilian **9.** Abominable Snowman **10.** Boa **11.** Mr Micawber **12.** Margaret
Drabble **13.** A fish **14.** Cursor **15.** Croydon **16.** Claire King

General Quiz 126

Answers on page 487

1. Who won the first of his five Olympic gold medals in the coxed fours in 1984?

2. What was the first name of the French novelist Proust?

3. Which Pound was a US poet?

4. Which Irish athlete won a gold at 5,000 and 10,000 metres at the 1998 European Championships?

5. Which English artist exhibited a shark preserved in a tank of formaldehyde?

6. What is the collective noun for a group of crows?

7. Who wrote *The Madness of King George*?

8. Which residential district of west London was laid out in squares by Thomas Cubitt?

9. In which country is Arnhem Land?

10. In which city is the Ashton Gate football ground?

11. On which river is the Kariba Dam?

12. Which former *Neighbours* actor starred in the 2002 film *The Count of Monte Cristo*?

13. Which Formula One team was founded in 1966 by a New Zealand driver?

14. Oakland is linked by bridge to which Californian city?

15. Which journalist was editor of *Punch* from 1953–7?

16. What is the name of the loading mark painted on the hull of merchant ships?

Answers to page 487
GENERAL QUIZ 128: **1.** CAT scan **2.** Camp David **3.** Matt Biondi
4. Ramadan **5.** Oysters **6.** Congress of Vienna **7.** U2 **8.** Chile and Argentina
9. Swindon **10.** Red squirrel **11.** Ure **12.** Star Wars **13.** Russell Crowe
14. Personal identification number **15.** Lake **16.** Cello

General Quiz 127

Answers on page 484

1. Which member of the New Kids on the Block appeared in the 1999 movie *The Sixth Sense?*

2. Which lighthouse is situated 14 miles south of Plymouth?

3. Which two countries have mountain ranges called Sierra Nevada?

4. What can be pygmy, elephant or hero?

5. What was the Rump in the 17th century?

6. Which English film star made her debut in *Heavenly Creatures?*

7. A wisent is another name for which animal?

8. What nationality was racing driver Nelson Piquet?

9. What was supposedly first spotted in the Himalayas in 1832?

10. The anaconda is a species of which snake?

11. Which *David Copperfield* character is thought to be based on Dickens' own father?

12. Who wrote *The Millstone* and *The Gates of Ivory?*

13. What is a dory?

14. What symbol indicates the current entry position on a computer screen?

15. Fairfield Halls are in which London borough?

16. Which former *Emmerdale* actress stars in *Bad Girls?*

Answers to page 484
GENERAL QUIZ 125: **1.** Rupert Graves **2.** Angelina Jolie **3.** Spa **4.** Romania
5. Exaggeration **6.** Dove **7.** Jazz **8.** Outer Hebrides **9.** 41 **10.** USA **11.** Tokyo
12. Denmark **13.** Sheffield Shield **14.** Sheep and goats **15.** Arthur Scargill
16. 18th

General Quiz 128

Answers on page 485

1. What is a computerised axial tomography scan better known as?

2. What is the official country home of US Presidents?

3. Which American swimmer won eight Olympic gold medals between 1984 and 1992?

4. What is the name given to the month of Muslim fasting?

5. With which sea food is Whitstable associated?

6. Which Congress agreed the settlement of Europe after the Napoleonic Wars?

7. Which band released the 1991 album 'Achtung Baby'?

8. Which two countries own regions of Tierra del Fuego?

9. Diana Dors and Melinda Messenger both hailed from which town?

10. Which native British rodent has the Latin name *Sciurus*?

11. On which river does Ripon stand?

12. What was the popular name for Ronald Reagan's Strategic Defense Initiative?

13. Which actor played a former tobacco company executive who blew the whistle on the industry in the 1999 movie *The Insider*?

14. What does PIN stand for?

15. What kind of geographical feature is an oxbow?

16. What musical instrument does Julian Lloyd Webber play?

Answers to page 485
GENERAL QUIZ 126: 1. Steve Redgrave 2. Marcel 3. Ezra Pound 4. Sonia O'Sullivan 5. Damien Hirst 6. A murder 7. Alan Bennett 8. Belgravia 9. Australia 10. Bristol 11. Zambezi 12. Guy Pearce 13. McLaren 14. San Francisco 15. Malcom Muggeridge 16. Plimsoll line

General Quiz 129

Answers on page 490

1. Which river forms the boundary between New South Wales and Victoria?

2. Which quintessential British actor made his film debut as a Mexican in a *Hopalong Cassidy* movie?

3. Murcia is a region of which country?

4. Which former England football captain died in 1993?

5. What does the London tower Monument commemorate?

6. What don't Mercury and Venus have that all other planets do?

7. What instrument did Glenn Miller used to play?

8. Richard O'Sullivan and Tessa Wyatt starred on which Seventies sitcom?

9. Who earned his big break as Han Solo in *Star Wars*?

10. Which 45-year-old became the oldest boxer ever to win a world championship when he knocked out Michael Moorer in 1994?

11. Which Florida city is the oldest in the USA?

12. What feat did Richard Branson and Per Lindstrand accomplish in 1987?

13. Who got married in a Berlin air-raid shelter on 29 April 1945 and committed suicide together the next day?

14. Who was married to Olive in *On the Buses*?

15. Which US space shuttle exploded on take-off in 1986?

16. What is Tiger Woods' real first name?

Answers to page 490
GENERAL QUIZ 131: **1.** 1936 **2.** Three Wise Men **3.** Boris Becker **4.** George Formby **5.** *Auf Wiedersehen, Pet* **6.** Meryl Streep **7.** Riyal **8.** Egypt **9.** 'Redshirts' **10.** Catherine Morland **11.** Types of light bulb **12.** Coca-Cola **13.** Lucy Ewing **14.** LL Cool J **15.** Wiltshire **16.** The Birmingham Six

General Quiz 130

Answers on page 491

1. Who defeated Charles II at the Battle of Worcester in 1651?

2. Which Beatle nearly died at the age of six after his appendix burst?

3. Which American state forms the southern border of Missouri?

4. Which English county has its own parliament, the Stannary?

5. What was the maiden name of Australian tennis player Margaret Court?

6. Whose 1992 book was titled *Sex*?

7. Which impressionist made his debut on TV's *Junior Showtime*?

8. What does 'leprechaun' mean in old Irish?

9. On which river does Leicester stand?

10. What stage name was adopted by Lee Yuen Kam?

11. According to the Old Testament, which city's wall crumbled to the blast of Joshua's trumpets?

12. What was the name of the cross-eyed lion in *Daktari*?

13. On what date is the festival of Epiphany?

14. Which football club were later disqualified after winning the 1993 European Champions' Cup?

15. Whose funeral did Prince Philip controversially attend in 1989?

16. What was the name of the band in the TV series *Tutti Frutti*?

Answers to page 491
GENERAL QUIZ 132: **1.** Dundee United **2.** A chesterfield **3.** Bill Bryson **4.** Darren Gough **5.** Ted Bovis **6.** Adelaide **7.** 'Opposite feet' **8.** Jeffrey Archer **9.** Weasel **10.** Bob Carolgees **11.** Francis Bacon **12.** Michael Douglas **13.** John **14.** Wilkie Collins **15.** Monza **16.** Cape Town

General Quiz 131

Answers on page 488

1. In which year did George VI become King of England?

2. What are the Magi more generally known as?

3. Which unseeded player won the men's singles at Wimbledon in 1985?

4. Who sang about 'Mr Wu'?

5. Oz, Dennis and Moxey were characters in which TV series?

6. Who starred in Sophie's Choice, Out of Africa and Death Becomes Her?

7. What is the currency of Saudi Arabia?

8. Sinai is a peninsula in which country?

9. What nickname was given to the army assembled by Italian patriot Garibaldi?

10. Who is the heroine in Jane Austen's Northanger Abbey?

11. What are fluorescent and filament?

12. In 1985, which company had to re-introduce its old product when customers complained about the taste of the new one?

13. Who was nicknamed the 'Poison Dwarf' in Dallas?

14. Which rap artist starred in the 1999 movie Deep Blue Sea?

15. In which English county is Avebury?

16. Which sextet were released in 1991 after the Court of Appeal quashed their convictions?

Answers to page 488
GENERAL QUIZ 129: 1. Murray 2. David Niven 3. Spain 4. Bobby Moore 5. Great Fire of London 6. Moons 7. Trombone 8. Robin's Nest 9. Harrison Ford 10. George Foreman 11. St Augustine 12. The first transatlantic crossing by hot-air balloon 13. Hitler and Eva Braun 14. Arthur 15. Challenger 16. Eldrick

General Quiz 132

Answers on page 489

1. Which Scottish football club plays at Tannadice Park?

2. What can be a man's overcoat or a sofa?

3. Which American-born travel writer sent *Notes from a Small Island*?

4. Which England fast bowler is nicknamed 'Dazzler'?

5. Who did Paul Shane play in *Hi-De-Hi*?

6. Which Australian city is named after William IV's queen?

7. What does the Greek word 'antipodes' mean?

8. Who wrote *Not a Penny More, Not a Penny Less*?

9. The badger is a member of which family of animals?

10. Who appears on TV with a dog called Spit?

11. What name was shared by an English philosopher and an Irish painter?

12. Who won an Oscar for his portrayal of a tough businessman in the movie *Wall Street*?

13. What was the Christian name of Sherlock Holmes' companion Dr Watson?

14. Who wrote *The Woman in White*?

15. Which Grand Prix circuit features the Lesmo curves?

16. Which town is overlooked by Table Mountain?

Answers to page 489
GENERAL QUIZ 130: **1.** Oliver Cromwell **2.** Ringo Starr **3.** Arkansas
4. Cornwall **5.** Margaret Smith **6.** Madonna **7.** Joe Longthorne **8.** 'Small body'
9. Soar **10.** Bruce Lee **11.** Jericho **12.** Clarence **13.** 6 January **14.** Marseilles
15. Emperor Hirohito of Japan **16.** The Majestics

General Quiz 133

Answers on page 494

1. On which island is Ronaldsway airport?

2. Who was Gerald Ford's Vice-President?

3. At what age does a filly become a mare?

4. From which country are the band Midnight Oil?

5. What is the US equivalent of a post code?

6. Who directed *Lock, Stock and Two Smoking Barrels*?

7. In the NATO phonetic alphabet, which word represents the letter 'G'?

8. In *A Tale of Two Cities*, who was Sidney Carton's doppelganger?

9. Which bird was on the reverse side of the last farthing?

10. Who wrote *Brighton Rock* and *Monsignor Quixote*?

11. Who played Cruella de Vil in *101 Dalmatians*?

12. Who captained the British Lions rugby team on their triumphant tour to South Africa in 1974?

13. Which early film comedian was noted for his trademark horn-rimmed glasses and straw hat?

14. Llandrindod Wells is the administrative headquarters of which county?

15. In which ocean is the Sargasso Sea?

16. What name is given to the widow of a king?

Answers to page 494
GENERAL QUIZ 135: 1. Eight 2. Fish 3. A bird 4. Agent Cooper in *Twin Peaks* 5. One Thousand Guineas 6. 'Nasty Nigel' 7. Edinburgh 8. Jeroboam 9. Special Air Service 10. Elgin City and Peterhead 11. Jaw 12. Ruff 13. Paris 14. Giant panda 15. Alan Jones 16. Rubber plant

General Quiz 134

Answers on page 495

1. What is the equivalent of the Red Cross in Muslim countries?

2. In which country is Linate airport?

3. Mrs Danvers is the sinister housekeeper in which novel?

4. What did Trevor Chappell do in 1980 to prevent New Zealand winning a Test match against Australia?

5. Which zoo is situated north-east of Tamworth?

6. What is the name of Prince Edward's TV production company?

7. *Hamlet* was the prince of which country?

8. Who played Queen Elizabeth I in *Blackadder II* ?

9. The Heartbreakers backed which American singer?

10. Which Nightingale reads the ITV news?

11. St Peter Port is the capital of which of the Channel Islands?

12. Which British national newspaper folded in 1971?

13. Which minister earned the nickname 'Milk Snatcher' after abolishing free milk for schoolchildren?

14. Which African country's national coach was banned from football for life by the king after the team were eliminated from the 1998 World Cup qualifiers by Kenya?

15. What is the capital of Belarus?

16. Which movie directed by Robert Redford won the Oscar for Best Picture in 1980?

Answers to page 495
GENERAL QUIZ 136: **1.** The Eagles **2.** *One Man and His Dog* **3.** Dickie Bird **4.** All three were Hollywood actors born in Vancouver, Canada **5.** Woody Allen **6.** Sigourney Weaver **7.** 'Relax' **8.** George I **9.** Kentucky **10.** Felix **11.** Leicester City **12.** Lee Kuan Yew **13.** Australia **14.** Ray Stubbs **15.** China, Laos and Cambodia **16.** Saigon

General Quiz 135

Answers on page 492

1. How many legs do spiders have?

2. With which food is London's Billingsgate Market associated?

3. What is a spoonbill?

4. Which TV agent had a thing about cherry pie?

5. In horse racing, which of the Guineas is for fillies only?

6. What nickname did TV executive Nigel Lythgoe earn after his appearances as a judge on *Popstars*?

7. In which city is Murrayfield Stadium?

8. What name is given to a wine bottle four times the ordinary size?

9. In military parlance, what does SAS stand for?

10. Which two football clubs were elected to the Scottish League in 2000?

11. Whereabouts in the human body is the maxilla?

12. Which bird gets its name from the frill of feathers around the neck of the male?

13. Which European city is famous for its Latin quarter?

14. Which animal can eat almost 100lb of bamboo shoots in a single day?

15. Which Australian was Formula One World Champion in 1980?

16. Which house plant was the Latin name *Ficus elastica*?

Answers to page 492
GENERAL QUIZ 133: **1.** Isle of Man **2.** Nelson Rockefeller **3.** Four **4.** Australia **5.** Zip code **6.** Guy Ritchie **7.** Golf **8.** Charles Darnay **9.** Wren **10.** Graham Greene **11.** Glenn Close **12.** Willie John McBride **13.** Harold Lloyd **14.** Powys **15.** Atlantic **16.** Dowager

General Quiz 136

Answers on page 493

1. Don Henley is the drummer with which band?

2. Katy Cropper was the first woman to win which TV competition?

3. Which chirpy cricket umpire retired from the game in 1998?

4. What do Yvonne De Carlo, Michael J. Fox and Barbara Parkins have in common?

5. Who said of death: 'There is the fear that there is an afterlife but no one will know where it's being held'?

6. Which actress chose her first name from a character in the novel *The Great Gatsby*?

7. Which song shot to the top of the charts in 1984 after Radio 1 DJ Mike Read announced that he was refusing to play it because of its sexual content?

8. Which English king was known as 'The Turnip-Hoer'?

9. In which American state is Fort Knox?

10. Which cartoon cat was created by Pat Sullivan in 1919?

11. Peter Taylor managed which Premiership football club at the start of the 2001–2 season?

12. Who was Prime Minister of Singapore from 1959–90?

13. Wattle is the national flower of which country?

14. Which former Tranmere Rovers full-back is part of the BBC's soccer team?

15. Which three countries border Vietnam?

16. What was the former name of Ho Chi Minh City?

Answers to page 493
GENERAL QUIZ 134: **1.** The Red Crescent **2.** Italy **3.** *Rebecca* **4.** He bowled underarm along the ground **5.** Twycross **6.** Ardent **7.** Denmark **8.** Miranda Richardson **9.** Tom Petty **10.** Mary Nightingale **11.** Guernsey **12.** *Daily Sketch* **13.** Margaret Thatcher **14.** Algeria **15.** Minsk **16.** *Ordinary People*

General Quiz 137

Answers on page 498

1. Who laid out his BBC boss with a turkey?

2. What has 336 dimples?

3. What is a cupel used for?

4. Whose 2001 album was titled 'Fever'?

5. Jennifer Ehle is the daughter of which actress?

6. On which river does Newbury stand?

7. Which band's first hit was 'Pictures Of Matchstick Men'?

8. How many players are there on a basketball team?

9. Who was the original choice to play Frank Spencer?

10. Who was Britain's only Conservative Prime Minister between 1964 and 1979?

11. In which country is Odense?

12. Who was always coming up with 'cunning plans'?

13. Which actor's real name is Maurice Micklewhite?

14. Which African country was ruled by Idi Amin in the 1970s?

15. Which jockey beat cancer to win the 1981 Grand National on Aldaniti?

16. One of which composer's notebooks fetched £2.3 million in auction at Sotheby's in May 1987?

Answers to page 498
GENERAL QUIZ 139: **1.** Macy Gray **2.** Johnny Vaughan **3.** Talking Heads
4. Russia **5.** Wrestling **6.** New Zealand **7.** A large antelope **8.** Ice skating
9. Botany Bay **10.** Hellas **11.** Kenny Everett **12.** Medici **13.** Golf
14. Pickettywitch **15.** Sheffield **16.** Topper

General Quiz 138

Answers on page 499

1. What job did Ricky Tomlinson's Mike Bassett hold in a 2001 film?

2. What is the name for a female calf?

3. Which mallet-wielding TV presenter gave Chris Evans his big break?

4. In which year did Creedence Clearwater Revival have a UK number one hit with 'Bad Moon Rising'?

5. Bismarck is the capital of which American state?

6. What did former Manchester United goalkeeper Alex Stepney once do while shouting at a team-mate?

7. Keanu Reeves, Dennis Hopper and Sandra Bullock starred in which 1994 thriller movie?

8. Whereabouts in the human body is the lacrimal gland?

9. Helen Burns is a character in which Charlotte Brontë novel?

10. Which country marks the western border of Oman?

11. The Needles can be found on which island?

12. Who composed the opera *The Rake's Progress*?

13. Norman Greenbaum and Doctor and the Medics had UK number one hits at 16-year intervals with which song?

14. Which town in North Yorkshire is famous for its annual bed race?

15. Which artificial stimulant was banned from the World Worm-Charming Championships?

16. The treacherous Goodwin Sands are situated off the coast of which English county?

Answers to page 499
GENERAL QUIZ 140: **1.** Lucy Liu **2.** Truth **3.** Woodlouse **4.** Diving
5. Elephant **6.** Accrington, Barrow, Gateshead and Bradford Park Avenue
7. John Laurie (Frazer) **8.** Sirius (Dog Star) **9.** The Vatican **10.** Ten
11. Tenerife **12.** Honeybus **13.** Tennessee **14.** Yellow **15.** The Iron Age
16. Morocco

General Quiz 139

Answers on page 496

1. Which singer did Lord Snowdon call the rudest woman he'd ever photographed?

2. Which former *Big Breakfast* presenter was in something *'Orrible* in 2001?

3. Which US band on the road to nowhere were originally called The Artistics?

4. With what country was Berwick-upon-Tweed officially at war for 110 years until 1966?

5. At which sport could you fall victim to a flying mare or a half Nelson?

6. The Chatham Islands belong to which country?

7. What is a kudu?

8. Canada's Kurt Browning was a world champion at which sport?

9. Whereabouts in Australia did Captain Cook land in 1770?

10. What is the Greek name for Greece?

11. Whose TV characters included Mr Angry of Mayfair and Marcel Wave?

12. Which family ruled Florence from 1434 to 1737?

13. Of what sport is Sergio Garcia a leading exponent?

14. Which group had 'That Same Old Feeling' in 1970?

15. In which city is the Crucible Theatre, venue for the World Snooker Championships?

16. What was the name of Hopalong Cassidy's horse?

Answers to page 496
GENERAL QUIZ 137: 1. Alan Partridge 2. A golf ball 3. Assaying gold
4. Kylie Minogue 5. Rosemary Harris 6. River Kennet 7. Status Quo 8. Five
9. Norman Wisdom 10. Edward Heath 11. Denmark 12. Baldrick
13. Michael Caine 14. Uganda 15. Bob Champion 16. Mozart

General Quiz 140

Answers on page 497

1. Who plays Ling in *Ally McBeal* and Alex in *Charlie's Angels: The Movie*?

2. What does the name of the Russian newspaper *Pravda* mean?

3. Which common garden creature is really a crustacean?

4. At what sport does Greg Louganis participate?

5. What animal has a gestation period of 21 months?

6. Which four former Football League clubs played in the Unibond League Premier Division in 2001–2?

7. Which member of the *Dad's Army* cast was actually in the Home Guard during World War Two?

8. Which is the brightest star in the sky?

9. Where is the Sistine Chapel?

10. How many frames are there in a game of tenpin bowling?

11. Which is the largest of the Canary Islands?

12. Which band couldn't let Maggie go in 1968?

13. Nashville is the capital of which American state?

14. What colour are the flowers of a tansy?

15. What age followed the Bronze Age?

16. In which country is the port of Tangier?

Answers to page 497
GENERAL QUIZ 138: **1.** England football manager **2.** Heifer **3.** Timmy Mallett **4.** 1969 **5.** North Dakota **6.** Dislocated his jaw **7.** *Speed* **8.** The eye **9.** *Jane Eyre* **10.** Yemen **11.** Isle of Wight **12.** Stravinsky **13.** 'Spirit In The Sky' **14.** Knaresborough **15.** Washing-up liquid **16.** Kent

General Quiz 141

Answers on page 502

1. Which building on the river Jumna near Agra was constructed by 20,000 workmen?

2. Which actress starred in *There's Something About Mary* and *Being John Malkovich*?

3. What nationality is James Last?

4. What is special about the echidna and the duck-billed platypus?

5. Where did *Rosie and Jim* live?

6. Where would you find futtock plates?

7. Qantas is the national airline of which country?

8. Which French oceanographer commanded the boat *Calypso*?

9. Which Belgian tennis player got to the final of the Wimbledon ladies' singles in 2001?

10. Which actor, famous for playing a TV soap thug, was voted Rector of Glasgow University in 1999?

11. In which African country is the city of Constantine?

12. Who wrote *Hedda Gabler*?

13. Which Australian squash player won the British Women's Open title a record 16 years in succession from 1962–77?

14. Which Premiership football club plays at the Riverside Stadium?

15. Francisco Lopez was a 19th-century dictator of which South American country?

16. How many points is the letter 'X' worth in Scrabble?

Answers to page 502
GENERAL QUIZ 143: **1.** 64 **2.** Sigmund Freud **3.** Walton **4.** State Earnings-Related Pension Schemes **5.** Terry-Thomas **6.** Yo-yo **7.** It is the smallest house in Britain **8.** Botswana **9.** Millwall **10.** 1984 **11.** A musical instrument **12.** Swedish **13.** Preston Sturges **14.** Styx **15.** The Mediterranean **16.** Haircut 100

General Quiz 142

Answers on page 503

1. Birmingham Bullets and Leicester Riders are teams in which sport?

2. Shirley Manson is the singer with which band?

3. Which cricketer was dropped after flying a Tiger Moth during a match on the 1991 tour of Australia?

4. What is the name of the clown on *The Simpsons*?

5. Which country makes Nokia mobile phones?

6. Which animated children's TV series featured the Hemulen?

7. Which former chairman of British Rail is the namesake of *Spiderman*'s alter-ego?

8. Which is the oldest bridge across the River Seine in Paris?

9. What pen name was used by writer Eric Arthur Blair?

10. What does UNESCO stand for?

11. What is a sequoia?

12. Aurora borealis are otherwise known as what?

13. Who plays Waynetta Slob to Harry Enfield's Wayne?

14. What did Englishman Harry Brearley invent in 1913?

15. Which car manufacturing company was named after the ten-year-old daughter of Austrian financier and motor-racing enthusiast Emil Jellinek?

16. Which boxer was nicknamed 'The Louisville Lip'?

Answers to page 503
GENERAL QUIZ 144: **1.** Dodo **2.** Chaka Khan **3.** Newmarket **4.** South Pole **5.** The badger parade **6.** Honeysuckle **7.** Strand **8.** Italy **9.** East Sussex **10.** Duran Duran **11.** Kamikaze **12.** Mercury **13.** Lusaka **14.** Show-jumping **15.** Olive Oyl **16.** Cloud

General Quiz 143

Answers on page 500

1. How many squares are there on a draughts board?

2. Which Austrian physician pioneered the study of the unconscious mind?

3. Which Essex resort is 'on the Naze'?

4. Of what is SERPS an acronym?

5. On which British comedy actor was Basil Brush's voice based?

6. Which child's game was developed from a Filipino weapon?

7. What is special about a 19th-century fisherman's cottage on the quay at Conwy, North Wales?

8. Which country has the highest percentage of female heads of household in the world?

9. Who were the first Third Division club to reach the semi-finals of the FA Cup?

10. In which year did George Michael reach number one in the UK with 'Careless Whisper'?

11. What is a dulcimer?

12. What nationality was the playwright August Strindberg?

13. To what did US film director and writer Edmond Biden change his name?

14. In Greek mythology, which river surrounded the underworld?

15. Which sea did the Romans refer to as *mare nostrum*?

16. Which band sang about their 'Favourite Shirts' in 1981?

Answers to page 500
GENERAL QUIZ 141: **1.** Taj Mahal **2.** Cameron Diaz **3.** German **4.** They are the world's only egg-laying mammals **5.** On a canal boat **6.** On a ship **7.** Australia **8.** Jacques Cousteau **9.** Justine Henin **10.** Ross Kemp (Grant Mitchell) **11.** Algeria **12.** Henrik Ibsen **13.** Heather McKay **14.** Middlesbrough **15.** Paraguay **16.** Eight

General Quiz 144

Answers on page 501

1. Which extinct bird's name is Dutch for 'fat bum'?

2. Whose first UK hit was 'I'm Every Woman'?

3. On which racecourse is the One Thousand Guineas run?

4. What was Roald Amundsen the first person to reach?

5. Harry Hill was distraught to see which parade repeatedly cancelled?

6. What is another name for a woodbine when it grows in your garden?

7. According to the TV commercials, which cigarette were you never alone with?

8. Which footballing country won the 1982 World Cup?

9. In which English county is Ashdown Forest?

10. Which Eighties band released the album 'Seven And The Ragged Tiger'?

11. Which Japanese military word means 'divine wind'?

12. Hg is the chemical symbol for which element?

13. What is the capital of Zambia?

14. At which sport did Richard Meade represent his country?

15. Which damsel-in-distress has vital statistics of 19–19–19?

16. Cumulus and cirrus are types of what?

Answers to page 501
GENERAL QUIZ 142: 1. Basketball 2. Garbage 3. David Gower 4. Krusty
5. Finland 6. *The Moomins* 7. Peter Parker 8. Pont Neuf 9. George Orwell
10. United Nations Educational, Scientific, and Cultural Organisation
11. A redwood tree 12. The northern lights 13. Kathy Burke 14. Stainless
steel 15. Mercedes 16. Muhammad Ali

General Quiz 145

Answers on page 506

1. Where did Moses receive the Ten Commandments?

2. Whose 1983 album was titled 'Hearts And Bones'?

3. In which US state are the Black Hills?

4. Whose best-selling album was 'Jagged Little Pill'?

5. Which two actresses created *Upstairs Downstairs*?

6. Which is the nearest seaside resort to London?

7. In which country is Hockenheim motor racing circuit?

8. How many shillings were there in a guinea?

9. What squat sea bird has the Latin name *Fratercula arctica*?

10. Which sporting event was inspired by the exploits of Pheidippides?

11. What name was given to England's boundary areas with Wales and Scotland?

12. 'Logo' is derived from the Greek word for what?

13. What has been the official spoken language of China since 1917?

14. What is a runnel?

15. What is a unit for measuring the warmth of fabrics and clothes?

16. The House of Keys is part of the government of which island?

Answers to page 506
GENERAL QUIZ 147: **1.** Flounce **2.** *Last Orders* **3.** Bishop **4.** Mancunian
5. Slowly **6.** Swimming **7.** Frankie Abbott **8.** Brad Pitt **9.** Hawaii **10.** Danny
Boyle **11.** Martha and the Muffins **12.** Gig **13.** Coldplay **14.** Timothy West
15. Play it (it's a musical intrument) **16.** 28

General Quiz 146

Answers on page 507

1. What colour was Roy Orbison's Bayou?

2. Who was appointed manager of Coventry City FC in October 2001?

3. According to Blackadder, who had a brain the size of 'a weasel's wedding tackle'?

4. In what sport did Britain's Jason Queally win a gold medal at the 2000 Sydney Olympics?

5. Who was Noah's niggly wife in the children's TV series?

6. The North Foreland is a promontory in which county of England?

7. What are natives of Kazakhstan called?

8. What colour is umber?

9. What does a trichologist study?

10. For which international rugby team does Keith Wood play?

11. Which singer/songwriter had a hit in 2000 with 'Babylon'?

12. Who played TV cop *T. J. Hooker*?

13. What did officials at Ascot consider banning from the Royal Enclosure in 1971?

14. Which slender eating implements can be made from wood, plastic or ivory?

15. What are chitterlings?

16. Which 2001 film starred John Cleese and Woody Harrelson?

Answers to page 507
GENERAL QUIZ 148: 1. Scotland 2. Fraser River 3. German 4. Fair Isle
5. A millionth of a second 6. Behind your stomach 7. Esther Rantzen
8. Jamiroquai 9. Keanu Reeves 10. Stock, Aitken and Waterman
11. Weather forecast 12. H. E. Bates 13. South Africa 14. Campaign for Real
Ale 15. Spend it 16. Tony awards

General Quiz 147

Answers on page 504

1. What can be an expression of indignation or a deep frill on a dress?

2. Which 2001 film starred Michael Caine and Bob Hoskins as part of a gang of drinking buddies who scatter their friend's ashes off Margate Pier?

3. In chess, which piece can only move diagonally?

4. What is a native of Manchester called?

5. What does the musical term 'largo' mean?

6. At what sport did Britain's Judy Grinham win gold in the 1956 Olympics?

7. Who was 'mummy's little soldier' in *Please, Sir!*?

8. Who played Austrian mountaineer Heinrich Harrer in the 1997 movie *Seven Years in Tibet*?

9. Which island was the setting for *Magnum PI*?

10. Who directed *Trainspotting* and *The Beach*?

11. Which band longed to go to 'Echo Beach'?

12. What can be a two-wheeled horse-drawn carriage or a pop concert?

13. Which band recorded the album 'Parachutes'?

14. To whom is actress Prunella Scales married?

15. What would you do with a sackbut?

16. In the imperial system of weight, how many pounds are there in a quarter?

Answers to page 504
GENERAL QUIZ 145: **1.** Mount Sinai **2.** Paul Simon **3.** South Dakota **4.** Alanis Morissette **5.** Jean Marsh and Eileen Atkins **6.** Southend **7.** Germany **8.** 21 **9.** Puffin **10.** Marathon **11.** The Marches **12.** 'Word' **13.** Mandarin **14.** A small stream **15.** Tog **16.** Isle of Man

General Quiz 148

Answers on page 505

1. *Caledonia* was the Roman name for which country?

2. Vancouver stands at the mouth of which river?

3. What nationality were the original Vandals?

4. Which Shetland island gives its name to a type of knitting pattern?

5. How long is a microsecond?

6. Where does your pancreas lie?

7. Which TV presenter made her name on *Braden's Week*?

8. Who released the album 'Synkronized'?

9. Who starred in *The Matrix, Sweet November* and *Hardball*?

10. Mike, Matt and Pete were better known as which Eighties hitmakers?

11. What does Isobel Lang present on the BBC?

12. Who wrote *My Uncle Silas*?

13. In which country was golfer Retief Goosen born?

14. What does CAMRA stand for?

15. What would you do with a kina in Papua New Guinea?

16. Which US theatre awards are named after actress Antoinette Perry?

Answers to page 505
GENERAL QUIZ 146: **1.** Blue **2.** Roland Nilsson **3.** Prince Regent **4.** Cycling **5.** Nellie **6.** Kent **7.** Kazakhs **8.** Yellow/brown **9.** Hair **10.** Ireland **11.** David Gray **12.** William Shatner **13.** Hot pants **14.** Chopsticks **15.** Animal intestines, prepared as a food **16.** *Scorched*

General Quiz 149

Answers on page 510

1. What is the Italian dish zuppa inglese?

2. What type of animals did *ALF* most enjoy eating?

3. What colour is the leather on the seats in the House of Commons?

4. Which ship sank in the film *A Night to Remember?*

5. What action causes all your bodily functions to stop momentarily?

6. Which country produces the cheese Gaperon?

7. On this earth, what outnumber humans by approximately 100 million to one?

8. How long are baby kangaroos at birth?

9. What carnivores can smell humans up to 20 miles away?

10. Who released the best-selling UK album of 1999, 'Come On Over'?

11. The Road Hole is part of which championship golf course?

12. *Jason King* was a spin-off from which TV series?

13. In which country is Eindhoven?

14. Which mountain in Alaska was named after a former US President?

15. What is London's Central Criminal Court more commonly known as?

16. How many lines are there in a sonnet?

Answers to page 510
GENERAL QUIZ 151: **1.** The Andes **2.** Sebastian Coe **3.** Robert Maxwell **4.** Joy **5.** Marvin **6.** Mexico **7.** Pavement **8.** Nine **9.** Winston Churchill **10.** The little dog **11.** Five **12.** Australia **13.** 'Angel Of Harlem' **14.** Cardiff **15.** Badger **16.** Great grey slug

General Quiz 150

Answers on page 511

1. At which 2001 Grand Prix did Michael Schumacher secure his fourth Formula One World Drivers' Championship?

2. Which poet laureate wrote detective novels under the name Nicholas Blake?

3. What year followed 1BC?

4. What is the national anthem of Australia?

5. Where is the Old Man of Coniston?

6. Which puppet is known in Germany is Balduin Schwupp?

7. Which British boxing hero from the 2000 Sydney Olympics turned professional shortly afterwards?

8. Flashman was the school bully in which novel?

9. Which footballer teamed up with Lindisfarne for a 1990 re-make of 'Fog On The Tyne'?

10. In which country is the Po River?

11. Which actress was known as 'America's Sweetheart'?

12. What is Monday's child said to be?

13. Which Hollywood dancer was born Eugene Curran?

14. Ratabaga is another name for which vegetable?

15. In which century was the Book of Kells produced?

16. The capital of which country switched from Alma-Ata to Astana in 1997?

Answers to page 511
GENERAL QUIZ 152: **1.** Florida **2.** Giraffes **3.** Michelle Pfeiffer **4.** French **5.** Cordon bleu **6.** The Cure **7.** The Oaks **8.** Portugal **9.** Marlon Brando **10.** 1938 **11.** The Pony Express **12.** The Velvet Underground **13.** Gordon Strachan **14.** Skiffle **15.** Tobermory **16.** Regina

General Quiz 151

Answers on page 508

1. What is the second highest mountain range in the world?

2. Which British athlete took silver in the 800 metres and gold in the 1,500 metres at both the 1980 and 1984 Olympics?

3. Who bought the *Mirror* newspaper group in 1984?

4. What are you supposed to feel if you see two magpies?

5. Who was the Paranoid Android in *The Hitch-Hiker's Guide to the Galaxy*?

6. Which country's national emblem depicts an eagle on a cactus devouring a snake?

7. What do Americans call a 'sidewalk'?

8. An ennead is a set of how many?

9. Which former Prime Minister wrote the four-volume *History of the English-Speaking Peoples*?

10. In the nursery rhyme 'Hey Diddle Diddle', which animal laughed to see such fun?

11. How many pillars of Islam are there?

12. In which continent is the Great Dividing Range of mountains?

13. Which U2 song was a tribute to singer Billie Holiday?

14. Which city lies at the mouth of the River Taff?

15. On children's TV, who was Simon Bodger's puppet pet?

16. Which creature mates in mid-air, hanging from a rope of slime?

Answers to page 508
GENERAL QUIZ 149: **1.** Trifle **2.** Cats **3.** Green **4.** The *Titanic* **5.** Sneezing **6.** France **7.** Insects **8.** An inch **9.** Polar bears **10.** Shania Twain **11.** St Andrews **12.** *Department S* **13.** The Netherlands **14.** Mount McKinley **15.** Old Bailey **16.** 14

General Quiz 152

Answers on page 509

1. In which American state are the Everglades?

2. Which are the only animals born with horns?

3. Who spread herself across a piano in *The Fabulous Baker Boys*?

4. What nationality was the artist Degas?

5. What name indicating cookery of a high standard is also given to a dish made with ham and cheese and a white sauce?

6. Which band had a 1983 hit with 'The Love Cats'?

7. Which was run first – The Derby or The Oaks?

8. Braganza was the royal house of which European country from 1640–1910?

9. Which actor's portrayal of biker Johnny in *The Wild One* created a rebel image?

10. In which year was the Munich Agreement?

11. What system of mail-carrying by relays of horse-riders was employed in parts of the USA in the 19th century?

12. Of which influential band was Lou Reed a member before going solo?

13. Which football club manager left Coventry City after just a few weeks of the 2001–2 season?

14. Which music style was pioneered by Lonnie Donegan?

15. Which Womble wore a black bowler hat?

16. What is the state capital of the Canadian province of Saskatchewan?

Answers to page 509
GENERAL QUIZ 150: 1. Hungarian 2. Cecil Day-Lewis 3. AD 1 4. 'Advance Australia Fair' 5. In the Lake District 6. Basil Brush 7. Audley Harrison 8. *Tom Brown's Schooldays* 9. Paul Gascoigne 10. Italy 11. Mary Pickford 12. Fair of face 13. Gene Kelly 14. Swede 15. 8th 16. Kazakhstan

General Quiz 153

Answers on page 514

1. In which Charles Dickens novel does Estella appear?

2. Which jockey served a year in prison for tax evasion in 1987?

3. What is the collective noun for a group of geese in flight?

4. To what part of the body does the word 'phrenic' refer?

5. Who won the Oscar for Best Actor at the 2002 Academy Awards?

6. Who designed the Church of the Holy Family in Barcelona?

7. In which castle is St George's Chapel?

8. Which British racing driver retired from Formula One in 2000?

9. Who painted his mother in 1871?

10. What is vellum?

11. Which rock 'n' roller was the title of a 1995 hit for Weezer?

12. What was American Sally Ride's claim to fame in 1983?

13. Under what name did Archie Leach become famous?

14. In which sport do countries compete for the Swaythling Cup?

15. Which Football League team plays at the Bescot Stadium?

16. What links the mammal *Odobenus rosmarus* to The Beatles?

Answers to page 514
GENERAL QUIZ 155: **1.** Maxwell **2.** Dorset **3.** Diana Dors **4.** Tasman Sea
5. Portugal **6.** He was the first East German to play for the new unified
Germany **7.** Carol Vorderman **8.** Beetroot **9.** Mickey Mouse **10.** Earthquakes
11. 'Greenhouse effect' **12.** 144 **13.** *Macbeth* **14.** 'Blue' **15.** Seven
16. George V

General Quiz 154

Answers on page 515

1. To which member of the royal family was Bette Midler referring when she said: 'She loves nature in spite of what it did to her'?

2. Who recorded the album 'Tubular Bells'?

3. In which country is Lake Bala?

4. With which film studios was producer Michael Balcon associated?

5. At which castle did the investiture of the Prince of Wales take place?

6. Which ITV barrister first appeared in a BBC *Play for Today*?

7. What is the only native North American marsupial?

8. Which city stands at the mouth of the Hudson river?

9. Who was allegedly responsible for the Massacre of the Innocents?

10. What does RNLI stand for?

11. Who ran through the town in his nightgown?

12. Which bird gets its name from a quill-like protrusion of feathers behind its ear?

13. Which novel was based on the adventures of Alexander Selkirk?

14. As whom was Scottish outlaw Robert MacGregor known to friend and foe?

15. At which sport was Beryl Burton a national champion?

16. Which BBC horse-racing presenter played Statto in *Fantasy Football League*?

Answers to page 515
GENERAL QUIZ 156: 1. Harry Palmer 2. John Major 3. Chuck Berry
4. Georgia 5. Amazon 6. Nigel Bruce 7. Elephants 8. Sting 9. Minotaur
10. Alistair 11. Lake Eyre 12. Erle Stanley Gardner 13. Hippopotamus
14. Victor Hugo 15. Flower arranging 16. Lancashire

General Quiz 155

Answers on page 512

1. Who owned a silver hammer in a Beatles track?

2. Where in England would you find Wool?

3. Who became a screen sex symbol after changing her surname from Fluck?

4. What sea separates New Zealand and Australia?

5. If you sailed due east from New York, which land would you encounter next?

6. In what way was German international footballer Matthias Sammer a trailblazer in 1990?

7. Who showed her flair for figures by wearing a low-cut turquoise mini dress to the 2000 BAFTA Awards?

8. What is the main ingredient of borscht?

9. Which rodent made his debut in the 1928 film *Plane Crazy*?

10. What does a seismologist study?

11. Which environmental phrase was first coined by Swedish scientist Svante Arrhenius?

12. How many are there in a gross?

13. Which Shakespeare play opens with three witches?

14. Which colour provided a hit for Eiffel 65 in 1999?

15. How many times did Stephen Hendry win the World Snooker Championships in the 1990s?

16. Which English king married Mary of Teck?

Answers to page 512
GENERAL QUIZ 153: 1. *Great Expectations* 2. Lester Piggott 3. Skein
4. Diaphragm 5. Denzel Washington 6. Antonio Gaudi 7. Windsor Castle
8. Johnny Herbert 9. James Whistler 10. A type of parchment 11. 'Buddy Holly' 12. She was the first American woman in space 13. Cary Grant
14. Table tennis 15. Walsall 16. It's the Latin name for the walrus, as in The Beatles' song 'I Am The Walrus'

General Quiz 156

Answers on page 513

1. Which secret agent did Michael Caine play in *The Ipcress File*?

2. Which British Prime Minister's father was once a circus trapeze artist?

3. Which US rock star served two years in jail in 1962 for taking a girl across State borders for 'immoral purposes'?

4. In which country do 100 tetri make a lari?

5. Which river has some 1100 tributaries?

6. Who played Watson to Basil Rathbone's Sherlock Holmes?

7. What are the only mammals that can't jump?

8. What can a jellyfish still do when it's dead?

9. Which creature was said to be half bull, half man?

10. What was the name of Crystal Tipps' dog?

11. What is Australia's largest salt lake?

12. Who created Perry Mason?

13. Which animal takes its name from the Greek for 'river horse'?

14. Who wrote *Les Misérables*?

15. What is ikebana the Japanese art of?

16. The Forest of Bowland is in which English county?

Answers to page 513
GENERAL QUIZ 154: **1.** Princess Anne **2.** Mike Oldfield **3.** Wales **4.** Ealing **5.** Caernarvon **6.** *Rumpole of the Bailey* **7.** The opossum **8.** New York **9.** King Herod **10.** Royal National Lifeboat Institution **11.** Wee Willie Winkie **12.** Secretary bird **13.** *Robinson Crusoe* **14.** Rob Roy **15.** Cycling **16.** Angus Loughran

General Quiz 157

Answers on page 518

1. Which planet has a pink sky?

2. According to old British legend, with which knight did Queen Guinevere have an affair?

3. Which sport – played only in the USA – boasts a World Series?

4. In which mountain country do yak live?

5. Who was *Callan*'s smelly sidekick?

6. Which Righteous Brothers song was used in the 1990 film *Ghost*?

7. Which fashion designer co-owned a shop with Malcolm McLaren?

8. Which envoy to the Archbishop of Canterbury was kidnapped in Beirut in 1987?

9. What colour are the stripes on the flag of Uruguay?

10. What unwanted distinction did Manchester United's Kevin Moran achieve in the 1985 FA Cup Final?

11. Stewart Copeland was the drummer with which successful trio?

12. Who was the unseen doorman in the US sitcom *Rhoda*?

13. Which capital city's pride is a form of saxifrage?

14. The Battle of St Albans was the first round in which conflict?

15. What is a cricket umpire signalling when he raises both arms aloft?

16. What is a jarrah?

Answers to page 518
GENERAL QUIZ 159: **1.** Les Dawson **2.** Leader of the army **3.** Erasure **4.** Batley **5.** Rimsky-Korsakov **6.** Japan **7.** Scout **8.** 9th **9.** Plover **10.** Backstroke **11.** Leonardo DiCaprio **12.** Lord Reith **13.** Lt Uhura **14.** Penguin **15.** USSR **16.** Centigrade

General Quiz 158

Answers on page 519

1. Which bird features on the coat of arms of the state of Louisiana?

2. What colour is the circle on the Japanese national flag?

3. Which adjoining country forms Moldova's western border?

4. In which country is the birr the official currency?

5. Which king's appendix caused his coronation to be delayed for six weeks?

6. Which comedian presided over the Daz Doorstep Challenge?

7. What nationality was jockey Scobie Breasley?

8. Who was Queen of the Netherlands from 1948–80?

9. Which singer's biggest hit, 'Me And Bobby McGee', was not released until after her death?

10. Which Gertrude was a noted English landscape gardener?

11. Which novelist died from typhoid two months after drinking a glass of tap water in a Paris hotel to prove that it was safe?

12. Which insect can live for over a week with its head cut off?

13. Which writer disappeared following *The Murder of Roger Ackroyd*?

14. Which Football League team had to apologise to their local rivals in September 2001 after calling them 'Scum' on an electronic scoreboard?

15. What is 'indie' short for in music?

16. In which county is Stow-on-the-Wold?

Answers to page 519
GENERAL QUIZ 160: **1.** 'Buffalo Bill' **2.** 1950 **3.** East Sussex **4.** Small circular dishes **5.** Electrocardiogram **6.** Beth **7.** President de Gaulle **8.** West Indies **9.** Denis Howell **10.** Marlon Brando (*The Godfather*) **11.** Burgos **12.** Nose **13.** Fiji **14.** A ballet movement **15.** France **16.** The Ram Jam Band

General Quiz 159

Answers on page 516

1. Who preceded Lily Savage as host of *Blankety Blank?*

2. What does the Japanese word 'shogun' mean?

3. Who took their 'Abba-Esque' EP to number one in 1992?

4. Who were the first winners of the Rugby League Challenge Cup?

5. Who composed the opera *The Snow Maiden?*

6. In which country was actress Liv Ullmann born?

7. What was the name of Tonto's horse?

8. In which century did reindeer become extinct in the wild in the UK?

9. To which family of birds does the lapwing belong?

10. Which is the only swimming stroke not started by a dive?

11. Who starred opposite Claire Danes in the 1996 movie *Romeo & Juliet?*

12. Who was the first managing director of the BBC?

13. Who was head of communications on the starship *Enterprise?*

14. Which is the only bird that walks upright?

15. Who did West Germany beat in the semi-finals of the 1966 World Cup?

16. What is the Celsius temperature scale otherwise known as?

Answers to page 516
GENERAL QUIZ 157: **1.** Mars **2.** Sir Lancelot **3.** Baseball **4.** Tibet **5.** Lonely **6.** 'Unchained Melody' **7.** Vivienne Westwood **8.** Terry Waite **9.** Blue and white **10.** He was the first player to be sent off in an FA Cup Final **11.** The Police **12.** Carlton **13.** London (London pride) **14.** The Wars of the Roses **15.** A six **16.** A type of eucalyptus tree from Australia

General Quiz 160

Answers on page 517

1. What was William Frederick Cody's alter ego?

2. In which year was the Princess Royal born?

3. In which county might you come face to face with the Long Man of Wilmington?

4. What are ramekins?

5. What is ECG an abbreviation for?

6. What was Dr Glover's first name in *Peak Practice*?

7. *The Day of the Jackal* was a novel about the attempted assassination of which world leader?

8. Who won cricket's first World Cup?

9. Whose appointment as Minister for Drought in 1976 coincided with the sudden end to the summer-long heatwave?

10. Who refused to accept his Best Actor Oscar for 1972 in protest over the plight of American Indians?

11. In which city's cathedral is El Cid buried?

12. What did Cyrano de Bergerac have that was longer than most men's?

13. Viti Levu is the largest of which group of islands?

14. What is a fouetté?

15. Which nation's post-war constitution was known as the Fourth Republic?

16. Which band backed Geno Washington?

Answers to page 517
GENERAL QUIZ 158: **1.** Pelican **2.** Red **3.** Romania **4.** Ethiopia **5.** Edward VII **6.** Shane Richie **7.** Australian **8.** Juliana **9.** Janis Joplin **10.** Gertrude Jekyll **11.** Arnold Bennett **12.** Cockroach **13.** Agatha Christie **14.** Norwich City (apologised to Ipswich Town) **15.** Independent **16.** Gloucestershire

General Quiz 161

Answers on page 522

1. Which animal has no vocal cords?

2. Which actor who starred in *Edward Scissorhands* has a phobia about clowns?

3. Which are the only birds that can see the colour blue?

4. Which band had a 1982 hit with 'Abracadabra'?

5. Which world motor-racing champion was killed in a car crash on the Guildford by-pass in 1959?

6. Who is leader of the Staines Massive?

7. Which one-time resident of Gravesend was the subject of a 1995 Disney film?

8. On which gulf is the town of Sorrento?

9. Who had his own Velvet Opera?

10. What is the American term for grilling food?

11. Scrooge featured in which Dickens novel?

12. Which tea party was the topic of a 1976 song by The Sensational Alex Harvey Band?

13. Who was 'The It Girl'?

14. Of what colour is leukophobia a fear?

15. Which country's currency is the tenge?

16. What was the name of *Hector Heathcote*'s faithful dog?

Answers to page 522
GENERAL QUIZ 163: **1.** On the wing **2.** The Sorbonne **3.** *Roget's Thesaurus*
4. 38th parallel **5.** Ermintrude **6.** 1989–90 **7.** Right Said Fred **8.** Jethro Tull
9. Calvin Coolidge **10.** Conductor **11.** *Home and Away* **12.** Golf **13.** Karate
14. Rex Hunt **15.** A venomous snake **16.** Michael Jackson

General Quiz 162

Answers on page 523

1. What stretches from West Gansu to the Gulf of Liaodong?

2. Which bridge in eastern England was the longest in the world when it was completed in 1980?

3. The poisonous plant deadly nightshade belongs to the same family as which vegetable?

4. What is the name for a pregnant goldfish?

5. In which group of islands is Martinique?

6. What canal, spelled backwards, is the name of a Greek god?

7. What was Grace in her US sitcom?

8. What are the Christian names of tennis's Williams sisters?

9. Which English city has a Hoe and a Sound?

10. Which politician was labelled 'Attila the Hen'?

11. Who played Yosser Hughes in *Boys From the Blackstuff*?

12. What is 'Buzz' Aldrin's real first name?

13. What nationality was the author Hilaire Belloc?

14. What is campanology?

15. A sousaphone is a large bass version of which musical instrument?

16. Who was quite contrary?

Answers to page 523
GENERAL QUIZ 164: **1.** Sex **2.** Egg yolks and wine **3.** Cinderella
4. Aconcagua (in Argentina) **5.** Gobi Desert **6.** Barbara Taylor Bradford
7. Ice hockey **8.** Barton Street **9.** 16th **10.** William **11.** Nemesis **12.** 1996
13. David Essex **14.** Petra **15.** Louis Theroux **16.** Venice

General Quiz 163

Answers on page 520

1. Where do swifts mate?

2. What is the University of Paris commonly known as?

3. Which collection of synonyms was first published in 1852?

4. Along which line of latitude is the border between North and South Korea based?

5. What was the name of the cow in *The Magic Roundabout*?

6. In which season did Liverpool Football Club last win the League title?

7. Who were 'Deeply Dippy' in 1992?

8. Which 18th-century agriculturist was not living in the past when he wrote *Horse-Hoeing Husbandry*?

9. Which Calvin became US President in 1923?

10. What was Herbert von Karajan?

11. Which TV soap is set in Summer Bay?

12. Which sport does Lee Westwood play?

13. Which martial art takes its name from the Japanese for 'empty hand'?

14. Who was governor of the Falklands at the time of the Argentine invasion?

15. What was the speckled band in the Sherlock Holmes story of that title?

16. Whose 1987 album was 'Bad'?

Answers to page 520
GENERAL QUIZ 161: 1. Giraffe 2. Johnny Depp 3. Owls 4. The Steve Miller Band 5. Mike Hawthorn 6. Ali G 7. Pocahontas 8. Gulf of Salerno 9. Elmer Gantry 10. Broiling 11. *A Christmas Carol* 12. 'The Boston Tea Party' 13. Clara Bow 14. White 15. Kazakhstan 16. Winston

General Quiz 164

Answers on page 521

1. What do oysters change depending on the temperature of the water around them?

2. What are the two main ingredients of zabaglione?

3. Who was Anastasia and Drizella's stepsister?

4. What is the highest mountain outside Asia?

5. What is the second largest desert in the world?

6. Who wrote *A Woman of Substance* and *Hold the Dream*?

7. In which sport do teams compete for the Stanley Cup?

8. In *The Bill*, which is the nearest station to Sun Hill?

9. In which century did Ivan the Terrible reign?

10. Which boy's name is sweet when applied to a member of the *Dianthus* family?

11. For which organisation did *The Champions* work?

12. In which year was Damon Hill Formula One World Champion?

13. Who was 'Gonna Make You A Star' in 1974?

14. Who was the first *Blue Peter* pet?

15. Which TV presenter conducts *Weird Weekends*?

16. In which city is the Rialto bridge?

Answers to page 521
GENERAL QUIZ 162: **1.** Great Wall of China **2.** Humber Bridge **3.** The potato **4.** Twit **5.** West Indies **6.** Suez **7.** Under Fire **8.** Venus and Serena **9.** Plymouth **10.** Margaret Thatcher **11.** Bernard Hill **12.** Edwin **13.** English **14.** Bell-ringing **15.** Tuba **16.** Mary

General Quiz 165

Answers on page 526

1. Which singer decided 'Heaven Is A Place On Earth'?

2. In which year did Edmund Hillary and Sherpa Tensing climb to the summit of Mount Everest?

3. Which British athlete won gold in the 3,000 metres steeplechase at the 1956 Olympics?

4. Which *Cold Feet* actor starred as an undercover cop in 2001 in the BBC film *Murphy's Law*?

5. Which former Italian Prime Minister was murdered in 1978?

6. Which country was the first to take the America's Cup for yachting outside the United States?

7. Agatha Christie's novel *The Mysterious Affair at Styles* introduced which character?

8. In which country is Flushing?

9. Line back and quarterback are positions in which game?

10. Who played John Nash in the 2002 film *A Beautiful Mind*?

11. Which artist worked as a labourer on the building of the Panama Canal?

12. Which Indie band used to be called On A Friday?

13. What was the name of The Cisco Kid's horse?

14. Which singer turned down the chance to play a waiter in an episode of *Miami Vice*?

15. Which artist sold just one painting in his lifetime – *Red Vineyard at Arles*?

16. Which Geordie actor has the middle name Golightly?

Answers to page 526
GENERAL QUIZ 167: **1.** Providence **2.** Estonia **3.** Bob Hoskins **4.** Gulf of Mexico **5.** Midge Ure **6.** Andean condor **7.** Mrs Hudson **8.** Australian **9.** Triassic **10.** Portugal **11.** The Blue Flames **12.** Vietnam **13.** Tanzania **14.** Betty Hutton **15.** Gillingham **16.** Prague

General Quiz 166

Answers on page 527

1. Which two countries fought the War of Jenkins' Ear?

2. Who was Dr David Banner transformed into?

3. What colour is a giraffe's tongue?

4. Transylvania is a part of which country?

5. Which band had 'A Glass Of Champagne' in 1975?

6. Which UK entrant for the Eurovision Song Contest said afterwards that he would rather stick needles in his eyes than compete again?

7. Which landlord of the Queen Vic was murdered in 1991?

8. What is the largest island in Europe?

9. Which group of London writers and artists included Virginia Woolf and Lytton Strachey?

10. Which Frenchman crossed the Niagara Falls on a tightrope in 1859?

11. In which country are the Blue Mountains?

12. What was the fighting name of German aviator Manfred von Richthofen?

13. Who wrote *The Mayor of Casterbridge*?

14. What colour is the Circle Line on a London Underground map?

15. In which month is the Indianapolis 500 motor race run each year?

16. What mathematical aids were invented by John Napier?

Answers to page 527
GENERAL QUIZ 168: 1. 6–6 2. The owl and the pussycat 3. Bristol Rovers 4. Spring-Heeled Jack 5. Warren 6. Philip 7. Apicius published the first known volume of recipes, in AD 62 8. Mrs Peacock 9. Kuala Lumpur 10. The Aces 11. Holly Hunter 12. The Two Ronnies 13. *Madame Bovary* 14. Jamaica 15. The Corrs 16. A monkey

General Quiz 167

Answers on page 524

1. What is the state capital of Rhode Island?

2. In which nation's currency do 100 sents make a kroon?

3. Which Cockney actor who thought it was good to talk was actually born in rural Bury St Edmunds?

4. Into which sea does the Mississippi flow?

5. Which Scot was the lead singer with Ultravox?

6. Which is the largest bird of prey in the world?

7. What was the name of Sherlock Holmes' housekeeper?

8. What nationality is golfer Steve Elkington?

9. In the geological time scale, which period preceded the Jurassic?

10. Which country owns Madeira?

11. Who were Georgie Fame's backing band?

12. Which nation's flag consists of a gold star on a red background?

13. Dodoma is the capital of which African country?

14. Which Hollywood actress was known as 'The Blonde Bombshell'?

15. Which Football League club plays at Priestfield Stadium?

16. Which is further north – Paris, Stuttgart or Prague?

Answers to page 524
GENERAL QUIZ 165: **1.** Belinda Carlisle **2.** 1953 **3.** Chris Brasher **4.** James Nesbitt **5.** Aldo Moro **6.** Australia **7.** Hercule Poirot **8.** The Netherlands **9.** American football **10.** Russell Crowe **11.** Paul Gauguin **12.** Radiohead **13.** Diablo **14.** George Michael **15.** Vincent van Gogh **16.** Robson Green

General Quiz 168

Answers on page 525

1. At what score does a tie-break come into force in tennis?

2. Who went to sea in a beautiful pea-green boat?

3. Which Football League club were once called the Black Arabs?

4. Which legend of Victorian London was famed for his ability to breathe fire and jump great heights?

5. Who was the Welsh housemate in *This Life*?

6. Which boy's name means 'fond of horses'?

7. What connects the Roman Apicius and Delia Smith?

8. Which Cluedo suspect is known as Dona Violeta in Brazil?

9. The name of which eastern city means 'muddy estuary'?

10. Which band backed Desmond Dekker?

11. Who won a Best Actress Academy Award in 1993 for her role in *The Piano*?

12. Which comedy duo starred on TV in *The Picnic*?

13. Which novel by Gustave Flaubert caused a stir over its tale of a country doctor's wife being driven to suicide by a string of affairs?

14. Michael Manley was Prime Minister of which Caribbean country?

15. Whose 1999 album was titled 'Talk On Corners'?

16. What is a mangabey?

Answers to page 525
GENERAL QUIZ 166: **1.** Britain and Spain **2.** *The Incredible Hulk* **3.** Blue **4.** Romania **5.** Sailor **6.** Michael Ball **7.** Eddie Royle **8.** Britain **9.** The Bloomsbury Group **10.** Charles Blondin **11.** Australia **12.** 'The Red Baron' **13.** Thomas Hardy **14.** Yellow **15.** May **16.** Logarithms

General Quiz 169

Answers on page 530

1. Which work of art was originally bought by King Francis I of France to hang in his bathroom?

2. Who put in his thumb and pulled out a plum and said 'what a good boy am I'?

3. What fraction of Finland is within the Arctic Circle?

4. Which actor quit the movie *10* early in filming, enabling Dudley Moore to make his Hollywood breakthrough?

5. In which country is the Ormeli waterfall?

6. Which first permanent British settlement in North America was named after the king of the time?

7. The knesset is which country's parliament?

8. Who was the quack doctor in *The Fall and Rise of Reginald Perrin*?

9. Which Ruby was the winning jockey in the 2000 Grand National?

10. Who commanded the *Bounty*?

11. What is the Koh-i-noor?

12. Which singer was known as the 'Big O'?

13. Which magazine was founded by DeWitt Wallace in 1922?

14. Which Middlesex and England cricketer was the face of Brylcreem in the early Fifties?

15. Which TV cop's sidekick was Bobby Crocker?

16. Which American state is known as the 'Tar Heel State'?

Answers to page 530
GENERAL QUIZ 171: **1.** Jelly **2.** London and Paris **3.** Canada **4.** Henry Rider Haggard **5.** Mike Hailwood **6.** Chicago **7.** Spring equinox **8.** Brandy **9.** Australia **10.** August (*Dan August*) **11.** Chester **12.** Pat Garrett **13.** Graham McPherson **14.** Michael York **15.** The Bluetones **16.** *Gladiators*

General Quiz 170

Answers on page 531

1. Who did Prince Rainier of Monaco marry in 1956?

2. In which African country is the port of Mombasa?

3. From which country did Iceland achieve total independence in 1944?

4. Which radio programme celebrated its 60th anniversary in 2002?

5. Who were the first London club to win the Football League Championship?

6. Which is the highest capital city in the world?

7. What duck is a fish?

8. Who is *Emmerdale*'s lesbian vet?

9. Who painted *The Blue Boy*?

10. Which county cricket team have played at Sophia Gardens?

11. In which southern hemisphere country are the Southern Alps?

12. The daddy-longlegs is the popular name for which insect?

13. What is the national flower of Wales?

14. Which *Dad's Army* actor was married to Hattie Jacques?

15. Which fastening product takes its name from 'velvet' and 'crochet'?

16. As whom is guitarist Dave Evans better known?

Answers to page 531
GENERAL QUIZ 172: 1. Arkle 2. Jan Hammer 3. *Raging Bull* 4. Doncaster 5. Ann Sheridan 6. James II 7. Tennessee Williams 8. Wisconsin 9. Yellow River 10. Iceland 11. Little Miss Muffet 12. Medicine Woman 13. Morocco 14. The Pet Shop Boys 15. Union Berlin 16. St Mary Mead

General Quiz 171

Answers on page 528

1. What is the American name for jam?

2. In 1919, which two cities were linked by the world's first air service?

3. In which country is the Great Slave Lake?

4. Which Rider was an English novelist?

5. Which Englishman won nine world motorcycling titles between 1961 and 1967?

6. In which American city did house music originate?

7. What used to take place in Aries but has now moved into Pisces?

8. Armagnac is a type of which spirit?

9. Off which country's northern coastline is the Gulf of Carpentaria?

10. What month of the year shared its name with a TV detective played by Burt Reynolds?

11. Which English racecourse is situated on the Roodee?

12. Who shot Billy the Kid?

13. What is Suggs' real name?

14. Which British actor began as Michael Johnson until taking his stage name from a brand of cigarettes?

15. Which band's 1996 album was 'Expecting To Fly'?

16. Warrior, Trojan and Lightning all featured on which TV contest?

Answers to page 528
GENERAL QUIZ 169: 1. *Mona Lisa* 2. Little Jack Horner 3. One third
4. George Segal 5. Norway 6. Jamestown 7. Israel 8. Doc Morrissey 9. Ruby
Walsh 10. Captain Bligh 11. A diamond 12. Roy Orbison 13. *Reader's Digest*
14. Denis Compton 15. *Kojak* 16. North Carolina

General Quiz 172

Answers on page 529

1. Which horse won a third Cheltenham Gold Cup in 1966?

2. Who wrote the theme music to *Miami Vice*?

3. For which movie did Robert de Niro win a Best Actor Oscar in 1980?

4. On which racecourse is the Lincoln run?

5. Who was Hollywood's 'Oomph Girl'?

6. Which King of England succeeded Charles II?

7. Who wrote *A Streetcar Named Desire*?

8. Milwaukee, Green Bay and Racine are towns in which American state?

9. What is China's Huang He river otherwise known as in the west?

10. The Westman Islands are situated off the coast of which country?

11. Who was eating curds and whey when disturbed by an arachnid?

12. What was Dr Quinn in the title of her TV series?

13. MA is the vehicle index mark for which country?

14. Who had a 1987 UK number one with 'It's A Sin'?

15. Which amateur soccer team reached the 2001 German Cup final?

16. In which village did Miss Marple live?

Answers to page 529
GENERAL QUIZ 170: **1.** Grace Kelly **2.** Kenya **3.** Denmark **4.** Desert Island Discs **5.** Arsenal (1931) **6.** La Paz **7.** Bombay duck **8.** Zoë Tate **9.** Thomas Gainsborough **10.** Glamorgan **11.** New Zealand **12.** Crane fly **13.** Daffodil **14.** John Le Mesurier **15.** Velcro **16.** The Edge

TV

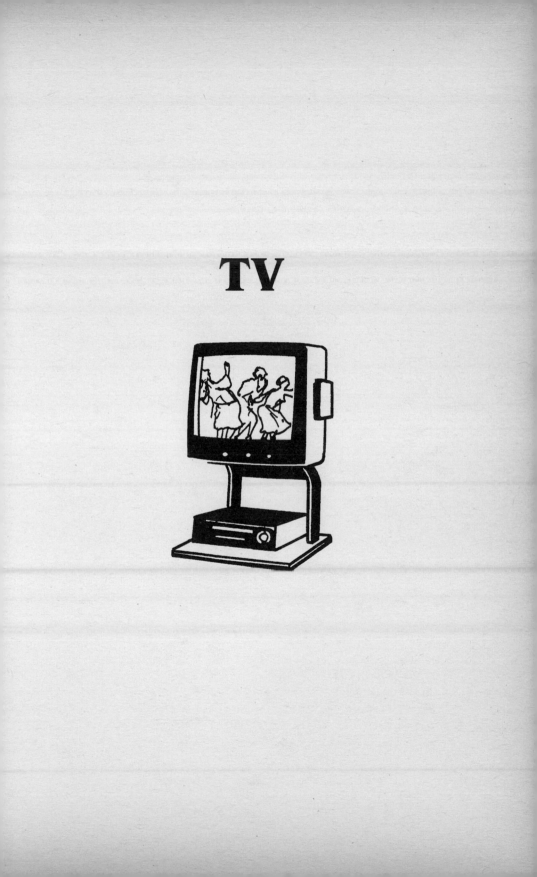

Cop Shows 1

Answers on page 536

1. Which police detective was played by Pauline Quirke?

2. Who created *Dixon of Dock Green*?

3. After what product did Maddie Hayes re-name her business the Blue Moon Detective Agency?

4. Who played *Matt Houston*?

5. Lt Samuels was boss to which detective duo?

6. Which racetrack tout was the chief informant in *77 Sunset Strip*?

7. What was 'Fancy' Smith's real name in *Z Cars*?

8. DCS John Kingdom was the mainstay of which Seventies police series?

9. Which future *Hi-De-Hi!* star played DS Smith's wife Betty in *Hunter's Walk*?

10. What was the name of the Assistant DA on *Hill Street Blues*?

11. Who replaced Ray Vecchio as Fraser's partner in *Due South*?

12. Who starred as *The Expert*?

13. Whose policeman husband was murdered in the opening episode of *The Gentle Touch*?

14. What was Dempsey's Christian name in *Dempsey and Makepeace*?

15. Which cop-playing actress always had to be seen at the wheel of a stationary police car because she couldn't drive?

16. In which cop series did Farrah Fawcett make her TV debut?

Answers to page 536
CHILDREN'S TV 1: **1.** Pink and white striped **2.** Orange **3.** *Pipkins*
4. Elephant **5.** Henry the janitor **6.** Oscar **7.** Hadji **8.** Winston **9.** Amanda Barrie **10.** The Penguin **11.** Mr Crockett **12.** Peter **13.** *Postman Pat*
14. Commissioner Gordon **15.** Perry Masonry **16.** Sam

Sport 1

Answers on page 537

1. Which former Scottish international footballer is a studio expert on ITV's *The Premiership*?

2. Which Virgin Radio DJ presents ITV's snooker coverage?

3. Who goes to the Boot Room as part of Sky's soccer coverage?

4. Which Walley used to be a BBC soccer commentator?

5. James Allen is an ITV commentator on which sport?

6. Which sports programme obtained a scoop by televising the world's first four-minute mile in 1954?

7. Which judo champion won *The Superstars* in 1978 and 1979?

8. But which Rugby League player seized *The Superstars* title in 1980?

9. Which year's FA Cup final was the first to be televised in full?

10. Which 1964 event produced the first action replay?

11. Which commentator said of the 1952 Boat Race: 'It's a desperately close race. I don't know who's in front, it's either Oxford or Cambridge'?

12. Who was the BBC's whispering voice of snooker?

13. On which sport did Des Lynam specialise as a radio commentator?

14. Who switched from the BBC to ITV in 1964 to front *World Of Sport*?

15. Who retired as a BBC commentator in May 1981 at the age of 74?

16. Which year's British Open golf championship was the first to be televised live?

Answers to page 537
POT LUCK 1: **1.** Sri Lanka **2.** Michael Palin **3.** Sarah Greene **4.** Jimmy Savile **5.** Noele Gordon **6.** Arthur Billett **7.** Do It Yourself **8.** Cliff Michelmore **9.** Jeremy Beadle **10.** *Grandad* **11.** French and Saunders **12.** Irene Handl **13.** Pauline **14.** Steve Owen (Martin Kemp) **15.** Nick Ross and Lynn Faulds Wood **16.** Doc Cox

Children's TV 1

Answers on page 534

1. What colour was *Bagpuss*?

2. What colour were the Froglets in *Clangers*?

3. Hartley Hare, Tortoise and Topov the monkey were all regulars on which show?

4. What kind of animal was Mumfie?

5. Who was transformed into ace detective Hong Kong Phooey?

6. Who was Astronut's Earth pal?

7. Which little Indian boy accompanied Jonny Quest on his adventures?

8. What was the name of *Hector Heathcote*'s faithful dog?

9. Who presented *Hickory House* before moving to Weatherfield?

10. Which *Batman* villain was played by Burgess Meredith?

11. Who ran the garage in *Camberwick Green*?

12. What was 'Tucker' Jenkins's real name?

13. PC Selby was the constable in which series?

14. Who was Gotham City's Police Commissioner?

15. Which crack TV barrister appeared in *The Flintstones*?

16. Which hired hand helped Daddy Woodentop?

Answers to page 534
COP SHOWS 1: 1. *Maisie Raine* 2. Ted Willis 3. Blue Moon shampoo 4. Lee Horsley 5. *Cagney and Lacey* 6. Roscoe 7. William 8. *New Scotland Yard* 9. Ruth Madoc 10. Irwin Bernstein 11. Stanley Kowalski 12. Marius Goring 13. Maggie Forbes 14. James 15. Jill Gascoine (*The Gentle Touch*) 16. *Harry O*

Pot Luck 1

Answers on page 535

1. From which island did Arthur C. Clarke introduce his *Mysterious World*?

2. Which traveller undertook a *Hemingway Adventure* in 1999?

3. Which former *Blue Peter* presenter hosted the fashion show *Posh Frocks and New Trousers*?

4. Who first fixed it in 1975?

5. Which ex-*Crossroads* star presented the admag *Homes and Gardens*?

6. Which 78-year-old was sacked from *Gardeners' World* for being too old?

7. W.P. Matthew was the first TV expert in which field?

8. Who presented *So You Think You Can Drive* in 1965?

9. Which *Game For a Laugh* host insisted that *People Do the Funniest Things*?

10. As what was Charlie Quick better known on children's TV?

11. Which comedy duo starred in *Let Them Eat Cake*?

12. Who played Granny in *Metal Mickey*?

13. Who is the sadistic careers adviser in *The League of Gentlemen*?

14. Which EastEnders character died in a dramatic car explosion in 2002?

15. Who were the original presenters of *Watchdog*?

16. Which Doc was a presenter on *That's Life*?

Answers to page 535
SPORT 1: **1.** Ally McCoist **2.** Russ Williams **3.** Andy Gray **4.** Walley Barnes **5.** Motor racing **6.** *Sportsview* **7.** Brian Jacks **8.** Keith Fielding **9.** 1938 **10.** The Grand National **11.** John Snagge **12.** Ted Lowe **13.** Boxing **14.** Eamonn Andrews **15.** Eddie Waring **16.** 1955

Comedy 1

Answers on page 540

1. What was the name of the girls' landlady in *Girls on Top*?

2. Which show featured the 'Fork Handles' sketch?

3. Which river-based sitcom starred Nigel Davenport and Sheila White?

4. Which medical prodigy was played by Neil Patrick Harris?

5. Which of the Pythons presented the menacing game show 'Blackmail'?

6. What was the name of Jeffrey Fourmile's wife in *George and Mildred*?

7. Who played Bill Macgregor in *Second Thoughts*?

8. What was Elaine's job in *Seinfeld*?

9. Who was the Jim in *The Seven Faces of Jim*?

10. Which group of comedians starred in *A Show Called Fred*?

11. Who was bed-ridden in *'Allo 'Allo*?

12. And what were the names of the two upper-class British Flying Officers in *'Allo 'Allo*?

13. Who played *Mr Aitch* in 1967?

14. Who wrote *Open All Hours*?

15. Which hypochondriac was played by Peter Bowles in *Only When I Laugh*?

16. Which double act starred in an *Imaginatively-Titled Show* in 1994?

Answers to page 540
WILDLIFE 1: **1.** *The Waltons* **2.** Vienna **3.** The Andes **4.** French **5.** Chris Kelly **6.** James Fisher **7.** Slimbridge **8.** 1969 **9.** Anglia **10.** Gerald and Lee Durrell **11.** *Bellamy on Botany* **12.** London Zoo **13.** *Life in the Freezer* **14.** Duke **15.** *The Range Rider* **16.** Wombat

Corrie 1

Answers on page 541

1. Which potman doubled as Bet Lynch's chauffeur?

2. Who first converted the corner shop into a mini market?

3. Who left for Zaire after marrying reformed alcoholic Ron Cooke?

4. Which ex-con called Minnie Caldwell 'Ma'?

5. Which scheming Rovers barmaid was played by Eva Pope?

6. What was the name of the Rovers' biker chick barmaid?

7. With which cosmetics company did Elsie Tanner take a job as a rep in 1970?

8. Who shopped Mike Baldwin for drink driving in 1988?

9. Who moved in with Rita Fairclough at No. 7 in 1987?

10. Which teenage rebel followed pop star Brett Falcon to London and joined a hippie commune?

11. What is the name of Steve McDonald's brother?

12. Who was the teetotal, lay-preacher boss of Gamma Garments?

13. What did Sean Skinner do for a living?

14. Who took in Henry Wakefield as a lodger following the death of her husband?

15. How much compensation did Alf Roberts receive for injuries sustained when a timber lorry ploughed into the Rovers Snug?

16. Which of Sally Webster's lovers later held her and the girls hostage?

Answers to page 541
DRAMAS 1: 1. *The Girl From UNCLE* 2. *Heart and Home* 3. Russ Abbot
4. *A Sense of Guilt* 5. Dill 6. *Lytton's Diary* 7. *The Life and Loves of a She Devil* 8. Nigel Davenport 9. Avril 10. Kate Butler 11. Mike Bullen
12. *Reckless* 13. Maggie 14. *Ballykissangel* 15. Michael Elphick 16. *Mission Impossible*

Wildlife 1

Answers on page 538

1. Which TV family had a dog called Reckless?

2. What was the name of Rigsby's cat in *Rising Damp*?

3. In which part of the world did Armand Denis propose to Michaela?

4. What nationality was Jacques Cousteau?

5. Who succeeded Desmond Morris as presenter of *Zoo Time*?

6. Who presented *News From the Zoos* in the 1960s?

7. From which Gloucestershire wildfowl trust did Peter Scott introduce countless editions of *Look*?

8. Which year saw the last edition of *Look*?

9. Which ITV company is associated with *Survival*?

10. Which husband and wife team presented *The Amateur Naturalist*?

11. What was the title of David Bellamy's first TV series?

12. Which zoo sponsored *Zoo Quest*?

13. Which David Attenborough series visited Antarctica?

14. What was the name of Jed Clampett's dog in *The Beverly Hillbillies*?

15. Which Western hero owned a horse called Rawhide?

16. What kind of animal wee'd on Liza Goddard during an episode of *Skippy the Bush Kangaroo*?

Answers to page 538
COMEDY 1: 1. Lady Carlton 2. *The Two Ronnies* 3. *Don't Rock the Boat*
4. *Doogie Howser, MD* 5. Michael Palin 6. Ann 7. James Bolam
8. Publishing editor 9. Jimmy Edwards 10. The Goons 11. Edith's mother
Fanny 12. Fairfax and Carstairs 13. Harry H Corbett 14. Roy Clarke
15. Archie Glover 16. Punt & Dennis

Dramas 1

Answers on page 539

1. What was April Dancer better known as?

2. For which fictitious magazine did *Kate* work?

3. Which comedian went straight in *September Song*?

4. Which raunchy Andrea Newman series was described by *Radio Times* as having 'more pairing than Noah's Ark'?

5. What was Tinker's surname in *Lovejoy*?

6. What did Peter Bowles pen for the *Daily News* in 1985?

7. Which Fay Weldon series spawned a 1989 film starring Roseanne Barr?

8. Who played King George III in *Prince Regent*?

9. What was the name of Jack Rolfe's daughter in *Howard's Way*?

10. Who did Lesley Vickerage play in *Soldier, Soldier*?

11. Who created *Cold Feet*?

12. What were Robson Green and Francesca Annis in the title of a medical drama?

13. Who runs the mess room kitchen in *London's Burning*?

14. Father Aidan O'Connell was the new priest in which village?

15. Who played news agency boss Harry Salter in *Harry*?

16. Jim Phelps tackled cases of International intrigue in which US series?

Answers to page 539
CORRIE 1: **1.** Fred Gee **2.** Alf Roberts **3.** Maggie Clegg **4.** Jed Stone **5.** Tanya Pooley **6.** Samantha Failsworth **7.** Charm Cosmetics **8.** Ida Clough **9.** Alan Bradley **10.** Lucille Hewitt **11.** Andy **12.** Leonard Swindley **13.** Bookmaker **14.** Hilda Ogden **15.** £800 **16.** Greg Kelly

EastEnders 1

Answers on page 544

1. Which vicar lusted after Kathy Mitchell?

2. Who was shot when Dougie Briggs laid siege to the Vic?

3. Who fell pregnant to Conor Flaherty?

4. Which family had a member called Kofi?

5. To whom did Annie Palmer sell her shares in the Health Club?

6. Who spent four months in jail after running over and killing a girl on Christmas Eve 1992?

7. Who died of a pulmonary embolism while giving birth?

8. How many husbands has Pat Evans had?

9. On which TV game show did Arthur Fowler once appear?

10. Who gave Lofty guitar lessons in 1988?

11. Who got Phil Mitchell to burn down the car lot so that he could claim on the insurance?

12. In which public building did Beppe di Marco end his relationship with Sam Mitchell?

13. To whom did Jamie Mitchell lose his virginity?

14. Who did Ian Beale marry in 2001?

15. Who played Tony Hills?

16. Who stole Arthur Fowler's prize leeks in 1986?

Answers to page 544
QUIZ AND GAME SHOWS 1: **1.** *Naked Jungle* **2.** Channel 5
3. Amanda Barrie **4.** Frank Bruno **5.** Leslie Grantham **6.** Gillian Taylforth
7. *What's My Line?* **8.** *3-2-1* **9.** *The Desert Forges* **10.** Holland **11.** Anthea
Turner **12.** 100 **13.** Robert Fabian **14.** *Call My Bluff* **15.** Yorkshire
Television

Pot Luck 2

Answers on page 545

1. What does *CSI* stand for in the title of an imported Channel 5 drama series?

2. Which Irish politician did Trevor Eve play in a drama series co-starring Francesca Annis?

3. Which rock musician and husband of Caroline Aherne led the studio band on *The Mrs Merton Show*?

4. Actress Belinda Lang is the daughter of which Fifties quiz show host?

5. *Relative Strangers* was a spin-off from which sitcom?

6. What was the prize for winning *Survivor*?

7. Which children's animation, made in 1971, has been repeated every year since, making it the second longest-running on TV?

8. Who was the accident-prone soul food specialist in *Chef!*?

9. Which TV presenter is the brother of radio broadcaster Janice Long?

10. Who played the odious David Brent in *The Office*?

11. Which former *ER* regular returned to the series in 2002?

12. Which *Hi-De-Hi!* actor died in 1996 in his mid forties?

13. Whose first straight role was that of game show host *Bob Martin*?

14. Who starred as *The Baron*?

15. What was Florence Macarthy Knox generally known as in *The Irish RM*?

16. What was René's codename in *'Allo 'Allo*?

Answers to page 545
COP SHOWS 2: **1.** Richard 'Cheech' Marin **2.** Agnes **3.** *Man in a Suitcase* **4.** Barrington Pheloung **5.** Wee Jock **6.** George Cross **7.** Mickey Dolenz **8.** Bobby Simone **9.** Tony Clark (*Between the Lines*) **10.** Toronto **11.** Meldrick **12.** *Millennium* **13.** *Picket Fences* **14.** Paul Riley **15.** Harry Morgan **16.** Derek Thompson

Quiz & Game Shows 1

Answers on page 542

1. In which naturists' game show did Keith Chegwin appear nude in 2000?

2. And on which channel was the controversial series shown?

3. Which former *Coronation Street* actress was once a hostess on *Double Your Money*?

4. Which boxing personality was one of the presenters in the revival of *It's a Knockout*?

5. Which ex-*EastEnder* co-presents *Fort Boyard*?

6. And which ex-*EastEnder* co-presented the children's game show *On Safari*?

7. Eamonn Andrews, David Jacobs, Penelope Keith and Angela Rippon have all chaired which classic panel game?

8. Which primetime ITV game show was axed in 1987 after a nine-year run?

9. Richard Fairbrass and Gabrielle Richens host which Channel 5 adventure game show?

10. From which country did *You Bet!* originate?

11. Which former *Blue Peter* presenter hosted *Change Your Life Forever*?

12. What score must contestants not exceed when spinning the wheel on *The Price Is Right*?

13. Which retired policeman was custodian of the questions on *The $64,000 Question*?

14. Which panel game lasted just six months in its native USA but has been running for nearly 30 years in the UK?

15. Which ITV company made *Winner Takes All*?

Answers to page 542
EASTENDERS 1: 1. Alex Healy 2. Michelle Fowler 3. Ruth Fowler
4. The Taverniers 5. Grant Mitchell 6. Pat Butcher 7. Cindy Beale
8. Four – Pete Beale, Brian Wicks, Frank Butcher and Roy Evans
9. *Cat and Mouse* 10. James Willmott-Brown 11. Frank Butcher 12. The Natural History Museum 13. Janine Butcher 14. Laura Dunn 15. Mark Homer 16. Tom Clements

Cop Shows 2

Answers on page 543

1. Which half of comedy duo Cheech and Chong played *Nash Bridges'* partner Joe Dominguez?

2. What was Miss Dipesto's Christian name in *Moonlighting*?

3. What was bounty hunter McGill better known as in a Sixties series?

4. Who wrote the theme music for *Inspector Morse*?

5. Who was killed in a hit-and-run during the first series of *Hamish Macbeth*?

6. Which bravery award did Jack Frost win?

7. Which Monkee played the Mayor in *Pacific Blue*?

8. In *NYPD Blue*, which officer told Andy Sipowicz to 'kiss my French-Portuguese ass'?

9. Harry Naylor and Mo Connell assisted which SIB officer?

10. Which city's streets had to be dirtied to pass for Chicago in *Due South*?

11. What was Detective Lewis's Christian name in *Homicide: Life on the Street*?

12. Frank Black is the hero in which cop show from *X Files* creator Chris Carter?

13. In which US series did Tom Skerritt play local sheriff Jimmy Brock?

14. Which Sun Hill DC has a brother who is always in trouble?

15. Who played Bill Gannon in *Dragnet* 20 years before starring in *M*A*S*H*?

16. Which *Casualty* star played DS Jimmy Fenton in *The Gentle Touch*?

Answers to page 543
POT LUCK 2: 1. Crime Scene Investigation 2. Charles Stewart Parnell (*Parnell and the Englishwoman*) 3. Peter Hook 4. Jeremy Hawk 5. *Holding the Fort* 6. £1 million 7. *Mr Benn* 8. Everton 9. Keith Chegwin 10. Ricky Gervais 11. Dr Susan Lewis (Sherry Stringfield) 12. Simon Cadell 13. Michael Barrymore 14. Steve Forrest 15. 'Flurry' 16. Nighthawk

Comedy 2

Answers on page 548

1. Who is the lethal vet in *The League of Gentlemen*?

2. What relation were Paul Shane and Su Pollard in *You Rang, M'Lord*?

3. Which international performer's only venture into the world of sitcoms was to star in *The Strange World of Gurney Slade*?

4. As a youngster, which US sitcom star of the Fifties was sent to reform school for attacking his teacher?

5. Who played the prissy Laurence Bingham in *Doctor at Large*?

6. Who were the Jack and Jeremy in *Jack and Jeremy's Real Lives*?

7. What did Sgt Major Williams call Gunner Graham in *It Ain't Half Hot Mum*?

8. In which sitcom did Prunella Scales play widow Sarah France?

9. In which series did Clive Dunn's real-life wife play his screen daughter?

10. Which game show host was straight man in *The Arthur Haynes Show*?

11. In 'The Kipper and the Corpse' episode of *Fawlty Towers*, what was Dr Price kept waiting for?

12. What was Foggy Dewhurst's role in the army?

13. What was Mr Rumbold's Christian name in *Are You Being Served*?

14. Who hosted *South of Watford*?

15. Who worked for funeral directors Gateman, Goodbury and Graves?

16. What was Peter Duffley's job in *The Peter Principle*?

Answers to page 548
NAME THE YEAR 1: **1.** 1985 **2.** 1986 **3.** 1983 **4.** 1960 **5.** 1983 **6.** 1980 **7.** 1995 **8.** 1997 **9.** 1956 **10.** 1965 **11.** 1974 **12.** 1971 **13.** 1956 **14.** 1980 **15.** 1956 **16.** 1985

Soaps 1

Answers on page 549

1. In real-life, which owner of the Rovers Return in *Coronation Street* was once married to the owner of the Black Swan in *Family Affairs?*
2. Who arrived in *Coronation Street* in 1974 with her friend Tricia Hopkins to work at the Mark Brittain Warehouse?
3. Who died in 1993 two months after marrying *Emmerdale*'s Annie Sugden?
4. Which globetrotting journalist fell for David Hunter in *Crossroads?*
5. Which couple left Brookside Close for Basingstoke in 1990?
6. Who was the female head of the di Marco clan in *EastEnders?*
7. Who married Rita Jacks in *Peyton Place?*
8. Which *Coronation Street* character once brewed beer in the bath during a brewery strike?
9. In *Emmerdale*, who did Kathy Tate marry in 1996?
10. In *Neighbours*, which daughter of Jim Robinson married Philip Martin?
11. Which *Prisoner: Cell Block H* inmate once stole Lizzie Birdsworth's false teeth?
12. What was the nickname of Crossroads Motel proprietor Tommy Lancaster?
13. What was the name of Alf Stewart's spinster sister in *Home and Away?*
14. In *Brookside*, who was given a mercy killing by her daughter and son-in-law?
15. Who had a secretary called Sly?
16. When Bet Lynch was kidnapped during Weatherfield Rag Week, how much did the Rovers regulars raise to set her free?

Answers to page 549
CATCHPHRASES 1: 1. Mike Reid 2. Dick Emery 3. Benton Fraser (*Due South*) 4. Young Mr Grace (*Are You Being Served?*) 5. The Lovely Wobbly Randy Old Ladies 6. Jim Bowen (*Bullseye*) 7. Edward and Tubbs (*The League of Gentlemen*) 8. Ken Goodwin 9. Roy Walker (*Catchphrase*) 10. Ken Dodd 11. Sgt Joe Friday (*Dragnet*) 12. 'Allo 'Allo 13. Mavis Riley/Wilton 14. Jimmy Krankie 15. Jimmy Anderson (*The Fall and Rise of Reginald Perrin*) 16. Blakey

Name the Year 1

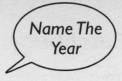
Name The Year

Answers on page 546

In which year were the following programmes first shown on British TV?

1. Dempsey and Makepeace

2. The Golden Girls

3. Knight Rider

4. It's a Square World

5. The A-Team

6. Play Your Cards Right

7. Star Trek: Deep Space Nine

8. An Unsuitable Job for a Woman

9. The Billy Cotton Band Show

10. Public Eye

11. The Zoo Gang

12. Jason King

13. The Buccaneers

14. Buck Rogers in the 25th Century

15. Gunsmoke

16. The Secret Diary of Adrian Mole, Aged $13\frac{3}{4}$

Answers to page 546
COMEDY 2: 1. Mr Chinnery 2. Father and daughter 3. Anthony Newley
4. Phil Silvers 5. Richard O'Sullivan 6. Jack Dee and Jeremy Hardy 7. 'Mr
Lah-de-dah Gunner Graham' 8. *After Henry* 9. *My Old Man* 10. Nicholas
Parsons 11. Sausages 12. Sign-writer 13. Cuthbert 14. Ben Elton
15. Herman Munster 16. Bank manager

Catchphrases 1

'NICE TO SEE YOU, TO SEE YOU NICE'

Answers on page 547

1. Which Cockney comic's catchphrase was 'Terr-i-fic'?

2. Which comedian had a camp character who used to say: 'Hello, Honky Tonk'?

3. Which courteous TV law enforcer would say: 'Thank you kindly'?

4. Who used to tell his staff: 'You've all done very well'?

5. Which Harry Enfield creations would chorus: 'Young Man!'?

6. Which game show host warned: 'Keep out of the black and into the red – you get nothing in this game for two in a bed'?

7. Who inquire of customers: 'Are you local'?

8. Which of *The Comedians* had the catchphrase: 'Settle down now'?

9. Which game show host told contestants: 'Say what you see'?

10. Which comedian tells his audience: 'How tickled I am'?

11. Which TV cop wanted 'Just the facts, ma'am'?

12. On which sitcom would an ageing master-of-disguise whisper: 'It is me – Leclerc'?

13. Which *Coronation Street* character's plaintive cry of 'I don't really know' became a catchphrase thanks to impressionist Les Dennis?

14. Who yells: 'Fandabidozi'?

15. Who was prone to a 'cock-up on the catering front'?

16. Which *On the Buses* inspector used to say: 'I 'ate you, Butler'?

Answers to page 547
SOAPS 1: **1.** Natalie Barnes (Denise Welch is the ex-wife of David Easter) **2.** Gail Potter **3.** Leonard Kempinski **4.** Angela Kelly **5.** Billy and Sheila Corkhill **6.** Rosa **7.** Norman Harrington **8.** Stan Ogden **9.** Dave Glover **10.** Julie **11.** Franky Doyle **12.** 'Bomber' **13.** Celia **14.** Gladys Charlton **15.** JR Ewing **16.** £4.56

Dramas 2

Answers on page 552

1. Why was *Edward and Mrs Simpson* not shown in France until 1986?

2. Which Australian actress starred in *Within These Walls*?

3. What did Roger Moore have to give up to appease Tony Curtis on *The Persuaders*?

4. Who faked his death in *Widows*?

5. Who played Peter Barkworth's wife in *Telford's Change*?

6. In which series did Dennis Waterman play chancer Thomas Gynn?

7. Declan McConnochie, Jimmy Destry and Max Lubin were yuppie bankers in which 1989 series?

8. Which agent named Toby sought to destroy *Callan*?

9. Who played Robby Box's girlfriend Jan in *Big Deal*?

10. Which *Casualty* night shift manager died of a heart attack?

11. Which singing soldiers teamed up for *Ain't Misbehavin'*?

12. Which long-suffering sitcom wife once played Queen Victoria in *Edward the Seventh*?

13. What is female Judge Cone's nickname in *Ally McBeal*?

14. Who did Lt Philip Gerard relentlessly pursue?

15. What was survival expert James Capen Adams better known as?

16. 'Three Stars Will Shine Tonight' was the theme music to which Sixties medical drama?

Answers to page 552
EMMERDALE 1: **1.** Hunter **2.** Mandy Dingle **3.** Pete Whiteley **4.** Kathy Tate **5.** Jackie Merrick **6.** Seth Armstrong **7.** Tina Dingle **8.** Viv Windsor **9.** Beverly Callard **10.** Claire King (Kim Tate) **11.** Victoria **12.** Kate Hughes **13.** Rachel Hughes **14.** Frank Tate **15.** Seth Armstrong **16.** Butch Dingle

Pot Luck 3

Answers on page 553

1. Which member of the aristocracy presented the ITV arts programme *Tempo*?

2. Which pair were *Living It Up* in 1958?

3. Which comedy duo enraged viewers in 1988 over a sketch about a cat in a microwave?

4. How did *M*A*S*H* writer Larry Gelbart get around the US network ban on the word 'virgin'?

5. From which radio programme was *The Day Today* derived?

6. On which TV series did Frank Sinatra make a guest appearance as a New York cop?

7. Who was the arch prankster on *Candid Camera*?

8. Which captain, who first appeared on TV in 1957, took to the seas for 13 new adventures in 1998?

9. Who said 'Opportunity Knocks' from 1987?

10. Which gangster actor swapped sides to star in the Fifties series *I'm The Law*?

11. Who is Alistair McGowan's female counterpart on his show *Alistair McGowan's Big Impression*?

12. Which ex-*Tomorrow's World* presenter fronted the 1978 documentary series *Connections*?

13. Who played Lucinda in *Grange Hill* and Dawn in *Brookside* before hitting the big time in *EastEnders*?

14. Who was the voice of Buzby in the BT commercials?

15. Who narrated the movie series *The Hollywood Greats*?

16. As whom was Richard Hearne better known?

Answers to page 553
COMEDY 3: **1.** *Never Mind the Horrocks* **2.** Aveline **3.** Bradley Hardacre (*Brass*) **4.** Jo Brand **5.** *Kate & Allie* **6.** Dennis Pennis **7.** Ronald Wolfe and Ronald Chesney **8.** Vic Reeves **9.** *The Vicar of Dibley* **10.** Harry Worth **11.** Mollie Sugden and William Moore **12.** Jesse **13.** Crilly **14.** *Blackpool Night Out* **15.** Dick Clement and Ian La Frenais **16.** Principal Skinner

Emmerdale 1

THE WOOLPACK

Answers on page 550

1. Which TV Gladiator helped the Woolpack tug-of-war team beat the Malt Shovel in 1995?

2. Who went into business with a mobile burger van?

3. Which husband of Lynn was run over and killed by a car in 1990?

4. Who opened the Old School Tea Rooms with money from her divorce settlement?

5. Who got engaged to a nurse after his motorcycle accident?

6. Who did Alan Turner narrowly beat to be elected parish councillor in 1985?

7. Who dumped Luke McAllister at the altar in revenge for the death of her brother?

8. Which colourful character does Deena Payne play?

9. Which future *Coronation Street* regular called herself Beverly Sowden when playing Jackie Merrick's girlfriend Angie Richards in *Emmerdale Farm* in 1983?

10. Which former *Emmerdale* actress's first screen kiss was with Mel Smith in *Alas Smith and Jones*?

11. What is the name of Jack Sugden's daughter?

12. Who did Joe Sugden marry in 1989?

13. Who broke off her engagement to Michael Feldmann in 1992?

14. Who bought Home Farm in 1989?

15. Whose donkey ran amok at the 1985 village fete?

16. Which character did Paul Loughran play?

Answers to page 550
DRAMAS 2: 1. The Duchess of Windsor, who lived in France, had it banned there until her death 2. Googie Withers 3. Smoking 4. Harry Rawlins 5. Hannah Gordon 6. *Stay Lucky* 7. *Capital City* 8. Toby Meres 9. Sharon Duce 10. Ewart Plimmer 11. Robson and Jerome 12. Annette Crosbie 13. 'Whipper' 14. Dr Richard Kimble 15. 'Grizzly' 16. *Dr Kildare*

Comedy 3

Answers on page 551

1. What was the title of the one-off special starring Jane Horrocks in 1996?

2. In *Bread*, who was Nellie Boswell's only daughter?

3. Who had sons named Austin and Morris?

4. Who looked at life *Through the Cakehole*?

5. Susan Saint James and Jane Curtin starred as best friends in which US sitcom?

6. Hugh Grant, Madonna and Michael Heseltine were among those quizzed by which spoof interviewer in a 1995 special?

7. Who were known as the writing Two Ronnies?

8. Which comedian born Jim Moir used to work on a pig farm?

9. As what is Geraldine Granger better known?

10. Whose final TV series was *Oh Happy Band!*?

11. Which real-life husband and wife starred in *My Husband and I*?

12. Who was famed for his diets on *The Fast Show*?

13. What was *Father Ted*'s surname?

14. On which 1964 variety show did the Beatles dress up as dustmen for a sketch with Mike and Bernie Winters?

15. Who created *The Likely Lads* and *Porridge*?

16. Who is the headmaster at Bart and Lisa's school in *The Simpsons*?

Answers to page 551
POT LUCK 3: **1.** Lord Harewood **2.** Arthur Askey and Richard Murdoch
3. Hale and Pace **4.** By inventing a soldier from the Virgin Islands
5. *On the Hour* **6.** *Magnum P.I.* **7.** Jonathan Routh **8.** *Captain Pugwash*
9. Bob (Monkhouse) **10.** George Raft **11.** Ronni Ancona **12.** James Burke
13. Letitia Dean **14.** Bernard Cribbins **15.** Barry Norman
16. Mr Pastry

Cop Shows 3

Answers on page 556

In which police series have the following characters appeared?

1. PC Lauderdale

2. Jonathan Quayle Higgins III

3. Detective Baldwin Jones

4. PC Henry Snow

5. Detective Saperstein

6. WDC Viv Martella

7. Miss Lemon

8. Della Street

9. Captain C.Z. Stern

10. Detective Neal Washington

11. DI Bob Croft

12. PC Jock Weir

13. Neil the Bus

14. DS Toolan

15. Detective Mark Petrie

16. DS Dennis Becker

Answers to page 556
SOAPS 2: **1.** Minnie Caldwell **2.** Pat Hancock **3.** Adam **4.** Nick Bates
5. She was killed in a hit-and-run **6.** Jane Templeton **7.** *The Newcomers*
8. Gareth Hunt **9.** The Woolpackers **10.** Scott **11.** Paul Robinson
12. Bet Lynch **13.** Shannon Reed **14.** Rosie Banks **15.** Lindsey Corkhill
16. Schoolteacher

Children's TV 2

Answers on page 557

1. Which *Coronation Street* actress used to play Mrs Muddle in *Pipkins*?

2. Which action series starred Graydon Gould as George Keeley?

3. What was *Orlando's* lucky charm called?

4. Who exchanged *Play Away* for *Brideshead Revisited*?

5. Who was the Hot Chestnut Man?

6. Which former presenter of *The Big Breakfast* once played Charlie in *Byker Grove*?

7. Which bushy-haired girl owned a dog called Alistair in a 1970s animation?

8. Who shared his home with a cat named Za Za?

9. Flopsy the rag doll and Pilliwig the toy clown were characters in which series?

10. What was the name of the musical frog with Pinky and Perky?

11. Which *Emmerdale* actor used to play Chris Longworth in *Grange Hill*?

12. Which Liverpool pop star was taken to hospital after being knocked out on *The Sooty Show* in the early Seventies?

13. Who was *Marine Boy's* mermaid companion?

14. Which 2001 series was about Irish boy Jamie Custer's quest to be a comedian?

15. Which puppet assisted Phillip Schofield on *Going Live!*?

16. What is the connection between the gardener in *The Herbs* and a character played by James Hazeldine in *London's Burning*?

Answers to page 557
LOCATIONS I: **1.** Russia **2.** *After Henry* **3.** Seattle **4.** *Monarch of the Glen* **5.** *Ally McBeal* **6.** Shane Longman **7.** France **8.** *Oh Happy Band!* **9.** *Picket Fences* **10.** *The Peter Principle* **11.** New Rochelle **12.** Millstone Manor **13.** Washington, D.C. **14.** *Howard's Way* **15.** Madrid County, California **16.** Hyacinth Bucket

Soaps 2

Answers on page 554

1. In *Coronation Street*, who agreed to marry Albert Tatlock to improve her pension, but backed down when she realised she would be worse off financially?

2. Which hospital porter did David Easter play in *Brookside*?

3. Which Carrington called himself Michael Torrance in *Dynasty*?

4. Who in *Emmerdale* was hailed a hero for foiling a 1988 Post Office raid despite pocketing some of the loot?

5. How did Debbie Bates meet an untimely end in *EastEnders*?

6. Who died from a brain tumour after marrying *Crossroads*' Hugh Mortimer?

7. George Harbottle and Bert Harker were characters in which Sixties soap?

8. Which New Avenger stars in *Night and Day*?

9. Which soap group had a 1996 hit with 'Hillbilly Rock Hillbilly Roll'?

10. What is the name of the Booths' son in the new *Crossroads*?

11. Who did Gail Lewis marry in *Neighbours*?

12. Who was appointed manager of the Rovers Return in 1985?

13. Who did Isla Fisher play in *Home and Away*?

14. Whose sister was Mo McGee in *Brookside*?

15. Which lipstick lesbian in *Brookside* caught her mum in bed with her girlfriend?

16. What was Bev Mansfield's job in *Emmerdale*?

Answers to page 554
COP SHOWS 3: 1. *Dixon of Dock Green* 2. *Magnum P.I.* 3. *NYPD Blue* 4. *Softly, Softly* 5. *Kojak* 6. *The Bill* 7. *Agatha Christie's Poirot* 8. *Perry Mason* 9. *Hooperman* 10. *Hill Street Blues* 11. *The Gentle Touch* 12. *Z Cars* 13. *Hamish Macbeth* 14. *A Touch of Frost* 15. *Cagney and Lacey* 16. *The Rockford Files*

Locations 1

Answers on page 555

1. Which country was the principal setting for *Reilly – Ace of Spies?*

2. Which sitcom was set in Stipton?

3. In which US city is the police series *Millennium* set?

4. The Glenbogle Estate features in which Scottish drama series?

5. Cage/Fish and Associates are the firm in which cult US series?

6. What was the name of the bank in *Capital City?*

7. Which country was the setting for the Seventies series *Crime of Passion?*

8. Which musical sitcom was set in Nettlebridge?

9. Which police series is set in Rome, Wisconsin?

10. Which banking sitcom was set in the fictitious town of Aldbridge?

11. In which New York suburb did the Petrie family live in *The Dick Van Dyke Show?*

12. What was the name of the manor in *Grace and Favour?*

13. From which city did Maxwell Smart operate in *Get Smart?*

14. Tarrant was the fictional setting for which boating saga?

15. What was the name of *Cade's County?*

16. Which sitcom monster lived in Blossom Avenue?

Answers to page 555
CHILDREN'S TV 2: **1.** Sue Nicholls **2.** *The Forest Rangers* **3.** The Gizzmo **4.** Jeremy Irons **5.** Johnny Morris **6.** Donna Air **7.** Crystal Tipps **8.** Hector (*Hector's House*) **9.** *Torchy, the Battery Boy* **10.** Morton **11.** Ben Freeman **12.** Gerry Marsden **13.** Neptina **14.** *Custer's Last Stand-Up* **15.** Gordon the Gopher **16.** Both were called Bayleaf

Dramas 3

Answers on page 560

1. Who played *Moll Flanders* before joining *ER*?

2. Which of the *LA Law* firm of McKenzie, Brackman, Chaney and Kuzak died in the first episode?

3. Which English actress created a stir as C.J. Lamb in *LA Law*?

4. Which 1966 drama about a hypothetical nuclear attack on Britain was banned until 1985 for fear that it would frighten elderly people to death?

5. Which Mike Leigh play starred Roger Sloman and Alison Steadman?

6. And what were the names of their characters?

7. Who played Captain Richard Gaunt in *The Regiment*?

8. What did Trevor Chaplin and Jill Swinburne investigate?

9. With which swing band did Eric and Eddie sing in *Ain't Misbehavin'*?

10. Who played *Bill Brand* in the 1976 political drama?

11. Ten years after starring in the 1978 film *The Thirty-Nine Steps*, who reprised the role on TV as *Hannay*?

12. What was Anthony Blake better known as in a 1974 US series?

13. Which George Eliot novel was the subject of a 1994 BBC adaptation starring Robert Hardy?

14. Which *ER* medic had a brain tumour removed?

15. At what sport did Mickey Noades excel in *Give Us a Break*?

16. And who played him?

Answers to page 560
CHILDREN'S TV 3: 1. *Ponies* 2. He could extend his arms and legs
3. Rosalie 4. Bungle 5. Leila Williams 6. Christopher Trace 7. Ollie Beak
8. Mr Troop 9. Mr Quelch 10. Posh Paws 11. Brown Sauce
12. 'I Wanna Be a Winner' 13. There was already a cat food called 'Top Cat' in the UK 14. Garner Hall 15. Prince Knut 16. Zammo McGuire

Brookside 1

Answers on page 561

1. Which Scottish nurse shared a house with Pat Hancock and Kate Moses?

2. Which loan shark put pressure on Mandy Jordache?

3. In 1997, who discovered that her groom-to-be was already married and a murderer?

4. Which dog was run over and killed in 1997?

5. Which family moved into the bungalow in 1998?

6. Who did Gizzmo Hawkins and Ducksie Brown hang around with?

7. Who learned in 1994 that her late husband had been having an affair for 12 years with an ex-prostitute?

8. Who met his future wife when she served him with spot cream?

9. Which house did the cult occupy in 1994?

10. Who was Nicholas Black's sinister drug-taking friend?

11. What was the name of Ron Dixon's father?

12. Which character did Brian Regan play?

13. Who was the first Brookside death?

14. Who accused Peter Harrison of rape?

15. From which firm was Bobby Grant made redundant?

16. Which of the Farnhams' nannies fled the country as an illegal immigrant?

Answers to page 561
POT LUCK 4: 1. Phillip Schofield 2. Esther Rantzen 3. 1994 4. Pete McCarthy 5. *The Girlie Show* 6. Mike Reid 7. Siobhan Redmond 8. Charlotte Coleman 9. *How Do They Do That?* 10. Del Boy 11. Margo Leadbetter 12. Hannah Waterman (as Laura Dunn she married Ian Beale) 13. Peter Wyngarde 14. *Taggart* 15. *Opportunity Knocks* 16. Peter Hawkins

Children's TV 3

Answers on page 558

1. What animals live at *Starhill*?

2. What were Twizzle's special powers?

3. Besides Florence, who was the other girl in *The Magic Roundabout*?

4. What was the name of the bear in *Rainbow*?

5. Which *Blue Peter* presenter married Fred Mudd of the Muddlarks?

6. Which *Blue Peter* presenter split his trousers when bending down to feed England's largest pig?

7. Which puppet once described folk singer Jon Pertwee as an 'old folker'?

8. Who was the *Trumpton* Town Clerk?

9. Which form-master made life hell for Billy Bunter?

10. What was the name of the dinosaur mascot on *Multi-Coloured Swap Shop*?

11. Under what name did a group of *Swap Shop* presenters appear on *Top of the Pops*?

12. And what was the title of their song?

13. Why was TC known as *Boss Cat* in Britain?

14. Where did Major Forbes live in *Postman Pat*?

15. What was the name of Noggin the Nog's son?

16. Who did Lee McDonald play in *Grange Hill*?

Answers to page 558
DRAMAS 3: **1.** Alex Kingston **2.** Chaney **3.** Amanda Donohoe **4.** *The War Game* **5.** *Nuts in May* **6.** Keith and Candice-Marie **7.** Christopher Cazenove **8.** *The Beiderbecke Affair* **9.** The Ray Smiles Orchestra **10.** Jack Shepherd **11.** Robert Powell **12.** *The Magician* **13.** *Middlemarch* **14.** Dr Mark Greene **15.** Snooker **16.** Robert Lindsay

Pot Luck 4

Answers on page 559

1. Who presented stories of courage about people that were *One in a Million?*

2. Who awarded *Hearts of Gold* to deserving cases?

3. When was *That's Life* axed?

4. Which offbeat presenter conducted *Travelog?*

5. Which late-night Channel 4 show was hosted by Sara Cox, Rachel Williams and Sarah Cawood?

6. Which comedian-turned-soap star played Arthur Mullard's brother in *Yus My Dear?*

7. Who played *Bulman's* sidekick Lucy McGinty?

8. Who starred as Jess in *Oranges Are Not the Only Fruit?*

9. Which BBC factual series has been presented by Eamonn Holmes, Esther McVey and Desmond Lynam?

10. In a recent poll, who did *Radio Times* readers vote best male sitcom character?

11. And who was named best female sitcom character?

12. Which *Minder* actor's daughter got married in *EastEnders* in 2001?

13. Which actor, famous for playing a flamboyant Sixties detective, was born Cyril Louis Goldbert?

14. 'Killer' was the pilot show for which detective series?

15. Which talent show gave the world Peters and Lee, Bonnie Langford and Freddie Starr?

16. Who was the voice of *The Flowerpot Men* and the Daleks?

Answers to page 559
BROOKSIDE 1: **1.** Sandra Maghie **2.** Kenny Maguire **3.** Julia Brogan (Jack Sullivan) **4.** Cracker **5.** The Shadwicks **6.** Damon Grant **7.** Penny Crosbie **8.** Rod Corkhill **9.** No. 5 **10.** Charlie Dawson **11.** Cyril **12.** Terry Sullivan **13.** Gavin Taylor **14.** Diana Corkhill **15.** Fairbanks Engineering **16.** Anna Wolska

Soaps 3

Answers on page 564

1. Who played a *Coronation Street* slob but was once a velvet-voiced Granada TV continuity announcer?

2. What was the name of Stan Harvey's sister in *Crossroads*?

3. Which Rugby League international played himself in an *Emmerdale* match organised by Terry Woods in 1996?

4. What was the name of the di Marcos' restaurant in *EastEnders*?

5. Which former *Coronation Street* star plays Auntie Wainwright in *Last of the Summer Wine*?

6. Which *Neighbours* character was in turn a shopkeeper, a romantic novelist and a financial adviser?

7. Which two Farnham children were killed in 1997 on their way home to Brookside Close?

8. Which *Santa Barbara* character received a letter of sympathy from the White House when she was temporarily blinded?

9. Which two *Emergency – Ward 10* actors later married in real life?

10. Who played police officer Nick Parrish in *Home and Away*?

11. Which fully-dressed character in *The Colbys* was banned from kissing his wife's foot for fear of encouraging foot-fetishists?

12. In *Emmerdale Farm*, who had a gypsy curse put on him in 1986?

13. What did *Emmerdale* village used to be called?

14. Who in *Coronation Street* had a sister called Debs Brownlow?

15. Who plays Jamie Mitchell in *EastEnders*?

16. Who preceded Shughie McFee as *Crossroads'* head chef?

Answers to page 564
COMEDY 4: 1. *Citizen Smith* 2. *Hi-De-Hi!* 3. *Love Thy Neighbour* 4. *Hugh and I* 5. *The Vicar of Dibley* 6. *The Royle Family* 7. *The Fall and Rise of Reginald Perrin/The Legacy of Reginald Perrin* 8. *'Allo 'Allo* 9. *2 Point 4 Children* 10. *Roseanne* 11. *Caroline in the City* 12. *Game On* 13. *Drop the Dead Donkey* 14. *Whack-O!* 15. *Are You Being Served?* 16. *Rhoda*

Cop Shows 4

Answers on page 565

1. Which aristocratic sleuth was played by Ian Carmichael?

2. Who was Malcolm MacGruder's partner?

3. What was David Small better known as?

4. Alec Peters, Ron Smollett and Cathy Marshall were officers in which series?

5. Which *Hill Street Blues* tough guy was given a hard time by his mum for not ringing her regularly?

6. Which quirky US series featured an episode written in iambic pentameters?

7. What was the name of the pink helicopter in *Riptide*?

8. What did *77 Sunset Strip*'s Kookie never leave home without?

9. In Kookie's hip language, what did 'antsville' mean?

10. Who played DCI Tom Haggerty in *Special Branch*?

11. Pru Standfast and 'Fred' Smith were members of which undercover team?

12. Out of 271 cases, how many did *Perry Mason* lose?

13. Which Eighties detective drove a black Ferrari Spider sports car?

14. What was Lewis's Christian name in *Inspector Morse*?

15. Which *Doctor Who* played *Campion*?

16. Which detective had a sidekick called Barney O'Keefe?

Answers to page 565
CORRIE 2: **1.** Susan and Peter Barlow **2.** Arthur Dewhurst **3.** Audrey Bright **4.** Len Fairclough **5.** William Ivory **6.** Heavey **7.** Nita **8.** Gail Potter and Suzie Birchall **9.** Portugal **10.** Tina Hobley **11.** Blackpool **12.** Jenny **13.** Rita Fairclough **14.** Betty Turpin **15.** Curly Watts **16.** Eddie Yeats

Comedy 4

Answers on page 562

In which sitcoms did the following characters appear?

1. Harry Fenning

2. Barry Stewart-Hargreaves

3. Barbie Reynolds

4. Arthur Wormold

5. Jim Trott

6. Dave Best

7. Joan Greengross

8. Helga Geerhart

9. Bill Porter

10. Leon Carp

11. Richard Karinsky

12. Martin Henson

13. Damien Day

14. Oliver Pettigrew

15. Shirley Brahms

16. Ida Morgenstern

Answers to page 562
SOAPS 3: 1. Bernard Youens (Stan Ogden) 2. Sheila 3. Martin Offiah
4. Guiseppe's 5. Jean Alexander 6. Philip Martin 7. Matthew and Emily
8. Augusta Lockridge 9. John Alderton and Jill Browne 10. Bruce
Roberts 11. Jeff Colby 12. Amos Brearly 13. Beckindale 14. Natalie
Barnes 15. Jack Ryder 16. Mr Lovejoy

Corrie 2

Answers on page 563

1. Which twins were born in 1965?

2. With which local butcher did Annie Walker take a cruise to Greece in 1971?

3. Which schoolgirl eloped to Gretna Green in 1968 to marry Dickie Fleming?

4. Who spent a night in jail after being drunk and disorderly at Alf Roberts's stag night in 1978?

5. Which *Common as Muck* writer played Eddie Ramsden in the Street?

6. What was Maxine Peacock's maiden name?

7. What was the name of Vikram Desai's sister?

8. Which two girls lodged with Elsie Tanner in the late Seventies?

9. To which country did Elsie Tanner finally move in 1984?

10. Who played barmaid Samantha Failsworth?

11. In which resort did Alan Bradley die?

12. What was the name of Alan Bradley's headstrong daughter?

13. Who turned down Alf Roberts's marriage proposal in 1985?

14. Who first became a barmaid at the Rovers in 1969?

15. Who did Emily Bishop take in as a lodger in November 1983?

16. Who wrote off Annie Walker's beloved Rover by backing his dustcart into it?

Answers to page 563
COP SHOWS 4: 1. *Lord Peter Wimsey* 2. Jenny Loud 3. *Lanigan's Rabbi* 4. *The Bill* 5. Mick Belker 6. *Moonlighting* 7. The Screaming Mimi 8. His comb 9. A crowded room 10. Patrick Mower 11. *C.A.T.S. Eyes* 12. Three 13. 'Sonny' Crockett (*Miami Vice*) 14. Robbie 15. Peter Davison 16. *Mark Saber*

Dramas 4

Answers on page 568

1. Who links *Minder* to the World Cup?

2. What happened to the father of Sam Ryan (*Silent Witness*)?

3. Who lost the role of *Sharpe* after being injured in a football match?

4. Who played husband and wife Peter and Sally Higgins in *The Shillingbury Tales*?

5. What is the Christian name of *Dr Quinn: Medicine Woman*?

6. In which Eighties series did a determined civil servant try to expose a sinister agency called Le Pouvoir?

7. Which 1961 series was set in a fictional West End department store?

8. What was Ian Hendry's Alex Lambert known as in the title of a 1966 ITV series?

9. Which former Avenger won a BAFTA for her performance as Helena Vesey in 1989?

10. What was the name of Father O'Connell's beautiful sister in *Ballykissangel*?

11. And who played her?

12. Which nightclub did John Kline manage in *Gangsters*?

13. In *Howard's Way*, who was Tom Howard's drunken partner in the Mermaid Yard?

14. What was the name of Nigel Le Vaillant's character in *Casualty*?

15. Which war provided the backdrop for *By The Sword Divided*?

16. Who played Mary Hammond in *The Brothers*?

Answers to page 568
COP SHOWS 5: 1. Don Beech 2. Duggie Brown 3. *Cribb* 4. Carolyn Pickles – she starred in *Bluebell* and played DCI Kim Reid in *The Bill* 5. Anna Carteret 6. Margery Allingham 7. *Cannon* 8. Thomas Magnum 9. *Jonathan Creek* 10. Hercule Poirot 11. *Starsky and Hutch* 12. Jack Frost 13. Kris 14. *Hart of the Yard* 15. Kevin Dobson 16. *Shoestring*

Children's TV 4

Answers on page 569

In which children's programmes have the following characters appeared?

1. Mr Peregrine

2. Willie Munn

3. Lady Rosemary

4. The Iron Chicken

5. Mr Guinea Pig

6. Pom Pom the poodle

7. Chief Kalamakooya

8. Horace Hare

9. Ramsbottom the snake

10. Mr Turnip

11. Granny Dryden

12. Snorky

13. Chief O'Hara

14. Sticks

15. Captain Haddock

16. Princess Thousandbeauty

Answers to page 569
COMEDY 5: 1. Jeffrey Archer 2. Dave Allen 3. Rik Mayall 4. Nursie
5. Sean Hughes 6. *The Day Today* 7. Rik Mayall and Adrian Edmondson
8. Harry Enfield 9. *The Goodies* 10. David Jason 11. *Fairly Secret Army*
12. Hungarian 13. Light bulbs 14. John Lithgow 15. Roger Rees
16. Jackie

Cop Shows 5

Answers on page 566

1. Which bent Sun Hill copper returned to England in 2001?

2. Which comedian went straight as a lab technician in *The Enigma Files?*

3. *Waxwork* was the pilot show for which detective series?

4. Who links the Bluebell Girls and *The Bill?*

5. Who played Kate Longton in *Juliet Bravo?*

6. Which novelist created *Campion?*

7. Which portly detective thrashed a Lincoln Continental around the streets of Los Angeles?

8. TC and Rick assisted which private eye?

9. Which unusual investigator worked for illusionist Adam Klaus?

10. Which detective utilises his 'little grey cells'?

11. Which cops had an informant called Huggy Bear?

12. R.D. Wingfield created which TV detective?

13. What was the name of Jill Munroe's younger sister in *Charlie's Angels?*

14. Which 1980 series transported a bungling Scotland Yard detective to San Francisco?

15. Who played Bobby Crocker in *Kojak?*

16. Which dishevelled detective had a landlady named Erica Bayliss?

Answers to page 566
DRAMAS 4: 1. Dennis Waterman who starred in *The World Cup – A Captain's Tale* 2. He was murdered by Irish terrorists 3. Paul McGann 4. Robin Nedwell and Diane Keen 5. Michaela 6. *Bird of Prey* 7. *Harpers West One* 8. *The Informer* 9. Diana Rigg (*Mother Love*) 10. Orla 11. Victoria Smurfit 12. The Maverick 13. Jack Rolfe 14. Dr Julian Chapman 15. The English Civil War 16. Jean Anderson

Comedy 5

Answers on page 567

1. Who sent a tape of his voice to *Spitting Image* so that they could improve their impersonation of him?

2. Which Irish comedian accidentally exposed himself to nuns during a convent play at the age of four?

3. Who played Lord Flashheart in *Blackadder II*?

4. Who in *Blackadder II* had an udder fixation?

5. Which Sean starred in *Sean's Show*?

6. Which series featured a reporter by the name of Peter O'Hanra'h'ahanrahan?

7. Who performed as The Dangerous Brothers?

8. Who was the voice of *Billy the Fish*?

9. Which trio were criticised by Mary Whitehouse for being 'too sexually orientated'?

10. Which comedy actor was born David White?

11. What did Major Harry Kitchener Wellington Truscott form?

12. What nationality was Granville's unknown father thought to be in *Open All Hours*?

13. What did Jerry Seinfeld used to sell for a living?

14. Who was originally offered the role of Frasier in *Cheers*?

15. Which British actor played fraudulent tycoon Robin Colcord in *Cheers*?

16. What was the name of *Roseanne's* sister?

Answers to page 567
CHILDREN'S TV 4: 1. *Muffin the Mule* 2. *Chigley* 3. *The Herbs*
4. *Clangers* 5. *Tales of the Riverbank* 6. *Torchy, the Battery Boy* 7. *Four Feather Falls* 8. *Pinky and Perky* 9. *The Sooty Show* 10. *Whirligig*
11. *Postman Pat* 12. *The Banana Splits* 13. *Batman* 14. *Here Come the Double Deckers* 15. *Hergé's Adventures of Tintin* 16. *The Singing Ringing Tree*

Pot Luck 5

Answers on page 572

1. Which show aimed to reunite people with unclaimed cash and valuables?

2. Which *Auf Wiedersehen, Pet* actor ran *Heartburn Hotel*?

3. Ford Kiernan and Greg Hemphill starred in which BBC sketch show?

4. What is Mac's full name in *Doctors*?

5. Which BBC channel was launched in September 1998?

6. Who narrated the military docusoap *Guns and Roses*?

7. Which former child star plays Danny Sorenson in *NYPD Blue*?

8. Who described tales of *Motoring Madness* in 2000?

9. What was the name of Channel 5's motoring programme which launched in 2002?

10. Which newsreader presented *Britain's Most Wanted* with Kirsty Young?

11. Who looked at the changing status of women in society in *The Lipstick Years*?

12. Which sitcom stars Kathy Burke and James Dreyfus?

13. In 2000, which Scottish comedienne played a neurotic lesbian in her first sitcom?

14. Which former *Magpie* presenter has a Tory politician brother?

15. Who became a presenter on *Panorama* after failing to win Hereford for the Liberals at the 1959 General Election?

16. Who were *Men Down Under* in 2000?

Answers to page 572
SOAPS 4: 1. Ken Dodd 2. Terence and Jason Donovan (Doug Willis and Scott Robinson) 3. Angela Griffin (Fiona Middleton in *Coronation Street*) 4. Christopher 5. JC Bradley 6. *Dynasty* 7. Vanessa Downing 8. *Crossroads* 9. Marie Lancaster 10. Postman 11. Austria 12. George 13. Benny Hawkins 14. Max Derwin 15. Bessie Street 16. Bernard Butler

Locations 2

Answers on page 573

1. Who is the most famous resident of Staines?

2. Which city was the setting for *And the Beat Goes On*?

3. Who lived at 1313 Mockingbird Lane?

4. Who was MP for the fictional North Yorkshire constituency of Haltemprice?

5. Which police series was set in Eastland?

6. Which sitcom featured the Portofino Guest House, Bridlington?

7. What was the name of the store where Leonard Swindley worked as assistant manager in *Pardon the Expression*?

8. Along which river did *The Vital Spark* steam in *Para Handy – Master Mariner*?

9. The goings-on at Brent Park Cricket Club provided the humour in which sitcom?

10. In which continent was *Top Secret* set?

11. Which father and son lived at Oil Drum Lane, Shepherd's Bush?

12. Who lived at 38 Froxbury Mansions and drank at Pomeroy's Wine Bar?

13. Shamatawa was the setting for which stirring police series of 1960?

14. Who lived on a street named Cemetery Ridge?

15. And who drove a bus to Cemetery Gates?

16. What was the name of the school in *Please, Sir!*?

Answers to page 573
SPORT 2: **1.** Golf **2.** *Let's Go* **3.** Bernard Braden (with Huw Thomas)
4. John Rickman **5.** *Sports Anorak of the Year* **6.** Clive Graham **7.** Peter
Alliss **8.** Nicky Horne **9.** 1960 **10.** Robin Cousins **11.** *On the Ball*
12. *Fantasy Football League* **13.** Horse racing **14.** 1953 British Grand Prix
15. *Pot Black* **16.** Peter Moore

Soaps 4

Answers on page 570

1. Which Liverpudlian comedian booked into *Crossroads* as a guest in 1973?

2. Which father and son actors appeared in *Neighbours* although unrelated on screen?

3. Who played one of the few Holiday Village guests at *Emmerdale* before setting up business in Weatherfield?

4. Which baby did Pam and Bobby Ewing adopt in *Dallas*?

5. Who was Jules Bradley's builder father?

6. Of which American soap was Rudolf Hess said to be a big fan?

7. Who played the first Pippa in *Home and Away*?

8. Which soap had a working title of *The Midland Road*?

9. In *Coronation Street*, who was the mother of Eddie Ramsden's son?

10. What was Fergus Jamieson's job in *Take the High Road*?

11. In which country did *Brookside*'s Jonathan Gordon-Davies first meet Cheryl Boyanowsky?

12. What was Lofty's real name in *EastEnders*?

13. Which *Crossroads* character was temporarily blinded in a hit-and-run?

14. In *Family Affairs*, which cab driver died of a heart attack?

15. At which school did Ken Barlow become a teacher in 1961?

16. What was the name of Elsie Tanner's hairdresser nephew?

Answers to page 570
POT LUCK 5: **1.** *Find a Fortune* **2.** Tim Healy **3.** *Chewin' the Fat* **4.** Dr Brendan McGuire **5.** BBC Choice **6.** Amanda Redman **7.** Rick Schroder **8.** Andrew Sachs **9.** *5th Gear* **10.** Dermot Murnaghan **11.** Lowri Turner **12.** *Gimme Gimme Gimme* **13.** Rhona Cameron (*Rhona*) **14.** Jenny Hanley (Jeremy Hanley) **15.** Robin Day **16.** Martin Clunes and Neil Morrissey

Sport 2

Answers on page 571

1. Apart from football, which other sport did Gary Lineker present for the BBC in 2001?

2. What was the name of ITV's new Saturday afternoon sports programme for 1959?

3. And which Canadian was one of the co-presenters?

4. Which ITV horse-racing commentator used to doff his trilby to viewers?

5. Which sporting quiz was hosted by Rory McGrath?

6. Which Clive was 'in the paddock' for the BBC's early horse-racing coverage?

7. Who commentated on *Pro-Celebrity Golf*?

8. Which disc jockey was chosen to present Channel 4's first American football game because he knew nothing about the sport?

9. In which year was the Grand National first televised?

10. Which ice skater was named BBC Sports Personality of the Year for 1980?

11. Which soccer preview programme was revived by ITV in 1998?

12. Which show ran a jokey reconstruction called 'Phoenix from the Flames'?

13. John Hanmer commentates on which sport?

14. Which was the first Formula One Grand Prix to be televised?

15. Which snooker series began in 1969?

16. Which Peter used to read the horse-racing results on ITV?

Answers to page 571
LOCATIONS 2: **1.** Ali G **2.** Liverpool **3.** *The Munsters* **4.** Alan B'Stard **5.** *The Chief* **6.** *Constant Hot Water* **7.** Dobson and Hawks **8.** The Clyde **9.** *Outside Edge* **10.** South America **11.** *Steptoe and Son* **12.** *Rumpole of the Bailey* **13.** *Royal Canadian Mounted Police* **14.** *The Addams Family* **15.** Stan Butler (*On the Buses*) **16.** Fenn Street Secondary Modern

Name the Year 2

Name The Year

Answers on page 576

In which year did the following programmes first appear on British TV?

1. *Supercar*

2. *Van Der Valk*

3. *Dial 999*

4. *The Crystal Maze*

5. *It Takes a Thief*

6. *Our Man at St Mark's*

7. *We'll Meet Again*

8. *The Legacy of Reginald Perrin*

9. *The Fall Guy*

10. *Crime Traveller*

11. *You've Been Framed*

12. *Lassie*

13. *Five O'Clock Club*

14. *The Huckleberry Hound Show*

15. *The Likely Lads*

16. *Whatever Happened to the Likely Lads?*

Answers to page 576
COMEDY 6: 1. George Clooney 2. Linda La Hughes 3. Stan Meadowcroft 4. *Steptoe and Son* 5. Lisa Maxwell 6. Marcel the monkey 7. *You're Only Young Twice* 8. *Up Pompeii!* 9. Mervyn 10. The Fairchilds 11. Hercules the horse 12. *Atletico Partick* 13. *Brighton Belles* 14. Gordon Brittas 15. *The Brothers McGregor* 16. Kenny Everett

Westerns 1

Answers on page 577

1. Who was the voice of Matt Dillon on radio but was considered the wrong shape to play the marshal in *Gunsmoke* on TV?

2. Which Western hero's real name was Nat Cutler?

3. Which female card shark tried to outsmart Bret Maverick?

4. John Wayne, Bette Davis and Ronald Reagan all guest-starred in which series?

5. *The Men From Shiloh* was the sequel to which Western series?

6. Which US series was re-named *Tenderfoot* in the UK?

7. What was the name of Big John Cannon's younger brother in *The High Chaparral*?

8. What was *Gunsmoke* re-named during its initial run in the UK?

9. Which songwriter played Jonesy in *Laramie*?

10. Who had a friend called Trampas?

11. Who was the eldest of the three Cartwright brothers in *Bonanza*?

12. And which actor played him?

13. For which company did Jim Hardie work?

14. Who married Victoria Montoya in *The High Chaparral*?

15. Which 13-year-old orphan joined the *Wagon Train*?

16. Which Western's theme song was 'Home on the Range'?

Answers to page 577
POT LUCK 6: **1.** *It Takes a Thief* **2.** Jeremy Lloyd **3.** Joe Longthorne **4.** Michael Crawford **5.** The first epilogue on British TV **6.** Oracle **7.** David Niven **8.** Glyn Worsnip **9.** *The Partridge Family* **10.** David Soul **11.** *Seconds Out* **12.** New Zealand **13.** Chris Evans **14.** The washboard **15.** Prince Philip **16.** *Panorama*

Comedy 6

Answers on page 574

1. Which heartthrob actor barked for a gay dog in *South Park?*

2. Who does Kathy Burke play in *Gimme Gimme Gimme?*

3. What was the name of the handyman in *Dinnerladies?*

4. Which series was voted best Sixties sitcom by *Radio Times* readers in 2001?

5. Which female impressionist was a regular on *The Les Dennis Laughter Show?*

6. Which of the *Friends* cast was sacked for vomiting live worms on set?

7. Flora Petty and Cissie Lupin lived in a retirement home in which series?

8. Hernia, Pussus Galoria and Stovus Primus were characters in which sitcom?

9. What was Noote's Christian name in *All Gas and Gaiters?*

10. Which *Brass* family were the poor relations of the Hardacres?

11. Who died in a 1970 episode of *Steptoe and Son* but recovered for the film two years later?

12. Which 1995 soccer sitcom combined airs of Spain and Scotland?

13. Which British version of *The Golden Girls* was dropped half-way through its run?

14. Which leisure centre boss was appointed European Minister for Sport in 1994?

15. Paul Barber and Philip Whitchurch played which siblings?

16. Which comedy performer was born Maurice Cole?

Answers to page 574
NAME THE YEAR 2: 1. 1961 2. 1972 3. 1958 4. 1990 5. 1968 6. 1963 7. 1982 8. 1996 9. 1982 10. 1997 11. 1990 12. 1956 13. 1963 14. 1960 15. 1964 16. 1973

Pot Luck 6

Answers on page 575

1. In which series did Robert Wagner play cat-burglar Alexander Mundy?

2. Which comedy scriptwriter was once married to Joanna Lumley?

3. Which singer/impressionist is best-known for his take-off of Shirley Bassey?

4. Which actor, born Michael Dumble Smith, took his stage name from a passing biscuit lorry?

5. What TV innovation took place at 10.30pm on Palm Sunday, 18 March 1951?

6. What was ITV's Teletext service originally known as?

7. Avenger Patrick Macnee is a cousin of which debonair film star?

8. Which former *That's Life* presenter described life in *The Paras*?

9. Keith, Laurie, Danny, Christopher and Tracy were the kids in which TV family?

10. Which actor, famed for playing a TV cop, used to wear a ski mask when billed as the Mystery Singer on *The Merv Griffin Show* in the US?

11. In which 1981 sitcom did Robert Lindsay play a boxer?

12. In which country was investigative reporter Roger Cook born?

13. Who presented the golf travelogue, *Tee Time*?

14. In which unusual musical instrument did Deryck Guyler specialise?

15. Who was the first member of the Royal Family to grant a TV interview?

16. On which programme did the historic interview take place?

Answers to page 575
WESTERNS 1: **1.** William Conrad **2.** 'Hawkeye' **3.** Sam Crawford **4.** *Wagon Train* **5.** *The Virginian* **6.** *Sugarfoot* **7.** Buck **8.** *Gun Law* **9.** Hoagy Carmichael **10.** *The Virginian* **11.** Adam **12.** Pernell Roberts **13.** Wells Fargo **14.** Big John Cannon **15.** Barnaby West **16.** *The Range Rider*

Cop Shows 6

Answers on page 580

1. Officers Lowery, Valentine and Roussakoff appear in which US police series?

2. Which US actor, famous for playing a TV cop, was born John Joseph Ryan?

3. What was the name of *Maisie Raine*'s dodgy brother?

4. How did young PC Sweet die in *Z Cars*?

5. Which was the first case to be investigated by Jeremy Brett in *The Adventures of Sherlock Holmes*?

6. Which TV investigator wrote novels under the name of Mark Caine?

7. Which singer made his acting debut in an episode of *McCloud*?

8. Which police sergeant retired to run the Aidensfield Arms?

9. Which Cockney detective was helped out by his cousin Tel?

10. What were *Starsky and Hutch*'s Christian names?

11. What did Steve Keller become on leaving the force in *The Streets of San Francisco*?

12. Which TV detective was modelled on a character in Dostoevsky's *Crime and Punishment*?

13. Which TV detective had only one arm?

14. Who rose from Police Constable to Detective Inspector on TV between 1955 and 1976?

15. In which series did George Bulman first appear?

16. Whose novels inspired *Midsomer Murders*?

Answers to page 580
CHILDREN'S TV 5: 1. *The Woodentops* 2. Dusty 3. Scottish hedgehog
4. Mr Onion 5. Six 6. Yogi Bear (Yogi Berra) 7. The Hillbilly Bears
8. Morph 9. Nick Park 10. Tinky Winky 11. Tinky Winky 12. Stanley
Unwin 13. *Inigo Pipkin* 14. Oliver Postgate 15. *Sesame Street* 16. Rick
Jones

Emmerdale 2

THE
WOOLPACK

Answers on page 581

1. Who were the happy couple in the first *Emmerdale Farm* wedding?

2. Who suffered a fatal heart attack in October 1991?

3. Who was the village policeman for 14 years until 1994?

4. What was Kim Tate's maiden name?

5. Who had an affair with timber consultant Stephen Fuller?

6. Which sitcom star played a solicitor in *Emmerdale* in 1986?

7. Which nanny had an affair with Zoë Tate?

8. Who were forced to move out of Emmerdale Farm in 1997 to make way for an access road to Demdyke Quarry?

9. Who had an abortion following her affair with Charlie Aindow?

10. Which cast member had a hit with 'Just This Side of Love' in 1990?

11. Which former *Emmerdale* actor is the brother of Hywel Bennett?

12. Who was banned from driving for a year in 1988 after failing a breathalyser?

13. In which country did Joe Sugden die?

14. Which son was born to Kim and Frank Tate in 1995?

15. Who turned up as chauffeur at Eric Pollard's 1997 wedding while on the run from the police?

16. Which newlywed feared that he might have inherited Huntington's disease?

Answers to page 581
DRAMAS 5: **1.** Margi Clarke **2.** *When the Boat Comes In* **3.** *Where The Heart Is* **4.** Gurkha Tank Battle **5.** Ray McAnally **6.** *Danger Man* **7.** Dennis Potter **8.** The Inland Revenue **9.** The Teletones **10.** Paul **11.** Tim Vincent **12.** Douglas Fairbanks Jr **13.** Colin Baker **14.** *The Cinder Path* **15.** *Down to Earth* **16.** Contessa di Contini

Children's TV 5

Answers on page 578

1. Which programme went out on Friday's strand of *Watch With Mother*?

2. What was the name of Tex Tucker's talking dog in *Four Feather Falls*?

3. What kind of creature was Spike McPike in *The Three Scampies*?

4. Who taught the Chives in *The Herbs*?

5. How many firemen did Captain Flack have under his command at *Trumpton*?

6. Which cartoon character took his name from a famous baseball player?

7. Pa Rugg was the head of which animated family?

8. Which plasticine character made his debut in *Take Hart*?

9. And which future Oscar-winner created him?

10. Which of the *Teletubbies* has a triangular aerial on his head?

11. And which of the *Teletubbies* has become a gay icon?

12. Which master of goobledygook starred in *The Secret Service*?

13. Which series changed its name to *Pipkins*?

14. Who wrote and narrated *Bagpuss*?

15. On which street did Mr Hooper run a sweet shop?

16. Who presented *Play School* and *Fingerbobs*?

Answers to page 578
COP SHOWS 6: **1.** *Brooklyn South* **2.** Jack Lord **3.** Kelvin **4.** He drowned while making a heroic rescue attempt **5.** 'A Scandal in Bohemia' **6.** *Jason King* **7.** John Denver **8.** Oscar Blaketon (*Heartbeat*) **9.** *Hazell* **10.** Dave and Ken **11.** Teacher **12.** *Columbo* **13.** Mark Saber **14.** Andy Crawford (*Dixon of Dock Green*) **15.** *The XYY Man* **16.** Caroline Graham

Dramas 5

Answers on page 579

1. Who played Queenie in *Making Out*?

2. Jack Ford was the central character in which Seventies series?

3. The Skelthwaite Arms is the watering hole in which drama?

4. Which board game did Lloydy invent in *Preston Front*?

5. Which actor won a BAFTA for his role as Labour Prime Minister Harry Perkins in *A Very British Coup*?

6. Which British series of the 1960s was called *Secret Agent* when shown in the US?

7. A 1965 play, *The Confidence Course*, was which writer's first TV work?

8. For whom did 'Charley' work initially in *The Darling Buds of May*?

9. Which singing group did *The Hello Girls* form?

10. What was *Dangerfield*'s Christian name?

11. And which former *Blue Peter* presenter played *Dangerfield*'s son?

12. Which Hollywood star introduced an ITV anthology series from 1955?

13. Which future *Doctor Who* played Paul Merroney in *The Brothers*?

14. In which Catherine Cookson story did Catherine Zeta-Jones play Victoria Chapman?

15. Which rural series stars Pauline Quirke as Faith Addis?

16. Which of *The Protectors* had a karate-chopping chauffeur named Chino?

Answers to page 579
EMMERDALE 2: 1. Frank Blakey and Janie Harker 2. Henry Wilks 3. Sgt MacArthur 4. Barker 5. Dolly Skilbeck 6. Richard Wilson 7. Sophie Wright 8. Jack and Sarah Sugden 9. Dolly Skilbeck 10. Malandra Burrows 11. Alun Lewis (Vic Windsor) 12. Alan Turner 13. Spain 14. James 15. Sam Dingle 16. Biff Fowler

Comedy 7

Answers on page 584

1. Which movie star gurgled baby Maggie Simpson's first words on *The Simpsons*?

2. Why didn't Tony Hancock learn his lines for 'The Blood Donor'?

3. Who did Eric Idle's Julius Caesar do an impression of in the *Monty Python* sketch 'Historical Impressions'?

4. What was Edmund's title in the first *Blackadder* series?

5. What was the name of the Goods' goat in *The Good Life*?

6. In which series did Tony Selby play the sadistic Corporal Marsh?

7. What was Morecambe and Wise's theme song in their early ITV shows?

8. Which series changed its title to *His Lordship Entertains* when it switched from ITV to BBC?

9. Whose characters included Apricot Lil and Slack Alice?

10. Who was Eric Barker's wife and frequent co-star?

11. In which 1991 series did John Gordon-Sinclair play struggling thespian Robert Neilson?

12. Who played Fat Bob opposite Steve Coogan's Paul Calf?

13. Which TV bar closed in 1993?

14. Which *Doctor Who* was left *Holding the Fort*?

15. Who replaced Jeffrey Fairbrother as Entertainments Officer in *Hi-De-Hi!*?

16. What was the name of the family in *Keep it in the Family*?

Answers to page 584
MUSIC 1: **1.** *The Protectors* **2.** Tony Christie **3.** Lynsey De Paul **4.** *Walk On By* **5.** Tony Hatch and Jackie Trent **6.** *Minder* **7.** Stephanie de Sykes **8.** *Never Mind the Buzzcocks* **9.** The John Barry Seven **10.** 'Hit and Miss' **11.** The Firm **12.** Jacky had a 1968 hit with the theme from *White Horses* and, three years later, as Jackie Lee had another hit with the theme from *Rupert* **13.** The Dickies **14.** The Barron Knights **15.** 'Trumpton Riots' **16.** Mike Holoway

Soaps 5

Answers on page 585

In which soaps have the following characters appeared?

1. Tish Hope

2. Anne-Marie Wade

3. Maggie Redman

4. Emma Nightingale

5. Rod Norman

6. Vicky Dean

7. Morag Bellingham

8. Keith Rooney

9. Afton Cooper

10. Jane Harris

11. Dulcie Froggatt

12. Kimberley Taylor

13. Sol Patrick

14. Brian Blair

15. Doug Beatty

16. Lorna Cartwright

Answers to page 585
POT LUCK 7: **1.** Jean Alexander **2.** Honor Blackman **3.** *Good Morning With Anne and Nick* **4.** Peter Dulay **5.** 1998 **6.** Ulrika Jonsson **7.** *Game for a Laugh* **8.** *WKRP in Cincinnati* **9.** Annie and Clarabel **10.** Nicholas Parsons **11.** *All Rise for Julian Clary* **12.** Lulu, Mike Yarwood and Ray Fell **13.** Victoria Wood **14.** Ronnie Barker **15.** Anthony Andrews **16.** Jessica Walter

Music 1

Answers on page 582

1. 'Avenues and Alleyways' was the theme song to which drama series?

2. And who had a hit with it?

3. Who had a hit in 1974 with the theme from *No – Honestly*?

4. Which series (which took its title from a Burt Bacharach number) told the 'story of popular song'?

5. Which husband-and-wife team composed the theme song for *Neighbours*?

6. 'I Could Be So Good For You' was the theme to which series?

7. Which singer, playing a *Crossroads* guest, took her song in the programme, 'Born With a Smile On My Face', to number two in the charts in 1974?

8. Which series asks the teams to spot faded stars in an identity parade?

9. Who had a hit with the instrumental theme to *Juke Box Jury*?

10. And what was the theme's appropriate title?

11. Which group had a 1987 hit with 'Star Trekkin''?

12. What is the link between 'White Horses' and 'Rupert'?

13. Who had a hit with the theme from *The Banana Splits*?

14. Which comedy band sang 'Get Down Shep'?

15. Which Half Man Half Biscuit number told of civil unrest in the world of children's television?

16. Which member of Seventies pop band Flintlock played one of *The Tomorrow People*?

Answers to page 582
COMEDY 7: **1.** Liz Taylor **2.** He had been involved in a car accident
3. Eddie Waring **4.** Duke of Edinburgh **5.** Geraldine **6.** *Get Some In!*
7. 'Two of a Kind' **8.** *Hark at Barker* **9.** Larry Grayson **10.** Pearl Hackney
11. *An Actor's Life for Me* **12.** John Thomson **13.** *Cheers* **14.** Peter Davison
15. Clive Dempster **16.** The Rush family

Pot Luck 7

Answers on page 583

1. Which former *Coronation Street* actress spent five years as a librarian?

2. Who once knocked out wrestler Jackie Pallo during rehearsals for *The Avengers*?

3. What was the BBC's answer to *This Morning*?

4. Who took over as presenter of *Candid Camera* in 1974?

5. In which year did Lisa Riley replace Jeremy Beadle as presenter of *You've Been Framed*?

6. Who rose from being a secretary at TV-am to interviewing Prime Minister John Major before the 1997 election?

7. Which Eighties prankfest was based on the US show *People Are Funny*?

8. Gary Sandy starred in a US sitcom about which radio station?

9. What are the names of *Thomas the Tank Engine*'s two carriages?

10. In 2001, which former game show host attacked programmes which humiliate people?

11. In which series did Julian Clary hold court?

12. Who were the *Three of a Kind* in the 1967 series of that name?

13. Which comedienne started out performing topical songs on *That's Life*?

14. Who wrote *His Lordship Entertains* under the pseudonym Jonathan Cobbald?

15. Who was originally cast as Bodie in *The Professionals*, only to be dropped because he looked too much like Martin Shaw?

16. Who played San Francisco police chief *Amy Prentiss*?

Answers to page 583
SOAPS 5: 1. *Crossroads* 2. *Crossroads* 3. *Coronation Street* 4. *Emmerdale*
5. *EastEnders* 6. *A Country Practice* 7. *Home and Away* 8. *Brookside*
9. *Dallas* 10. *Neighbours* 11. *Coronation Street* 12. *Coronation Street*
13. *Hollyoaks* 14. *Take the High Road* 15. *Compact* 16. *EastEnders*

Locations 3

Answers on page 588

1. Which sitcom was set in the canteen of Manchester firm HWD Components?

2. Which police series patrolled Seaport?

3. Which Ronnie Barker character lived at Chrome Hall?

4. Which sitcom was set at Paradise Lodge?

5. Which children's character lived in Stray Town?

6. Which female detective worked out of Bessomer Street Police Station?

7. What was the name of *The Brothers'* firm?

8. Which series was set in the Bayview Retirement Home, Bournemouth?

9. The Buffalo Pass, Scalplock and Defiance railroad line was the setting for which Western?

10. In which town did *The Waltons* live?

11. In which area of Britain was the sitcom *Watching* set?

12. Which Second World War series was set around the sleepy Suffolk town of Market Wetherby?

13. Which fictional north-eastern town was the setting for *When the Boat Comes In*?

14. Which English resort was the setting for the first series of *September Song*?

15. Which Fifties adventure series was set on the island of Portobello in the Spanish Main?

16. For which magazine did Jane Lucas work in *Agony*?

Answers to page 588
COMEDY 8: **1.** Harvey Nicks **2.** Jim Moir (aka Vic Reeves) **3.** Paul Merton **4.** Dr Strangepork **5.** *My Family* **6.** *Absolutely Fabulous* **7.** Belinda Purcell **8.** Liza Goddard **9.** Shepherd **10.** Brenda Blethyn **11.** Ronnie Corbett **12.** Penelope Keith **13.** Aggie Macdonald **14.** Chambers **15.** Angus Deayton **16.** A knotted handkerchief

Sci Fi 1

Answers on page 589

In which sci fi series have the following characters appeared?

1. Orac

2. Lyta Alexander

3. Neelix

4. Ham Tyler

5. Vizlor Turlough

6. Sam Loover

7. Lt Gen. Heywood Kirk

8. Tom Weston

9. Simon King

10. Hal Sterling

11. Dr John Ridge

12. Pal Kenzy

13. Professor Spiro

14. Dan Erickson

15. Quark

16. Kate Kestrel

Answers to page 589
POT LUCK 8: 1. Manuel's pet rat 2. Gerry Anderson 3. Nine 4. Jimmy Jewel 5. *Meet the Wife* 6. Nicholas Lyndhurst 7. *New Faces* 8. Fulton Mackay (Mr Mackay) 9. *Pardon the Expression* 10. Bill Owen 11. 'Buddy Boy' 12. Dulcie Gray 13. The Netherlands 14. *The Big Breakfast* 15. Bob Larbey 16. Tattoo

Comedy 8

Answers on page 586

1. Where do Edina and Patsy love to shop in *Absolutely Fabulous*?

2. Who very nearly decided to use Craig Wildfowl as his stage name?

3. Which comedian took his stage name from a south London borough?

4. Who was the fiendish villain in *The Muppet Show*'s 'Pigs in Space' serial?

5. Which domestic comedy stars Robert Lindsay as a dentist and Zoë Wanamaker as a tour guide?

6. Twiggy and Stephen Gately guested in the first episode of which returning series in 2001?

7. With which music teacher did rock star Nigel Cochrane fall in love in *Roll Over Beethoven*?

8. And who played her?

9. What was Queenie's surname in *Queenie's Castle*?

10. Who played Miriam Dervish in *Outside Edge*?

11. Which Edinburgh-born comedian had a post-war job as a civil servant responsible for the rationing of animal food?

12. Who starred in *No Job For a Lady*?

13. What was the name of the Scottish housekeeper in *Life with the Lyons*?

14. What was Thelma's maiden name in *Whatever Happened to the Likely Lads*?

15. Which member of the *Have I Got News For You* team once had soccer trials with Crystal Palace?

16. What did a Gumby wear on his head in *Monty Python's Flying Circus*?

Answers to page 586
LOCATIONS 3: 1. *Dinnerladies* 2. *Z Cars* 3. Lord Rustless 4. *You're Only Young Twice* 5. Twizzle 6. *Maisie Raine* 7. Hammond Transport Services 8. *Waiting for God* 9. *Iron Horse* 10. Walton's Mountain 11. Merseyside 12. *We'll Meet Again* 13. Gallowshield 14. Blackpool 15. *The Adventures of Long John Silver* 16. *Person* magazine

Pot Luck 8

Answers on page 587

1. Who or what was the other Basil in *Fawlty Towers*?

2. Which innovative TV producer created his first soundproof studio by nailing 1500 empty egg boxes to the walls of a Slough warehouse?

3. For how many years did the hospital documentary *Jimmy's* run?

4. Which late actor and half of a comedy double act with his cousin was born James Marsh?

5. Which sitcom featured feuding husband and wife Thora and Freddie Blacklock?

6. As a boy, which comedy actor used to host the Saturday morning magazine *Our Show*?

7. Mickie Most, Clifford Davis and Arthur Askey were regular panellists on which talent show?

8. Which officer of Slade Prison was later posted to *Fraggle Rock*?

9. Which Sixties sitcom was a spin-off from *Coronation Street*?

10. Which future sitcom star played Inspector Lestrade in the 1951 TV adaptation of *Sherlock Holmes*?

11. What was *Mister Ed*'s nickname for Wilbur Post?

12. To which actress was *Boyd QC*'s Michael Denison married?

13. In which country did the *Big Brother* concept originate?

14. 'Snap, Cackle and Pop' was the entertainment news segment on which show?

15. Who is John Esmonde's usual writing partner?

16. Which midget lived on *Fantasy Island*?

Answers to page 587
SCI FI I: **1.** *Blake's 7* **2.** *Babylon 5* **3.** *Star Trek: Voyager* **4.** *V* **5.** *Doctor Who* **6.** *Joe 90* **7.** *The Time Tunnel* **8.** *The Guardians* **9.** *Counterstrike* **10.** *Otherworld* **11.** *Doomwatch* **12.** *Star Cops* **13.** *Captain Zep – Space Detective* **14.** *Land of the Giants* **15.** *Star Trek: Deep Space Nine* **16.** *Terrahawks*

TV Chefs 1

Answers on page 592

1. Which Indian cookery expert took part in *Friends for Dinner?*

2. Who compiled a *Seafood Lovers' Guide?*

3. Michael Smith and Glyn Christian filled the cookery slot on which daytime magazine programme?

4. Which Emma helps out on *Food and Drink?*

5. Who presented his *Barbecue Bible?*

6. Which TV chef used to be a stand-up comedian at The Comedy Store?

7. Which presenter left *Food and Drink* in 1999?

8. Which early TV chef died in 1970?

9. Which TV chef learnt to cook in the kitchen of his parents' Essex pub?

10. Which husband and wife team presided over the 'Happy Cooking' sequence in the children's magazine show *Lucky Dip?*

11. Which TV chef played drums in a band called Scarlet Division?

12. Which TV cook also managed the radio station Classic FM?

13. Who has presented both Summer and Winter Collections on TV?

14. Which 1993 *Masterchef* finalist has since become a TV chef in his own right?

15. Who presented the fun cookery series *Party of a Lifetime?*

16. Which TV cook invariably has a glass of wine in his hand?

Answers to page 592
CORRIE 3: 1. The Orinoco 2. Max Wall 3. Albert Tatlock 4. Liz McDonald 5. Vera Duckworth 6. Mollie Sugden 7. Friday 8. Ben Kingsley 9. Julia Stone 10. Fiona Allen (*Smack the Pony*) 11. Mike Baldwin 12. Irma Barlow 13. Vicky Arden 14. Mark Casey 15. Jon Lindsay 16. Les Clegg

Dramas 6

Answers on page 593

1. Which dyslexic actress played Lady Glencora in *The Pallisers*?

2. Which actor pleaded *Take Me* on ITV in 2001?

3. Which 2001 series starring Sheila Hancock, Timothy West and Stephen Tompkinson was set in neighbouring bedrooms?

4. Which *Auf Wiedersehen, Pet* star used to be employed as a court Jester at mock Elizabethan banquets?

5. Which Geordie actor used to work as a shipyard draughtsman?

6. Which actress shaved her head for her role as Tryphaena in *The Cleopatras*?

7. Why did militant students in Prague postpone a rally in the Sixties?

8. Which 1983 series revolved around hustler Mickey Noades?

9. Who became manageress of a fashion house in *Howard's Way*?

10. What links *Ivanhoe* and the *Carry On* films?

11. What was the name of 'Mother's' Amazonian secretary in *The Avengers*?

12. Which was the first US mini-series to be shown in Britain?

13. Who enjoyed *A Kind of Loving* before putting out the flames of passion in *London's Burning*?

14. Who played Hitler in *The Death of Adolf Hitler*?

15. Which 1995 series saw the return of *Widows'* Dolly Rawlins?

16. Which actress who played a police officer in *Cracker* switched to the wrong side of the law to help commit *Daylight Robbery*?

Answers to page 593
COMEDY 9: 1. Harry Hill 2. Steve Coogan 3. Corinne Tate 4. David Jason 5. Paul Shane 6. Duane 7. Mr Gumby 8. Arthur Atkinson 9. Reggie Perrin 10. *Don't Ask Us – We're New Here* 11. Ainsley Harriott 12. A courtroom 13. *Vic Reeves Big Night Out* 14. Peter Davison and Robert Glenister 15. *Ripping Yarns* 16. Jimmy Tarbuck

Corrie 3

Answers on page 590

1. Which club did Laurie Frazer own?

2. Which comedian played Elsie Tanner's friend Harry Payne?

3. Who blamed an outbreak of food poisoning on Annie Walker's pies, only to find the real cause was on his own allotment?

4. Which Street resident had an affair with a gangster named Fraser?

5. Who took her first driving lessons in June 1986 after winning a car in a competition?

6. Which comedy actress played Nellie Harvey, landlady of The Laughing Donkey?

7. On which day of the week did *Coronation Street* originally go out?

8. Who chatted up Irma Ogden and Valerie Barlow before playing Gandhi?

9. Which *femme fatale* was hired by Greg Kelly to wreck Mike Baldwin's reputation?

10. And which star of a sketch show played her?

11. When Hilda Ogden won a raffle prize of a date with 'Mr Wonderful', who turned out to be the mystery man?

12. Who snatched a baby in 1970 shortly after losing her husband and son?

13. What was the name of Alec Gilroy's granddaughter?

14. Which Mark worked as a mechanic at the garage with Kevin Webster?

15. Which con man and impostor was played by Owen Aaronovitch?

16. Who was admitted to a mental hospital in 1968 suffering from alcoholism?

Answers to page 590
TV CHEFS 1: 1. Madhur Jaffrey 2. Rick Stein 3. *Pebble Mill at One*
4. Emma Crowhurst 5. Ainsley Harriott 6. Ainsley Harriott 7. Chris
Kelly 8. Philip Harben 9. Jamie Oliver 10. Fanny and Johnnie Cradock
11. Jamie Oliver 12. Michael Barry 13. Delia Smith 14. Ross Burden
15. Ainsley Harriott 16. Keith Floyd

Comedy 9

Answers on page 591

1. Who had a 'big brother Alan' on his TV shows?

2. Whose lesser-known characters include trivia-obsessed Guy Crump and museum curator Tim Fleck?

3. Whose baby in *Soap* was possessed by the devil?

4. Who did producer Humphrey Barclay discover performing in a Bournemouth pier theatre before launching him on TV in *Do Not Adjust Your Set*?

5. Which comedy actor used to work as a morgue porter?

6. What was Doberman's Christian name in *The Phil Silvers Show*?

7. Which *Monty Python* character used to say: 'My brain hurts'?

8. Which music-hall comic did Paul Whitehouse play in *The Fast Show*?

9. Who founded a shop named Grot?

10. Which BBC sketch show of 1970 gave early exposure to Maureen Lipman and Richard Stilgoe?

11. Who supported *Davro* in 1990 before becoming a TV chef?

12. What was the setting for the ITV sitcom *Can We Get On Now, Please*?

13. Wavy Davy appeared in which show of the early Nineties?

14. Who played the two rival brothers in *Sink or Swim*?

15. Which Michael Palin series was inspired by an old annual?

16. Which comedian was a Butlin's Redcoat before making his TV debut in *Comedy Bandbox* in 1963?

Answers to page 591
DRAMAS 6: **1.** Susan Hampshire **2.** Robson Green **3.** *Bedtime* **4.** Tim Healy **5.** Robson Green **6.** Amanda Boxer **7.** So that they could watch *The Forsyte Saga* **8.** *Give Us a Break* **9.** Jan Howard **10.** The executive producer of *Ivanhoe* was *Carry On* creator Peter Rogers **11.** Rhonda **12.** *Rich Man, Poor Man* **13.** Clive Wood **14.** Frank Finlay **15.** *She's Out* **16.** Geraldine Somerville

Pot Luck 9

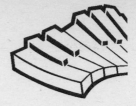

Answers on page 596

1. Who narrated *The World at War*?

2. Which late soccer commentator was a decorated bomber pilot in the war?

3. Who was the principal presenter of *The White Heather Club*?

4. Which Channel 4 drama series of 2000 was about a group of barristers in a Yorkshire city?

5. Who plays the headmaster in the school drama *Hope and Glory*?

6. Who visited *Magnificent Monuments* in 2000?

7. What was the title of Alan Whicker's series about British expatriates in the USA?

8. Who was the first presenter of *What the Papers Say*?

9. Which ex-*Coronation Street* actress and daughter of series creator Kay Mellor starred in *Fat Friends*?

10. Which series featured cook Clarissa Dickson Wright and hill farmer Johnny Scott?

11. Who played Bernard Black in *Black Books*?

12. In which year did BBC2 begin transmission?

13. Who played salesman Gareth Cheeseman in his comedy series?

14. Which flamboyant pianist played the villain Chandell in *Batman*?

15. Denis Tuohy, Joan Bakewell, Sheridan Morley and Tony Bilbow all had turns at presenting which BBC2 arts show?

16. Who was the first presenter of the consumer programme *We Can Work It Out*?

Answers to page 596
QUIZ AND GAME SHOWS 2: **1.** Melinda Messenger **2.** Lisa Tarbuck **3.** Eamonn Holmes **4.** Jackie Rae **5.** Marion Ryan **6.** Nine **7.** Bob Monkhouse **8.** Jimmy Hanley **9.** Jadene Doran **10.** Eamonn Andrews **11.** *Busman's Holiday* **12.** *Family Feud* **13.** Vincent Price **14.** William Rushton **15.** Kenny Everett **16.** *The Generation Game*

Soaps 6

Answers on page 597

1. Which *Howard's Way* star played goalkeeper Kenny Craig in *United!*?

2. Rod Taylor, Gina Lollobrigida, Kim Novak and Lana Turner all appeared in which US soap?

3. Which resident of Brookside Close was found dead at a guest house in Llandudno?

4. Which impressionist played singer Kate Loring in *Crossroads*?

5. Who ran a photographic business in Weatherfield in the early 1970s?

6. In *Neighbours*, what were the names of Cheryl Stark's two sons?

7. What was Krystle Carrington's maiden name?

8. What was Bob Grove's job in *The Grove Family*?

9. Who is Cat Matthews' errant husband in *Family Affairs*?

10. Who got Sonia Jackson pregnant in *EastEnders*?

11. Who was an Assistant District Attorney in *Dallas*?

12. Which racist targeted Mick Johnson's pizza parlour in *Brookside*?

13. What is the name of Mick Johnson's flash brother?

14. What sort of birds did *Crossroads'* Wilf Harvey fancy?

15. In which Sixties soap did a young Jenny Agutter play Kirsty Kerr?

16. Which Ramsay Street regular is played by Tom Oliver?

Answers to page 597
WILDLIFE 2: 1. Twizzle 2. Ricky North 3. Minnie Caldwell (*Coronation Street*) 4. Jim Newton 5. Dr Marsh Tracy (*Daktari*) 6. Jimmy Gibson (*Supercar*) 7. Sandy and Bud Ricks 8. Rusty 9. Victoria Gordon 10. Jimmy Corkhill (*Brookside*) 11. Mavis Wilton (*Coronation Street*) 12. Mrs Pumphrey (*All Creatures Great and Small*) 13. Martin Crane (*Frasier*) 14. Percy Sugden (*Coronation Street*) 15. Geoff Pearce (*London's Burning*) 16. Tonto

Quiz & Game Shows 2

Answers on page 594

1. Which busty model presents Fort Boyard?

2. Which former *Big Breakfast* presenter became the new host of *Blockbusters* on Sky in 2000?

3. Who presents the daytime quiz *Playing for Time*?

4. Who was the first host of *The Golden Shot*?

5. Which mother of singing twins was the resident songstress on *Spot the Tune*?

6. How many contestants begin each edition of *The Weakest Link*?

7. Who tested powers of recall in *Memory Masters*?

8. Which father of a *Magpie* presenter was previously a host on *Dotto*?

9. Who was Chris Evans's female co-host on *Don't Forget Your Toothbrush*?

10. Who hosted the satellite quiz *Top of the World*?

11. What did Julian Pettifer send contestants on?

12. What was the name of the American version of *Family Fortunes*?

13. Which horror movie star appeared on the first edition of *Celebrity Squares*?

14. Who always occupied the centre square on *Celebrity Squares*?

15. Whose voice introduced *Celebrity Squares*?

16. Sally Meen and Melanie Stace are associated with which game show?

Answers to page 594
POT LUCK 9: **1.** Laurence Olivier **2.** Kenneth Wolstenholme **3.** Andy Stewart **4.** *North Square* **5.** Lenny Henry **6.** Fred Dibnah **7.** *Living With Uncle Sam* **8.** Kingsley Martin **9.** Gaynor Faye **10.** *Clarissa and the Countryman* **11.** Dylan Moran **12.** 1964 **13.** Steve Coogan **14.** Liberace **15.** *Late Night Line-Up* **16.** Judy Finnegan

Wildlife 2

Answers on page 595

Which TV characters owned the following animals?

1. Footso the cat

2. Champion the Wonder Horse

3. Bobby the cat

4. Fury

5. Judy the chimp

6. Mitch the monkey

7. Flipper

8. Rin-Tin-Tin

9. Black Beauty

10. Cracker the dog

11. Harriet the budgerigar

12. Tricki-Woo

13. Eddie the dog

14. Randy the budgerigar

15. Bruno the boxer dog

16. Scout the horse

Answers to page 595
SOAPS 6: 1. Stephen Yardley 2. *Falcon Crest* 3. Petra Taylor 4. Kate
Robbins 5. Ernest Bishop 6. Brett and Darren 7. Jennings 8. Builder
9. Dave 10. Martin Fowler 11. Cliff Barnes 12. George Webb 13. Ellis
14. Pigeons 15. *The Newcomers* 16. Lou Carpenter

Comedy 10

Answers on page 600

1. Who wrote *One Foot in the Grave*?

2. Who was Rik's favourite singer in *The Young Ones*?

3. Which one-time friend of Prince Andrew played the lesbian Cissy Meldrum in *You Rang, M'Lord*?

4. What was the name of Jessica Tate's husband in *Soap*?

5. Who was *Mr Magoo's* nephew?

6. Which *Carry On* star teamed up with Victor Spinetti for *Two in Clover*?

7. Who started his series with a shop-window routine where he used his reflection to make it look as if he was waving all four limbs at once?

8. *The Phantom Raspberry Blower of Old London Town* was a serial within which show?

9. Which English teacher did Barry Evans play in *Mind Your Language*?

10. Who played the grandmother in *The Kumars at No. 42*?

11. Who was the unseen proprietor in *Drop the Dead Donkey*?

12. Which US sitcom of the 1990s featured numerous clips of old shows?

13. Who used to have a character called Kenny the kangaroo?

14. What was Warren Webber's nickname in *Happy Days*?

15. Which Sixties series sent a model of BBC Television Centre into space?

16. What was Mark Taylor's job in *Joking Apart*?

Answers to page 600
CORRIE 4: 1. 1989 2. Sam Kingston 3. Emma Taylor 4. Gail Tilsley 5. Ena Sharples 6. Christine Hardman 7. Jonathan Guy Lewis 8. Stan and Hilda Ogden 9. Minnie Caldwell 10. Len Fairclough 11. Jackie 12. Jack Walker 13. The Ogdens 14. Jill Summers 15. Danny Hargreaves 16. Eunice Nuttall

Dramas 7

Answers on page 601

1. Which two actors played Harvey Moon?

2. Which *Where the Heart Is* character was killed in a road accident Involving a runaway horse?

3. Who played holiday rep Nicki Matthews in *Sunburn*?

4. What was the name of the barman at the Winchester Club in *Minder*?

5. Which member of the *Auf Wiedersehen, Pet* gang hails from Bristol?

6. Who was Steed and Tara King's portly boss in *The Avengers*?

7. Who drowned after falling off a bridge in *Dawson's Creek*?

8. *Callan* stemmed from a play in which ITV series?

9. Which series caused old ladies to report sightings of suspicious one-armed men?

10. Which seafaring hero is played by Ioan Gruffudd?

11. Who did Francis Urquhart push off a roof in *House of Cards*?

12. What was the name of the Howards' spoilt daughter in *Howard's Way*?

13. Who played the ultra-possessive mother in *Mother Love*?

14. Which sadistic Nazi was played by Anthony Valentine in *Colditz*?

15. Who tackled such cases as the Penge Bungalow Murders and the Great Grimsby Fish Fraud?

16. Who tried unsuccessfully to dispose of several thousand condoms in *Porterhouse Blue*?

Answers to page 601
CHILDREN'S TV 6: 1. Officer Dibble 2. Freddie 3. Mr Bronson 4. The Soup Dragon 5. Dylan 6. *Camberwick Green* 7. Bella 8. Mike Read 9. Dai Station 10. *Rainbow* 11. Terry Scott 12. Horatio 13. *Play School* 14. Simon Groom 15. John Craven 16. 13

Corrie 4

Answers on page 598

1. In which year did *Coronation Street* add a third weekly episode?

2. Who is the Street's resident male stripper?

3. Which policewoman married Curly Watts?

4. Who had an affair with her husband's Australian cousin?

5. Which Street legend made her last appearance in 1980 before moving to St Anne's?

6. Who was talked down from jumping off a factory roof by Ken Barlow?

7. Which love rat cheated on Sharon Gaskell?

8. Irma Barlow was whose daughter?

9. Who took in ex-convict Jed Stone as a lodger?

10. Who did Rita Littlewood marry in 1977?

11. What is the name of Tyrone Dobbs' mouthy mother?

12. Which landlord of the Rovers died while visiting his daughter Joan in Derbyshire?

13. Whose front room boasted a 'muriel'?

14. Who played Phyllis Pearce?

15. Who opened a hardware shop with Sally Webster?

16. Who married Fred Gee?

Answers to page 598
COMEDY 10: 1. David Renwick 2. Cliff Richard 3. Catherine Rabett
4. Chester 5. Waldo 6. Sid James 7. Harry Worth 8. *The Two Ronnies*
9. Jeremy Brown 10. Meera Syal 11. Sir Royston Marchant 12. *Dream On* 13. Michael Barrymore 14. 'Potsie' 15. *It's a Square World*
16. Comedy scriptwriter

Children's TV 6

Answers on page 599

1. Which custodian of the law was constantly outsmarted by *Boss Cat*?

2. In *HR Pufnstuf*, what was the name of Jimmy's talking flute?

3. Which authoritarian *Grange Hill* teacher wore a toupee?

4. In *Clangers*, who lived in the soup wells?

5. Who was the spaced-out bunny on *The Magic Roundabout*?

6. Which series began: 'Here is a box, a musical box, wound up and ready to play'?

7. Which of the *Tweenies* is blue?

8. Who was the General Manager of *Saturday Superstore*?

9. Who looked after Llaniog Station in *Ivor the Engine*?

10. Moony and Sunshine were early puppets on which series?

11. Who provided the voice of Penfold in *Dangermouse*?

12. What was *Captain Pugwash*'s Christian name?

13. Hamble and Humpty were toys on which series?

14. Which *Blue Peter* presenter praised a couple of door ornaments with the words: 'What a beautiful pair of knockers'?

15. Who encouraged a 'News Swap' on *Multi-Coloured Swap Shop*?

16. How many episodes of *Mr Benn* were made?

Answers to page 599
DRAMAS 7: **1.** Kenneth Cranham and Nicky Henson **2.** Peggy Snow **3.** Michelle Collins **4.** Dave **5.** Bomber **6.** 'Mother' **7.** Abby Morgan **8.** *Armchair Theatre* **9.** *The Fugitive* **10.** *Hornblower* **11.** Mattie Storin **12.** Lynne **13.** Diana Rigg **14.** Major Mohn **15.** *Rumpole of the Bailey* **16.** Zipser

Comedy 11

Answers on page 604

1. Who was General Melchett's sycophantic aide in *Blackadder Goes Forth*?

2. What was the job of *Frasier*'s dad Marty Crane before retirement?

3. Which comedian was born Leslie Townes Hope in Eltham, London, in 1903?

4. Which one-time England football manager had a cameo role in an episode of *The Upper Hand*?

5. Who was heavily disguised as a TV interviewer in *The Rutles*' spoof Beatles documentary *All You Need Is Cash*?

6. What is Homer Simpson's favourite drinking haunt?

7. What was the name of the newspaper in *Hot Metal*?

8. Which sitcom featured Chris and Fliss Hawthorne?

9. As a salesman for which company did Maxwell Smart work undercover in *Get Smart*?

10. Who played Badvoc in *Chelmsford 123*?

11. Miss Tibbs and Miss Gatsby were permanent guests at which establishment?

12. Which Seventies sitcom was retitled *Three's Company* in the US?

13. What did Colin Watkins dream of being in *Colin's Sandwich*?

14. Which of *The Munsters* was normal?

15. Who starred as *Mulberry*?

16. Who was Selwyn Froggitt's brother?

Answers to page 604
CHILDREN'S TV 7: **1.** Boss Cat **2.** Wacky Races **3.** The Herbs **4.** Clangers **5.** Ivor the Engine **6.** The Banana Splits **7.** Here Come the Double Deckers **8.** Bagpuss **9.** Pinky and Perky **10.** The Sooty Show **11.** The Wombles **12.** The Saga of Noggin the Nog **13.** Postman Pat **14.** Camberwick Green **15.** Trumpton **16.** The Flintstones

Westerns 2

Answers on page 605

1. Who played *Tenderfoot*?

2. Who was the for-hire hero of *Have Gun, Will Travel*?

3. What was Don Diego's alias?

4. Sheriff Clay Hollister was the peacekeeper in which Western?

5. Which *Wagon Train* actor died part-way through the series?

6. Which medic was the central character in *Frontier Doctor*?

7. Who was the ineffective town marshal in *The Rifleman*?

8. What was the name of the family in *Bonanza*?

9. Josh Randall was the enigmatic hero of which Western?

10. Who was the drover in *Rawhide*?

11. Which series featured a housekeeper named Daisy Cooper?

12. Who played *Shotgun Slade*?

13. In which American state was *The Virginian* set?

14. Which judge was the first ranch owner in *The Virginian*?

15. In which Western did Lee Majors play a bastard son Heath?

16. *Laredo* was a spin-off from which popular Western?

Answers to page 605
EASTENDERS 2: **1.** Debbie Wilkins and Andy O'Brien **2.** PR executive
3. Kelvin **4.** Cindy Beale **5.** Kat Slater **6.** Donna Ludlow **7.** Lisa O'Brien
8. Arthur Fowler and Christine Hewitt **9.** Aidan Brosnan **10.** Taxi
driver **11.** Etta **12.** Kool for Kutz **13.** Debbie Bates **14.** Paul Bradley
15. Hardware **16.** Tony Hills

Children's TV 7

Answers on page 602

Which children's programmes featured the following characters?

1. Spook
2. Penelope Pitstop
3. Dill the dog
4. The Froglets
5. Evans the Song
6. Snorky
7. Sticks
8. Gabriel the toad
9. Basil Bloodhound
10. Kipper the cat
11. Tomsk
12. Thor Nogson
13. Mrs Goggins
14. Captain Snort
15. Captain Flack
16. Dino

Answers to page 602
COMEDY 11: 1. Captain Darling 2. Police officer 3. Bob Hope 4. Kevin Keegan 5. George Harrison 6. Moe's 7. *The Daily Crucible* 8. *The Cuckoo Waltz* 9. The Pontiac Greeting Card Company 10. Rory McGrath 11. *Fawlty Towers* 12. *Man About the House* 13. A thriller writer 14. Marilyn 15. Karl Howman 16. Maurice

EastEnders 2

Answers on page 603

1. Who had kittens called Starsky and Hutch?

2. What was Jan Hammond's occupation?

3. What was the name of Tony Carpenter's son?

4. Who arranged to have Ian Beale shot?

5. Which character is played by Jessie Wallace?

6. Who did Kathy Beale give away for adoption at 15?

7. Who left her newborn baby on Diane Butcher's doorstep on Christmas Day 1990?

8. Who slept together for the first time on Christmas Day 1992?

9. Who tried to commit suicide by jumping off a tower block after seeing his sporting dreams shattered?

10. What does Charlie Slater do for a living?

11. Who was Celestine Tavernier's wife?

12. What was the name of the hairdressing salon set up by Steve Elliot and Della Alexander?

13. Who was killed in a road accident in 1995, a year after marrying Nigel Bates?

14. Who played Nigel Bates?

15. What sort of shop did Ted Hills run in Walford?

16. Who slept with both Tiffany Raymond and her brother Simon?

Answers to page 603
WESTERNS 2: 1. Will Hutchins 2. Paladin 3. *Zorro* 4. *Tombstone Territory* 5. Ward Bond 6. Bill Baxter 7. Micah Torrance 8. The Cartwrights 9. *Wanted: Dead or Alive* 10. Mushy 11. *Laramie* 12. Scott Brady 13. Wyoming 14. Henry Garth 15. *The Big Valley* 16. *The Virginian*

Emmerdale 3

Answers on page 608

1. Who died in the first episode of *Emmerdale Farm*?

2. Andrew Burt originally played which character?

3. What was the name of Lynn Whiteley's husband?

4. Who was Annie Sugden's father?

5. Who was kidnapped in revenge for his father's mysterious army past?

6. Which of the McGann clan plays Sean Reynolds?

7. Which simple village girl married Butch Dingle?

8. Whose daughter Peggy died of a brain haemorrhage?

9. In which year did *Emmerdale* go five nights a week?

10. What crashed on the village in 1993?

11. Which Sixties TV personality turned up as Betty Eagleton's old flame?

12. Who had relationships with both Chris and Zoë Tate?

13. At which sport was Terry Woods once a professional?

14. In 2001, who was revealed to be Zak Dingle's secret son?

15. In which country did Jack Sugden live before returning to the Dales?

16. Who played Dave Glover before moving to *Casualty*?

Answers to page 608
DRAMAS 8: **1.** *Danger UXB* **2.** *The Fugitive* **3.** *London's Burning*
4. *Casualty* **5.** *Peak Practice* **6.** *Sword of Freedom* **7.** *Pennies From Heaven*
8. *Soldier, Soldier* **9.** *ER* **10.** *Boys From the Blackstuff* **11.** *Dick Turpin*
12. *Howard's Way* **13.** *House of Cards* **14.** *Kavanagh QC* **15.** *The
Professionals* **16.** *Probation Officer*

Children's TV 8

Answers on page 609

1. Which *Play School* toy was replaced in 1986 by a black doll, Poppy?

2. Who narrated *Postman Pat*?

3. Who became the *Blue Peter* baby in 1968?

4. Which former *Neighbours* actor took over temporarily from Phillip Schofield as host of *Going Live!*?

5. Who hosted the 'Double Dare' segment on *Going Live!*?

6. Who urges youngsters: *Get Your Own Back*?

7. What are Norb and Dag?

8. Which cat is tormented by cockroaches?

9. Which programme was censured in 1964 over a ginger-pop recipe described by the Temperance Union as 'a dangerously alcoholic brew'?

10. Who was Ollie Beak's shaggy-dog sidekick?

11. Which pussy cat was the mainstay of *Small Time*?

12. Which Douglas was a *Magpie* presenter?

13. What was the name of Shari Lewis's young sheep puppet?

14. Which singing puppets made six appearances on *The Ed Sullivan Show*?

15. Who played Ginger in *Biggles* before having a hit with 'Johnny Remember Me'?

16. Who provides the voice of the toy lion in *Teletubbies*?

Answers to page 609
POT LUCK 10: **1.** *On the Braden Beat* **2.** Paul and Pauline Calf **3.** *QED* **4.** Alan A. Freeman **5.** Mary Stavin **6.** 1947 **7.** Derek Griffiths **8.** Robert Kee **9.** Paul **10.** Colour television **11.** Ayshea Brough **12.** Kate Humble **13.** *Miss World* **14.** Pauline Quirke **15.** Custard **16.** Roald Dahl

Dramas 8

Answers on page 606

In which series past and present have the following characters appeared?

1. Lt Brian Ash

2. Donna Taft

3. George Green

4. Josh Griffiths

5. Dr Alex Redman

6. Marco del Monte

7. Arthur Parker

8. Marsha Stubbs

9. Dr Kerry Weaver

10. Loggo Logmond

11. Swiftnick

12. Polly Urquhart

13. Francis Urquhart

14. Jeremy Aldermarten

15. George Cowley

16. Philip Main

Answers to page 606
EMMERDALE 3: 1. Jacob Sugden 2. Jack Sugden 3. Pete 4. Sam Pearson
5. Will Cairns 6. Stephen 7. Emily Wylie 8. Annie Sugden 9. 2000
10. A plane 11. Leslie Randall 12. Charity Dingle 13. Rugby League
14. Cain Dingle 15. Italy 16. Ian Kelsey

Pot Luck 10

Answers on page 607

1. On which show did Peter Cook's character E.L. Wisty make his debut?

2. Which brother and sister appeared in *Three Fights, Two Weddings and a Funeral*?

3. Which long-running documentary series was replaced by *Living Proof* in 1999?

4. Which *New Faces* panellist had a bowl of sugar tipped over him after describing a singer as 'too camp'?

5. Which Miss Sweden was crowned *Miss World* in 1977?

6. In which year did Sylvia Peters join the BBC?

7. Which Derek was the first presenter of *Don't Ask Me*?

8. Who presented *Ireland: A Television History*?

9. Who was Florence's male friend on *The Magic Roundabout*?

10. What innovation came to British TV in 1967?

11. Who was the Ayshea in *Lift Off With Ayshea*?

12. Which Kate has presented *Top Gear*?

13. Coverage of which contest passed from the BBC to ITV in 1980?

14. Which actress, best known for comedy roles, played a murderess in *The Sculptress*?

15. Who was *Roobarb*'s chief adversary?

16. Which author introduced *Tales of the Unexpected*?

Answers to page 607
CHILDREN'S TV 8: **1.** Hamble **2.** Ken Barrie **3.** Daniel Scott
4. Kristian Schmid **5.** Peter Simon **6.** Dave Benson-Phillips **7.** *The Angry Beavers* **8.** Oggy **9.** *Blue Peter* **10.** Fred Barker **11.** Willum **12.** Douglas Rae **13.** Lamb Chop **14.** Pinky and Perky **15.** John Leyton **16.** Eric Sykes

Comedy 12

Answers on page 612

In which sitcoms did the following characters appear?

1. Dave Charnley
2. Gary Strang
3. Carter Brandon
4. Tony Webster
5. Chrissy Plummer
6. Norman Bormann
7. Dave Best
8. Dan Conner
9. Marjory Frobisher
10. Diana Trent
11. Peggy Ollerenshaw
12. Lionel Hardcastle
13. Dick Lucas
14. Gemma Palmer
15. Charles Brown
16. Jack Jones

Answers to page 612
SOAPS 7: **1.** Emma Bunton **2.** Wentworth Detention Centre **3.** Donna Reed **4.** Michael Crawford **5.** Edward Clayton **6.** Maureen Holdsworth **7.** Grant – by a year **8.** Brian Jarvis **9.** Janice Gifford **10.** Derek Owen **11.** Lane Ballou **12.** Graham Norton **13.** Jim McDonald **14.** Billy Kennedy **15.** Chrissy Rogers **16.** Marilyn Chambers

TV Chefs 2

Answers on page 613

1. Which TV chef is the son of a celebrated Irish presenter?

2. Who reminded the nation *How to Cook*?

3. Who was Jilly Goolden's wine-tasting partner on *Food and Drink*?

4. Which Glynn presented the cookery slot on *Breakfast Time*?

5. Who talked about the *Fruits of the Sea*?

6. Which channel broadcasts *Kitchen Invaders*?

7. Who was the cook on *Multi-Coloured Swap Shop*?

8. Who presented *Food and Drink* for one series only in 1991?

9. Which cookery programme celebrates its 20th anniversary in 2002?

10. Which husband and wife team conducted the 'Happy Cooking' slot on the Fifties children's show *Lucky Dip*?

11. What was Fanny Cradock's real Christian name?

12. Which TV chef refused to take part in a Benny Hill sketch because he thought it questioned his professionalism?

13. Which Fern presented *Ready Steady Cook*?

14. Complete the title: *Can't Cook...*

15. Which George was a TV cook in the Sixties?

16. Who presented *Farmhouse Kitchen*?

Answers to page 613
SCI FI 2: **1.** Tuvok **2.** *The Tomorrow People* **3.** *Timeslip*
4. Romanadvoratrelundar **5.** World Aquanaut Security Patrol
6. Catherine Sakai **7.** Architect **8.** Ros Henderson **9.** Oz **10.** *StarTrek*
11. Professor Matt Matic **12.** Auron **13.** *The X Files* **14.** Safe-cracking
15. Whoopi Goldberg **16.** Buck Rogers

Soaps 7

Answers on page 610

1. Which Spice Girl mugged Jules Tavernier in *EastEnders*?

2. What was the name of the jail in *Prisoner: Cell Block H*?

3. Who took over from Barbara Bel Geddes as Miss Ellie in *Dallas*?

4. Which international stage musical star once played a patient in *Emergency – Ward 10*?

5. Who played Stan Harvey in *Crossroads* and Arthur Parkinson in *Brookside*?

6. Who was left high and dry when her beau's water bed burst in *Coronation Street*?

7. Who is the younger of the two Mitchell brothers in *EastEnders*?

8. Which *Crossroads* character married his father's secretary in 1965?

9. What was her name?

10. What was the name of the supervisor in *Albion Market*?

11. Who was the singer at Lute-Mae Sanders' casino in *Flamingo Road*?

12. Which camp Channel 4 comic made a guest appearance on *Brookside*?

13. Who barged on in Fiona Middleton's *Coronation Street* wedding to Alan McKenna?

14. Which *Neighbours* character was played by Jesse Spencer?

15. Who walked out on her *Brookside* family during her daughter's wedding reception?

16. Who married Donald Fisher in *Home and Away*?

Answers to page 610
COMEDY 12: **1.** *Drop the Dead Donkey* **2.** *Men Behaving Badly* **3.** *I Didn't Know You Cared* **4.** *The Fall and Rise of Reginald Perrin* **5.** *Man About the House* **6.** *The New Statesman* **7.** *The Royle Family* **8.** *Roseanne* **9.** *To the Manor Born* **10.** *Waiting for God* **11.** *Hi-De-Hi!* **12.** *As Time Goes By* **13.** *Are You Being Served?* **14.** *Solo* **15.** *Sykes* **16.** *Dad's Army*

Sci Fi 2

Answers on page 611

1. Who was the Vulcan security officer on *Star Trek: Voyager?*

2. Which group of individuals were Homo Superior?

3. Liz Skinner and Simon Randall were time travellers in which children's sci fi series?

4. What was Romana's full name in *Doctor Who?*

5. What did WASP stand for in *Stingray?*

6. Which Buddhist was Jeffrey Sinclair's occasional girlfriend in *Babylon 5?*

7. What was David Vincent's profession in *The Invaders?*

8. Who was the computer genius in *Bugs?*

9. Which werewolf became Willow's boyfriend in *Buffy the Vampire Slayer?*

10. Which programme was perceived by its creator as being like *Wagon Train* in space?

11. Who was the navigator and designer of *Fireball XL5?*

12. From which planet did Cally hail in *Blake's 7?*

13. Well-Manicured Man featured in which series?

14. What was Parker's criminal speciality in *Thunderbirds?*

15. Which comedy actress played bartender Guinan in *Star Trek: The Next Generation?*

16. Whose space capsule was Ranger 3?

Answers to page 611
TV CHEFS 2: **1.** Mark Wogan **2.** Delia Smith **3.** Oz Clarke **4.** Glynn Christian **5.** Rick Stein **6.** BBC1 **7.** Delia Smith **8.** Paul Heiney **9.** *Food and Drink* **10.** Fanny and Johnnie Cradock **11.** Phyllis **12.** Philip Harben **13.** Fern Britton **14.** *Won't Cook* **15.** George Villiers **16.** Dorothy Sleightholme

Cop Shows 7

Answers on page 616

1. Who starred in *Second Sight*?

2. What was the name of Jean Darblay's husband in *Juliet Bravo*?

3. What was Adam Dalgliesh's father?

4. What did *Hunter* christen his hefty Magnum revolver?

5. Who took over from Kookie at the parking lot in *77 Sunset Strip*?

6. What was *Serpico's* Christian name?

7. Which detective had sons named Harvey Junior and Michael?

8. Who played *Barney Miller*?

9. Who is De Pauli's partner in *Liverpool One*?

10. Chris Tierney, Fabio Cavalcanti and Anna Holz comprised which team of crime-busters?

11. Who did Patrick Mower play in *Target*?

12. Which British police series ran for 16 years from 1962 to 1978?

13. Who was *Banacek's* chauffeur?

14. Rooster was a jive-talking pimp on which show?

15. What was Ricardo Tubbs's undercover identity in *Miami Vice*?

16. Who was Jack Killian's engineer at the radio station?

Answers to page 616
COMEDY 13: **1.** John Lennon **2.** Les Dawson **3.** Dorothy in *Men Behaving Badly* **4.** Leonard Rossiter **5.** Joe **6.** Terry Collier in *Whatever Happened to the Likely Lads?* **7.** Carla Lane **8.** Bernard Hedges in *Please, Sir!* **9.** Paddy **10.** *Porridge* **11.** Lewis Collins **12.** *Curry and Chips* **13.** Sheridan **14.** 'Shirley Temple' **15.** *Friends* **16.** Michael Bates

Name the Year 3

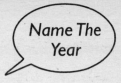

Answers on page 617

In which year were the following programmes first shown on British TV?

1. Tomorrow's World

2. Doctor Who

3. Some Mothers Do 'Ave 'Em

4. Max Headroom

5. The World of Tim Frazer

6. The Word

7. Dinnerladies

8. Dallas

9. Roseanne

10. The Phil Silvers Show

11. Rowan and Martin's Laugh-In

12. The New Statesman

13. The Ruth Rendell Mysteries

14. Hamish Macbeth

15. The Flowerpot Men

16. The Dick Van Dyke Show

Answers to page 617
QUIZ AND GAME SHOWS 3: 1. Ulrika Jonsson 2. John Anderson
3. Helicopter 4. Card Sharks 5. The Price Is Right 6. Magnus Magnusson
(Mastermind) 7. Hexagonal 8. Family Fortunes 9. Una Stubbs and Lionel
Blair 10. Phillip Schofield 11. Chris Tarrant 12. Wednesday at Eight
13. Bernie the Bolt 14. Chris Tarrant 15. Robin Ray 16. Ask the Family

Comedy 13

Answers on page 614

1. Which Beatle played a lavatory attendant in a *Not Only...But Also* sketch?

2. Which comedian described his face as resembling 'a sack of spanners'?

3. Who wore a T-shirt bearing the words 'Don't Even Think About It' after an appendectomy?

4. Who played an escaped convict in an episode of *Steptoe and Son*?

5. What is the name of Mary's quiet husband in *The Royle Family*?

6. Who called Mönchengladbach 'the West Hartlepool of West Germany'?

7. Who wrote *The Mistress*?

8. Which sitcom teacher did Penny Wheeler marry?

9. What was the name of the militant shop steward in *The Rag Trade*?

10. *Prisoner and Escort* was the pilot show for which hit series?

11. Who played the 'cuckoo' in *The Cuckoo Waltz*?

12. Which controversial Johnny Speight sitcom starred Eric Sykes and Spike Milligan?

13. Who was Hyacinth Bucket's wonderful son?

14. What did Alf Garnett call son-in-law Mike because of his long hair?

15. 'I'll Be There For You' is the theme song to which US sitcom?

16. Who blacked up to play Rangi Ram in *It Ain't Half Hot Mum*?

Answers to page 614
COP SHOWS 7: **1.** Clive Owen **2.** Tom **3.** A vicar **4.** 'Simon' **5.** J.R. Hale
6. Frank **7.** Mary Beth Lacey **8.** Hal Linden **9.** DC Mark Callaghan
10. *TECX* **11.** DS Steve Hackett **12.** *Z Cars* **13.** Jay Drury **14.** *Baretta*
15. Rico Cooper **16.** Billy Po

Quiz & Game Shows 3

Answers on page 615

1. Who launched a *Charm Offensive* in 2001?

2. Who was the no-nonsense referee on *Gladiators*?

3. What was Anneka Rice's mode of transport in *Treasure Hunt*?

4. What was the US title of *Play Your Cards Right*?

5. Which game show returned to ITV in 1995 after a seven-year absence?

6. Which quiz show host encouraged contestants to 'Pass' if they didn't know the answer?

7. What shape are the blocks on *Blockbusters*?

8. Which game show's computer used to be called 'Mr Babbage'?

9. Who were the original team captains on *Give Us a Clue*?

10. Which former occupant of the broom cupboard hosted *Talking Telephone Numbers*?

11. Which former teacher presented *Man O Man*?

12. *Name That Tune* was a segment of which variety show in the 1970s?

13. Derek Young, Alan Bailey and Johnny Baker all played which role on *The Golden Shot*?

14. Who was the host of *Everybody's Equal*?

15. Who was the first chairman of *Call My Bluff*?

16. Alan Titchmarsh hosted the revival of which Sixties quiz in 1999?

Answers to page 615
NAME THE YEAR 3: **1.** 1965 **2.** 1963 **3.** 1973 **4.** 1985 **5.** 1960 **6.** 1990 **7.** 1998 **8.** 1978 **9.** 1989 **10.** 1957 **11.** 1968 **12.** 1987 **13.** 1987 **14.** 1995 **15.** 1952 **16.** 1963

Locations 4

Answers on page 620

1. On which island does *Thomas the Tank Engine* operate?

2. Which Western hero stayed at the Hotel Carlton, San Francisco?

3. Which Seventies sitcom husband and wife moved to 46 Peacock Crescent, Hampton Wick?

4. What was the name of the school in *Hope and Glory*?

5. Which north-west London suburb was home to *The Grove Family*?

6. Which Nineties sitcom was set at Farnaby Manor?

7. Which detective lived at St Mary Mead?

8. In which town did the *Frontier Doctor* work?

9. What was the name of the ranch in *The Virginian*?

10. In which city was *North Square*?

11. Who drank at the Scarsdale Working Men's Club?

12. What was the name of the school featured in *Press Gang*?

13. Tundish Hall aimed to discourage what in a 1993 BBC drama?

14. What was the name of the taxi firm in *Roger Roger*?

15. Near which city was the ranch in *Bonanza*?

16. In which town did *The Rifleman* operate?

Answers to page 620
CHAT SHOWS 1: **1.** Jeremy Clarkson **2.** *Pass the Mic* **3.** Matthew Wright **4.** Mel and Sue **5.** Leeza Gibbons **6.** Russell Harty **7.** Clive James **8.** Michael Parkinson **9.** Jonathan Ross **10.** Rowland Rivron **11.** Oliver Reed **12.** George Best **13.** Jonathan Ross **14.** Clive Anderson **15.** Selina Scott **16.** *Russell Harty Plus One*

Dramas 9

Answers on page 621

1. What was Danny Kavanagh's addiction in *The Lakes*?

2. Who faked his death in *Widows*?

3. What was the name of the cook played by Ricky Tomlinson in *Roughnecks*?

4. *To Play the King* was the sequel to which series?

5. What did Jack Maddox initially do for a living in *The House of Eliott*?

6. Which series was based on Simon Nye's novel *Wideboy*?

7. Which series told the stories of student nurses at St Angela's Hospital?

8. Who played Paul Craddock in *A Horseman Riding By*?

9. In which quirky series was Maggie O'Connell a trained pilot?

10. Who wrote the 1976 *Play For Today* production *Bar Mitzvah Boy*?

11. Which character played on TV by Anthony Valentine and Nigel Havers was created by E.W. Hornung?

12. Who resigned from *St Elsewhere* after mooning at the new Chief of Services?

13. As what were Peregrine Smith, Brigadier Davidson and Richard Hurst better known?

14. Who played Nicky Hutchinson in *Our Friends in the North*?

15. In which European city did *The Fortunes of War* open?

16. Who vowed revenge on *The Charmer*?

Answers to page 621
POT LUCK 11: **1.** Edward Enfield (father of Harry) **2.** *Operation Good Guys* **3.** Felixstowe, Gothenburg and Amsterdam **4.** Rachel Hunter **5.** Jeremy Beadle **6.** *Big Strong Boys* **7.** Freeman **8.** Pauline Quirke **9.** Stephen Mangan **10.** Ben and Alexander **11.** Glen Hugill **12.** *Get Your Kit Off* **13.** Jeff Banks **14.** 1983 **15.** Ant and Dec **16.** Sarah Kennedy

Chat Shows 1

Answers on page 618

1. Which motormouth has his own chat show?

2. Which BBC2 talk show was conducted by Luke Hyams?

3. Who hosts the Channel 5 talk show *The Wright Stuff*?

4. Which comedy double act presented *Light Lunch*?

5. Which Leeza has her own talk show?

6. Which chat show host was mocked for his 'you are, are you not?' style of questioning?

7. Which Australian fronted *Saturday Night People*?

8. Which chat show host wrote and narrated *The Woofits*?

9. Who hosted *The Last Resort*?

10. Who played Dr Martin Scrote on *The Last Resort*?

11. Which hell-raising actor appeared to be very, very drunk on *Aspel & Company*?

12. And which footballer was very, very drunk on *Wogan*?

13. Who fronted *Saturday Zoo*?

14. Who talked back on Channel 4?

15. Which *Wogan* stand-in flirted with guest Prince Andrew?

16. In which series did Russell Harty have late-night conversations with just one guest each week?

Answers to page 618
LOCATIONS 4: **1.** Sodor **2.** Paladin in *Have Gun, Will Travel* **3.** *George and Mildred* **4.** Hope Park **5.** Hendon **6.** *Mulberry* **7.** Miss Marple **8.** Rising Springs, Arizona **9.** Shiloh **10.** Leeds **11.** Selwyn Froggitt **12.** Norbridge High **13.** *The Riff Raff Element* **14.** Cresta Cabs **15.** Virginia City **16.** North Fork, New Mexico

Pot Luck 11

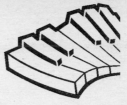

Answers on page 619

1. Which father of a comedian had a stint as an investigative reporter on *Watchdog*?

2. DI Beach and DS Ash are prime movers in which police spoof?

3. Between which three ports did the *Triangle* ferry sail?

4. Which of Rod Stewart's wives appeared in *Shortland Street*?

5. Which prankster was the first presenter of *You've Been Framed*?

6. What are DIY experts Jake Robinson and Gavin Lowe otherwise known as?

7. Which family were the subjects of *In a Land of Plenty*?

8. Which Bird of a Feather starred in *Office Gossip*?

9. Who played Adrian Mole in *The Cappuccino Years*?

10. What are the Christian names of Armstrong and Miller?

11. Who presents *The Mole*?

12. In which Channel 5 game show are members of the public encouraged to part with their clothing?

13. Which Jeff presented *The Clothes Show*?

14. In which year did the BBC launch *Breakfast Time*?

15. Which double act were *Unzipped*?

16. Who was the female face on *Game For a Laugh*?

Answers to page 619
DRAMAS 9: **1.** Gambling **2.** Harry Rawlins **3.** Cinders **4.** *House of Cards* **5.** Photographer **6.** *Frank Stubbs Promotes* **7.** *Angels* **8.** Nigel Havers **9.** *Northern Exposure* **10.** Jack Rosenthal **11.** *Raffles* **12.** Dr Donald Westphall **13.** *The Rat Catchers* **14.** Christopher Eccleston **15.** Bucharest **16.** Donald Stimpson

Sport 3

Answers on page 624

1. Who retired as BBC horse racing commentator in 1997 after 50 years in the job?

2. On which sport did Henry Longhurst commentate for the BBC?

3. What is the name of ITV's new Saturday afternoon update of the football scores?

4. Tony Jardine is a studio expert for which sport?

5. Who was named BBC Sports Personality of the Year in 1986 and 1992?

6. Who was the last presenter of *Sportsview*?

7. Which Idwal was an occasional commentator on *Match of the Day*?

8. Which former England manager is part of ITV's Premiership coverage?

9. Who scored the first goal on *Match of the Day*?

10. Peter Lloyd presented which children's sports programme?

11. Which Peter previewed the day's soccer on *World of Sport*?

12. Which former Warwickshire captain is a Channel 4 cricket commentator?

13. Which two Welsh Rugby Union skippers have been team captains on *A Question of Sport*?

14. Which Tim reads the football results on *Grandstand*?

15. Who presents *On Side*?

16. Hamilton Bland was a BBC commentator on which sport?

Answers to page 624
COMEDY 14: 1. Minehead 2. 'Cupcake' 3. Albert Steptoe 4. Lance Corporal Jones 5. *The Liver Birds* 6. Lurcio 7. *Curry and Chips* 8. Blamire 9. Harry Grout 10. The Grumbleweeds 11. *Feet First* 12. Evadne 13. *Lucky Feller* 14. David Jason 15. Peter Jones and Sheila Hancock 16. Robin Bailey

Soaps 8

Answers on page 625

1. Whose house on Brookside Close was daubed with anti-gay slogans?

2. Who played Hugh Mortimer in *Crossroads*?

3. Which family moved into 9 Coronation Street in 1983?

4. What did Des Clarke do for a living in *Neighbours*?

5. What is *High Road* farmer Tom Kerr more commonly known as?

6. What was the name of Alan Jackson's grandmother in *EastEnders*?

7. Who created *The Colbys*?

8. Which travelling salesman did Kath Brownlow fall for in *Crossroads*?

9. To which country did Ray Langton go on leaving Weatherfield?

10. Who played Mike Young in *Neighbours* and David Croft in *Home and Away*?

11. Which future movie star played PR man Crispin Ryder in *Crossroads*?

12. Where did Ernest and Emily Bishop go for their *Coronation Street* honeymoon?

13. Who was paid $150,000 an episode for her three appearances in *Dynasty*?

14. For what crime was Bea Smith doing time in *Prisoner: Cell Block H*?

15. Kevin Laffan created which soap?

16. What was the name of Annie Hart's husband in *Family Affairs*?

Answers to page 625
CHILDREN'S TV 9: **1.** 'Gaz Top' **2.** Ostrich **3.** Mr Rusty **4.** Paddy and Mary **5.** *Grange Hill* **6.** Velma **7.** Milo **8.** Teenage Mutant Hero Turtles **9.** Penelope Keith **10.** No Slacking **11.** Soo **12.** Bertie Bonkers **13.** *Sketch Club* **14.** Green **15.** Jones the Steam **16.** *Bonehead*

Comedy 14

Answers on page 622

1. In which English town did Mr Hilter stand for election in *Monty Python's Flying Circus*?

2. What was Private Cook's nickname in *The Army Game*?

3. Who memorably ate pickled onions in the bath?

4. Who was the local butcher in *Dad's Army*?

5. Dawn and Beryl were the original flatmates in which series?

6. Who did Frankie Howerd play in *Up Pompeii!*?

7. In which series did Spike Milligan play a Pakistani?

8. Which *Last of the Summer Wine* character left the show in 1976 to pursue a widow?

9. Who was the prison 'Mr Big' in *Porridge*?

10. Who had their own *Radio Show* on TV from 1983?

11. What was the title of John Esmonde and Bob Larbey's 1979 soccer sitcom?

12. What is the Christian name of Dr Hinge in *Hinge and Bracket*?

13. 'Shorty' Mepstead was the girl-shy hero of which sitcom?

14. Who played him?

15. Which two *Rag Trade* actors were reunited in *Mr Digby, Darling*?

16. Who took over as *Potter* following the death of Arthur Lowe?

Answers to page 622
SPORT 3: **1.** Peter O'Sullevan **2.** Golf **3.** *The Goal Rush* **4.** Motor racing
5. Nigel Mansell **6.** Frank Bough **7.** Idwal Robling **8.** Terry Venables
9. Roger Hunt (Liverpool) **10.** *Seeing Sport* **11.** Peter Lorenzo
12. Dermot Reeve **13.** Cliff Morgan and Gareth Edwards **14.** Gudgin
15. John Inverdale **16.** Swimming

Children's TV 9

Answers on page 623

1. What did *How 2* presenter Gareth Jones used to call himself?

2. What kind of creature was Octavia in *Pipkins*?

3. Who owned a barrel-organ in *The Magic Roundabout*?

4. What were the names of Mickey Murphy's children in *Camberwick Green*?

5. A Somerset Women's Institute demanded the instant scrapping of which children's programme in 1979?

6. Who is the brains of Scooby Doo's gang?

7. Which of the *Tweenies* is purple?

8. Leonardo and Michelangelo were members of which gang?

9. Who provides the voice of the toy bear on *Teletubbies*?

10. What was the name of the Chuckle Brothers' boss in *Chucklevision*?

11. Who joined *The Sooty Show* in 1964 amidst accusations of bringing sex into children's television?

12. What was the name of the baby elephant with *Pinky and Perky*?

13. Which Sixties art series was presented by Adrian Hill?

14. What colour was *Ivor the Engine*?

15. And who drove him?

16. Happy and Fingers were members of whose gang?

Answers to page 623
SOAPS 8: **1.** Paul and Annabelle Collins **2.** John Bentley **3.** The Duckworths **4.** Bank manager **5.** Inverdarroch **6.** Blossom **7.** Aaron Spelling **8.** John Latchford **9.** Holland **10.** Guy Pearce **11.** Malcolm McDowell **12.** Edale **13.** Sophia Loren **14.** Murdering her husband **15.** *Emmerdale Farm* **16.** Chris

Brookside 2

Answers on page 628

1. At which number Brookside Close did the Grants live?

2. Which couple divorced and re-married in 1993?

3. Whose boyfriends Simon Howe and Clint Moffat both ended up dead?

4. What was Eleanor Kitson's occupation?

5. Who was Mick Johnson's schoolteacher stalker?

6. Who died in jail in 1995?

7. Which former star of *The Comedians* played Ray Piper?

8. Who hurled a brick through the window of her lover Tim Derby's house?

9. Who shot himself at the end of the 1985 siege?

10. Whose affair with Jerome Johnson ended his relationship with Nikki Shadwick?

11. To whom did Sinbad propose via the electronic scoreboard at Everton's Goodison Park?

12. Who squirted a corrosive liquid at Jacqui Dixon's eyes?

13. What was the name of Peter Phelan's sister?

14. Which animal rights activist was Louise Hope's long-lost father?

15. Who gave birth to a Down's syndrome baby named Alice?

16. What was Sue Sullivan's maiden name?

Answers to page 628
QUIZ AND GAME SHOWS 4: **1.** Captain Sensible **2.** 'Nasty' Nick Bateman **3.** Julian Clary **4.** Annabel Croft **5.** *The Golden Shot* **6.** Chesney Hawkes **7.** Frank Muir and Robert Morley **8.** Boswell Taylor **9.** Geoffrey Wheeler **10.** Lennie Bennett **11.** Martyn Lewis **12.** *3-2-1* **13.** *The $64,000 Question* **14.** *The Krypton Factor* **15.** *Take Your Pick* **16.** *Pets Win Prizes*

Sci Fi 3

Answers on page 629

1. Who created *Land of the Giants*?

2. What was the sequel to *Battlestar Galactica*?

3. At what speed was *The Six Million Dollar Man* capable of running?

4. From which American state did Captain Kirk hail?

5. Which *Doctor Who* assistant was played by Bonnie Langford?

6. What was Avon's Christian name in *Blake's 7*?

7. What are the three castes of Minbari in *Babylon 5*?

8. In *The Time Tunnel*, which pair were rescued from the deck of the *Titanic* just before it sank?

9. What did SHADO stand for in *UFO*?

10. Which 13-part series starring James Garner told the story of America's space programme?

11. Which series was the first to feature the Wedgwood family?

12. Vic Perrin and Kevin Conway have both played the Control Voice in which series?

13. What is the name of Lady Penelope's ocean-going cruiser?

14. In *Babylon 5*, which disease wiped out the Markab race?

15. What was the name of Dr Beverly Crusher's genius son in *Star Trek: The Next Generation*?

16. Who was Titan's inept agent in *Stingray*?

Answers to page 629
DRAMAS 10: **1.** Jesse **2.** Foxy **3.** Hobie **4.** *The Glittering Prizes* **5.** Jack Davenport **6.** Peter Horton **7.** *Grafters* **8.** *Kate* **9.** Richard Todd **10.** Quentin Crisp **11.** *The Brothers* **12.** Sandra **13.** Assumpta Fitzgerald **14.** Adam Williams **15.** Jimmy Nail **16.** *ER*

Quiz & Game Shows 4

Answers on page 626

1. Who sings the theme song to *Big Break*?

2. Who won *The Weakest Link*'s reality TV special in 2001?

3. Who took over as host of *Mr and Mrs* in 1999?

4. Who starred in *Interceptor*?

5. Andrea Lloyd, Anita Richardson and Carol Dilworth were the first hostesses on which game show?

6. Carol Dilworth is the mother of which pop star?

7. Who were the first team captains on *Call My Bluff*?

8. Who was the chief question-setter on *Television Top of the Form*?

9. Who asked the questions on *Winner Takes All*?

10. Which comic hosted *Punchlines* and *Lucky Ladders*?

11. Which former newsreader hosted *Today's the Day*?

12. Which game show featured a team of hostesses called The Gentle Secs?

13. On which US game show was *Double Your Money* based?

14. Which show aimed to find Britain's 'Superperson'?

15. Which show featured the Yes/No Interlude?

16. Which Saturday evening animal game show was hosted by such diverse talents as Danny Baker and Dale Winton?

Answers to page 626
BROOKSIDE 2: 1. No. 5 2. Max and Patricia Farnham 3. Katie Rogers
4. Solicitor 5. Jenny Swift 6. Beth Jordache 7. Duggie Brown 8. Sammy
Rogers 9. John Clarke 10. Nisha Batra 11. Marcia Barrett 12. Leanne
Powell 13. Fee 14. Marcus Seddon 15. Patricia Farnham 16. Harper

Dramas 10

Answers on page 627

1. Who was the Duke cousins' wily old uncle in *The Dukes of Hazzard*?

2. Who did Tim Healy play in *Common as Muck*?

3. What was the name of Mitch's son in *Baywatch*?

4. Adam Morris was the central character in which Seventies drama about academic life?

5. Who played Miles in *This Life*?

6. Which husband of Michelle Pfeiffer appeared in *thirtysomething*?

7. In which series do Robson Green and Stephen Tompkinson play builders?

8. Which 1970 drama starred Phyllis Calvert as an agony aunt?

9. Which film star played Heathcliff in the 1953 BBC version of *Wuthering Heights*?

10. Which outrageous character did John Hurt play in *The Naked Civil Servant*?

11. Which Seventies series featured the trials and tribulations of the Hammond family?

12. What was the name of John Hallam's wife in *London's Burning*?

13. In *Ballykissangel*, who died in Father Peter Clifford's arms after electrocuting herself?

14. Which of the *Cold Feet* characters is a systems analyst?

15. Who created and starred in *Crocodile Shoes*?

16. In which series did Alan Alda return to the operating theatre as Dr Gabriel Lawrence?

Answers to page 627
SCI FI 3: **1.** Irwin Allen **2.** *Galactica 1980* **3.** 60 mph **4.** Iowa **5.** Melanie Bush **6.** Kerr **7.** Religious, Warrior and Worker **8.** Tony Newman and Doug Phillips **9.** Supreme Headquarters, Alien Defence Organisation **10.** *Space* **11.** *Target Luna* **12.** *The Outer Limits* **13.** *Seabird* **14.** Drafa **15.** Wesley **16.** X20

Soaps 9

Answers on page 632

1. Which *Coronation Street* character blew up his own boat?

2. Which hugely popular actor once played a psychopathic gardener in *Crossroads*?

3. Which schizophrenic interrupted Grant Mitchell's carving of the Christmas turkey to call him the Devil Incarnate?

4. What was Dorothy Burke's profession in *Neighbours*?

5. In *Dallas*, who did Pam Ewing marry during a dream sequence?

6. Which former *Z Cars* actor played Angus Hart in *Family Affairs*?

7. Who was Pippa's second husband in *Home and Away*?

8. Who married Sammy Rogers in *Brookside*?

9. Which international musical star played Caroline Winthrop in *Crossroads* back in 1968?

10. To which country did *Coronation Street*'s Chalkie Whiteley emigrate?

11. The Crown and the Bull were pubs in which Sixties soap?

12. In which soap have locals drunk at Bev's Bar?

13. Who went on to become a famous TV face after playing Dr Richard Moone in *Emergency – Ward 10*?

14. Which *Coronation Street* couple had a baby called Ben in December 2001?

15. Who burnt down the E20 club in 2001?

16. Which financial adviser of Hugh Mortimer first arrived at *Crossroads* in 1978?

Answers to page 632
WILDLIFE 3: **1.** Greyhound **2.** Amanda Burton **3.** Masai Mara **4.** *The Dog Listener* **5.** Trude Mostue and Steve Leonard **6.** Great Dane **7.** John Noakes **8.** Fred the tortoise who had to be hastily renamed Freda **9.** *Predators* **10.** *The World About Us* **11.** David Bellamy **12.** Rolf Harris **13.** Ornithology **14.** Chris Packham **15.** *Salty* **16.** Bear

Children's TV 10

Answers on page 633

1. Which sister of John Mills talked to *Muffin the Mule*?

2. Who lived in a basket with *Andy Pandy* and Looby Loo?

3. Who presented *Record Breakers* until his death in 1994?

4. Which Tony was a *Magpie* presenter?

5. Which member of *Rag, Tag and Bobtail* was a hedgehog?

6. Who gave up reading the stories on *Picture Book* to play Maid Marian in *The Adventures of Robin Hood*?

7. Which all-action game show on *Going Live!* was presented by Peter Simon and Shane Richie?

8. Who presented *Live and Kicking* alongside Zoë Ball?

9. Which family had twins called Willy and Jenny?

10. What kind of animal was Midge in *Mary, Mungo and Midge*?

11. Who was billed as 'the greatest secret agent in the world'?

12. Which cartoon horse was the fastest draw in the west?

13. What colour was *Roobarb*?

14. Pilchard the cat appears with which handyman?

15. Who narrated the stories of *Joe*?

16. Who was a *Blue Peter* presenter from 1962 to 1971?

Answers to page 633
NAME THE YEAR 4: 1. 1992 2. 1962 3. 1982 4. 1973 5. 1985 6. 1963
7. 1984 8. 1987 9. 1957 10. 1964 11. 1974 12. 1973 13. 1977 14. 1953
15. 1993 16. 1968

Wildlife 3

Answers on page 630

1. What breed of dog was Grant Mitchell's Frieda in *EastEnders*?

2. Which actress went in search of bears in 2000 for *Born to be Wild*?

3. On which African game reserve was Channel 5's *Passion for the Wild* filmed?

4. As what is Jan Fennell better known?

5. Who are *Vets in the Wild*?

6. What breed of dog is Scooby-Doo?

7. Which ex-*Blue Peter* presenter was *Mad About Pets* in 1999?

8. Which *Blue Peter* pet had a sex change?

9. Which wildlife series looks at natural-born killers?

10. Which BBC2 natural history series ran from 1967 to 1986?

11. Who was *Up a Gumtree*?

12. Who introduced us to the *Amazing World of Animals*?

13. Tony Soper specialised in which field of natural history?

14. Which Chris was a presenter on *The Really Wild Show*?

15. Which sea-lion had his own series?

16. What kind of animal was *Gentle Ben*?

Answers to page 630
SOAPS 9: **1.** Des Barnes **2.** David Jason **3.** Joe Wicks **4.** School headmistress **5.** Mark Graison **6.** Ian Cullen **7.** Michael Ross **8.** Owen Daniels **9.** Elaine Paige **10.** Australia **11.** *The Newcomers* **12.** *Brookside* **13.** John Alderton **14.** Curly and Emma Watts **15.** Melanie Owen **16.** Adam Chance

Name the Year 4

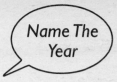

Answers on page 631

In which year did the following programmes first appear on British television?

1. Gladiators

2. That Was The Week That Was

3. Fame

4. That's Life

5. Howard's Way

6. The Telegoons

7. Spitting Image

8. French and Saunders

9. Jim's Inn

10. Bewitched

11. The Planet of the Apes

12. Warship

13. Robin's Nest

14. The Good Old Days

15. The Detectives

16. Please, Sir!

Answers to page 631
CHILDREN'S TV 10: **1.** Annette Mills **2.** Teddy **3.** Roy Castle
4. Bastable **5.** Rag **6.** Patricia Driscoll **7.** Run the Risk **8.** Jamie Theakston
9. The Woodentops **10.** Mouse **11.** Dangermouse **12.** Quick Draw McGraw
13. Green **14.** Bob the Builder **15.** Lee Montague **16.** Valerie Singleton

Comedy 15

Answers on page 636

1. What nationality is Armando Iannucci of *The Saturday Night Armistice*?

2. Which dull Yorkshireman was tested in a *Ripping Yarns* story?

3. Which Australian was a regular on *Hancock's Half-Hour*?

4. Who played the condescending continuity announcer in *Victoria Wood – As Seen On TV*?

5. Who performed the opening theme song each week on *That Was The Week That Was*?

6. Which two comedy actors brought *One-Upmanship* to television?

7. What is Roz's surname in *Frasier*?

8. Which *Only Fools and Horses* character persisted in calling Rodney 'Dave'?

9. What in 1975 was 'Britain's smallest television network'?

10. Which character was the 'man' in *Man About the House*?

11. In which US sitcom did Larry Hagman play Anthony Nelson?

12. Who wrote *I Didn't Know You Cared*?

13. Who hosted *Friday Night Live*?

14. In which decade was the Richard Wilson sitcom *High & Dry* set?

15. Who played Competitive Dad on *The Fast Show*?

16. Who was Alan Partridge's loyal PA?

Answers to page 636
DRAMAS 11: **1.** Rula Lenska **2.** Nancy Mitford **3.** *Sword of Freedom* **4.** Derek Hatton **5.** Jimmy Nail and Christopher Fairbank **6.** John McArdle **7.** Andrew Ray (son of Ted) **8.** *Will Shakespeare* **9.** The Majestics **10.** Vincent **11.** Joe **12.** Glenda Jackson (*Elizabeth R*) **13.** Kenneth Branagh **14.** *Bird of Prey* **15.** Sir Laurence Olivier **16.** *The Sullivans*

Music 2

Answers on page 637

1. Which group were created by *Popstars Australia*?

2. Which Spice Girl presented *This Is My Moment*?

3. Who failed an audition for *The Monkees* before joining a Seventies supergroup?

4. Which Seventies group had their own series, *Shang-A-Lang*?

5. Who co-presented the first *Ready, Steady, Go!* with Keith Fordyce?

6. Which presenter of *The Tube* was suspended in 1987 for swearing during a trailer for the show?

7. What was the name of the first dance troupe on *Top of the Pops*?

8. Which punk band, having heard that they were expected to trash their *Top of the Pops* dressing-room, gave it a good spring-clean instead?

9. Which Sixties Merseybeat star presented *Discotheque*?

10. Which *Carry On* star used to host *Six-Five Special*?

11. Which flu-ridden *Top of the Pops* DJ fainted into Alan Freeman's arms at the start of one show?

12. Who was reprimanded for saying, 'It's effing freezing' on *The Tube*?

13. Which team of Boys were regulars on *Oh Boy!*?

14. And who were their female counterparts on the show?

15. Which band provided the *Top of the Pops* theme but refused to appear on the show?

16. Which of Basil Brush's sidekicks presented *Get It Together*?

Answers to page 637
LOCATIONS 5: 1. Sydney 2. *The Liver Birds* 3. Carlisle Crescent
4. Africa 5. *High Road* 6. St Elegius 7. Brussels 8. *The Likely Lads* 9. *The Virginian* 10. *Angels* 11. Melbourne 12. *High Street Blues* 13. *Rosie and Jim* 14. Melbourne 15. Boston 16. Cumbria

Dramas 11

Answers on page 634

1. Who played 'Q' in *Rock Follies*?

2. Whose novels were adapted for TV in 2001 as *Love in a Cold Climate*?

3. Which swashbuckling series starred Edmund Purdom?

4. Which radical politician sought legal advice because he thought *GBH*'s Michael Murray was based on him?

5. Which two *Auf Wiedersehen, Pet* actors were regulars in *Crocodile Shoes*?

6. Which former *Brookside* actor played Tonbridge in *The Cazalets*?

7. Which son of a famous Fifties comedian played King George VI in *Edward and Mrs Simpson*?

8. Which was the first ITV series to be sold to Russia?

9. What was the name of the band in *Tutti Frutti*?

10. And which member of the band set himself alight on stage?

11. What was *Hine*'s Christian name?

12. Which actress shaved her forehead and wore a false nose to play an English monarch?

13. Who starred as Ernest Shackleton in the 2002 drama?

14. Henry Jay was the civil servant hero of which series?

15. Which esteemed actor made his TV debut in a 1958 production of Ibsen's *John Gabriel Borkman*?

16. Which 1970s Australian series starring Paul Cronin depicted family life during the Second World War?

Answers to page 634
COMEDY 15: **1.** Scottish **2.** Eric Olthwaite **3.** Bill Kerr **4.** Susie Blake
5. Millicent Martin **6.** Richard Briers and Peter Jones **7.** Doyle **8.** Trigger
9. *Rutland Weekend Television* **10.** Robin Tripp **11.** *I Dream of Jeannie*
12. Peter Tinniswood **13.** Ben Elton **14.** 1940s **15.** Simon Day **16.** Lynn

Locations 5

Answers on page 635

1. Near which Australian city is Summer Bay supposed to be?

2. Which sitcom flatmates lived in Huskisson Street?

3. What was the name of the London crescent in *The Crezz*?

4. Which continent was the principal setting for *The Flame Trees of Thika*?

5. Which soap is set In Glendarroch?

6. Which hospital was commonly known as *St Elsewhere*?

7. In which European capital were *TECX* based?

8. Who worked at Ellisons' Electrical on Tyneside?

9. Which Western was set in Medicine Bow?

10. Which nurses moved from London to Heath Green Hospital, Birmingham?

11. Erinsborough is said to be a suburb of which city?

12. Which short-lived, shop-based Eighties sitcom was set in Hatford?

13. Who lived on the narrowboat *Ragdoll*?

14. Which city was the setting for *The Sullivans*?

15. In which city was *St Elsewhere* set?

16. In which English county was *Porridge*'s Slade Prison?

Answers to page 635
MUSIC 2: **1.** Bardot **2.** Mel B **3.** Stephen Stills **4.** The Bay City Rollers **5.** David Gell **6.** Jools Holland **7.** The GoJos **8.** The Stranglers **9.** Billy J. Kramer **10.** Jim Dale **11.** Tony Blackburn **12.** Paula Yates **13.** The Dallas Boys **14.** The Vernon Girls **15.** Led Zeppelin **16.** Roy North

Corrie 5

Answers on page 640

1. To whom did Elsie Lappin speak the first words on *Coronation Street*?

2. Who was taken to Weatherfield Hospital after suffering a stroke in the first month of the *Street*?

3. Who leaked town hall secrets to Ken Barlow at the *Gazette*?

4. Who did Billy Williams marry in the 1990s?

5. What was Albert Tatlock's favourite tipple?

6. Which singer played Malcolm Nuttall, Kevin Webster's love rival?

7. Whose wrongful imprisonment led to her being dubbed 'the Weatherfield One'?

8. Who slumped dead over her milk stout in 1964?

9. Who jilted Leonard Swindley at the altar?

10. Which layabout is played by Bruce Jones?

11. What sort of business did Len Fairclough run?

12. Which couple moved into 13 Coronation Street in 1964?

13. Which of Ken Barlow's wives committed suicide?

14. What did Harry Hewitt do for a living?

15. Who was Derek Wilton's rival for the hand of Mavis Wilton?

16. Which member of the Barlow family perished under the wheels of a bus?

Answers to page 640
QUIZ AND GAME SHOWS 5: **1.** Aztec, Futuristic, Medieval and Industrial **2.** Sharron Davies **3.** Michael Aspel **4.** Gordon Burns **5.** Arthur Marshall **6.** Nine **7.** Wiggling her bottom **8.** *Take Your Pick* **9.** Kenny Everett **10.** Sarah Kennedy **11.** *Concentration* **12.** Three **13.** *The Generation Game* **14.** Charlie Williams **15.** Jilly Cooper **16.** Richard O'Brien

Pot Luck 12

Answers on page 641

1. Which camp comic did *All Rise* for?

2. Who was the first gardening guru on *Pebble Mill at One*?

3. Who was the Gary in *Cue Gary*?

4. Which sitcom star used to play Jeremy Parsons QC on *Crown Court*?

5. Which show invited celebrities to 'Grab a Grand'?

6. Which company did Meridian succeed as franchise-holder for the south and south-east of England?

7. What were the Special Intelligence Force better known as in a 1978 drama series starring Roy Marsden?

8. Which 1980 documentary led to the suspension of diplomatic relations between Britain and Saudi Arabia?

9. Until 1957, what was the name of the one-hour gap in early-evening programmes designed to allow mothers to put children to bed?

10. Who is Norman Pace's comedy partner?

11. Which presenter earned her big break on *Braden's Week*?

12. Who ran a motorcycle courier service called The Texas Rangers?

13. Which Ferrari used to present *Eurotrash*?

14. Who plays Jenny Gifford in *Cold Feet*?

15. What kind of establishment was the setting for the sitcom *Chalk*?

16. Which children's request show was presented by Michael Aspel?

Answers to page 641
SCI FI 4: **1.** John Cleese **2.** Londo Mollari **3.** Miles O'Brien **4.** *The Tripods* **5.** John Duttine **6.** *Fireball XL5* **7.** *Max Headroom* **8.** *Blake's 7* **9.** *Buffy the Vampire Slayer* **10.** Steven Houghton **11.** Mr Sulu **12.** Japanese **13.** Alan **14.** Diana **15.** John **16.** Boris Karloff

Quiz & Game Shows 5

Answers on page 638

1. What were the original four zones in *The Crystal Maze*?

2. Which swimmer took the name 'Amazon' on *Gladiators*?

3. Who was chairman of *Give Us a Clue* from 1979 to 1984?

4. Who presented *The Krypton Factor*?

5. Which Arthur was a team captain on *Call My Bluff*?

6. In *The Weakest Link*, how many correct answers have to be strung together in a round to win the maximum £1,000?

7. What was *Double Your Money* hostess Jean Clarke criticised for doing?

8. In which series did contestants have to choose between opening the box or taking the money?

9. Which *Blankety Blank* panellist once produced a packet of Spanish peanuts called Bum in the middle of a question?

10. Which star of *Game For a Laugh* succeeded Julian Pettifer as host of *Busman's Holiday*?

11. Nick Jackson hosted the revival of which game show in 1988?

12. How many pairs of contestants took part in each *Bullseye*?

13. Which show always featured a cuddly toy among its prizes?

14. Which of *The Comedians* hosted *The Golden Shot*?

15. Who won *The Weakest Link*'s author special in February 2002?

16. Which creator of *The Rocky Horror Show* presented *The Crystal Maze*?

Answers to page 638
CORRIE 5: 1. Florrie Lindley 2. Ena Sharples 3. Wendy Crozier
4. Betty Turpin 5. Rum 6. Michael Ball 7. Deirdre Rachid 8. Martha
Longhurst 9. Emily Nugent 10. Les Battersby 11. Building 12. Stan and
Hilda Ogden 13. Janet Reid 14. Bus inspector 15. Victor Pendlebury
16. Ida

Sci Fi 4

Answers on page 639

1. Which *Monty Python* star played an art critic in the *Doctor Who* story *City of Death?*

2. Who is Centauri ambassador on *Babylon 5?*

3. Who was the pessimistic operations director aboard *Star Trek: Deep Space Nine?*

4. Which three-legged alien machines ruled Earth in a 1984 BBC sci fi series?

5. Who played Bill Masen in the 1981 version of *The Day of the Triffids?*

6. Which was the first Gerry Anderson series to be fully networked on American TV?

7. Which computer-generated TV presenter took his name from a car park sign?

8. Zen, Orac and Slave were computers on which series?

9. *Angel* was a spin-off from which series?

10. Who took over from Craig McLachlan as Ed in *Bugs?*

11. Who was the chief navigator in the original *Star Trek?*

12. And what nationality was he?

13. Which of the Tracy family in *Thunderbirds* is an accomplished racing driver?

14. Who was the alien leader in *V?*

15. Who was the only member of *The Tomorrow People* to appear in all eight series?

16. Which master of the macabre introduced *Out of This World?*

Answers to page 639
POT LUCK 12: **1.** Julian Clary **2.** Peter Seabrook **3.** Gary Wilmot
4. Richard Wilson **5.** *Noel's House Party* **6.** TVS **7.** *The Sandbaggers*
8. *Death of a Princess* **9.** The Toddlers' Truce **10.** Gareth Hale **11.** Esther
Rantzen **12.** Ken Boon **13.** Lolo Ferrari **14.** Fay Ripley **15.** A school
16. *Ask Aspel*

Children's TV 11

Answers on page 644

1. What was Constable Knapweed's number in *The Herbs*?

2. What musical instrument did Gabriel play in *Bagpuss*?

3. In which village did Mr Dagenham act as salesman?

4. Whose footsteps did Bill and Ben dread hearing?

5. Railroad supervisor Bart McClelland was the hero of which adventure series?

6. On which white dolphin did *Marine Boy* hitch a ride?

7. What was the name of the tortoise in *The Flowerpot Men*?

8. Which duo provided the laughs on *Going Live!*?

9. What was Mexican Pete's favourite dance on *Whirligig*?

10. Which international rock star's father used to run Lenny the Lion's fan club?

11. Which newspaper was run by Peter, Andy, Tubby, Swot and 'Fred'?

12. Spike the cactus grows in whose shop?

13. What is *Aunt Boomerang* according to the title of a BBC1 children's series?

14. Which former punk singer played Aunt Boomerang?

15. And which Sixties pop star played *Uncle Jack*?

16. Who was *Uncle Jack* always trying to outfox?

Answers to page 644
EASTENDERS 3: 1. Joe Wicks 2. Michael French 3. Bianca Jackson 4. Manor Wood 5. Andrea 6. Vanessa 7. Den and Angie Watts 8. Ian Beale 9. Michelle 10. Sharon Watts 11. Eibhlin O'Donnell 12. Tony and Hannah Carpenter 13. Naima Jeffery 14. Huw Edwards 15. Matthew Rose 16. Ethel Skinner

Dramas 12

Answers on page 645

1. Which British comedienne plays *Ally McBeal's* analyst?

2. Robby Box was the gambler hero of which series?

3. And who played Robby Box?

4. Which *Northern Exposure* character was a Native American?

5. Who did James Herriot marry in *All Creatures Great and Small?*

6. Which *Casualty* charge nurse married Dr Baz Hayes in 1998?

7. In which decade was *The Grand* set?

8. What was Louisa Trotter better known as?

9. Which series starred Nigel Havers as a former Boer War soldier living in Devon?

10. Which gangster's mansion did the lads renovate in series two of *Auf Wiedersehen, Pet?*

11. Which newspaper-based series was the forerunner of *Hadleigh?*

12. Which TV barrister had a wife Lizzie and teenage children Kate and Matt?

13. What type of dancer did Purdey from *The New Avengers* used to be?

14. Which tough businessman liked to play *The Power Game?*

15. How many children were there in *The Waltons?*

16. Who did Bernard Hepton play in *Tinker, Tailor, Soldier, Spy?*

Answers to page 645
POT LUCK 13: **1.** *Noel's House Party* **2.** 'You're a Star' **3.** Carl Wayne
4. Gwen Taylor **5.** Victor Sylvester **6.** Clive James **7.** Bamber Gascoigne
8. Teddy Johnson and Pearl Carr **9.** Bernard Braden **10.** *Challenge Anneka*
11. Taxidermy **12.** William Franklyn **13.** Dawn French **14.** Susan Tully
15. 1992 **16.** Denise Van Outen

EastEnders 3

Answers on page 642

1. Who felt guilty because his sister Karen had been killed in a car crash?

2. Who played David Wicks?

3. Who caught Ricky Butcher *in flagrante* with Natalie Price in 1995?

4. What was the name of Roy Evans's car dealership?

5. What is the name of Natalie's mother?

6. Which fake fiancée fleeced Barry Evans?

7. Which pair went to Venice in 1986?

8. Who used to run the 'Meal Machine'?

9. Which Fowler sold timeshares for a while?

10. Who was adopted at the age of three by Den and Angie Watts?

11. Who was Eddie Royle's Irish girlfriend?

12. From which couple did Colin Russell buy his flat?

13. Who was the first proprietor of the First Till Last Mini-Market?

14. Which *EastEnders* character shared his name with a BBC newsreader?

15. Who was found guilty of the manslaughter of Saskia Duncan?

16. Which Queen Vic regular wore an orange wig?

Answers to page 642
CHILDREN'S TV 11: **1.** PC 29 **2.** Banjo **3.** *Camberwick Green* **4.** The gardener **5.** *Union Pacific* **6.** Splasher **7.** Old Slowcoach **8.** Trevor and Simon **9.** The Mexican Hat Dance **10.** David Bowie **11.** *Adventure Weekly* **12.** *Mopatop's Shop* **13.** *Barmy* **14.** Toyah Willcox **15.** Paul Jones **16.** Vixen

Pot Luck 13

Answers on page 643

1. 'Wait Till I Get You Home' was a segment on which show?

2. What was the original theme song to *New Faces*?

3. And who sang it?

4. Who played Rita Simcock in *A Bit of a Do*?

5. Which pioneer of 'slow, slow, quick, quick, slow' presented *Television Dancing Club*?

6. Who investigated *Fame in the Twentieth Century*?

7. Who was the first presenter of ITV's *Cinema*?

8. Who came second in the 1959 Eurovision Song Contest with 'Sing Little Birdie'?

9. Which Canadian TV personality became chairman of *The Brains Trust* in 1957?

10. Which Anneka Rice series developed from the 1988 Children in Need event?

11. What was Sam Tyler's hobby in *Three Up, Two Down*?

12. Who hosted the Seventies panel game *Masterspy*?

13. Who starred in *Murder Most Horrid*?

14. Which former *EastEnders* actress has since returned as a director on the show?

15. In which year was UK Gold established?

16. Which presenter used to be part of a pop group called Those 2 Girls?

Answers to page 643
DRAMAS 12: **1.** Tracey Ullman **2.** *Big Deal* **3.** Ray Brooks **4.** Ed Chigliak **5.** Helen Alderson **6.** Charlie Fairhead **7.** 1920s **8.** *The Duchess of Duke Street* **9.** *A Horseman Riding By* **10.** Ally Fraser **11.** *Gazette* **12.** *Kavanagh QC* **13.** Ballerina **14.** John Wilder **15.** Seven **16.** Toby Esterhase

Comedy 16

Answers on page 648

1. Which secret agent soundalike did George Baker play in *Up Pompeii!*?

2. Who had the hots for Nurse G-G-G-Gladys Emmanuel?

3. Which series did Peter Sallis once describe as being '*Just William* with pension books'?

4. In *The Simpsons*, who are the kids' favourite cartoon characters?

5. Which Fifties show was originally titled *You'll Never Get Rich* in the US?

6. Which Seventies hit stemmed from a play called *The Banana Box*?

7. What was the name of the incompetent builder in *Fawlty Towers*?

8. Who was the hopeless medic in *The Fall and Rise of Reginald Perrin*?

9. Who was married to Boycie in *Only Fools and Horses*?

10. What was Mike Selway's job in *A Fine Romance*?

11. What relation was Chachi to the Fonz in *Happy Days*?

12. Which comedians won £250,000 for charity in a 2001 *Who Wants to be a Millionaire* special?

13. Who revealed that an anagram of his own name was 'Anal Delve'?

14. Which dance troupe livened up *The Kenny Everett Video Show*?

15. Who played Brian Drake in *Lame Ducks*?

16. Marta Kauffman and David Crane created which hit sitcom?

Answers to page 648
SOAPS 10: **1.** Steps **2.** Cliff Barnes **3.** Chris Tate **4.** Four – Peter Mark Richman, Lloyd Bochner, Paul Burke and Charles Bateman **5.** Kevin Kline **6.** *Neighbours* **7.** 'Mum' **8.** Rosemary Hunter **9.** Elsa **10.** Ken Farrington (Billy Walker in the *Street*) **11.** Darren Roebuck **12.** Martino Lazzeri **13.** Halliwell **14.** Anthony Stephens **15.** Maureen Flynn **16.** Woody

Catchphrases 2

'NICE TO SEE YOU, TO SEE YOU NICE'

Answers on page 649

1. Which juvenile exclaims: 'Eat my shorts!'

2. Which comedian insists: 'It's the way I tell 'em'?

3. Which Kenny Everett character promised: 'It's all done in the best possible taste'?

4. Who turned an audience member's deaf cat into a national catchphrase?

5. And what was it?

6. Which disturbed individual said: 'I can do that'?

7. Whose road rage exploded with moans of 'Drat and triple drat'?

8. Which Seventies sitcom character popularised the word 'Magic!'?

9. Which children's TV character said: 'Time for bed'?

10. Which series states: 'The truth is out there'?

11. Which quiz show host said: 'I've started so I'll finish'?

12. Which chaotic couple's catchphrase is 'To me, to you'?

13. Who repeatedly told Hokey Wolf: 'You're my hero, Hokey'?

14. Which cartoon character said: 'Just a cotton-pickin' minute'?

15. Who wishes his listeners 'good mental health'?

16. Who referred to ''er indoors'?

Answers to page 649
DRAMAS 13: **1.** Beatrice and Evangeline **2.** *The Final Cut* **3.** Glover
4. *A Family at War* **5.** Joel Fleischman **6.** Jim Pratt **7.** Anne **8.** *Upstairs, Downstairs* **9.** *Within These Walls* **10.** Carol Johnson **11.** Bill Nighy
12. 'Diesel' **13.** Niamh Quigley **14.** Tom Baker **15.** World War Two
16. John

Soaps 10

Answers on page 646

1. Which pop band came to stay at the new Crossroads Hotel?

2. In *Dallas*, who ended up owning Ewing Oil?

3. Who was Kathy Bates's second husband in *Emmerdale*?

4. How many different actors played the weird C.C. Capwell in *Santa Barbara*?

5. Which movie star once played Woody Reed in the US soap *Search For Tomorrow*?

6. On which soap did the Pet Shop Boys' Chris Lowe make an appearance?

7. What was Jeanette Brooks's nickname in *Prisoner: Cell Block H*?

8. Which *Crossroads* wife was committed to a psychiatric hospital in 1980?

9. Who was married to Jack Gates in *Family Affairs*?

10. And which former *Coronation Street* actor played Jack Gates?

11. Which doctor left *Brookside* in 2001?

12. Who plays Alex Bell in *Hollyoaks*?

13. What surname was *Coronation Street*'s Alma using when she died?

14. In *Coronation Street*, who pursued Rita Sullivan despite having a sick wife?

15. Which gypsy girl was knocked off her bicycle and killed on the morning of her intended wedding to *Crossroads*' Benny Hawkins?

16. Which jailbird boyfriend was briefly reunited with *Neighbours*' Steph Scully in 2000?

Answers to page 646
COMEDY 16: **1.** James Bondus **2.** Arkwright **3.** *Last of the Summer Wine* **4.** Itchy and Scratchy **5.** *The Phil Silvers Show* **6.** *Rising Damp* **7.** O'Reilly **8.** Doc Morrissey **9.** Marlene **10.** Landscape gardener **11.** Cousin **12.** David Baddiel and Frank Skinner **13.** Dave Allen **14.** Hot Gossip **15.** John Duttine **16.** *Friends*

Dramas 13

Answers on page 647

1. What were the names of the Elliott sisters in *The House of Eliott*?

2. What was the title of the last series in the *House of Cards* trilogy?

3. Which surname linked *Peak Practice*'s Dr Beth with a family in *Emmerdale*?

4. The rush home to see which dour tale of wartime Liverpool regularly brought traffic in Copenhagen to a standstill in the 1970s?

5. What was the name of the fish-out-of-water doctor in *Northern Exposure*?

6. Who owned J.P. Electrics in *Playing the Field*?

7. Which of James Onedin's wives died in childbirth?

8. Thirteen episodes of which period drama were banned in the US for 17 years because they dealt with homosexuality and adultery?

9. Faye Boswell, Helen Forrester and Susan Marshall were all prison governors in which series?

10. Which of the girls in *Gold* inherited money from an ex-punter?

11. Who played womanising Professor Mark Carleton in *The Men's Room*?

12. What was Des Moyle's nickname in *Preston Front*?

13. Which daughter of the local entrepreneur married PC Ambrose Egan in *Ballykissangel*?

14. Which ex-*Doctor Who* played eccentric professor of surgery Geoffrey Hoyt in *Medics*?

15. During which war was *Manhunt* set?

16. What was Sutherland's Christian name in *Sutherland's Law*?

Cop Shows 8

Answers on page 652

1. Which private eye took on *An Unsuitable Job for a Woman*?

2. Which TV detective had a wife named Steve?

3. For whom did Nick Mancuso work?

4. What did 'Ten-four' mean in *Highway Patrol*?

5. Carol White played Cathy Ward in which ground-breaking *Wednesday Play*?

6. Who changed his name to Jonathan Smith when returning to Earth in *Highway to Heaven*?

7. Who created *London's Burning*?

8. Who employed Rocky Cassidy as a despatch rider?

9. Emma Hart was the rags-to-riches heroine of which series?

10. Which *Soldier, Soldier* character was blown up on exercise in New Zealand?

11. Which trio of super-agents worked for Nemesis?

12. What was antiques dealer John Mannering better known as?

13. In which series did Dolly Rawlins turn to crime?

14. Which 1978 play by Roy Minton was banned from British television until 1991?

15. Who played the Bard in *Will Shakespeare*?

16. Who starred opposite John Stride in *Wilde Alliance*?

Answers to page 652
COMEDY 17: 1. Tommy Cooper 2. Rolf Harris 3. Bernard Levin 4. *Not Only…But Also* 5. The Spanish Inqusition 6. Daphne Moon 7. Karl Howman 8. *Not Only…But Also* 9. *Not the Nine O'Clock News* 10. Mr Mole 11. Julia Hills 12. Jasper Carrott 13. Tom Patterson 14. *The Dick Van Dyke Show* 15. *Hot Metal* 16. George Cole

News 1

Answers on page 653

1. Which original anchor man for *News at Ten* presented the news for Thames before retiring in 1992?

2. In which year did Trevor McDonald join ITN?

3. Which former ITN newsreader narrated *Arthur C. Clarke's Mysterious World*?

4. Which pregnant newsreader sang 'Hello, Young Lovers' on Russell Harty's show?

5. In 1963, Tim Hewat became the first producer of which hard-hitting current affairs series?

6. Which Peter read the news on *The Big Breakfast*?

7. To which tune did Angela Rippon demonstrate her dancing talents on *The Morecambe and Wise Show*?

8. Which confrontational interviewer became front man of *Newsnight* in 1989?

9. Robin Day, George Fitch and Tim Brinton were travelling reporters on which early ITV series?

10. Which Macdonald was a reporter on *Tonight*?

11. What relation is Peter Snow to Jon Snow?

12. Rob Butler reads the news on which channel?

13. Who introduced the Swingometer into election-night coverage?

14. And what nationality was he?

15. Which Zeinab read the Channel 4 News?

16. Which newsreader highlighted the Ethiopian famine of 1984?

Answers to page 653
POT LUCK 14: **1.** *Top Gear* **2.** Michael Palin **3.** Gaby Roslin **4.** Paul Shane **5.** *Will and Grace* **6.** *Fortean TV* **7.** *It'll Be Alright on the Night* **8.** *Martians* **9.** Ward **10.** Nick Hancock **11.** Harry Enfield **12.** *Celebrity Sleepover* **13.** Angus Deayton **14.** Channel 4 **15.** Robert Downey Jr **16.** *Cheaters*

Comedy 17

Answers on page 650

1. Who died on *Live From Her Majesty's* in 1984?

2. Which entertainer made one of his first TV appearances in the *Hancock's Half Hour* episode 'The Flight of the Red Shadow'?

3. Who did astrologer Katina squirt with a plastic lemon on *That Was The Week That Was*?

4. Which Sixties show featured the Gerry Anderson parody 'Superthunderstingcar'?

5. Cardinals Ximanez, Fang and Biggles made up which fiendish *Monty Python* triumvirate?

6. What character does Jane Leeves play in *Frasier*?

7. Who succeeded Robert Lindsay as Jakey Smith in *Get Some In!*?

8. On which series were 'Poets Cornered'?

9. Constable Savage appeared in a sketch on which show?

10. Who did Lollipop Love in a 1970s sitcom?

11. Who was the female member of the *Who Dares Wins* team?

12. Who pioneered '*Sun* reader jokes'?

13. Who was renowned for his home-made wine in *The Fall and Rise of Reginald Perrin*?

14. Rob and Laura Petrie were the married couple on which show?

15. Greg Kettle was a gutter journalist in which Eighties comedy?

16. Who played David Bliss on radio and TV in *A Life of Bliss*?

Answers to page 650
COP SHOWS 8: 1. Cordelia Gray 2. *Paul Temple* 3. The FBI
4. 'Message received and understood' 5. *Cathy Come Home* 6. Arthur
Morton 7. Jack Rosenthal 8. Ken Boon 9. *A Woman of Substance*
10. Fusilier Vinny Bowles 11. *The Champions* 12. *The Baron* 13. *Widows*
14. *Scum* 15. Tim Curry 16. Julia Foster

Pot Luck 14

Answers on page 651

1. With which BBC2 series was Vicki Butler-Henderson associated?

2. Who went *Full Circle* in 1997?

3. Which popular BBC presenter made her name on the children's show *Motormouth*?

4. Who starred as theatrical agent Harry James in the sitcom *Very Big Very Soon*?

5. In 2001, which US sitcom beat *Friends* to win the Emmy for Outstanding Comedy Series?

6. On which Channel 4 series does Father Lionel Fanthorpe explore bizarre phenomena?

7. Which series, first airing in 1977, marked its 13th edition in August 2001?

8. What creatures are *Butt-Ugly* in an ITV children's series?

9. Which Ali is one of the presenters on *Gardening Neighbours*?

10. Who presented *Sex and Stopping: A History of Contraception*?

11. Which comedian offered an irreverent *Guide to the North* in 2001?

12. Michael Winner, Vanessa Feltz and Jeremy Beadle all became house-guests in which series?

13. Who presented *The Temptation Game* and *The Lying Game*?

14. Which channel screens *The Sopranos*?

15. Who plays Larry Paul in *Ally McBeal*?

16. Which Channel 5 show exposes unfaithful partners?

Answers to page 651
NEWS 1: 1. Andrew Gardner 2. 1973 3. Gordon Honeycombe 4. Jan Leeming 5. *World in Action* 6. Peter Smith 7. 'Let's Face the Music and Dance' 8. Jeremy Paxman 9. *Roving Report* 10. Macdonald Hastings 11. Cousin 12. Channel 5 13. Robert McKenzie 14. Canadian 15. Zeinab Badawi 16. Michael Buerk

Dramas 14

Answers on page 656

In which series have the following characters appeared?

1. Charlie Endell

2. Landburgher Gessler

3. Spider Scott

4. Sheriff Harry S. Truman

5. Bradford Webster

6. Guy Buchanan

7. Lord Alex Marchmain

8. Charles Frere

9. Diane Ralston

10. Father MacAnally

11. Frank Carver

12. Kevin Medhurst

13. Mary Fisher

14. Martin Ashford

15. Billy Thomas

16. George Warleggan

Answers to page 656
LOCATIONS 6: 1. *The Bill* 2. Manchester 3. *The District Nurse* 4. *Nash Bridges* 5. Causton 6. Fulchester Crown Court 7. *Softly, Softly* 8. Liverpool 9. René Artois (*'Allo 'Allo*) 10. *Dalziel and Pascoe* 11. *A Horseman Riding By* 12. *Soap* 13. Denton 14. The Porters (*2 Point 4 Children*) 15. San Francisco 16. Lowlands

Quiz & Game Shows 6

Answers on page 657

1. Which quiz was based on the US series *College Bowl?*

2. Which sisters hosted *Your Kids Are in Charge?*

3. Which *What's My Line?* panellist was front page news after losing an ear-ring on the show?

4. And which comedian wore an eye-patch on *What's My Line?* after a blood vessel had burst?

5. What was TV's noughts-and-crosses game show?

6. And which Old Harrovian was the chief questionmaster?

7. Who made his name as the resident expert on *Going For a Song?*

8. How many correct answers must contestants get in the finale of *Wipeout?*

9. Which Arthur, not known for his speed of thought, was a regular guest on *Celebrity Squares* in the 1970s?

10. Which Millwall supporter presented the daytime sketching quiz *Win, Lose or Draw?*

11. Which London taxi driver won *Mastermind* in 1980?

12. In which show did young contestants have to go from gold to gold 'in 60 seconds or less'?

13. Who hosted *Take a Letter?*

14. Which former quiz show host was born Cedric Lange?

15. Which comedian hosted *Lucky Numbers?*

16. Which game show returned to ITV in 1992 after a 24-year absence?

Answers to page 657
EMMERDALE 4: **1.** Christine Sharp **2.** Alan Turner **3.** Angharad **4.** Barry Clegg **5.** Bare-knuckle fighting **6.** Ruth Pennington **7.** Stuart Wade **8.** Eric Pollard **9.** Inglebrook **10.** Shirley Foster **11.** Bridlington **12.** Seth Armstrong **13.** John Wylie **14.** Carlos Diaz **15.** Derek Warner **16.** Amos and Henry

Locations 6

Answers on page 654

1. Which police series investigates trouble on the Larkmead Estate?

2. In which English city was *The Grand* located?

3. Which series was set in the Welsh mining village of Pencwm?

4. Which police detective lived on a boat moored at North Pier, San Francisco?

5. Where is Inspector Barnaby based in *Midsomer Murders*?

6. What was the name of the court in *Crown Court*?

7. Which police series was set in Wyvern?

8. In which city did *The Wackers* live?

9. Who was a café proprietor in the French town of Nouvion?

10. Which police duo operate from the fictional Yorkshire town of Wetherton?

11. The Shallowford Estate was the fictional setting for which period drama?

12. Which sitcom was set in the town of Dunn's River, Connecticut?

13. Which town is the patch of Detective Inspector Jack Frost?

14. Which sitcom family lived at 142 Chepstow Road, Chiswick?

15. In which city did *McMillan and Wife* live?

16. What was the name of the university in *A Very Peculiar Practice*?

Answers to page 654
DRAMAS 14: 1. *Budgie/Charles Endell Esquire* 2. *The Adventures of William Tell* 3. *The XYY Man* 4. *Twin Peaks* 5. *The Third Man* 6. *Perfect Scoundrels* 7. *Brideshead Revisited* 8. *Howard's Way* 9. *The Knock* 10. *Ballykissangel* 11. *Love Hurts* 12. *London's Burning* 13. *The Life and Loves of a She Devil* 14. *Casualty* 15. *Ally McBeal* 16. *Poldark*

Emmerdale 4

Answers on page 655

1. Which of Joe Sugden's wives worked for the Milk Marketing Board?

2. Who became landlord of the Woolpack following the retirement of Amos Brearly?

3. What was the name of Bernard McAllister's wife?

4. To whom was Lisa Dingle previously married?

5. At which illegal sport did Zak Dingle and Ned Glover excel?

6. Who bought Joe Sugden a horse named Saint?

7. Who played Biff Fowler?

8. Which shady businessman did Elizabeth Feldmann marry?

9. In which cottage did Henry Wilks live before moving to the Woolpack?

10. Which one-time prostitute married Alan Turner?

11. Where was Amos Brearly born?

12. Which character is played by Stan Richards?

13. What is the name of Emily Dingle's father?

14. Who broke off his relationship with Nicola Blackstock in August 2001?

15. Who killed Harry Mowlam?

16. What did Sam Skilbeck call his two pet rabbits?

Answers to page 655
QUIZ AND GAME SHOWS 6: 1. *University Challenge* 2. Anthea and Wendy Turner 3. Barbara Kelly 4. Bob Monkhouse 5. *Criss Cross Quiz* 6. Jeremy Hawk 7. Arthur Negus 8. Six 9. Arthur Mullard 10. Danny Baker 11. Fred Housego 12. *Blockbusters* 13. Bob Holness 14. Jeremy Hawk 15. Shane Richie 16. *Take Your Pick*

Children's TV 12

Answers on page 660

1. Who was *The Brady Bunch*'s nutty housekeeper?

2. From which century did *Catweazle* originate?

3. John and Sue Peters were the young friends of which man of straw?

4. Which *Tiswas* favourite also presented *Saturday Scene*?

5. What was the name of the mole in *Barnaby*?

6. Katie Kookaburra was a friend of which pair of marsupials?

7. Which radio hero came to TV in 1979 with Tony Vogel in the title role?

8. Who starred as Luke Firbeck in *Luke's Kingdom*?

9. Who was the Matthew in *Rainbow*'s early singing trio Rod, Jane and Matthew?

10. On which Saturday morning show were contestants invited to Challenge Ant?

11. What was the name of *Yogi Bear*'s adversary Mr Ranger?

12. Prince Philip, George Harrison and Jerry Hall have all been victims of what?

13. Who was the evil witch in *H.R. Pufnstuf*?

14. King Dithers was a ruler in which series?

15. Which hound guarded Yakky Doodle?

16. What kind of animal was Babar?

Answers to page 660
SOAPS 11: **1.** Philip Winter **2.** Lance Smart **3.** Teresa Nolan **4.** Liam **5.** Armed robbery **6.** Carmen Silvera **7.** Fiction editor **8.** Malcolm **9.** Frank Barlow **10.** Sam Carne **11.** Ozcabs **12.** Grace Metalious **13.** Lorenzo Lamas **14.** Christopher Timothy **15.** Darius Perkins **16.** The Simpsons

Sci Fi 5

Answers on page 661

1. In what subject did Fox Mulder graduate from Oxford?

2. Which future movie star played friendly alien Willie in *V*?

3. What was George Sheridan's nickname in *Stingray*?

4. Which TV sci fi series started out as a sketch on a radio series called *Son of Cliché*?

5. Why had *Buffy the Vampire Slayer* been expelled from school in Los Angeles?

6. Which time traveller did Peter Firth play in two Eighties BBC productions?

7. In *Space: 1999*, who was the last survivor of the planet Psychon?

8. Which female impressionist played Flast, the Cryon leader, in the 1985 *Doctor Who* story 'Attack of the Cybermen'?

9. Which member of the *Star Trek: Voyager* crew was half-Klingon?

10. In which *Star Trek* series did Stephen Hawking make a guest appearance as himself?

11. Which two American astronauts ended up on *The Planet of the Apes*?

12. Who created *The Twilight Zone*?

13. Who played the third *Doctor Who*?

14. Which *Doctor Who* assistant was played by Wendy Padbury?

15. Who was the adopted son of Professor Ian McClaine?

16. Which series featured a magician named Tarot?

Answers to page 661
COP SHOWS 9: 1. Mike Burden 2. *Hazell* 3. District nurse 4. DS Jimmy Beck 5. *The Gold Robbers* 6. Agatha Troy 7. William Simons (PC Alf Ventress and Insp. Brad Fox) 8. Loretta Swit 9. *The Expert* 10. Phil Collins 11. *Mark Saber* 12. Antonia Fraser 13. Jill Kirkendall 14. Suzanne Fabray 15. *Z Cars* 16. Arthur Ward

Soaps 11

Answers on page 658

1. Which army deserter and motel handyman was the first man to have an affair with Jill Richardson in *Crossroads*?

2. Which mate of Martin Dibble in *Home and Away* failed to live up to his name?

3. Which *Brookside* wife committed suicide in 1986 by jumping off the Mersey Ferry?

4. What was the name of Nick Trip's son in *Family Affairs*?

5. And for what crime was the teenager given a custodial sentence?

6. Which *'Allo 'Allo* actress played Camilla Hope in *Compact*?

7. And what was Camilla's title on the magazine?

8. What was the name of Billy Kennedy's older brother in *Neighbours*?

9. In 1963, which *Coronation Street* character left his job at the Post Office to open a DIY shop?

10. What was 'Carney's' real name in *Crossroads*?

11. What was the name of Ali and Mehmet Osman's taxi firm in *EastEnders*?

12. Who wrote the original novel of *Peyton Place*?

13. Who played Lance Cumson in *Falcon Crest*?

14. Which former TV vet plays Mac in the BBC daytime soap *Doctors*?

15. Who was the first actor to play Scott Robinson in *Neighbours*?

16. Which family moved into 9 Brookside Close in 1996?

Answers to page 658
CHILDREN'S TV 12: 1. Alice Nelson 2. The 11th 3. *Worzel Gummidge*
4. Sally James 5. Maisie 6. Tingha and Tucker 7. *Dick Barton* 8. Olivia
Tobias 9. Matthew Corbett 10. *SM:TV Live* 11. John Smith 12. Sooty's
water pistol 13. Miss Witchiepoo 14. *Torchy, the Battery Boy* 15. Chopper
the Bulldog 16. Elephant

Cop Shows 9

Answers on page 659

1. Which sidekick of Reg Wexford did Jenny Ireland marry?

2. 'Choc' Minty was the sparring partner of which detective?

3. What was Maggie Bolton's job in *Heartbeat*?

4. Which twisted copper did Lorcan Cranitch play in *Cracker*?

5. Which villains were pursued by Peter Vaughan's DCS Cradock In a 1969 ITV series?

6. Who was Inspector Alleyn's artistic lady friend?

7. Which actor could be seen on the same night as one of the regular PCs in *Heartbeat* and as an Inspector in *The Inspector Alleyn Mysteries*?

8. Which *M*A*S*H* star played Christine Cagney in the pilot show of *Cagney and Lacey*?

9. What was pathologist Professor John Hardy known as in a 1968 BBC2 series?

10. Which singer played a con man in an episode of *Miami Vice*?

11. Which Fifties crime series was titled *The Vise* in the US?

12. Who created Jemima Shore?

13. Who does Andrea Thompson play in *NYPD Blue*?

14. What was the name of the boys' French receptionist on *77 Sunset Strip*?

15. *Softly, Softly* was a spin-off from which police series?

16. To whom did Lew Erskine report in *The FBI*?

Answers to page 659
SCI FI 5: **1.** Psychology **2.** Robert Englund **3.** 'Phones' **4.** *Red Dwarf*
5. Arson **6.** Dominick Hyde **7.** Maya **8.** Faith Brown **9.** B'Elanna Torres
10. *The Next Generation* **11.** Alan Virdon and Pete Burke **12.** Rod Serling
13. Jon Pertwee **14.** Zoë Herriot **15.** *Joe 90* **16.** *Ace of Wands*

Dramas 15

Answers on page 664

1. What relation were Siegfried and Tristan Farnon in *All Creatures Great and Small*?

2. Which successful character first appeared in a BBC *Play for Today* but was eventually snapped up by ITV in 1978?

3. Who injured himself in the eye while playing King Harold in *Churchill's People*?

4. In *Northern Exposure*, whose five previous boyfriends had all died in tragic accidents?

5. Who was married to Elliot in *thirtysomething*?

6. Who in *This Life* quit law to work in a restaurant?

7. What was the nickname of Fusilier Rawlins in *Soldier, Soldier*?

8. What was Brendan Kearney's job in *Ballykissangel*?

9. What colour suit did Boss Hogg usually wear in *The Dukes of Hazzard*?

10. Who played Lawrence Preston in *The Defenders*?

11. Which Nigel replaced another Nigel as the star of *Dangerfield*?

12. Who wrote *A Bit of a Do*?

13. In what field did Frank Carver make his fortune in *Love Hurts*?

14. Dr Roger Corder was the central character in which Sixties series?

15. And which future associate of Inspector Clouseau played him?

16. Who starred in *To Serve Them All My Days*?

Answers to page 664
COMEDY 18: 1. Kate O'Mara 2. Peter Cook and Dudley Moore
3. Solicitor 4. Doris 5. Joan Sanderson 6. MP 7. A record shop 8. Helen
Cooper 9. Plantagenet 10. *Beggar My Neighbour* 11. Richard Waring
12. Jimmy Clitheroe 13. Pinner 14. *Mind Your Language* 15. Basil
16. Peter Brough

Music 3

Answers on page 665

1. According to Mark Lamarr, what were Johnny Kidd, Alma Cogan and Terry Dene?

2. Which Harry Enfield and Paul Whitehouse creations hosted *Top of the Pops*?

3. Julian Lloyd-Webber's 'Variations' is the theme to which show?

4. Which miming singer wasn't ready for the sound track on *Pebble Mill at One*?

5. Which American star suffered a similar fate on *This Morning*?

6. Who wrote the *Coronation Street* theme?

7. Who briefly succeeded Pan's People as dance troupe on *Top of the Pops*?

8. Which *Top of the Pops* presenter met her future husband, Toploader's Dan Hipgrave, on the show?

9. Which show decided to ban miming in 1965?

10. Which country won the 2001 Eurovision Song Contest?

11. And who came 15th for the UK with 'No Dream Impossible'?

12. Which TV presenter was known as 'Queen of the Mods'?

13. On which regional programme did Bill Grundy appear to goad The Sex Pistols into swearing?

14. Following a mix-up, which guitar legend found himself miming to an Alan Price hit on *Top of the Pops*?

15. Which Meg presented *Get It Together*?

16. Which of *The Monkees* later had a solo hit with 'Rio'?

Answers to page 665
SOAPS 12: **1.** *Crossroads* **2.** *Hollyoaks* **3.** *Neighbours* **4.** *The Colbys*
5. *United!* **6.** *Brookside* **7.** *Peyton Place* **8.** *Home and Away* **9.** *Crossroads*
10. *Coronation Street* **11.** *Dallas* **12.** *Sons and Daughters* **13.** *Coronation Street* **14.** *EastEnders* **15.** *Emmerdale* **16.** *Brookside*

Comedy 18

Answers on page 662

1. Who played Patsy's sister Jackie in *Absolutely Fabulous?*

2. Which pair created the 'Dagenham dialogues'?

3. What was Alec Callender's profession in *May to December?*

4. What was the formidable Miss Ewell's Christian name in *Please, Sir!?*

5. And who played her?

6. What did Jean Price discover was *No Job For a Lady?*

7. Where did Wolfie's girlfriend Shirley work in *Citizen Smith?*

8. Which lesbian single mother joined the *Drop the Dead Donkey* team?

9. What was the distinctive Christian name of *The Magnificent Evans?*

10. Peter Jones and Reg Varney were adversaries in which 1967 sitcom?

11. Who wrote *Marriage Lines?*

12. Who was the Jimmy in *Just Jimmy?*

13. With which London suburb did Vince share his surname in *Just Good Friends?*

14. Which series was titled *What a Country!* when re-made for American TV?

15. Which character was dropped from the American ABC version of *Fawlty Towers?*

16. Which ventriloquist had a doll named Archie Andrews?

Answers to page 662
DRAMAS 15: **1.** Brothers **2.** *Rumpole of the Bailey* **3.** Dennis Waterman
4. Maggie O'Connell **5.** Nancy **6.** Egg **7.** 'Midnight' **8.** Schoolteacher
9. White **10.** E.G. Marshall **11.** Nigel Havers (taking over from Nigel Le Vaillant) **12.** David Nobbs **13.** Plumbing **14.** *The Human Jungle*
15. Herbert Lom **16.** John Duttine

Soaps 12

Answers on page 663

In which soaps have the following characters appeared?

1. Malcolm Ryder

2. Tony Hutchinson

3. Dr Beverly Marshall

4. Zachary Powers

5. Danny South

6. Sizzler

7. Elliott Carson

8. Finlay Roberts

9. Jim Baines

10. Chris Collins

11. Jordan Lee

12. Patricia Hamilton

13. Nellie Harvey

14. Rod Norman

15. Edna Birch

16. Cheryl Boyanowsky

Answers to page 663
MUSIC 3: **1.** *Jukebox Heroes* **2.** Smashey and Nicey **3.** *The South Bank Show* **4.** Owen Paul **5.** Gene Pitney **6.** Eric Spear **7.** Ruby Flipper **8.** Gail Porter **9.** *Ready, Steady, Go!* **10.** Estonia **11.** Lindsey Dracass **12.** Cathy McGowan **13.** *Today* **14.** Jimi Hendrix **15.** Meg Nicoll **16.** Mike Nesmith

Comedy 19

Answers on page 668

1. What was the first *Comic Strip Presents...* film?

2. *Mr Don and Mr George* was a spin-off from which sketch show?

3. Who was the compere of *Packet of Three*?

4. Who were *In Pieces* after *The Mary Whitehouse Experience*?

5. On which quiz show did *The Young Ones* appear?

6. What did the Bishop of Bath and Wells love to eat in *Blackadder II*?

7. Which politician was portrayed as a slug on *Spitting Image*?

8. Who did *Sykes* beat in a dream in the episode 'Sykes and a golfer'?

9. Which camp comic was born William White?

10. Which comedy impressionist used to work as an assistant in the menswear department of a Kingston store?

11. Which show introduced the Self-Righteous Brothers?

12. Which series revealed that 'Virginia Bottomley' is an anagram of 'I'm an evil Tory bigot'?

13. What was Kirk's surname in *Dear John...*?

14. Who played Albert in *Dear Mother – Love Albert*?

15. Who was Sharon and Tracey's man-eating neighbour in *Birds of a Feather*?

16. Who played Mindy to Robin Williams's Mork?

Answers to page 668
NAME THE YEAR 5: **1.** 1977 **2.** 1975 **3.** 1999 **4.** 1972 **5.** 1979 **6.** 1989
7. 1969 **8.** 1958 **9.** 1963 **10.** 1970 **11.** 1981 **12.** 1964 **13.** 1962 **14.** 1956
15. 1967 **16.** 1955

Pot Luck 15

Answers on page 669

1. Who left *Melrose Place* to play Charlotte York in *Sex and the City*?

2. Which survival challenge did the BBC screen in 2001?

3. What is *Mona* in the title of a children's series?

4. Simon Thomas, Matt Baker, Konnie Huq and Liz Barker were the presenters of which series in 2001?

5. Who dropped a viewer's prize clock on *Antiques Roadshow*, causing it to shatter into a hundred pieces?

6. Which transsexual won the 1998 Eurovision Song Contest?

7. Which fashion designer joined Antoine de Caunes presenting early episodes of *Eurotrash*?

8. Which *Dallas* star went on to appear in the sitcom *Step by Step*?

9. Which stony-faced comedian presents his *Happy Hour*?

10. In which religious sitcom was Philip Lambe the vicar?

11. Which former *Coronation Street* star supported Morecambe and Wise in their 1954 TV debut, *Running Wild*?

12. Who was the star of *Sez Les*?

13. Which presenter was once dubbed 'the thinking man's crumpet'?

14. Which yokel poet was a winner on *Opportunity Knocks* in 1975?

15. Who presented *The Big Big Talent Show*?

16. Which BBC channel was launched on 9 November 1997?

Answers to page 669
BROOKSIDE 3: **1.** Kevin **2.** Heather Haversham **3.** 'Growler' **4.** Katie Rogers **5.** Jason Shadwick **6.** Brussels **7.** Bruce Grobbelaar **8.** Jimmy Corkhill **9.** The Rogers **10.** Harry Cross **11.** Jim Wiggins **12.** Eddie Banks **13.** Mary Tamm **14.** The milkman **15.** Bristol **16.** Brian Kennedy

Name the Year 5

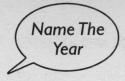

Name The Year

Answers on page 666

In which year did the following programmes first appear on British TV?

1. *Abigail's Party*

2. *The Cuckoo Waltz*

3. *The Grimleys*

4. *McCloud*

5. *Sapphire and Steel*

6. *Stay Lucky*

7. *Stars on Sunday*

8. *Your Life in Their Hands*

9. *The Dick Emery Show*

10. *A Family at War*

11. *The Hitch-Hiker's Guide to the Galaxy*

12. *Meet the Wife*

13. *Dr Finlay's Casebook*

14. *Whack-O!*

15. *At Last the 1948 Show*

16. *Quatermass II*

Answers to page 666
COMEDY 19: **1.** *Five Go Mad in Dorset* **2.** *Absolutely* **3.** Frank Skinner
4. *Newman and Baddiel* **5.** *University Challenge* **6.** Babies **7.** Kenneth Baker
8. Peter Alliss **9.** Larry Grayson **10.** Bobby Davro **11.** *Harry Enfield and Chums* **12.** *Drop the Dead Donkey* **13.** St Moritz **14.** Rodney Bewes
15. Dorien Green **16.** Pam Dawber

Brookside 3

Answers on page 667

1. What was the name of Harry Cross's son?

2. Who called off her 1985 wedding to businessman Tom Curzon?

3. What was Geoff Rogers' nickname?

4. Debbie Reynolds originally played which *Brookside* character?

5. And who did Vincent Price play?

6. In which European city did Margi Shadwick land a job?

7. Which former Liverpool footballer took part in a charity night for Tony Dixon at La Luz?

8. Who deliberately left Joey Godden stranded at the scene of an armed robbery?

9. Which family moved into 7 Brookside Close in 1987?

10. Whose garden gnomes went AWOL in 1983?

11. Who played Paul Collins?

12. Who had an affair with his daughter-in-law in 1996?

13. Which one-time assistant to *Doctor Who* played David Crosbie's sister-in-law?

14. Who spoke the first words on *Brookside*?

15. Where did Mandy Jordache go to live after leaving the Close?

16. Which hairdresser ended up in jail after a drugs deal went wrong?

Answers to page 667
POT LUCK 15: **1.** Kristin Davis **2.** *The Heat Is On* **3.** *The Vampire* **4.** *Blue Peter* **5.** Arthur Negus **6.** Dana International **7.** Jean-Paul Gaultier **8.** Patrick Duffy **9.** Jack Dee **10.** *All in Good Faith* **11.** Amanda Barrie **12.** Les Dawson **13.** Joan Bakewell **14.** Pam Ayres **15.** Jonathan Ross **16.** BBC News 24

Comedy 20

Answers on page 672

1. Which mouth-organist was repeatedly told 'Not now, Arthur' by Morecambe and Wise?

2. Which future *EastEnder* played Lyn in the 1977 revival of *The Rag Trade*?

3. Which *Only Fools and Horses* actor died in 1999?

4. Which comedy actress wanted to put Anne Robinson into Room 101 in 2002?

5. What was the title of the sequel to *I Love Lucy*?

6. Joan Cooper, who played Dolly Godfrey in *Dad's Army*, was married to which member of the show's cast?

7. Which sitcom centred around the meetings of the 1-2-1 Club?

8. Who starred in *Duck Patrol*?

9. With what surname was Prunella Scales born?

10. In his youth, which comedy great worked as junior clerk at the Westminster Bank in Oxford?

11. What did Albert Steptoe use to edge pastry for a pie?

12. Which show featured a tough TV cop named Monkfish?

13. Who ran a coffee shoppe in *Blackadder the Third*?

14. In which Seventies sitcom did the wife suggest: 'Chris-Fliss-Kiss'?

15. Which lofty US sitcom star of the 1960s worked as a copywriter for the J. Walter Thompson advertising agency while waiting for his acting break?

16. Which Python worked as script editor on early episodes of *The Liver Birds*?

Answers to page 672
DRAMAS 16: **1.** *Smiley's People* **2.** Donald Campbell **3.** Sir William Withey Gull, Queen Victoria's surgeon **4.** Clive Owen **5.** *Top Secret* **6.** *Trainer* **7.** *Casualty* **8.** *The Champions* **9.** Lynne Howard **10.** *Fox* **11.** *Out* **12.** Josie Ingham **13.** C.J. Parker **14.** *Gemini Man* **15.** The Brahms Network **16.** George Clooney

Commercials 1

Answers on page 673

1. Which cricketer's broken nose was used to promote the *Sunday Times* sports coverage?

2. Which insurance company commercials featured a talking baby?

3. Which supermodel advertised Walkers Crisps in 2002?

4. Which Liverpool and England footballer advertises Sporties breakfast cereal?

5. Producing which credit card elicited the response: 'That'll do nicely, sir'?

6. Which drink was 'probably the best lager in the world'?

7. Which unseen creatures featured in Milk Marketing Board adverts of the Sixties?

8. Which fictional husband and wife were dropped in 1976 after 18 years advertising their product?

9. Which beer refreshed the parts that others couldn't reach?

10. What instant potato product did 'martians' advertise in the 1970s and 1980s?

11. Why were the Leonard Rossiter/Joan Collins Cinzano ads dropped in 1983?

12. Anthony Head and Sharon Maughan were which coffee couple?

13. Who was so impressed with the shaver that he bought the company?

14. Who stripped off in a launderette to advertise Levi's?

15. Which suave actor whispered 'Sch-you-know-who' in the Sixties?

16. What was whispered in your ear in the 1960s if you didn't wash with Lifebuoy?

Answers to page 673
POT LUCK 16: **1.** Tony Blackburn **2.** Jim Davidson **3.** Brian Glover
4. Sharon Gless **5.** *Billy Bunter of Greyfriars School* **6.** Esther Rantzen
7. It was her father, Aaron **8.** Linda Evans **9.** Bill Owen and Brian Wilde
10. Paul Daniels **11.** *Full Circle* **12.** Isle of Wight **13.** Stacy Keach (Stacy
Keach Snr) **14.** Ron Moody **15.** By twitching her nose **16.** Jackson (Kate
and Glenda)

Dramas 16

Answers on page 670

1. What was the sequel to *Tinker, Tailor, Soldier, Spy*?

2. The story of which speed ace was told in the 1988 drama *Across the Lake*?

3. Who did Michael Caine name as *Jack the Ripper* in the 1988 mini-series?

4. Which actor's father won *New Faces* with his group Jess and the Gingerbreads?

5. Which Sixties series featured the adventures of British intelligence agent Peter Dallas?

6. Susannah York played stud owner Rachel Ware in which 1991 series?

7. Which series screened an episode about the aftermath of an Irish terrorist bombing the day before the Enniskillen atrocity?

8. Tremayne was the boss of which superhuman trio?

9. Who completed a solo transatlantic voyage in *Howard's Way*?

10. Which 1980 series starring Peter Vaughan centred around a South London criminal family?

11. What was Tom Bell's Frank Ross in 1978?

12. Who was the first female firefighter in *London's Burning*?

13. Who did Pamela Anderson play in *Baywatch*?

14. What was secret agent Sam Casey known as in the title of a 1976 US series?

15. Which secret agency did Bernard Samson form in *Game, Set and Match*?

16. By a strange coincidence, which American actor appeared in a sitcom called *E/R* in the early days of his career?

Answers to page 670
COMEDY 20: 1. Arthur Tolcher 2. Gillian Taylforth 3. Buster Merryfield
4. Jessica Stephenson 5. *The Lucy Show* 6. Arthur Lowe 7. *Dear John*
8. Richard Wilson 9. Illingworth 10. Ronnie Barker 11. His false teeth
12. *The Fast Show* 13. Mrs Miggins 14. *The Cuckoo Waltz* 15. Fred
Gwynne 16. Eric Idle

Pot Luck 16

Answers on page 671

1. Which DJ played a butler in *Noel's House Party*?

2. Which comedian boned bacon for a living before he became famous?

3. Which Yorkshire actor who died in 1997 used to wrestle under the name Leon Arras?

4. Who starred in *The Trials of Rosie O'Neill*?

5. Anthony Valentine, Michael Crawford, Melvyn Hayes and David Hemmings played schoolboys in which Fifties series?

6. Who presented *The Big Time*?

7. What special relationship did actress Tori Spelling have with the producer of *Beverly Hills 90210*?

8. Who was the original choice to play Pam Ewing in *Dallas*?

9. Which two *Last of the Summer Wine* actors barely exchanged words off-set?

10. Which TV personality used to be a local government auditor for Middlesbrough and District Council?

11. Which was the third of Michael Palin's worldwide expeditions?

12. On which island was Jeremy Irons born?

13. Which actor's father played Professor Carlson in *Get Smart*?

14. Which British actor was born Ronald Moodnick?

15. How did Samantha cast spells in *Bewitched*?

16. Which surname is shared by the actress who played Amanda King in *Scarecrow and Mrs King* and the narrator of the documentary series *Boss Women*?

Answers to page 671
COMMERCIALS 1: **1.** Mike Gatting **2.** Standard Life **3.** Helena Christensen **4.** Michael Owen **5.** American Express **6.** Carlsberg **7.** Humphreys **8.** Katie and Philip (Oxo) **9.** Heineken **10.** Smash **11.** Because Cinzano directors in Italy could see nothing funny about a man spilling his precious drink over a woman **12.** Gold Blend **13.** Victor Kiam **14.** Nick Kamen **15.** William Franklyn **16.** 'B.O.'

Music 4

Answers on page 676

1. Which girl band member was banned from appearing live on *The Big Breakfast* for six months in 1997 after she swore on air?

2. Which instrumental band provided the musical interludes on *The Comedians*?

3. Which children's pop show was introduced by Keith Chegwin?

4. Which international rock star has been an extra on *Coronation Street* and *EastEnders*?

5. Who created *Oh Boy!?*

6. Which Sixties star performed 'Somewhere' on *Top of the Pops* with one arm in plaster after being bitten by his dog?

7. Which Sixties number one hit was never played on *Top of the Pops*?

8. Which comedian vomited on the pavement while introducing a live edition of *The Tube* in 1984?

9. Who were the last band to appear on *The Tube*?

10. What job did 'Oi'll give it foive' girl Janice Nicholls do for 21 years?

11. Which Friday night series was axed in autumn 2000?

12. David Hepworth, Mark Ellen and Andy Kershaw all presented which rock show?

13. Babs, Ruth and Dee Dee were members of which TV dance troupe?

14. Which singer was it *Happening For* in a Sixties series?

15. Which Phil Lynott track became the *Top of the Pops* theme in 1981?

16. 'Stone Fox Chase' was the theme to which music show?

Answers to page 676
DRAMAS 17: **1.** Geraldine McEwan **2.** Francis Durbridge **3.** Adrian Lukis **4.** *Casualty* **5.** Mariette **6.** Rachel **7.** Miles Drentell **8.** Gerald **9.** Stella Gonet **10.** Sidney Tate **11.** Alan **12.** Angus **13.** Benjamin Shorofsky **14.** The Ashtons **15.** Peter O'Brien **16.** Irene

Pot Luck 17

Answers on page 677

1. Which private detective had a young sidekick named Geoffrey `Shawcross to do her leg work?

2. Which character was first seen as a comic strip in the Belgian weekly *Le Petit Vingtième*?

3. What was different about Samantha Stephens?

4. Which American actress was born Stefania Federkiewicz?

5. What was the sequel to *That Was The Week That Was*?

6. The plight of Ben Hardwicke was highlighted on which series?

7. Which comedian who died in 1986 was born Gerald Harrison?

8. Who played Anton Meyer in *Holby City*?

9. Which moustachioed Mike was a *TV-am* presenter?

10. Who presented *Classmates*?

11. Which Irish comedian went *In Search of the Great English Eccentric*?

12. Which BBC newsreader was born in Singapore?

13. Which ex-*EastEnder* used to be a singer with Mari Wilson and the Wilsations?

14. Which Liverpudlian comic used to be a hairdresser?

15. Which 1963 entertainment series was set in a pub?

16. In which year did *Points of View* start?

Answers to page 677
CHILDREN'S TV 13: 1. Mr Rusty 2. Dragon 3. Pinky and Perky
4. Terry Hall 5. *Play School* 6. Johnny Morris 7. Scooper 8. *Vision On*
9. Soccer 10. Arthur Lowe 11. John Le Mesurier 12. Melvyn Hayes
13. *See-Saw* 14. Charlie Mouse 15. Baron Greenback (*Dangermouse*)
16. Texas Pete

Dramas 17

Answers on page 674

1. Who starred in the 1978 version of *The Prime of Miss Jean Brodie?*

2. Who created *Paul Temple?*

3. Who played George Wickham in *Pride and Prejudice* before taking up a partnership in *Peak Practice?*

4. Which BBC drama series celebrated its 250th episode in March 1999?

5. Which of the Larkin daughters married 'Charley' in *The Darling Buds of May?*

6. Who did Milly spectacularly slap round the face in *This Life?*

7. In *thirtysomething*, for whom did Michael and Elliot go to work when their business collapsed?

8. What was the name of Polly Urquhart's husband in *Howard's Way?*

9. Who played Beatrice in *The House of Eliott?*

10. Who was the first Station Officer in *London's Burning?*

11. What was *Doctor Finlay's* Christian name?

12. And what was Dr Cameron's Christian name?

13. What was the name of the white-bearded music teacher in *Fame?*

14. Who were *A Family at War?*

15. Who played Shane Ramsay in *Neighbours* before becoming one of *The Flying Doctors?*

16. Who endured a loveless marriage to Soames in *The Forsyte Saga?*

Answers to page 674
MUSIC 4: **1.** All Saints' Melanie Blatt **2.** Shep's Banjo Boys **3.** *Cheggers Plays Pop* **4.** Robbie Williams **5.** Jack Good **6.** P.J. Proby **7.** 'Je t'aime...' **8.** Rik Mayall **9.** Duran Duran **10.** Chiropodist **11.** *TFI Friday* **12.** *Old Grey Whistle Test* **13.** Pan's People **14.** *Lulu* **15.** 'Yellow Pearl' **16.** *Old Grey Whistle Test*

Children's TV 13

Answers on page 675

1. Who owned *The Magic Roundabout*?

2. What kind of creature was Tarragon in *The Herbs*?

3. Whose show featured a pop group called the Beakles?

4. Who partnered Lenny the Lion?

5. Which children's series was the first programme to be seen on BBC2?

6. Who narrated *Tales of the Riverbank*?

7. Who was the leader of the Double Deckers?

8. Which 1964 series was the sequel to *For Deaf Children*?

9. What sport was played by *Murphy's Mob*?

10. Which *Dad's Army* star narrated *The Mr Men*?

11. And which *Dad's Army* star narrated *Bod*?

12. Which star of *It Ain't Half Hot Mum* was one of the Double Deckers?

13. Which series replaced *Watch With Mother* in 1980?

14. Who was the leader of the mice in *Bagpuss*?

15. Which villain kept a pet caterpillar called Nero?

16. Who was *Superted*'s arch enemy?

Answers to page 675
POT LUCK 17: **1.** Hetty Wainthropp **2.** Tintin **3.** She was a witch (*Bewitched*) **4.** Stefanie Powers **5.** *Not So Much a Programme, More a Way of Life* **6.** *That's Life* **7.** Dustin Gee **8.** George Irving **9.** Mike Morris **10.** Sarah Kennedy **11.** Dave Allen **12.** Fiona Bruce **13.** Michelle Collins **14.** Jimmy Tarbuck **15.** *Stars and Garters* **16.** 1961

Comedy 21

Answers on page 680

In which sitcoms did the following characters appear?

1. Will Stockdale

2. Arthur Simister

3. Norma Speakman

4. Blanco Webb

5. Ruth Jones

6. Emmet Hawksworth

7. Henry Yeatman

8. Norm Peterson

9. Darrin Stephens

10. Lionel Hardcastle

11. Mandy Wilkins

12. Michelle Dubois

13. Dorothy Zbornak

14. Howard Cunningham

15. Peter Barnes

16. 'Izzy' Comyn

Answers to page 680
SCI FI 6: **1.** Sapphire **2.** Valentine Dyall **3.** Georgia **4.** Windsor Davies
5. Scott **6.** The Mole **7.** 'The Tenth Planet' **8.** Gregory Harrison **9.** Terry
Nation **10.** Colonel Tigh **11.** Magrathea **12.** Deanna Troi **13.** *Space Patrol*
14. 42 **15.** Danny John-Jules **16.** Soolin

Soaps 13

Answers on page 681

1. Which *Emmerdale* schoolteacher had an affair with Kelly Windsor?

2. What was Stan Harvey's trade in *Crossroads*?

3. Which Brookside Close resident left for Las Vegas in 1989?

4. What was the name of Des Clarke's mother in *Neighbours*?

5. Which *EastEnders* couple first met at Butlin's, Clacton, in 1958?

6. Which real-life cricketer opened the refurbished Woolpack in 1995?

7. With which nurse did Martin Platt have an affair in *Coronation Street*?

8. What is the name of Ron Dixon's wife in *Brookside*?

9. Wendy Jane Walker and Joanna Foster have both played which *Coronation Street* character?

10. Which vicar married Crossroads Motel waitress Marilyn Gates in 1968?

11. Who was Sid Fairgate's divorced sister in *Knots Landing*?

12. Soap's first transsexual, Dominic, appeared in which series?

13. As whom was 'he' previously known?

14. Whose ex-husband staged an armed raid on the *Emmerdale* Post Office in 1994?

15. Which newlywed was shot dead in the aftermath?

16. Who did Charles Tingwell play in *Emergency – Ward 10*?

Answers to page 681
LOCATIONS 7: 1. Le Candide 2. *Torchy, the Battery Boy* 3. Packet of Three
4. Hampshire 5. The Brick 6. Tooting 7. *Mr Digby, Darling* 8. San Diego
9. *Batman* 10. Wembleham 11. Royston Vasey (*The League of Gentleman*)
is the real name of Roy 'Chubby' Brown 12. *Shelley* 13. *The Love Boat*
14. *The Lotus Eaters* 15. *The Last of the Baskets* 16. *The Grimleys*

Sci Fi 6

Answers on page 678

1. Which of *Sapphire and Steel* could see through time?

2. Who played The Black Guardian in *Doctor Who*?

3. From which American state did *Star Trek's* Dr McCoy hail?

4. Who provided the voice of Sgt Major Zero in *Terrahawks*?

5. Who is Jeff Tracy's eldest son?

6. What is the name of the burrowing tool carried on Thunderbird 2?

7. In which *Doctor Who* story did the Cybermen make their debuts?

8. Who played Logan in *Logan's Run*?

9. Who created *Survivors*?

10. Who was the second-in-command on *Battlestar Galactica*?

11. For which lost planet was Zaphod Beeblebrox heading at the start of *A Hitch-Hiker's Guide to the Galaxy*?

12. Which member of the crew in *Star Trek: The Next Generation* was half-Betazoid?

13. Which sci fi series featured a strange bird called the Gabblerdictum?

14. According to *The Hitch-Hiker's Guide to the Galaxy*, what was the answer to the Ultimate Question of Life, the Universe and Everything?

15. Who played Cat in *Red Dwarf*?

16. Which *Blake's 7* crack shot was played by Glynis Barber?

Answers to page 678
COMEDY 21: **1.** *No Time for Sergeants* **2.** *Leave It To Charlie* **3.** *The Royle Family* **4.** *Porridge* **5.** *Rising Damp* **6.** *Keeping Up Appearances* **7.** *Dad's Army* **8.** *Cheers* **9.** *Bewitched* **10.** *As Time Goes By* **11.** *Game On* **12.** *'Allo 'Allo* **13.** *The Golden Girls* **14.** *Happy Days* **15.** *A Sharp Intake of Breath* **16.** *Up the Garden Path*

Locations 7

Answers on page 679

1. Which restaurant was the Resistance headquarters in *Secret Army*?

2. Who lived in Topsy Turvy Land?

3. Which Channel 4 comedy series was staged at the fictitious Crumpsall Palladium?

4. In which county was the police series *Target* set?

5. What was the name of the bar/restaurant in *Northern Exposure*?

6. From which London suburb did *Citizen Smith* plan to lead the glorious revolution?

7. Which sitcom was set in the office of the Rid-O-Rat pest extermination company?

8. In which US city was *Harry O* originally based?

9. Who lived at Wayne Manor?

10. In which fictional village was *Jim's Inn*?

11. Which strange town gets its name from a blue comedian?

12. Which work-shy sitcom character lived at Pangloss Road in North London?

13. Which US series was set on board the *Pacific Princess* cruise liner?

14. Which Seventies drama series took place in Shepherd's Bar in the Cretan resort of Aghios Nikolaos?

15. Which Seventies sitcom starring Arthur Lowe was set in Little Clogborough-In-the-Marsh?

16. Which sitcom is set on the Jericho Council Estate, Dudley?

Answers to page 679
SOAPS 13: **1.** Tom Bainbridge **2.** Electrician **3.** Ralph Hardwick **4.** Eileen **5.** Frank and Pat Butcher **6.** Ian Botham **7.** Rebecca Hopkins **8.** Anthea **9.** Susan Barlow **10.** Rev Peter Hope **11.** Abby Cunningham **12.** *Santa Barbara* **13.** Sophia Capwell **14.** Viv Windsor **15.** Shirley Turner **16.** Dr Alan Dawson

Quiz & Game Shows 7

Answers on page 684

1. Which two comedians, who teamed up as Flanagan and Allen, both had stints presenting *Whose Baby?*

2. Which former quiz show host was the first to be voted off *Celebrity Weakest Link* in 2000 after answering 'moose' to the question: 'What C is a type of Canadian deer'?

3. Which *Neighbours* twins assisted Des O'Connor on *Take Your Pick?*

4. Which actor from *The Archers* read out the scores on *Telly Addicts?*

5. Which half of a short-lived comedy double act presented *Telly Quiz* in 1984?

6. Which quiz show host was a Canadian ex-pilot?

7. Shortly before his death in 1971, which quiz show host calculated that he had given away £500,000 in prizes?

8. Which host first left his mark when bitten by a ferret on TV?

9. Which game show host was the first comedian to be contracted by the BBC?

10. Who is Emma Forbes' actress mother?

11. Which game show host used to sell candy floss on Newquay beach?

12. On the death of which game show host in 1997 was it revealed that he was the real father of Paula Yates?

13. New *Crossroads* star Cindy Day used to be a hostess on which game show?

14. Which father and son have both presented ITV game shows?

15. Which quiz show host sang about 'nuts, whole hazelnuts' in a TV chocolate commercial?

16. Who was the first host of *The $64,000 Question?*

Answers to page 684
SCI FI 7: 1. Michael French 2. Michael Knight (*Knight Rider*)
3. Dr Stephen Franklin 4. Sam Shore 5. 'Dodo' 6. United Nations
Intelligence Taskforce 7. Fulvia 8. *Voyage to the Bottom of the Sea*
9. *The Six Million Dollar Man* 10. Charles Vaughan 11. Ray Bradbury
12. The Cyrius Cybernetics Corporation 13. Delenn 14. Hattie
Hayridge 15. *Quantum Leap* 16. Victor Carroon

Children's TV 14

Answers on page 685

1. Which sci fi epic replaced 'Chums' on *SM:TV Live* in 2001?

2. Who asks the questions on the puppet challenge *Clever Creatures*?

3. Who was the voice of Ollie Beak?

4. Which feline glove puppet received 400 fan letters a week in his heyday?

5. Which puppet was originally known simply as Teddy?

6. Which pair of animated space travellers used to feature in *Blue Peter*?

7. Which Saturday morning show invited youngsters to 'Stop the Snot'?

8. When changing back into his everyday attire, what did *Mr Benn* wear on his head?

9. Barnabas and Willy were members of whose crew?

10. Who insured the thumb and first two fingers of his right hand for £20,000?

11. Which programme featured a contest called 'Eat My Goal'?

12. Which Kirsten used to occupy the Children's BBC 'broom cupboard'?

13. Which children's talent show is hosted by members of a band?

14. Which band starred in the series *Miami 7*?

15. Keith Duffy, Kate Heavenor and Vernon Kay presented which Saturday morning show in 2000?

16. What was the name of *Camberwick Green's* postman?

Answers to page 685
BROOKSIDE 4: 1. Lee Banks 2. The Shadwicks 3. Roger Huntington
4. David Crosbie 5. Lyn Matthews 6. Audrey Manners 7. Grace
8. Sarah Greene 9. Shelagh O'Hara 10. 'Bumper' 11. Chris Myers
12. Carl Banks 13. Lance Powell 14. Dave Burns 15. Emily Shadwick
16. Gordon Collins

Sci Fi 7

Answers on page 682

1. Which *EastEnder* turned into a *Crime Traveller*?

2. Devon Miles assisted which sci fi hero?

3. What is the name of *Babylon 5*'s chief medical officer?

4. Which *Stingray* Commander was confined to a hoverchair after being crippled in a sea battle?

5. What was the nickname of *Doctor Who* assistant Dorothea Chaplet?

6. What did UNIT stand for in *Doctor Who*?

7. What was the name of the Mendusan Supreme Councillor in *Star Maidens*?

8. Richard Basehart and David Hedison starred in which Irwin Allen series?

9. Which US series contained an episode about an Irish terrorist group called the IBA?

10. Which of the *Survivors* was an architect?

11. Whose book inspired *The Martian Chronicles*?

12. Who built Marvin the Paranoid Android in *The Hitch-Hiker's Guide to the Galaxy*?

13. What is the name of the Minbari ambassador on board *Babylon 5*?

14. Which comedienne replaced Norman Lovett as Holly the *Red Dwarf* computer?

15. Scott Bakula and Dean Stockwell starred in which sci fi series?

16. What was the name of the contaminated astronaut in *The Quatermass Experiment*?

Answers to page 682
QUIZ AND GAME SHOWS 7: 1. Leslie Crowther and Bernie Winters
2. Nicholas Parsons 3. Gayle and Gillian Blakeney 4. Charles
Collingwood 5. Jerry Stevens 6. Hughie Green 7. Michael Miles
8. Richard Whiteley 9. Bob Monkhouse 10. Nanette Newman
11. Phillip Schofield 12. Hughie Green 13. *The Price Is Right* 14. Roy and
Mark Walker (*Catchphrase* and *Steal*) 15. Jeremy Hawk 16. Jerry
Desmonde

Brookside 4

Answers on page 683

1. Who had 'joyrider' painted across his head by vigilantes?

2. Which family had a dog called Candy?

3. Who had an affair with Diane McAllister?

4. Who bought 6 Brookside Close in 1993?

5. Who had children called Gavin and Allison?

6. With whom did David Crosbie have a one-night stand in 1994?

7. What was the name of Ralph Hardwick's first wife?

8. Which ex-*Blue Peter* presenter compered a charity fashion show for Patricia Farnham?

9. Who played Karen Grant?

10. What was the nickname of Geoff Rogers' friend Brian Humphries?

11. Who was Beth Jordache's gay university lecturer?

12. Who left to start a new life in Dubai in 1995?

13. Who had a Brazilian boyfriend named Fred?

14. Which reformed drug dealer moved in with Bev?

15. Who married Tim O'Leary in 2001?

16. Nigel Crowley and Mark Burgess both played which *Brookside* resident?

Answers to page 683
CHILDREN'S TV 14: 1. SM:TV 2099 2. Otis the Aardvark 3. Wally Whyton 4. Pussy Cat Willum 5. Sooty 6. *Bleep and Booster* 7. *Live and Kicking* 8. Bowler hat 9. *Captain Pugwash* 10. Harry Corbett 11. *SM:TV Live* 12. Kirsten O'Brien 13. *Steps to the Stars* 14. S Club 7 15. *FBI* 16. Peter Hazel

Cop Shows 10

Answers on page 688

1. Chief Inspector Barnard and DI Tony Baynham were characters in which 1998 police series?

2. In which series is DI Dave Creegan a member of the OSC?

3. And what does OSC stand for?

4. Which movie star played Mountie Sgt Buck Frobisher in *Due South*?

5. What was north country PC Tony Smith's nickname in *The Bill*?

6. Which actor/writer gained his big break as PC David Graham in *Z Cars*?

7. Who was Jim Taggart's first sidekick?

8. Which TV cop was *At Large* in 1971?

9. Which actor plays *Rebus*?

10. Who replaced Kookie as parking-lot attendant in *77 Sunset Strip*?

11. Where was *Parkin's Patch*?

12. Who were the two bickering Texan ranch-hands in *Matt Houston*?

13. Which TV cop was shot dead in 1949, only to come back to life six years later?

14. Which actor, best-known for playing TV cops, has twice married and divorced the same actress?

15. Which two fictional detectives examined real-life murder cases in *Second Verdict*?

16. What is WPC Rickman's Christian name in *The Bill*?

Answers to page 688
CATCHPHRASES 3: **1.** Hughie Green **2.** Barbara Woodhouse **3.** Del Boy **4.** *The Fast Show* **5.** Stavros **6.** Victor Meldrew's 'I don't believe it!' **7.** His wife Else **8.** *Rowan and Martin's Laugh-In* **9.** Hughie Green **10.** René in *'Allo 'Allo* **11.** *Vic Reeves Big Night Out* **12.** Arabella Weir **13.** Harry Enfield **14.** *Rowan and Martin's Laugh-In* **15.** The Self-Righteous Brothers **16.** *Strike It Lucky*

Children's TV 15

Answers on page 689

1. Which singer joined Roy Castle as presenter of *Record Breakers* in 1987?

2. Which BBC Saturday morning show came to an end in 1987?

3. What was the name of the Broomstick Man in *The Adventures of Twizzle*?

4. How did *Clangers* communicate?

5. Which former Radio 1 DJ was one of the original *Magpie* presenters?

6. What was the name of the Grouch in *Sesame Street*?

7. Pauline Quirke and Linda Robson were among the stars of which 1975 children's sketch show?

8. Which *Blue Peter* presenter was the son of a diplomat?

9. Which stately home was situated near *Chigley*?

10. And who lived there?

11. Who were the knockabout double-act *Mick and Montmorency*?

12. Which fearless knight was created by John Ryan?

13. Which children's TV characters were Britain's most successful chart act in 1974?

14. What was Mel Blanc, the voice of *Bugs Bunny*, allergic to?

15. What make of piano did *The Flintstones* own?

16. What relation was Scrappy-Doo to Scooby-Doo?

Answers to page 689
SOAPS 14: **1.** Divorce papers **2.** Vera Duckworth **3.** Emma Nightingale **4.** David Hunter's Uncle Timothy **5.** Melissa George **6.** Sonia Jackson **7.** Viv Windsor **8.** Claire Sweeney **9.** Muriel **10.** Jenna Wade **11.** Lou's Place **12.** Joanne Whalley **13.** Pat Sugden **14.** Tracy Corkhill **15.** Nicola Freeman **16.** Tony Caunter

Catchphrases 3

Answers on page 686

1. Which talent show host used to announce acts with the words: 'We really want to hear 'em, friends'?

2. Who ordered dogs and owners to go 'Walkies'?

3. Who enthused: 'Lovely jubbly'?

4. Which show included a catchphrase: '...which was nice'?

5. Which kebab shop owner used to say: 'Hello, Peeps'?

6. Which catchphrase did *Radio Times* readers vote their all-time favourite in 2001?

7. Who did Alf Garnett call a 'silly moo'?

8. Which Sixties show had a German soldier saying: 'Ver-r-ry interesting, but stupid'?

9. Who used to say: 'And I mean that most sincerely, folks'?

10. Who called his wife 'you stupid, stupid woman' whenever she caught him with his arms around a young girl?

11. On which show did the audience ask: 'What's on the end of the stick, Vic'?

12. Which *Fast Show* actress inquired: 'Does my bum look big in this'?

13. Who created a Brummie character who was only too happy to declare that he was 'considerably richer than you'?

14. On which Sixties show would you have heard the catchphrase: 'You bet your sweet bippy'?

15. Which Harry Enfield characters would tell the Pope: 'Oi, Pontiff, no!'?

16. On which game show did Michael Barrymore ask the audience: 'What is a hot spot not?'

Answers to page 686
COP SHOWS 10: **1.** *City Central* **2.** *Touching Evil* **3.** Organised and Serial Crime Unit **4.** Leslie Nielsen **5.** 'Yorkie' **6.** Colin Welland **7.** DS Peter Livingstone **8.** (Charlie) *Barlow* **9.** John Hannah **10.** J.R. Hale
11. Yorkshire **12.** Bo and Lamar **13.** George Dixon (killed in the film *The Blue Lamp* but revived on TV in *Dixon of Dock Green*) **14.** Don Johnson (Melanie Griffith) **15.** Charlie Barlow and John Watt **16.** Cass

Soaps 14

Answers on page 687

1. In 1986, what surprise did Dennis Watts give wife Angie over Christmas dinner in *EastEnders*?

2. Which *Coronation Street* character donated a kidney to save her grandson's life in 2000?

3. Who gave Zoë Tate *Emmerdale*'s first lesbian kiss?

4. Who was driving the car in the crash which crippled *Crossroads*' Sandy Richardson?

5. Who played Angel in *Home and Away*?

6. Which Walford teenager didn't know she was pregnant in 2000 until she started giving birth?

7. Who in *Emmerdale* was horrified to see someone else's head on her body in an underwear catalogue?

8. Which former soap actress was the face of Marks & Spencer's 2001 bra campaign?

9. What was the name of Jim Baines' agoraphobic wife in *Crossroads*?

10. Who did Priscilla Presley play in *Dallas*?

11. In *Neighbours*, what did The Waterhole change its name to?

12. Which movie star made one of her first TV appearances in *Coronation Street* as Pamela Graham?

13. Which *Emmerdale* driver was killed trying to avoid a flock of sheep?

14. Who painted her bedroom black in *Brookside*?

15. Who took over the running of the Crossroads Motel in 1985?

16. Which *EastEnder* played Dick Mitchell in *United!*?

Answers to page 687
CHILDREN'S TV 15: **1.** Cheryl Baker **2.** *Saturday Superstore* **3.** Jiffy **4.** By musical whistles **5.** Pete Brady **6.** Oscar **7.** *You Must Be Joking!* **8.** Christopher Wenner **9.** Wingstead Hall **10.** Lord Belborough **11.** Jack Edwardes and Charlie Drake **12.** Sir Prancelot **13.** *The Wombles* **14.** Carrots **15.** A Stoneway **16.** Nephew

Sci Fi 8

Answers on page 692

1. What was Trillian's Earthling name in *The Hitch-Hiker's Guide to the Galaxy?*

2. What was the name of the invisible scientist in the 1975 version of *The Invisible Man?*

3. And who played him?

4. What did the *Man From Atlantis* have instead of lungs?

5. Which space explorer had a pet hamster named Hamlet?

6. In *The Hitch-Hiker's Guide to the Galaxy*, what was the name of the Restaurant at the End of the Universe?

7. For what type of magazine was Chris Carter writing when he created *The X Files?*

8. Who was an agent for IADC?

9. What did IADC stand for?

10. Ham Tyler was a mercenary in which sci fi series?

11. How did Gerry Anderson come by the name *Thunderbirds?*

12. Dr Ann Mcgregor was a scientist in which Irwin Allen series?

13. In *The X Files*, who killed the Red-Headed Man?

14. What was the name of Gor's mother in *First Born?*

15. Which sci fi series originated from a Kurt Russell movie?

16. Who is First Officer on *Babylon 5?*

Answers to page 692
CHAT SHOWS 2: **1.** Ali G **2.** Clive James **3.** James Whale **4.** *Pebble Mill*
5. Frank Sinatra **6.** Ali G **7.** *Wogan* **8.** Russell Harty **9.** Mrs Merton
10. Dame Edna Everage **11.** Russell Harty **12.** Russell Harty, Janet
Street-Porter and Clive James **13.** An architect **14.** Danny Baker
15. Dame Edna Everage **16.** Frank Skinner

Comedy 22

Answers on page 693

1. *The Library Mob* was the working title for which enduring sitcom?

2. Which *M*A*S*H* soldier slept with a teddy bear?

3. What was the family surname in *Roseanne*?

4. Who played *Rosie*?

5. Which comedian was once accused of attacking a photographer with a tin of rice pudding?

6. Who did Alice Tinker marry in *The Vicar of Dibley*?

7. Who did Rowan Atkinson play in *The Thin Blue Line*?

8. Who was President of the Commerce bank in *The Beverly Hillbillies*?

9. And who was his prim assistant?

10. Which *Crossroads* star played Uncle Quentin in *Five Go Mad in Dorset*?

11. What was the name of the scabby maintenance man in *The Brittas Empire*?

12. Which Eighties sitcom featured a bemused waiter named Carlos?

13. Which pub was the regular haunt of Gary and Tony in *Men Behaving Badly*?

14. In which two subjects did Rodney Trotter gain GCSEs?

15. Which band were known as 'the Pre-fab Four'?

16. Who was the maligned mailman in *Seinfeld*?

Answers to page 693
EASTENDERS 4: 1. Annie 2. Kathy Beale 3. Dennis Watts 4. Nigel Bates 5. Matthew Rose 6. Arthur Fowler 7. Danny Taurus 8. Records 9. Mike Reid 10. Charlie Cotton 11. Janine Butcher 12. Martin Fowler 13. Auntie Nellie's 14. Clyde Tavernier 15. Darren Roberts 16. Dot Cotton

Chat Shows 2

Answers on page 690

1. Who interviewed Posh and Becks for Comic Relief in 2001?

2. Which Clive presented *Saturday Night Clive*?

3. Which talk show host is a former Surrey Junior Archery Champion?

4. On which daytime chat show from Birmingham was Alan Titchmarsh a regular interviewer?

5. Which singer did Clive James finally meet in a 1988 interview?

6. Which infamous interviewer did Richard Madeley impersonate on *This Morning*?

7. Which chat show went out three nights a week from 1985?

8. Who hosted *Eleven Plus* for ITV?

9. Which veteran chat show host began her career on Stockport local radio?

10. Which chat show host had her own Experience on ITV from 1987?

11. Who switched from ITV to BBC in 1980?

12. Which trio presented *Saturday Night People*?

13. What did Janet Street-Porter originally train to be?

14. Which former *New Musical Express* journalist had a short-lived Saturday night chat show?

15. Who conducted her chat show from her 'luxury Mayfair penthouse'?

16. What chat show host took his stage name from a member of his dad's dominoes team?

Answers to page 690
SCI FI 8: **1.** Trisha McMillan **2.** Dr Daniel Weston **3.** David McCallum **4.** Gills **5.** Jimmy Wedgwood **6.** Milliways **7.** A surfing magazine **8.** *Wonder Woman* **9.** Inter-Agency Defense Command **10.** *V* **11.** He named it after Thunderbird airfield in Arizona **12.** *The Time Tunnel* **13.** Mr X **14.** Mary **15.** *Stargate SG1* **16.** Susan Ivanova

EastEnders 4

Answers on page 691

1. What was the name of Mary Smith's young daughter?

2. Who had a wool stall on the market?

3. Who burnt down the Dagmar in revenge for the rape of Kathy Beale?

4. Which character did Paul Bradley play?

5. Who was forced into helping Steve Owen dispose of Saskia Duncan's body?

6. Who died in 1996 while digging his allotment?

7. Which singer tried to make sweet music with Pauline Fowler?

8. What did Barry Clark sell in the market?

9. Which former *EastEnders* star used to be a Hackney coalman?

10. Whose funeral clashed with the church blessing for Ricky and Sam Butcher?

11. Who brought head lice home from school in 1991?

12. Which character has been played by Jon Peyton Price and James Alexandrou?

13. Whose cat was found dead under Joe Wicks's bed?

14. Who went on the run after being framed for the murder of Eddie Royle?

15. Who staged a 'cultural evening' at the community centre which was really a front for a porn film and stripper?

16. And who wandered in on it and promptly fainted?

Answers to page 691
COMEDY 22: **1.** *Last of the Summer Wine* **2.** Radar **3.** Conner **4.** Paul Greenwood **5.** Vic Reeves **6.** Hugo Horton **7.** Inspector Raymond Fowler **8.** Milburn Drysdale **9.** Jane Hathaway **10.** Ronald Allen **11.** Colin Wetherby **12.** *Duty Free* **13.** The Crown **14.** Maths and Art **15.** *The Rutles* **16.** Newman

Sci Fi 9

Answers on page 696

In which sci fi series have the following characters appeared?

1. Major Don West

2. Susan Ivanova

3. Dr Katherine Pulaski

4. Sam Loover

5. Agent Jeffrey Spender

6. Bascom

7. Autolycus

8. Captain Del Tarrant

9. David Caulder

10. Dan Erickson

11. David Vincent

12. Lt. Warren Keffer

13. The Valeyard

14. Nathan Spring

15. Dr Helena Russell

16. Ensign Harry Kim

Answers to page 696
DOCUSOAPS 1: **1.** *The Matchmaker* **2.** *Newquay* **3.** *Turf Wars* **4.** Jessica Harrington **5.** Pauline Quirke **6.** *Sylvania Waters* **7.** Sydney **8.** *Airport* **9.** *Car Wars* **10.** *Court TV* **11.** *Great Ormond Street* **12.** *The Clampers* **13.** *Jamaica ER* **14.** Worcestershire **15.** Bristol **16.** Harmsworth

Pot Luck 18

Answers on page 697

1. On which Channel 4 late-night show did Ali G first appear?

2. Who devised *Come Dancing*?

3. On which series did Gerald the Gorilla make an impact?

4. Which show was voted worst sitcom by *Radio Times* readers in 2001?

5. Which former soap actress is the sister of Brian Rix?

6. In which Dennis Potter play did the adult cast dress as schoolchildren?

7. What was Bodie's Christian name in *The Professionals*?

8. In which ITV sitcom did Pat Phoenix play a seaside landlady?

9. What nationality was Leonard Sachs, chairman of *The Good Old Days*?

10. Which was the first programme to be seen on Channel 5?

11. Who went from playing Robin Hood to Prince Michael of Moldavia?

12. Nick Hancock and Paul Merton have both presented which Orwellian series?

13. Who changed her surname from Barr to Arnold after her second marriage?

14. Who presented *Fascinating Facts!*?

15. Which US comedy series featured the 'Flying Fickle Finger of Fate'?

16. Which holiday programme has been presented by Gaby Roslin and Davina McCall?

Answers to page 697
COMEDY 23: 1. Alexei Sayle 2. George Burns 3. *Roseanne* 4. McLaren 5. *Desmond's* 6. Grandpa 7. *Luv* 8. Edie Pegden 9. Sonny 10. Alan B'Stard (*The New Statesman*) 11. *Seven of One* 12. Geoffrey Lancashire (father of Sarah) 13. Dolly and Cissy 14. Harry Worth in *Here's Harry* 15. Fred Quilley 16. Albert Riddle

Docusoaps 1

Answers on page 694

1. Which docusoap was set in a dating agency?

2. Which English resort was the subject of a Channel 5 docusoap in 2001?

3. Which 2001 docusoap looked at the world of horse racing?

4. Which Ireland-based trainer was the subject of the series?

5. Who narrated *Lakesiders*?

6. Noeline Baker and Laurie Donaher were the heads of the household in which fly-on-the-wall series about a typical Australian family?

7. In the suburbs of which city did the family live?

8. On which series did Jeremy Spake make his name?

9. Which docusoap followed the work of the Avon and Somerset police car squad?

10. Which 1996 series took a look inside America's courtrooms?

11. Which children's hospital was the subject of a BBC series in 1996?

12. Motorists' enemy Ray Brown became the villain of which docusoap?

13. Which series followed the lives of staff and patients at Kingston Public Hospital, Jamaica?

14. Which county's hunt was the subject of the 1998 series *The Hunt*?

15. At which university were the students in *Vets' School*?

16. Which RSPCA hospital was the original subject of *Animal Hospital*?

Answers to page 694
SCI FI 9: **1.** *Lost in Space* **2.** *Babylon 5* **3.** *Star Trek: The Next Generation* **4.** *Joe 90* **5.** *The X Files* **6.** *TekWar* **7.** *Xena: Warrior Princess* **8.** *Blake's 7* **9.** *Moonbase 3* **10.** *Land of the Giants* **11.** *The Invaders* **12.** *Babylon 5* **13.** *Doctor Who* **14.** *Star Cops* **15.** *Space: 1999* **16.** *Star Trek: Voyager*

Comedy 23

Answers on page 695

1. Which product of the Comedy Store invariably wore a tight suit?

2. Which American comedian was born Nathan Birnbaum?

3. Who had kids called Becky, Darlene and DJ?

4. Who was the antagonistic black Scotsman in *Porridge*?

5. *Porkpie* was a spin-off from which series?

6. Which of *The Munsters* could change into a bat?

7. Which Carla Lane sitcom featured the proprietor of Craven's Ornamental Garden Requisites?

8. Who does Dame Thora Hird play in *Last of the Summer Wine*?

9. What was the name of Lenny Henry's character in *The Fosters*?

10. Which unscrupulous MP had a lesbian wife named Sarah?

11. In which Ronnie Barker anthology series did Arkwright and Granville first appear?

12. Which father of a popular actress wrote *The Cuckoo Waltz*?

13. What were the names of Godfrey's two sisters in *Dad's Army*?

14. Which comic ditherer had an unseen aunt called Amelia Prendergast?

15. Who was the crooked jockey in *Hi-De-Hi!*?

16. What was the name of the one armed washer-up in *Robin's Nest*?

Answers to page 695
POT LUCK 18: **1.** *The 11 O'Clock Show* **2.** Eric Morley **3.** *Not the Nine O'Clock News* **4.** *Chef!* **5.** Sheila Mercier (*Emmerdale Farm*) **6.** *Blue Remembered Hills* **7.** William **8.** *Constant Hot Water* **9.** South African **10.** *Family Affairs* **11.** Michael Praed **12.** *Room 101* **13.** *Roseanne* **14.** Jonathan Ross **15.** *Rowan and Martin's Laugh-In* **16.** *The Real Holiday Show*

Cop Shows 11

Answers on page 700

1. Which agent had a passion for cherry pie?

2. What make of car did *Fabian of the Yard* drive?

3. What was the name of Frank Furillo's ex-wife in *Hill Street Blues*?

4. For how many years did *Dixon of Dock Green* run?

5. Which rugged movie star got an early break as photographer sleuth Mike Kovac in *Man With a Camera*?

6. Which TV detective used a nasal spray?

7. Wo Fat was the arch villain in which police series?

8. Nicholas Freeling created which TV detective?

9. In which city did Father Dowling carry out his investigations?

10. Lucas was the young sidekick of which pipe-smoking detective?

11. For which TV company did Jemima Shore work?

12. Who married assistant DA Sylvia Costas?

13. Who played the title role in *Spenser: For Hire*?

14. Who played a PC in *Rosie* and a Superintendent in *Spender*?

15. Who ran the City of Angels Detective Agency before teaming up with a new partner?

16. Who had a Silent World in the title of an *Inspector Morse* case?

Answers to page 700
POT LUCK 19: 1. Chris Serle and Paul Heiney 2. *The Brains Trust*
3. *Don't Just Sit There* 4. Alice Beer 5. *Tomorrow's World* 6. *Tripper's Day*
7. Richard Madeley 8. Mrs Peacock 9. Gabrielle Drake 10. Miriam
11. Homburg 12. *The Day Today* 13. Humphrey Burton 14. *Captain Pugwash* 15. Tony Hatch 16. *Pilgrim's Rest*

Comedy 24

Answers on page 701

In which sitcoms did the following characters appear?

1. Del Cassidy
2. Roger Dervish
3. Michael Flaherty
4. Henry Cornor
5. Mildred Bates
6. Ralph Malph
7. Mr Barrowclough
8. Gavin Featherly
9. Bradley Hardacre
10. Burt Campbell
11. Sophia Petrillo
12. Hank Kingsley
13. Gary Sparrow
14. Manny Cohen
15. Kevin Arnold
16. Patrick Glover

Answers to page 701
COMMERCIALS 2: 1. Bernard Braden 2. Gina McKee 3. Heat Electric 4. Gary Lineker 5. Victor Lewis-Smith 6. Rory McGrath 7. Daz 8. Peter Martin 9. 'They've got the Jewson lot'? 10. The Shake 'n' Vac 11. Paul Daniels and Debbie McGee 12. The Brooke Bond chimps 13. Oxo 14. Jimmy Savile 15. Ben 16. Renault Mégane Scenic

Pot Luck 19

Answers on page 698

1. Which two former *That's Life* presenters were thrown *In at the Deep End*?

2. Hugh Ross Williamson was the first chairman of which BBC discussion programme of the 1950s?

3. What was the title of the follow-up to *Don't Ask Me*?

4. Which Alice presents *The Heaven and Earth Show*?

5. Howard Stableford, William Woollard and Judith Hann have all been presenters on which durable series?

6. What was Leonard Rossiter's last TV series?

7. Who hosts the wild weather programme *Eye of the Storm*?

8. Stephanie Beacham, Rula Lenska, Susan George and Joanna Lumley all played which character in *Cluedo*?

9. Who starred in *The Brothers* before playing Nicola Freeman in *Crossroads*?

10. What was the name of *Lovejoy*'s battered Morris Minor?

11. What sort of hat did *Hancock* usually wear?

12. On which show was Collaterlie Sisters a reporter?

13. Who was the first presenter of *Aquarius*?

14. 'The Hornblower' was the jaunty theme tune for which children's TV series?

15. Which straight-talking *New Faces* panellist was nicknamed 'the hatchet man'?

16. Which Nineties sitcom starring Gary Olsen was set in a transport café?

Answers to page 698
COP SHOWS 11: **1.** Dale Cooper (*Twin Peaks*) **2.** Humber Hawk **3.** Fay **4.** 21 **5.** Charles Bronson **6.** George Bulman **7.** *Hawaii Five-O* **8.** *Van Der Valk* **9.** Chicago **10.** *Maigret* **11.** Megalith **12.** Andy Sipowicz (*NYPD Blue*) **13.** Robert Urich **14.** Paul Greenwood **15.** Maddie Hayes (*Moonlighting*) **16.** Nicholas Quinn

Commercials 2

Answers on page 699

1. Which consumer programme presenter was sacked by the BBC for advertising Stork margarine?

2. Which noted actress played a chemist's shop assistant in the first British ad for condoms?

3. What did the Creature Comforts characters promote in 1990?

4. Which former England footballer has done a series of commercials for Walkers Crisps?

5. Who presented *Ads Infinitum*?

6. Which panellist on *They Think It's All Over* had a *Commercial Breakdown*?

7. Which soap powder sponsors *Emmerdale*?

8. Which actor from *The Royle Family* used to advertise Jewson?

9. And what was his tag line?

10. Which dance allegedly helped you to put the freshness back into your carpet?

11. Which celebrity husband and wife appear on the Heineken 'Close To You' ads?

12. Stanley Baxter, Bruce Forsyth and Kenneth Williams all provided the voices for which advertising favourites?

13. What cookery product did Sooty promote in 1956?

14. Who urged you to 'clunk-click every trip'?

15. What was the name of the Bird's Eye beefburger boy of the Seventies?

16. Which car ad showed prissy flight attendants singing Wheatus's 'Teenage Dirtbag'?

Answers to page 699
COMEDY 24: 1. *Caroline in the City* 2. *Outside Edge* 3. *Spin City* 4. *Not in Front of the Children* 5. *Hark at Barker* 6. *Happy Days* 7. *Porridge* 8. *The Brittas Empire* 9. *Brass* 10. *Soap* 11. *The Golden Girls* 12. *The Larry Sanders Show* 13. *Goodnight Sweetheart* 14. *Never Mind the Quality, Feel the Width* 15. *The Wonder Years* 16. *Father, Dear Father*